SPAA'91

3rd Annual ACM Symposium on Parallel Algorithms and Architectures

July 21-24, 1991
Hilton Head, South Carolina

Sponsored by
ACM SIGACT
ACM SIGARCH

In Cooperation with
IEEE and EATCS

The Association for Computing Machinery
11 West 42nd Street
New York, New York 10036

ISBN 0-89791-438-4

Additional copies may be ordered prepaid from:

ACM Order Department
P.O. Box 64145
Baltimore, MD 21264

ACM Order Number: 417910

3rd ANNUAL ACM SYMPOSIUM ON
PARALLEL ALGORITHMS AND ARCHITECTURES

July 21-24, 1991

The **3rd Annual ACM Symposium on Parallel Algorithms and Architectures** was held on July 21-24, 1991, at Hilton Head, South Carolina. The Symposium was sponsored by the ACM Special Interest Groups on Automata and Computability Theory (SIGACT) and Computer Architecture (SIGArch).

The papers in this volume were selected from 170 extended abstracts submitted to the Symposium. The entire Program Committee screened and discussed each submission. The Committee's decisions concerning acceptance and rejection were made on the basis of perceived quality, appropriateness to the theme of the Symposium, and anticipated interest to the participants. The submissions were not refereed; indeed, it is the hope of the Committee that polished and expanded versions of the accepted papers will find their way into the archival literature.

The Committee expresses its thanks to all who submitted papers for consideration.

Program Committee

Richard Anderson (U. Washington)
Sandeep Bhatt (Yale)
Richard Cole (NYU)
Mary Jane Irwin (Pennsylvania State U.)
Lennart Johnsson (Thinking Machines Corp.)
Tom Knight (MIT)
H. T. Kung (Carnegie-Mellon)
Thomas Lengauer (U. Paderborn)
Fabrizio Luccio (U. Pisa)
Yale Patt (U. Michigan)
Patrice Quinton (IRISA)
Arnold Rosenberg (U. Massachusetts)
Marc Snir (IBM Watson Research Ctr.)
Guri Sohi (U. Wisconsin)

1991 CONFERENCE COMMITTEE

Conference Chair:	*Tom Leighton* Massachusetts Institute of Technology
Conference Treasurer:	*Alok Aggarwal* IBM Watson Research Center
Local Arrangements Chair:	*Bill Aiello* Bell Communications Research
Program Chair:	*Arnold L. Rosenberg* University of Massachusetts at Amherst

SPAA STEERING COMMITTEE

Alok Aggarwal	Conference Treasurer
Bill Aiello	1991 Local Arrangements Chair
Doug deGroot	SIGArch Representative
Mark Franklin	SIGArch Representative
Dave Johnson	SIGACT Representative
Larry Larmore	1992 Local Arrangements Chair
Tom Leighton	1991 Conference Chair
Bruce Maggs	Corporate Affiliates Coordinator
Fillia Makedon	1990 Local Arrangements Co-Chair
Burkhard Monien	EATCS Representative
Christos Papadimitriou	IEEE-CS TC/MFC Representative
Franco Preparata	1990 Program Chair
Arny Rosenberg	1991 Program Chair
Larry Snyder	1992 Conference Chair
Paul Spirakis	1990 Local Arrangements Co-Chair

SPAA CORPORATE AFFILIATES

Computer Technology Institute	Patras, Greece
Massachusetts Institute of Technology	Cambridge, Mass.
NEC Research Institute	Princeton, N. J.

TABLE OF CONTENTS

Monday, July 22, 1991

Session 3

Tuesday, July 23, 1991

Invited Speaker:

Session 4

Session 5

Session 6

Wednesday, July 24, 1991

Invited Speaker

Session 7

Session 8

Session 9

Invited Speaker: Applications

Malvin Kalos

Director, Cornell Theory Center

"Architectural and Theoretical Implications of Monte Carlo Calculations"

SESSION 1

A Comparison of Sorting Algorithms
for the Connection Machine CM-2

Guy E. Blelloch
Carnegie Mellon University
Pittsburgh, PA 15213

Charles E. Leiserson
MIT
Cambridge, MA 02139

Bruce M. Maggs
NEC Research Institute
Princeton, NJ 08540

C. Greg Plaxton
University of Texas
Austin, TX 78712

Stephen J. Smith
Thinking Machines Corp.
Cambridge, MA 02142

Marco Zagha
Carnegie Mellon University
Pittsburgh, PA 15213

Abstract

We have implemented three parallel sorting algorithms on the Connection Machine Supercomputer model CM-2: Batcher's bitonic sort, a parallel radix sort, and a sample sort similar to Reif and Valiant's flashsort. We have also evaluated the implementation of many other sorting algorithms proposed in the literature.

Our computational experiments show that the sample sort algorithm, which is a theoretically efficient "randomized" algorithm, is the fastest of the three algorithms on large data sets. On a 64K-processor CM-2, our sample sort implementation can sort 32×10^6 64-bit keys in 5.1 seconds, which is over 10 times faster than the CM-2 library sort. Our implementation of radix sort, although not as fast on large data sets, is deterministic, much simpler to code, stable, faster with small keys, and faster on small data sets (few elements per processor). Our implementation of bitonic sort, which is pipelined to use all the hypercube wires simultaneously, is the least efficient of the three on large data sets, but is the most efficient on small data sets, and is considerably more space efficient. This paper analyzes the three algorithms in detail and discusses many practical issues that led us to the particular implementations.

1 Introduction

Parallel algorithms for sorting have been studied since at least the 1960's. An early advance in parallel sorting came in 1968 when Batcher discovered the elegant $\Theta(\lg^2 n)$-depth *bitonic sorting network*. For certain families of fixed interconnection networks such as the hypercube and shuffle-exchange, Batcher's bitonic sorting technique provides a parallel algorithm for sorting n numbers in $\Theta(\lg^2 n)$ time with n processors. The question of existence of a $o(\lg^2 n)$-depth sorting network remained open until 1983, when Ajtai, Komlós, and Szemerédi [2] provided an optimal $\Theta(\lg n)$-depth sorting network, but unfortunately, their construction leads to larger networks than those given by bitonic sort for all "practical" values

of n. Leighton [16] has shown that any $\Theta(\lg n)$-depth family of sorting networks can be used to sort n numbers in $\Theta(\lg n)$ time in the bounded-degree fixed interconnection network domain. Not surprisingly, the optimal $\Theta(\lg n)$-time fixed interconnection sorting networks implied by the AKS construction are also impractical.

In 1983, Reif and Valiant proposed a more practical $O(\lg n)$-time randomized algorithm for sorting [24], called *flashsort*. Many other parallel sorting algorithms have been proposed in the literature, including parallel versions of *radix sort* and *quicksort* [7], a variant of quicksort called hyperquicksort [27], smoothsort [21], column sort [16], Nassimi and Sahni's sort [19], and parallel merge sort [8].

Our paper reports the findings of a recent project undertaken at Thinking Machines Corporation to develop a fast sorting algorithm for the Connection Machine Supercomputer model CM-2. The primary goal of this project was to implement as fast a general-purpose sorting algorithm as possible. Our first step towards achieving this goal was to analyze and evaluate many of the parallel sorting algorithms that have been proposed in the literature.

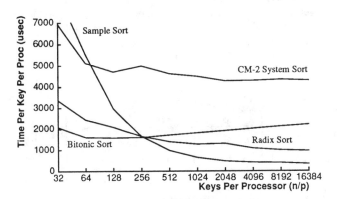

Figure 1: Actual running times for sorting 64-bit keys on a 32K Connection Machine CM-2. In the figure, the running times are divided by the number of keys per processor to permit extrapolation to machines with different numbers of processors. The term *processor*, as used in this paper, is a 32-bit wide so-called *"Sprint"* node, of which there are $p = 1024$ in a 32K CM-2. To determine the total running time of a sort involving n keys, multiply the time per key per processor in the figure by n/p.

After analyzing a number algorithms, we selected the three most promising alternatives for implementation: bitonic sort, radix sort, and sample sort. The running times to sort 64-bit keys on a 32K CM-2 are summarized in Figure 1. As is apparent from the figure, when the number of keys per processor (n/p) is large, sample sort is the fastest sorting algorithm. On the other hand, radix sort performs

*This research was supported in part by Thinking Machines Corporation, and in part by the Defense Advanced Research Projects Agency under Contracts N00014-87-0825 and F33615-90-C-1465. CM-2, Connection Machine, CM, *Lisp, Paris, and CMIS are trademarks of Thinking Machines Corporation.

reasonably well over the entire range of n/p, and it is deterministic, much simpler to code, stable, and faster with small keys. Although bitonic sort is the slowest of the three sorts when n/p is large, it is more space-efficient than the other two algorithms, and represents the fastest alternative when n/p is small.

In the remainder of the paper, we shall study the implementations of these three sorting algorithms. In each case, we describe and analyze the basic algorithm, as well as any enhancements and/or minor modifications that we introduced in order to optimize performance on the CM-2. After describing our programming model of the CM-2 in Section 2, Sections 3, 4, and 5 present our studies of bitonic sort, radix sort, and sample sort, respectively. In Section 6, we compare the relative performance of these three sorts, not only in terms of running time, but also with respect to such criteria as stability and space. Appendix A presents a brief analysis of other algorithms that were considered for implementation. Appendix B presents the probabilistic analysis of our sample sort implementation.

Notes on Timing: Due to the limited availability of a 64K CM-2, the only timings that we have been able to get on this largest configuration of a CM-2 were for the sample sort algorithm. The running time given in the abstract is taken from these measurements on the full 64K machine. For the sake of comparison, all other timings given in this paper were taken on a 32K machine. After the timings shown in Figure 1 were taken, the microcode for routing on the CM-2 was rewritten. For large numbers of elements per processor, the increased performance of routing should improve the running time of radix sort by almost a factor of 2 and the running time of sample sort by 20 percent.

2 The Connection Machine

This section describes the CM-2 Connection Machine and defines an abstract model of the machine that is used to describe all of the algorithms in this paper. By describing a particular algorithm in terms of the abstract model, the analysis can be applied to other parallel machines and approximate run-times can be generated by substituting appropriate values for certain parameters.

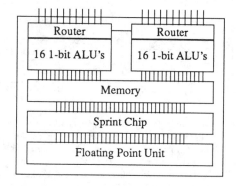

Figure 2: The organization of a CM-2 Sprint node.

The CM-2 is a single-instruction multiple-data (SIMD) computer. In its full 64K-processor configuration, it can be viewed as 2048 (2^{11}) so-called *Sprint* nodes configured as an 11-dimensional hypercube with *multiport* capability: all dimensions of the hypercube can be used at the same time. The Sprint nodes are controlled by a *front-end processor* (typically a Sun4 or Vax). Figure 2 illustrates

the organization of a Sprint node, which consists of the following chips:

- Two processor chips, each containing 16 1-bit processors, a 1-bit bidirectional wire to each of up to 11 neighboring nodes in the hypercube, and hardware for routing support.

- Ten DRAM chips, containing a total of between 256K bytes and 4M bytes of error-corrected memory, depending on the configuration. All recent machines contain at least 1M bytes of memory per node.

- A floating-point chip (FPU) capable of 32-bit and 64-bit floating-point arithmetic, as well as 32-bit integer arithmetic.

- A so-called "Sprint" chip that serves as an interface between the memory and the floating-point chip. The Sprint chip contains 128 32-bit registers and has the capability to convert data from the bit-serial format used by the 1-bit processors to the 32-bit word format used by the floating-point chip.

In this paper, we view each Sprint node as a single processor, rather than considering each of the 64K 1-bit processors on a fully configured CM-2 as separate processors. This point of view makes it easier to extrapolate our results on the CM-2 to other hypercube machines, which typically have 32 or 64-bit processors. Furthermore, it is closer to the way in which we viewed the machine when implementing the sorting algorithms.

We break the primitive operations of the CM-2 into four classes:

- *Arithmetic*: A local arithmetic or logical operation on each processor (Sprint node). Also included are global operations between the front end and Sprint nodes, such as broadcasting a word from the front end to all nodes.

- *Cube Swap*: Each processor sends and receives one message across each of the 11 dimensions of the hypercube. The CM-2 is capable of sending messages across all hypercube wires simultaneously.

- *Send*: Each processor sends a message to any other processor through the routing network. A message consists of a destination processor address, the data, and optionally, a memory address within the destination processor.

- *Scan*: A parallel-prefix (or suffix) computation on integers, one per processor. Scans operate on a vector of input values using an associative binary operator such as integer addition. (The only operator employed by our algorithms is addition.) As output, the scan returns a vector in which each position has the "sum," according to the operator, of those input values in lesser positions. For example, a plus-scan (integer addition as the operator) of the vector

$$[4 \quad 7 \quad 1 \quad 0 \quad 5 \quad 2 \quad 6 \quad 4 \quad 8 \quad 1 \quad 9 \quad 5]$$

yields

$$[0 \quad 4 \quad 11 \quad 12 \quad 12 \quad 17 \quad 19 \quad 25 \quad 29 \quad 37 \quad 38 \quad 47]$$

as the result of the scan.

Figure 3 gives estimated running times for each of the four classes of primitives on a 64K CM-2. We assume that each of $p = 2048$ processors contains n/p elements, for a total of n elements. Times are given for 64-bit data, except for scans, which operate on 32-bit data. With respect to the operation times, we have generally simplified our expressions by ignoring fixed overheads whenever they are small, concentrating instead on throughput. (For scans,

Operation	Symbolic Time	Actual Time
Arithmetic	$A \cdot (n/p)$	$1 \cdot (n/2048)$
Cube Swap	$Q \cdot (n/p)$	$40 \cdot (n/2048)$
Send (routing)	$R \cdot (n/p)$	$130 \cdot (n/2048)$
Scan (parallel prefix)	$3A \cdot (n/p) + S$	$3 \cdot (n/2048) + 50$

Figure 3: The time required for operations on a 64K Connection Machine CM-2. The value p is the number of processors (Sprint nodes), and n is the total number of elements being operated on. All operations are on 64-bit words, except for scans which are on 32-bit words. All times are in microseconds.

the fixed overhead is substantial, so we have included it explicitly.) Because of these simplifications, our analyses do not accurately model real time when the number of elements per processor is small. When n/p is large, however, they are accurate to within approximately 10 percent. Since most data on the CM-2 originates in the 1-bit processors, n/p is typically at least 32. As a practical matter, most sorting applications involve $n/p \geq 128$, and often, $n/p = 2048$ or much larger.

We now discuss the time estimates for each of the classes of operations in somewhat more detail.

The time A for arithmetic operations is nominally chosen to be 1 microsecond. For example, the cost of summing two integer values, including the costs of loading and storing the data into local memory and of incrementing a counter (assuming the operation is in a loop) is about $1.4A$. An indirect access in which different processors access potentially different memory locations requires about $3A$ time. Also, computing the maximum or minimum of two values require about $3A$ time, since these operations involve a compare followed by a conditional memory move.

The time Q for cube swapping is the same whether a processor sends one message across just one dimension of the hypercube or across all 11 dimensions of the hypercube. To fully exploit the communication bandwidth provided by the hypercube, it is desirable, of course, to use all dimensions simultaneously.

The time R given for a send is based on routing messages randomly, where each message is equally likely to go to any other processor. Some variation in this estimate occurs, because some routing patterns take longer than others.

Consider the cost of a single scan operation on the CM-2 when the number of elements per processor is large. In this case, the running time is only about $3A \cdot (n/p)$, since the fixed overhead S can be safely ignored. In the case of multiple independent scans, however, the fixed overhead S must be taken into consideration. The other operations have fixed overheads as well, but they are negligible by comparison.

Our programs for the CM-2 are written in Connection Machine assembly language (Paris) and high-level microcode (CMIS). In this paper, however, we describe our algorithms in English, and, where more precision is required, in a parallel vector pseudocode. We generally assume that the variable n refers to the number of keys to be sorted, and that p is the number of processors in the machine.

In the parallel vector pseudocode, we assume that data is stored in two kinds of variables: n-element vectors and scalars. Vectors are identified by capitalized variable names, while scalar variable names are uncapitalized. Parallel arithmetic operations on vectors are performed in an elementwise fashion. The special vector $Self$ refers to the vector of coordinate addresses ($Self[i] = i$). Cube swaps along one dimension of the hypercube are performed on a

vector V by an operation CUBE-SWAP(V, j), which returns a vector whose ith coordinate is $V[i + 2^j]$ if the jth bit of i (in binary) is 0, and $V[i - 2^j]$ if the jth bit of i is 1. Cube swaps along all dimensions simultaneously are described in English. Routing is accomplished by the operation SEND$(V, Dest)$, which returns the vector whose ith coordinate is that $V[j]$ such that $Dest[j] = i$. Scan operations are performed by a procedure SCAN(V) that returns the plus-scan of the vector.

3 Batcher's Bitonic Sort

Batcher's bitonic sort [5] is a parallel merge sort that is based upon an efficient technique for merging so-called "bitonic" sequences. A bitonic sequence is one that increases monotonically and then decreases monotonically, or can be circularly shifted to become so. One of the earliest sorts, bitonic sort was considered to be the most practical parallel sorting algorithm for many years. The theoretical running time of the sort is $\Theta(\lg^2 n)$, where the constant hidden by Θ is small. Moreover, bitonic sort makes use of a simple fixed communication pattern that maps directly to the edges of the hypercube; a general routing primitive need not be invoked when bitonic sort is implemented on the hypercube.

In this section, we discuss our implementation of bitonic sort. The basic algorithm runs efficiently on a hypercube architecture, but uses only one dimension of the hypercube wires at a time. The CM-2 hypercube has multiport capability, however, and by pipelining the algorithm, it is possible to make efficient use of all hypercube wires at once. This optimization results in a 5-fold speedup of the communication and over a 2-fold speedup in the total running time of the algorithm. Even with this optimization, the other two algorithms that we implemented outperform bitonic sort when the number n/p of keys per processor is large. When n/p is small, however, bitonic sort is the fastest of the three, and uses considerably less space than the other two.

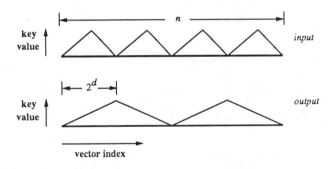

Figure 4: One application of procedure BITONIC-MERGE with n keys, converting 4 bitonic sequences into 2.

We shall not describe the operation of this well-known algorithm in detail; the interested reader is referred to [3, 10]. The key step is an operation called *bitonic merging,* which merges pairs of bitonic sequences to form larger bitonic sequences. For each pair, one bitonic sequence is sorted into ascending order, and the other into descending order. The resulting sequences are then concatenated to form new, larger, bitonic sequence. For the moment, let us assume that we have n input keys to be sorted and that we have $p = n$ processors, each with 1 key. For each integer d, $0 \leq d < \lg n$, the algorithm performs $n/2^{d+1}$ merges, where each merge produces a bitonic sequence of length 2^{d+1} from two bitonic sequences of length 2^d.

BITONIC-MERGE(Key, d)
1   **for** $j \leftarrow d - 1$ **downto** 0
2   **do** $Opposite \leftarrow$ CUBE-SWAP(Key, j)
3   **if** $Self\langle j \rangle \oplus Self\langle d \rangle$
4   **then** $Key \leftarrow \min(Key, Opposite)$
5   **else** $Key \leftarrow \max(Key, Opposite)$

In line 3, the operator $\oplus$ denotes the exclusive-or function, and the expression "$Self\langle j \rangle$" means the jth bit of the processor address, where $Self\langle 0 \rangle$ is the least significant bit.

To this point, we have assumed that the number of input keys n is equal to the number of processors p. In practice, it is important for a sorting algorithm to be able to cope with unequal values of n and p. As it happens, substantially different techniques yield the best hypercube algorithms currently known for the cases $n \ll p$ and $n \gg p$. This project focuses entirely on the development of sorting algorithms for the case $n \geq p$.

To handle multiple keys per processor, we view each key address as being composed of a processor address (high-order bits, which correspond to "physical" hypercube dimensions) and an index within the processor (low-order bits, which correspond to "virtual" hypercube dimensions). In a bitonic merge, communication occurs across successive dimensions, in descending order. Across any physical dimension, this communication is realized by a set of n/p cube-swaps. After processing the physical dimensions, what remains to be performed amounts to a bitonic merge within each processor. Given n keys and p processors, the CM-2 time for the bitonic merge becomes

$$T_{\text{merge}} = (n/p) \cdot (Q \cdot \max\{d - \lg(n/p), 0\} + 5A \cdot d),$$

where the coefficient 5 was determined empirically. (If $d \leq \lg(n/p)$, then the bitonic merges occur entirely within processors, and so the coefficient of Q is 0.)

The bitonic sort algorithm calls the BITONIC-MERGE subroutine once for each dimension.

BITONIC-SORT(Key, n)
1   **for** $d \leftarrow 1$ **to** $\lg n$
2   **do** BITONIC-MERGE(Key, d)

The time taken by the algorithm is

$$\begin{aligned}
T_{\text{bitonic}} &= \sum_{d=1}^{\lg n} T_{\text{merge}} \\
&= Q \cdot (n/p)(\lg p)(\lg p + 1)/2 \\
&\quad + 5A \cdot (n/p)(\lg n)(\lg n + 1)/2 \\
&\approx 0.5Q \cdot (n/p)\lg^2 p + 2.5A \cdot (n/p)\lg^2 n.
\end{aligned}$$ (1)

Let us examine this formula more closely. The times in Figure 3 indicate that Q is 40 times larger than A, and $\lg n$ is at most 2 or 3 times larger than $\lg p$ for all but enormous volumes of data. Thus, the first term in formula (1), corresponding to communication time, dominates the arithmetic time for practical values of n and p.

The problem with this naive implementation is that it is a single-port algorithm: communication occurs across only one dimension of the hypercube at a time. By using all of the dimensions virtually

all of the time, we can improve the algorithm's performance significantly. The idea is to use a multiport version of BITONIC-MERGE that pipelines the keys across all dimensions of the hypercube. In the multiport version, a call of the form BITONIC-MERGE(Key, d) is implemented as follows. On the first step, all processors cube-swap their first keys across dimension d. On the second step, they cube-swap their first keys across dimension $d - 1$, while simultaneously cube-swapping their second keys across dimension d. Continuing the pipelining in this manner, the total number of steps to move all the keys through all $d - \lg(n/p)$ physical dimensions is $n/p + d - \lg(n/p) - 1$. This algorithm is essentially equivalent to a pipelined bitonic merge on a butterfly network.

Thus, pipelining improves the time for bitonic merging to

$$T_{\text{multiport-merge}} = Q \cdot (n/p + d - \lg(n/p) - 1) + 5A \cdot (n/p)d.$$

By summing from $d = 1$ to $\lg p$, the time for the entire multiport bitonic sort, therefore, becomes

$$\begin{aligned}
T_{\text{multiport-bitonic}} &= Q \cdot (\lg p)(n/p + (\lg p)/2 - 1/2) \\
&\quad + 5A \cdot (n/p)(\lg n)(\lg n + 1)/2 \\
&\approx Q \cdot ((n/p)\lg p + 0.5\lg^2 p) \\
&\quad + 2.5A \cdot (n/p)\lg^2 n.
\end{aligned}$$ (2)

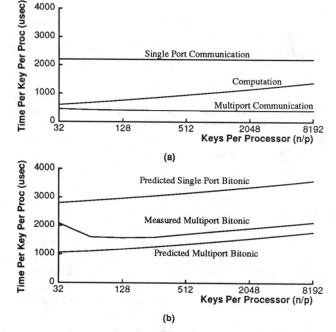

(a)

(b)

Figure 5: Bitonic sorting 64-bit keys on a 32K CM-2 ($p = 1024$). (a) The predicted single port communication is approximately 5 times the predicted multiport communication time. (b) The measured performance of multiport bitonic sort closely matches the predicted performance, but contains a fixed overhead.

Let us compare this formula with the single-port result of equation (1). For $n = O(p)$, the two running times do not differ by more than a constant factor. For $n = \Omega(p \log p)$, however, the coefficient of Q is $\Theta(\log p)$ times smaller in the multiport case. Thus, total communication time is considerably reduced by pipelining when n/p is large. Note that the number of arithmetic operations is not affected by pipelining.

Figure 5a shows the communication and computation components of the running time for both the single-port and multiport versions of bitonic sort. These times are generated from formulas (1) and (2). The computation component is equivalent for both algorithms. Figure 5b shows the predicted total time for the single-port and multiport bitonic, and the measured performance of our implementation of the multiport algorithm. The difference between predicted and measured times at low n/p is mostly due to the fact that our equations ignore constant overhead. The difference at high n/p is due to some overhead in our implementation caused by additional memory moves, effectively increasing the cost of the cube-swap (Q). This overhead could be eliminated by an improved implementation, but the resulting algorithm would still not be competitive with sample sort at high values of n/p.

Multiport bitonic sort can be further improved by using a linear-time serial merge instead of a bitonic merge in order to execute each "local" merge, that is, any merge that occurs entirely within a single processor. This variation yields a running time of:

$$T_{\text{multiport-bitonic}} \approx Q \cdot ((n/p) \lg p + 0.5 \lg^2 p) + A \cdot (n/p)(2.5 \lg^2 p + 10 \lg n).$$

where the constant 10 is an estimate, and is large because of the indirect addressing required by the implementation. For large n/p, this formula reduces the A term by a factor of 2 or more relative to equation 2. Once again, this improvement would not yield an algorithm that is close to the performance of the sample sort, so we decided not to implement it. Furthermore, the local merges could not be executed in place, so that the algorithm would lose one of its major advantages: it would no longer only require a fixed amount of additional memory.

4 Radix Sort

The second algorithm that we implemented is a parallel version of a counting-based radix sort [10, Section 9.3]. In contrast with bitonic sort, radix sort is not a *comparison sort*: it does not use comparisons alone to determine the relative ordering of keys. Instead, it relies on the representation of keys as b-bit integers. (Floating-point numbers can also be sorted using radix sort.) Our optimized version of radix sort is quite fast, and it was the simplest to code of the three sorting algorithms that we implemented.

The basic radix sort algorithm (whether serial or parallel) examines the keys to be sorted r bits at a time, starting with the least significant block of r bits in each key. Each time through the loop, it sorts the keys according to the r-bit block currently being considered in each key. Of fundamental importance is that this intermediate radix-2^r sort be *stable*: the output ordering must preserve the input order of any two keys whose r-bit blocks have equal values.

The most common implementation of the intermediate radix-2^r sort is as a counting sort. We first count to determine the *rank* of each key—its position in the output order—and then we permute the keys to their respective locations. The following pseudocode describes the implementation.

RADIX-SORT(Key)
1   for $i \leftarrow 0$ to $b-1$ by r
2   do $Rank \leftarrow$ COUNTING-RANK($r, Key\langle i, \ldots, i+r-1 \rangle$)
3           $Key \leftarrow$ SEND($Key, Rank$)

Since the algorithm requires b/r passes, the total time for a parallel sort is:

$$T_{\text{radix}} = (b/r) \cdot (R \cdot (n/p) + T_{\text{rank}})$$

where T_{rank} is the time taken by COUNTING-RANK.

The most interesting part of radix sort is the subroutine for computing ranks called in line 2. We first consider the simple algorithm underlying the Connection Machine library sort [7], which was programmed by one of us several years ago. In the following implementation of COUNTING-RANK, the vector $Block$ holds the r-bit values on which we are sorting.

SIMPLE-COUNTING-RANK($r, Block$)
1   $offset \leftarrow 0$
2   for $k \leftarrow 0$ to $2^r - 1$
3   do $Flag \leftarrow 0$
4   where $Block = k$ do $Flag \leftarrow 1$
5           $Index \leftarrow$ SCAN($Flag$)
6   where $Flag$ do $Rank \leftarrow offset + Index$
7           $offset \leftarrow offset +$ SUM($Flag$)
8   return $Rank$

In this pseudocode, the **where** statement executes its body only in those processors for which the condition evaluates to TRUE.

The SIMPLE-COUNTING-RANK procedure operates as follows. Consider the ith key, and assume that $Block[i] = k$. The rank of the ith key is the number $offset_k$ of keys j for which $Block[j] < k$, plus the number $Index[i]$ of keys for which $Block[j] = k$ and $j < i$. (Here, $offset_k$ is the value of $offset$ on the kth iteration of the **for** loop.) The code iterates over each of the 2^r possible values that can be taken on by the r-bit block on which we are sorting. For each value of k, the algorithm uses a scan to generate the vector $Index$ and updates the value of $offset$ to reflect the total number of keys whose $Block$ value is less than or equal to k.

To compute the running time of SIMPLE-COUNTING-RANKS, we refer to the running times of the CM-2 operations in Figure 3. On the CM-2, the SUM function can be computed as a by-product of the SCAN function, and thus no additional time is required to compute it. Assuming that we have p processors and n keys, the total time is

$$\begin{aligned} T_{\text{simple-rank}} &= 2^r \cdot (3A \cdot (n/p) + S) + 2^r(2A)(n/p) \\ &= A \cdot ((2+3)2^r(n/p)) + S \cdot 2^r, \end{aligned} \quad (3)$$

where the coefficient 2 of A in the last term of the first line of this equation was determined empirically.

The total time for this version of radix sort, call it SIMPLE-RADIX-SORT, that uses SIMPLE-COUNTING-RANKS on r-bit blocks of b-bit keys, is therefore

$$\begin{aligned} T_{\text{simple-radix}} \quad & (4) \\ &= (b/r)(R \cdot (n/p) + T_{\text{simple-rank}}) \\ &= (b/r)(R \cdot (n/p) + 5A \cdot 2^r(n/p) + S \cdot 2^r). \quad (5) \end{aligned}$$

(The library sort actually runs somewhat slower for small values of n/p, because of a large fixed overhead.) Notice from this formula that increasing r reduces the number of routings proportionally, but it increases the arithmetic and scans exponentially.

We can determine the value of r that minimizes $T_{\text{simple-radix}}$ by differentiating the RHS of equation (5) with respect to r and setting the result equal to 0. This gives

$$r = \lg\left(\frac{(n/p)R}{(n/p)5A + S}\right) - \lg(r \ln 2 - 1).$$

For large n/p (i.e., $n/p \gg (S/5A)$), the optimal value of r is

$$
\begin{aligned}
r &\approx \lg(R/5A) - \lg(r \ln 2 - 1) \\
&= 3.9 .
\end{aligned}
$$

This analysis is borne out in practice by the CM-2 library sort, which runs the fastest for large n/p when $r = 4$.

We now consider an improved version of parallel radix sort. The idea behind this algorithm was used by Cole and Vishkin as part of an optimal 2-ruling set algorithm [9]. We shall describe the new algorithm for counting ranks in terms of the physical processors, rather than in terms of the keys themselves. Thus, we view the length-n input vector $Block$ as a length-p vector, each element of which is a length-(n/p) array stored in a single processor. We also maintain a length-p vector $Index$, each element of which is a length-2^r array stored in a single processor. We shall describe the operation of the algorithm after giving the pseudocode:

COUNTING-RANK($r, Block$)
```
 1   for j ← 0 to 2^r − 1
 2       do Index[j] ← 0
 3   for j ← 0 to n/p
 4       do increment Index[Block[j]]
 5   offset ← 0
 6   for k ← 0 to 2^r − 1
 7       do count ← SUM(Index[k])
 8          Index[k] ← SCAN(Index[k]) + offset
 9          offset ← offset + count
10   for j ← 0 to n/p − 1
11       do Rank[j] ← Index[Block[j]]
12          increment Index[Block[j]]
13   return Rank
```

The basic idea of the algorithm is as follows. For all $Block$ values $k = 0, 1, \ldots, 2^r - 1$, lines 1–4 determine how many times each value k appears in each processor. Now, consider the ith processor and a particular value k. Lines 5–9 determine the final rank of the first key, if any, in processor i that has $Block$ value k. The algorithm calculates this rank by computing the number $offset_k$ of keys with $Block$ values less than k to which it adds the number of keys with $Block$ value equal to k that are in processors 0 through $i - 1$. These values are placed in the vector $Index[k]$. Having computed the overall rank of the first key in each processor, the final phase of the algorithm (lines 10–12) computes the overall rank of every key. This algorithm requires indirect addressing, since the processors must index their local arrays independently.

The total time for COUNTING-RANK is

$$
T_{\text{rank}} = A \cdot (2 \cdot 2^r + 10(n/p)) + S \cdot 2^r ,
$$

where the constants 2 and 10 were determined empirically. Comparing with the result obtained for SIMPLE-COUNTING-RANK, we find that the n/p and 2^r terms are now additive rather than multiplicative.

The time for RADIX-SORT is

$$
\begin{aligned}
T_{\text{radix}} &= (b/r)(R \cdot (n/p) + T_{\text{rank}}) \\
&= (b/r)(R \cdot (n/p) + S \cdot 2^r + A \cdot (2 \cdot 2^r + 10(n/p))) \\
&= (b/r)((n/p) \cdot (R + 10A) + 2^r(S + 2A)) . \quad (6)
\end{aligned}
$$

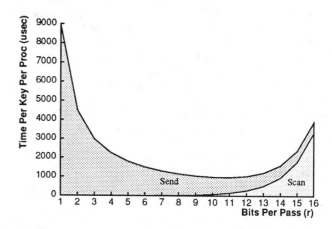

Figure 6: A breakdown of the total running time of radix sort into send time and scan time for sorting 64-bit keys ($b = 64$) with $n/p = 4096$. The total running time is indicated by the top curve. The two shaded areas represent the scan time and send time. As r is increased, the scan time increases and the send time decreases. (The arithmetic time is negligible.) For the parameters chosen, the optimal value of r is 11.

Figure 6 breaks down the running time of radix sort as a function of r for $n/p = 256$. As can be seen from the figure, as r increases, the send time diminishes and the scan time grows. We can determine the value for r that minimizes the total time of the algorithm by differentiating the RHS of equation (6) with respect to r and setting the result equal to 0. For large numbers of keys per processor, the value for r that we obtain satisfies

$$
\begin{aligned}
r &= \lg((n/p)(R + 10A)/(S + 2A)) - \lg(r \ln 2 - 1) \quad (7) \\
&\approx \lg(n/p) - \lg \lg(n/p) + 1.5 . \quad (8)
\end{aligned}
$$

For $n/p = 4096$, as in Figure 6, equation (8) suggests that we set $r \approx 10$, which indeed comes very close to minimizing the total running time. The marginally better value of $r = 11$ can be obtained by solving equation (7) numerically.

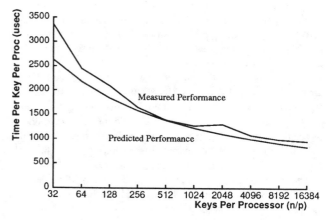

Figure 7: Predicted and measured performance of radix sort with 64-bit keys. Measured performance is on a 32K CM-2 and uses the empirically determined optimal values for r. Predicted performance was calculated using equation (9).

Unlike the choice of r dictated by the analysis of SIMPLE-RADIX-SORT, the optimal choice of r for RADIX-SORT grows with n/p. Consequently, for large numbers of keys per processor, the number

8

of passes of RADIX-SORT is smaller than that of SIMPLE-RADIX-SORT. When we substitute our choice of r back into equation (6), we obtain

$$T_{\text{radix}} \approx (n/p) \left(\frac{b}{\lg(n/p) - \lg\lg(n/p) + 1.5} \right) \cdot$$
$$(R + 10A + \frac{3}{\lg(n/p)}(S + 2A)) . \quad (9)$$

In our implementation of RADIX-SORT, the optimal values of r have been determined empirically. Figure 7 compares the performance predicted by equation (9) with the actual running time of our implementation.

5 Sample Sort

The third sort that we implemented is a sample sort [13, 15, 18, 24, 25, 29]. This sorting algorithm was the fastest for large sets of input keys, beating radix sort by more than a factor of 2. It also was the most complicated to implement. The sort is a randomized sort—it uses a random number generator—but its running time does not depend on the input distribution of keys. Rather, its performance depends only on the outputs of the random number generator. With high probability, the algorithm runs quickly.

Assuming n input keys are to be sorted on a machine with p processors, the algorithm proceeds in three phases:

1. A set of $p-1$ "splitter" keys are picked that partition the linear order of key values into p "buckets."

2. Based on their values, the keys are sent to the appropriate bucket, where the ith bucket is stored in the ith processor.

3. The keys are sorted within each bucket.

If necessary, a fourth phase can be added to load balance the keys, since the buckets do not typically have exactly equal size.

Sample sort gets its name from the way the $p - 1$ splitters are selected in the first phase. From the n input keys, a sample of $ps \le n$ keys are chosen at random, where s is a parameter called the *oversampling ratio*. This sample is sorted, and then the $p - 1$ splitters are selected by taking those keys in the sample that have ranks $s, 2s, 3s, \ldots, (p-1)s$.

Some sample sort algorithms [13, 18, 25, 29] choose an oversampling ratio of $s = 1$, but this choice results in a relatively large deviation in the bucket sizes. By choosing a larger value, as suggested by Reif and Valiant [24] and by Huang and Chow [15], we can guarantee with high probability that no bucket contains many more keys than the average. (The Reif-Valiant flashsort algorithm differs in that it uses buckets corresponding to $O(\lg^7 p)$-processor subcubes of the hypercube.)

The time for Phase 3 of the algorithm depends on the maximum number, call it L, of keys in a single bucket. Since the average bucket size is n/p, the efficiency by which a given oversampling ratio s maintains small bucket sizes can be measured as the ratio $L/(n/p)$, which will be referred to as the *bucket expansion*. The bucket expansion gives the ratio of the maximum bucket size to the average bucket size. The expected value of the bucket expansion depends on the oversampling ratio s and on the total number n of keys, and will be denoted by $\beta(s, n)$.

It is extremely unlikely that the bucket expansion will be significantly greater than its expected value. If the oversampling ratio is s,

then the probability that the bucket expansion is greater than some factor $\alpha > 1$ is

$$Pr[L > \alpha(n/p)] \le n e^{-(1-1/\alpha)^2 \alpha s/2} . \quad (10)$$

This bound is graphed in Figure 8. As an example, with an oversampling ratio of $s = 64$ and $n = 10^6$ keys, the probability that the largest bucket is more than 2.5 times as large as the average bucket is less than 10^{-6}.

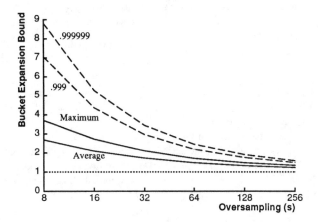

Figure 8: Bucket expansion for sample sorting $n = 10^6$ keys, as a function of oversampling ratio s. The dashed curves are theoretical upper bounds given by inequality (10) when setting the probability of being within the bound to $1 - 10^{-3}$ (the lower dashed curve) and $1 - 10^{-6}$ (the upper dashed curve). The solid curves are experimental values for bucket expansion. The upper solid curve shows the maximum bucket expansion found over 10^3 trials, and the lower solid curve shows the average bucket expansion over 10^3 trials. In practice, oversampling ratios of $s = 32$ or $s = 64$ yield bucket expansions of less than 2.

We shall see shortly that the running time of sample sort depends linearly on both the oversampling ratio and the bucket expansion. As is apparent from Figure 8, as the oversampling ratio s increases, the bucket expansion decreases. Thus, the oversampling ratio s must be carefully adjusted in order to obtain optimal performance.

We are now ready to discuss our implementation of the sample sort algorithm. Before executing Phase 1, however, the algorithm must do a little preprocessing. The reason is that the basic sample sort algorithm assumes that all input keys are distinct. If many keys happen to have the same value, failure to break ties consistently between them can result in an uneven distribution of keys to buckets. Consequently, before the first phase of the sample sort begins, we tag each key with its address, thereby guaranteeing that the tagged keys all have distinct values.

Phase 1: Selecting the splitters

The first phase of sample sort begins with each processor randomly selecting a set of s tagged keys from among those stored in its local memory. This selection process differs from that where each processor selects s tagged keys randomly from the entire set, as is done in both the Reif-Valiant [24] and Huang-Chow [15] algorithms. In terms of the size L of the largest bucket produced, our local-choice method yields results that are at least as good as the global-choice method. (A proof of this fact will appear in the final version of our paper.) Since the CM-2 is a distributed-memory machine, however, the local-choice method has an advantage in performance: no global communication is required. In our implementation, we typically pick $s = 32$ or $s = 64$, depending on the number of keys per processor in the input.

Once the sample of tagged keys has been determined, the keys in it are sorted across the machine using the simple version of radix sort described in Section 4. (Since radix sort is stable, the tags need not be sorted.) Since the sample contains many fewer keys than does the input, this step runs significantly faster than sorting all of the keys with radix sort. The splitters are now chosen as the tagged keys that have rank $s, 2s, 3s, \ldots, (p-1)s$. The actual extraction of the splitters from the sample is implemented as part of Phase 2.

The dominant time required by Phase 1 is the time for sorting the candidates:

$$T_{\text{candidates}} = RS(ps, p), \qquad (11)$$

where $RS(ps, p)$ is the time required to radix sort ps keys on p processors. Using the radix sort from the CM-2 library, we have $T_{\text{candidates}} \approx 7000A \cdot s$.

Notice that the time for Phase 1 is independent of the total number n of keys, since during the selection process, a processor need not look at all of its n/p keys in order to randomly select from them. Notice also that if we had implemented a global-choice sampling strategy, we would have had a term containing $R \cdot s$ in the expression.

Phase 2: Distributing the keys to buckets

Except for our local-choice method of picking a sample and the choice of algorithm used to sort the oversampled keys, Phase 1 follows both the Reif-Valiant and Huang-Chow algorithms. In Phase 2, however, we follow Huang-Chow more closely.

Each key can determine the bucket to which it belongs by performing a binary search of the sorted array of splitters. We implemented this part of the phase in a straightforward fashion: the front end reads the splitters one by one and broadcasts them to each processor. Then, each processor determines the bucket for each of its keys by performing a binary search of the array of splitters stored separately in each processor. Once we have determined to which bucket a key belongs, we throw away the tagging information used to make each key unique and route the keys directly to their appropriate buckets.

The time required by Phase 2 can be separated into the time for the broadcast, the time for the binary search, and the time for the send:

$$
\begin{aligned}
T_{\text{broadcast}} &= 50A \cdot p \\
T_{\text{bin-search}} &= 6.5A \cdot (n/p) \lg p \\
T_{\text{send}} &= R \cdot (n/p),
\end{aligned}
$$

where the constants 50 and 6.5 were determined empirically.

As is evident by our description and also by inspection of the formula for $T_{\text{broadcast}}$, the reading and broadcasting of splitters by the front end is a serial bottleneck for the algorithm. Our sample sort is really only a reasonable sort when n/p is large, however. In particular, the costs due to binary search outweigh the costs due to reading and broadcasting the splitters when $6.5(n/p) \lg p > 50p$, or equivalently, when $n/p > (50/6.5)p/\lg p$. For a 64K CM-2, we have $p = 2048$, and the preceding inequality holds when the number n/p of input keys per processor is at least 1432. This is not a particularly large number given that each processor on the CM-2 has a full megabyte of memory even when the machine is configured with only 1-megabit DRAM's.

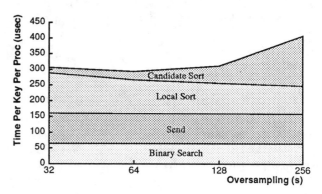

Figure 9: Breakdown of sample sort for various choices of the oversampling ratio s. The graph shows the measured running time for sorting 64-bit keys ($b = 64$) with $n/p = 16384$ keys per processor on a 32K CM-2 ($p = 1024$), where the height of each labeled region indicates the time for the corresponding component of the sort. As the oversampling ratio is increased, two effects may be observed: (i) the time for the candidate sort increases because there are more candidates to sort, and (ii) the time for the local sort decreases because the maximum bucket expansion diminishes. For these parameters, the total time is minimized at $s = 64$. ($T_{\text{broadcast}}$ is not shown, since it is negligible.)

Phase 3: Sorting keys within processors

The third phase sorts the keys locally within each bucket. The time taken by this phase is equal to the time taken by the processor with the most keys in its bucket. If the expected bucket expansion is $\beta(s, n)$, the largest bucket has expected size $(n/p)\beta(s, n)$.

We use a standard serial radix sort in which each pass is implemented using several passes of a counting sort (see, for example, [10, Section 9.3]). Radix sort was used, since it is significantly faster than comparison sorts such as quicksort. The serial radix sort requires time

$$T_{\text{local-sort}} = (b/r)A \cdot ((1.3)2^r + 10(n/p)\beta(s, n)), \quad (12)$$

where b is the number of bits in a key and 2^r is the radix of the sort. The first term in the coefficient of A corresponds to the b/r (serial) scan computations on a histogram of key values, and the second term corresponds to the work needed to put the keys in their final destinations.

We can determine the value of r that minimizes $T_{\text{local-sort}}$ by differentiating the RHS of equation (12) with respect to r and setting the result equal to 0. This yields $r \approx \lg(n/p) - 1$ for large n/p. With this selection of r, the cost of the first term in the equation is small relative to the second term. Typically, $b/r \approx 6$, and $\beta(s, n) \approx 2$, which yields

$$
\begin{aligned}
T_{\text{local-sort}} &\approx A \cdot 10 \cdot 6(n/p) \cdot 2 \\
&= 120A \cdot (n/p). \qquad (13)
\end{aligned}
$$

Discussion

The main parameter to choose in the algorithm is the oversampling ratio s. A larger s distributes the keys more evenly within the buckets, thereby speeding up Phase 3 of the algorithm. A larger s also means a larger sample to be sorted, however, thereby causing Phase 1 of the algorithm to take longer. Figure 9 shows the tradeoff we obtained experimentally, for $n/p = 16384$. As can be seen from the figure, choosing $s = 64$ is optimal in this case.

To obtain the arithmetic expression that describes the total running time of the sample sort, we sum the formulas for the phases. Figure 10 shows the experimental breakdown of times for the various tasks accomplished by the algorithm. These closely match the equation.

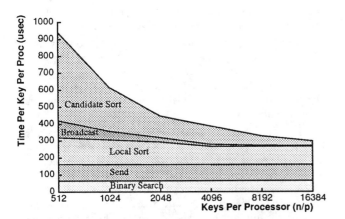

Figure 10: A breakdown of the actual running time of sample sort, as a function of the input size n. The graph shows actual running times for 64-bit keys on a 32K CM-2 ($p = 1024$). The per-key cost of broadcasting splitters decreases as n/p increases, since the total cost of the broadcast is independent of n. The per-key cost of the candidate sort decreases until there are 4K keys per processor; at this point, we increase the oversampling ratio from $s = 32$ to $s = 64$ in order to reduce the time for local sorting. The local sort improves slightly at higher values of n/p, because the bucket expansion decreases while the per-key times for send and binary search remain constant.

Let us look more closely at the formula for T_{sample} as n/p becomes large. The first two terms, which correspond to the sorting of candidates and the broadcasting of splitters, become insignificant. On a 64K CM-2, the other three terms grow proportionally. Specifically, the last two terms, which correspond to the send and local sort, take about the same time, and the third term, binary searching, takes about half that time. Thus, as n/p becomes large, the entire algorithm runs in less than 3 times the cost of a single send. Since T_{sample} is so close to the time of a single send, it is unlikely that any other sorting algorithm on the CM-2 can outperform it by much.

There were many variations of the sample sort algorithm that we considered implementing. We now discuss a few.

Splitter-directed routing. Rather than broadcasting the splitters, binary searching, and sending in Phase 2, we might have used the "splitter-directed routing" method from Reif and Valiant's flashsort. The idea is to send each key through the hypercube to its destination bucket. At each hypercube node, the key chooses one of two outgoing directions based on a comparison of the key to a splitter value stored at the node. Each key therefore follows a path through the network to its bucket based on $\lg p$ comparisons, one at each level of the network. On the CM-2, the algorithm can be pipelined across the cube wires in a way that is similar to the pipelined version of bitonic sort. The local processing required at each step of the routing is quite involved, however. It requires managing queues since a variable number of messages can arrive at each node. Our analysis indicated that although communication costs for splitter-directed routing might take less time than the communication costs required to simply route messages through the network, this advantage could not be exploited, because bookkeeping (arithmetic) costs would dominate. Our conclusion was that splitter-directed routing may be

Alg.	Stable	Load Bal.	Time/(n/p) $n/p = 64$	$n/p = 16K$	Mem.	Rank
Bitonic	no	yes	$1600\mu sec$	$2200\mu sec$	1.0	1.5
Radix	yes	yes	$2400\mu sec$	$950\mu sec$	2.1	1.0
Sample	no	no	$5500\mu sec$	$330\mu sec$	3.2	1.5

Figure 11: Summary of the three sorting algorithms assuming 64-bit keys. The *load balanced* column specifies whether the final result is balanced across the processors. The *time* column is the time to sort on a 1024-processor machine (32K CM-2). The *memory* column is the ratio, for large n/p, of the space taken by the algorithm to the space taken by the original data. The *rank* column is an approximate ratio, for large values of n/p, of the time of a rank to the time of a sort.

a reasonable option if it is supported by special-purpose hardware. Lacking that on the CM-2, the scheme that we chose to implement was faster and much simpler to code.

Smaller sets of keys. As implemented, sample sort is suitable only when the number n/p of keys per processor is large, especially since we broadcast the $p - 1$ splitters from the front end. One way to improve the algorithm when each processor contains relatively few input keys would be to execute two passes of phases 1 and 2. In the first pass, we can generate $\sqrt{p} - 1$ splitters and assign a group of $\sqrt{p}$ processors to each bucket. Each key can then be sent to a random processor within the processor group corresponding to its bucket. In the second pass, each group generates $\sqrt{p}$ splitters which are locally broadcast within the subcubes, and then keys are sent to their final destinations. With this algorithm, many fewer splitters need to be distributed to each processor, but twice the number of sends are required. This variation was not implemented, because we felt that it would not outperform bitonic for small values of n/p.

Load balancing. When the three phases of the algorithm are complete, not all processors have the same number of keys. Although some applications of sorting—such as implementing a combining send or heuristic clustering—do not require that the processor loads be exactly balanced, many do. Load balancing can be performed by first scanning to determine the destination of each sorted key and then routing the keys to their final destinations. The dominant cost in load balancing is the extra send. We implemented a version of sample sort with load balancing. With large numbers of keys per processor, the additional cost was only 30 percent, and the algorithm still outperforms the other sorts.

Key distribution. The randomized sample sort algorithm is insensitive to the distribution of keys, but unfortunately, the CM-2 message router is not, as was mentioned in Section 2. In fact, for certain patterns, routing can take up to two and a half times longer than normally expected. This difficulty can be overcome, however, by randomizing the location of buckets. For algorithms that require the output keys in the canonical order of processors, an extra send is required, as well as a small amount of additional routing so that the scan for load balancing is performed in the canonical order. This same send can also be used for load balancing.

6   Conclusions

This section compares the three sorting algorithms that we have implemented. Our goal in this project was to develop a system sort for the Connection Machine. Because of this goal, raw speed was not our only concern. Other issues included, space, stability, portability, and simplicity. Radix sort has several notable advantages with respect to such criteria. In particular, radix sort is stable, easy to code and maintain, performs reasonably well over the entire range of n/p, requires less memory than sample sort, and performs well on short keys.

Running Time. A graph of the actual running times of all three sorts along with the time of the original system sort was given in Figure 1. With many keys per processor, the sample sort is approximately three times faster than the other two sorts, and therefore based on pure performance, sample sort is the clear winner.

More informative than the raw running times are the equations for the running times, since they show how the running time is affected by the number of keys, the number of processors, and various machine parameters. If we assume that n/p is large, we can approximate the equations for the three algorithms as

$$
\begin{aligned}
T_{\text{bitonic}} &\approx (n/p)(Q \cdot (\lg p) &+ A \cdot 2.5(\lg^2 n)) \\
T_{\text{radix}} &\approx (n/p)(R \cdot 6 &+ A \cdot 80) \\
T_{\text{sample}} &\approx (n/p)(R &+ A \cdot (5 \lg p + 120)) .
\end{aligned}
$$

If Q, R and A are known, these equations can be used to give rough estimates of running times for the algorithms on other machines. We caution, however, that running times predicted in this fashion could err by as much as a factor of two. The A terms in the equations are likely to be the least accurate since the constants were all derived empirically for the CM-2, and they depend highly on the local capabilities of the processors.

The equations can also give an idea of how much would be gained in each sorting algorithm by improving various aspects of the CM-2. For example, we could analyze the effect of improving the time for a send. Based on the equations, we see that radix sort would benefit the most since its running time is dominated by the send (currently on the CM-2, $R = 130A$).

Space. A second important concern is the space required by each sorting algorithm. Bitonic sort executes in place and therefore requires only a small constant amount of additional memory for storing certain temporary variables. Our radix sort, using n keys each consisting of w 32-bit words, requires $2w(n/p) + 2^r$ 32-bit words of space per processor. The first term is needed for storing the keys before and after the send (the send cannot be executed in place), and the second term is needed for holding the bucket sums. Because of the first term, the space required by the sort is at least twice that required by the original data. The number in Figure 11 corresponds to the case $w = 2$ (64-bits) and $r = \lg(n/p) - 2$ (set to minimize the running time). Our sample sort requires a maximum of $2w(n/p)\beta(s, n) + 2^r + (w + 1)p$ 32-bit words of space in any processor. The first and second terms are needed for local radix sorting, and the third term is needed for storing the splitters within each processor. The number in Figure 11 corresponds to the case $w = 2$, $r = \lg(n/p) - 1$ (set to minimize the running time), and $\beta(s, n) \approx 1.5$ (determined from experimental values).

Ranking. Often, in practice, a "rank" is a more useful operation than a sort. For a vector of keys, the *rank* operation returns to each key the rank it would attain if the vector were sorted. This operation allows the user to rank the keys and then send a much larger block of auxiliary information associated with each key to the final sorted position. For each of the three algorithms that we implemented, we also implemented a version which generates the ranks instead of the final sorted order. To implement a rank operation in terms of a sort, the original index in the vector is tagged onto each key and is then carried around during the sort. Once sorted, the final index is sent back to the location specified by the tag (the key's original position). In a radix-sort-based implementation of the rank

operation, the cost of the additional send can be avoided by omitting the last send of radix sort, and sending the rank directly back to the index specified by the tag. Furthermore, as each block of the key is used by radix sort, that block can be thrown away, thereby shortening the message length of subsequent sends. Because of this, the time of "radix-rank" is only marginally more expensive than that of radix sort. For sample sort and bitonic sort, carrying the tag around slows down the algorithm by a factor of between 1.3 and 1.5.

Stability. Radix sort is stable, while the other two sorts are not. Bitonic sort and sample sort can be made stable by tagging each key with its initial index, as is done for the rank. In this case, however, not only must the tag be carried around during the sends, it must also be used in the comparisons. Sorting the extra tag can incur a slowdown of up to a factor of $3/2$.

Key Length. Another issue is sorting short keys—keys with perhaps 10, 16, or 24 significant bits. Sorting short keys is a problem that arises reasonably often in CM-2 applications. For short keys, the time required by bitonic sort is not at all improved over the 32-bit time. The time required by the sample sort is marginally improved since the cost of the local radix sort is reduced. The time required by radix sort, however, is essentially linearly proportional key length. Since r is typically in the range $10 \leq r < 16$, sorting 20 bits will require 2 passes instead of 3–4 for 32 bits and 5–7 for 64 bits.

A   Other Sorts of Sorts

Many algorithms have been developed for sorting on the hypercube and related networks such as the butterfly, cube-connected cycles, and shuffle-exchange. We considered a number of these algorithms before deciding to implement bitonic sort, radix sort, and sample sort. The purpose of this section is to discuss some of the other sorting algorithms considered and, in particular, to indicate why these alternatives were not selected for actual implementation.

Quicksort. It is relatively easy to implement a parallel version of quicksort on the CM-2 using segmented scans. First, a pivot is chosen at random and broadcast using scans. The pivot partitions the keys into *small* keys and *large* keys. Next, using scans, each small key is labeled with the number of small keys that precede it in the linear order, and each large key is labeled with the number of large keys that precede it, plus the total number of small keys. The keys are then routed to the locations specified by their labels. The new linear order is broken into two segments, the small keys and the large keys, and the algorithm is recursively applied to each segment. The expected number of levels of recursion is close to $\lg n$, and, at each level, the algorithm performs 1 route and approximately 7 scans. This algorithm has actually been implemented in a high level language (*Lisp) and runs about 2 times slower than the original system sort. We believed that we could not speed it up significantly, since the scan and route operations are already performed in hardware.

Hyperquicksort. The hyperquicksort algorithm [28] may be outlined as follows. First, each hypercube node sorts its n/p keys locally. Then, one of the hypercube nodes broadcasts its median key, m, to all of the other nodes. This key is used as a pivot. Each node partitions its keys into those smaller than m, and those larger. Next, the hypercube nodes exchange keys along the dimension 0 edges of the hypercube. A node whose address begins with 0 sends all of its keys that are larger than m to its neighbor whose address begins with 1. The neighbor sends back all of its keys that are smaller than m. As keys arrive at a node, they are merged into the sorted sequence of keys that were not sent by that node. Finally, the algorithm is recursively applied to the $p/2$-node subcubes whose addresses begin with 0 and 1, respectively.

The communication cost of hyperquicksort is comparable to that of the fully-pipelined version of bitonic sort. The expected cost is at least $Qn \lg p/2p$ since the algorithm uses the $\lg p$ dimensions one at a time and, for each dimension, every node expects to send half of its n/p keys to its neighbor. The cost of bitonic sort is always $Q \cdot (\lg p)(n/p + (\lg p)/2 - 1/2)$ (see Section 3).

The main advantage of bitonic sort over hyperquicksort is that its performance is not affected by the initial distribution of the keys to be sorted. Hyperquicksort relies on a random initial distribution to ensure that the work each processor has to do is reasonably balanced. Although hyperquicksort may perform less arithmetic than bitonic sort in the best case, it uses indirect addressing, which is relatively expensive on the CM-2.

Sparse enumeration sort. The Nassimi-Sahni sorting algorithm [19], which will be referred to as *sparse enumeration sort*, is used when the number of items to be sorted, n, is smaller than the number of processors, p. In the special case $n = \sqrt{p}$, sparse enumeration sort is a very simple algorithm indeed. The n records are initially stored one-per-processor in the n lowest-numbered processors; viewing the processors of the hypercube as forming a two-dimensional $n \times n$ array, the input records occupy the first row of the array. Sparse enumeration sort proceeds by performing a set of n parallel column broadcasts (from the topmost entry in each column) followed by n parallel row broadcasts (from the diagonal positions) so that the processor at row i and column j of the array contains a copy of the ith and jth items. At this point, all pairs of items can be simultaneously compared in constant time, and prefix operations over the rows can be used to compute the overall rank of each item. The ith row is then used to route a copy of item i to the column corresponding to its output rank. Finally, a set of n parallel column routes is used to move each item to its sorted output position in the first row. For values of n strictly less than $\sqrt{p}$, sparse enumeration sort proceeds in exactly the same fashion; n^2 processors are used and the remaining $p - n^2$ processors are idle. Thus, sparse enumeration sort runs in $O(\lg n)$ time when $n \leq \sqrt{p}$.

Sparse enumeration sort generalizes the preceding algorithm in an elegant manner to obtain a smooth tradeoff between $O(\lg n)$ performance at $n = \sqrt{p}$ and $O(\lg^2 n)$ performance at $n = p$ (the performance of bitonic sort). In this range, sparse enumeration sort is structured as a (p/n)-way merge sort; after the ith set of parallel merges, the n items are organized into $n(n/p)^i$ sorted lists of length $(p/n)^i$. The ith set of merges is performed in $O(i \lg(p/n))$ time using a constant number of bitonic merges, prefix operations, and monotone routes. Monotone routes are a special class of routing operations that can be performed deterministically, on-line in a collision-free manner. On the CM-2, monotone routes would be implemented using cube swaps; the entire implementation of sparse enumeration sort would not make use of the CM-2 router. A straightforward computation shows that the overall time complexity of sparse enumeration sort is $O(\lg^2 n/ \lg(p/n))$ time.

For sufficiently large values of the ratio $p/n > 1$, one would expect sparse enumeration sort to be the algorithm of choice. In particular, for the case $n = \sqrt{p}$ there is little doubt that sparse enumeration sort would run faster than any other algorithm currently known. However, our project was primarily geared towards the case $n \gg p$, certainly to $n \geq p$, and so sparse enumeration sort was not a candidate for implementation.

Column sort. Column sort is an elegant parallel sorting technique that has found a number of significant applications [16]. Column sort sorts n keys using two primitive operations. The first primitive operation is to sort $n^{1/3}$ separate sets (called columns) of $n^{2/3}$ keys each. Depending on the particular application, this sorting primitive may either be accomplished by a recursive call or, more typically, by some other sorting algorithm. The second primitive operation is to route all n keys according to a fixed permutation. Alternating between sorts and routes 4 times suffices to sort all n elements.

If $n \geq p^3$, then column sort runs extremely efficiently; the sorting primitive is executed as a local sort. Furthermore, all of the fixed permutations required by column sort are straightforward to implement in a greedy, collision-free manner. In terms of the CM-2, they can be implemented with a simple sequence of cube swaps rather than by invoking the router. As another implementation optimization, we remark that the "standard" column sort algorithm is not pipelined and would only make use of a $1/\lg p$ fraction of the CM-2 wires at any given time. A $\Theta(\lg p)$ speedup can be achieved by pipelining, and there are at least two approaches worthy of consideration. The first approach is to partition the data at each processor into $\lg p$ equal-sized sets, interleave $\lg p$ column sorts, and then merge the resulting $\lg p$ sorted lists. The second approach is to pipeline each of the routing operations in a single application of column sort.

The main drawback of column sort is that, for $n \leq p^3$, some degree (depending on the ratio n/p) of recursion is necessary in order to perform the sorting primitive; sets of $n^2/3$ items occupy more than a single processor. We chose not to implement column sort because it appeared that the condition $n \geq p^3$ would not be satisfied in many cases of interest, and a close analysis of critical sections of the potential code indicated that a recursive version of column sort would provide little, if any, improvement over either radix sort or sample sort. Furthermore, the relative performance of column sort would tend to degrade quite severely for small values of the ratio n/p.

The asymptotic performance of column sort is best understood by considering arithmetic and communication costs separately. The following analysis will assume that $n \geq p^{1+\epsilon}$, where ϵ denotes an arbitrary positive constant, which implies a bounded depth of recursion. Under this assumption, the total arithmetic cost of column sort is $\Theta((n/p) \lg n)$, which is optimal for any comparison-based sort. With pipelining, the communication cost of column sort is $\Theta(n/p)$, which is optimal for *any* sorting algorithm.

To summarize, we felt that although column sort might turn out to be the best algorithm at unusually high loads ($n \geq p^3$), its mediocre performance at high loads ($p^2 \leq n \leq p^3$), and poor performance at low to moderate loads ($p \leq n \leq p^2$), made other alternatives more attractive. Note that column sort could well be a useful component of a hybrid sorting scheme that automatically selects an appropriate algorithm depending upon the values of n and p.

Non-adaptive smoothsort. There are a number of variants of the smoothsort algorithm, all of which are described in [21]. The most practical variant, and the one of interest to us here, is the non-adaptive version of smoothsort algorithm. The structure of this algorithm, hereinafter referred to simply as "smoothsort", is similar to that of column sort; both algorithms make progress by ensuring that under a certain partitioning of the data into subcubes, the distribution of ranks of the items within each subcube is similar. The benefit of performing such a "balancing" operation is that after the subcubes have been recursively sorted, all of the items can immediately be routed close to their correct position in the final sorted order (i.e., the subcubes can be approximately merged in an oblivious fashion). The effectiveness of the algorithm is determined by how close (in terms of number of processors) every item is guaranteed to come to its correct sorted position. It turns out that for both column sort as well as smoothsort, the amount of error decreases as the load per processor, n/p, is increased.

As noted in the preceding section, for $n \geq p^3$, column sort can be applied without recursion. This is due to the fact that after merging the balanced subcubes, every item has either been routed to the correct processor i, or it has been routed to one of processors $i - 1$ and $i + 1$. Thus, the sort can be completed by performing local sorts followed by merge-and-split operations between odd and even pairs of adjacent processors. As a simple optimization, it is more efficient to sort the ith largest set of n/p items to the processor with the ith largest standard Gray code instead of processor i; this permits the merge-and-split operations to be performed between adjacent processors.

The main difference between column sort and smoothsort is that the "balancing" operation performed by smoothsort (the cost of which is related to that of column sort by a small constant factor) guarantees an asymptotically smaller degree of error. For this reason, smoothsort can be applied without recursion over a larger range of values of n and p, namely, for $n \geq p^2$. Interestingly, the balancing operation of smoothsort is based upon a simple variant of merge-and-split: the "merge-and-unshuffle" operation. Essentially, the best way to guarantee similarity between the distribution of ranks of the items at a given pair of adjacent processors A and B is to merge the two sets of items, assign the odd-ranked items in the resulting sorted list to processor A (say), and the even-ranked items to processor B; this is precisely the effect of a merge-and-unshuffle operation. The balancing operation of smoothsort amounts to performing $\lg p$ sets of such merge-and-unshuffle operations, one over each of the hypercube dimensions. As in the case of column sort, there are at least two ways to pipeline the balancing operation in order to take advantage of the CM-2's ability to communicate across all of the hypercube wires at once.

At high loads ($p^2 \leq n \leq p^3$), we felt that smoothsort might turn out to be the fastest algorithm. However, like column sort, the performance of smoothsort degrades (relative to that of other algorithms) at low to moderate loads ($p \leq n \leq p^2$), and this was the overriding factor in our decision not to implement smoothsort. For unusually high loads ($n \geq p^3$), it is likely that column sort would slightly outperform smoothsort because of a small constant factor advantage in the running time of its balancing operation on the CM-2. Thus, the ideal hybrid sorting scheme might employ column sort for $n \geq p^3$, smoothsort for $p^2 \leq n \leq p^3$, and some other sort for $n \leq p^2$. It should be mentioned that for $n \geq p^{1+\epsilon}$, the asymptotic performance of smoothsort is the same as that of column sort, both in terms of arithmetic as well as communication. Smoothsort outperforms column sort for smaller values of n/p, however. For a detailed analysis of the runing time of smoothsort, the reader is referred to [21].

Theoretical results. This subsection summarizes a number of "theoretical" sorting results—algorithms with optimal or near-optimal asymptotic performance but which remain impractical due to large constant factors and/or non-constant costs that are not accounted for by the model of computation. In certain instances, a significant additional penalty must be paid in order to "port" the algorithm to the particular architecture provided by the CM-2.

A number of algorithms have been developed for sorting on Parallel Random Access Machines (PRAMs). The fastest comparison-based sort is Cole's parallel merge sort [8]. This algorithm requires optimal $O(\lg n)$ time to sort n items on an n-node exclusive-read exclusive-write (EREW) PRAM. Another way to sort in $O(\lg n)$ time is to emulate the AKS sorting circuit [2, 20]. The constants hidden by the O-notation are large, however. For sorting n integers in the range $[1, n(\lg n)^{O(1)}]$, it is possible to match the linear processor-time product obtained by sequential bucket sort [23].

If one is interested in emulating a PRAM algorithm on a fixed interconnection network such as the hypercube or butterfly, the cost of the emulation must be taken into account. Since emulation schemes tend to be based on routing, and the cost of routing seems to be intimately related to that of sorting, it is perhaps unlikely that any sorting algorithm developed for the PRAM model will lead to an optimal solution in the fixed interconnection network model.

For the hypercube and related networks such as the butterfly, cube-connected cycles, and shuffle-exchange, there have been recent asymptotic improvements in both the deterministic and randomized settings. A deterministic, $O(\lg n(\lg \lg n)^2)$ algorithm for the case $n = p$ is described in [11]. An $O(\lg n)$ algorithm that admits an efficient bit-serial implementation and also improves upon the asymptotic failure probability of the Reif-Valiant flashsort algorithm is presented in [17]. Unfortunately, both of these algorithms are quite impractical. The reader interested in theoretical bounds should consult the aforementioned papers for further references to previous work.

B Probabilistic Analysis of Sample Sort

This appendix analyzes the size of the buckets created by the sample sort of Section 5. Recall the method for creating buckets. First, each of the p processors partitions its n/p keys into s groups of n/ps and selects one candidate at random from each group. Thus, there are a total of exactly ps candidates. Next, the candidates are sorted, and every sth candidate in the sorted order is chosen to be a splitter. The keys lying between two successive splitters form a bucket. Theorem B.3 shows that it is unlikely that this method assigns many more keys than average to any one bucket.

B.1 Hoeffding's Inequality

The proof of Theorem B.3 uses two lemmas. The first of these is a famous inequality due to Hoeffding [14].

Lemma B.1 *Let X_i be a random variable that is equal to 1 with probability q_i and to 0 with probability $1 - q_i$, for $1 \leq i \leq n$. Let $W = \sum_{1 \leq i \leq n} X_i$. Then $E(W) = \sum_{1 \leq i \leq n} q_i$. Let $q = E(W)/n$ and let Z be the sum of n random variables each equal to 1 with probability q, and 0 with probability $1 - q$. Note that $E(W) = E(Z) = qn$. If k is an integer and $k \leq qn - 1$, then*

$$\Pr(W \leq k) \leq \Pr(Z \leq k).$$

B.2 The Partition Method

Sample sort's method of choosing candidates is a special case of the following method, which we call *Method P*, where the P stands for Partition. Let S be the set of n keys, and let b be a positive integer. Partition S into m subsets $S_1, \ldots, S_m$, each of cardinality less than or equal to b. For $1 \leq i \leq m$, do the following. With probability $|S_i|/b$, decide to take a candidate from set S_i. If you decide to take a candidate from S_i, then choose a key at random from S_i. Note that independent of how the keys are partitioned, each key has probability $1/b$ of becoming a candidate, and the expected number of candidates is n/b. The sample sort algorithm is the case in which $m = n/b$ and $|S_i| = b$, for $1 \le i \le m$. Another special case that is easier to analyze than the general case is that in which $m = n$, and $|S_i| = 1$, for $1 \le i \le m$, i.e., each key independently chooses to be a candidate with probability $1/b$. We call this special case *Method I*, where the I stands for Independent. The following lemma relates Methods I and P.

Lemma B.2 *Let T denote an arbitrary subset of S, and let Y_I and Y_P denote the number candidates chosen from T by methods I and P, respectively. If k is an integer and $k \le (|T|/b) - 1$, then*

$$\Pr(Y_P \le k) \le \Pr(Y_I \le k).$$

Proof: Let $T_i = S_i \cap T$, for $1 \le i \le m$. Each set T_i contributes 1 candidate with probability $|T_i|/b$ (note that $|T_i| \le |S_i| \le b$), and 0 candidates otherwise. Now define $|T|$ 0-1 random variables as follows. For each non-empty T_i, define $|T_i|$ random variables, where the first random variable is equal to 1 with probability $|T_i|/b$ and 0 otherwise, and the remaining $|T_i| - 1$ random variables are always 0. Call the resulting set of $|T|$ random variables $X_1, \ldots, X_{|T|}$ (order is unimportant), and let Y_P denote the random variable equal to $\sum_{1 \le i \le |T|} X_i$. Note that

$$E(Y_P) = \sum_{1 \le i \le m} |T_i|/b = |T|/b,$$

and that Y_P is the random variable corresponding to the number of candidates chosen from the set T by Method P. Define Y_I to be the sum of $|T|$ $(1/b)$-biased Bernoulli trials. Note that Y_I is the random variable corresponding to the number of candidates chosen from the set T by Method I. Hence, substituting $W = Y_P$ and $Z = Y_I$ into Hoeffding's inequality, we have

$$\Pr(Y_P \le k) \le \Pr(Y_I \le k)$$

for $k \le E(Y_P) - 1 = E(Y_I) - 1 = (|T|/b) - 1$. $\square$

B.3 Bounding the Maximum Bucket Size

With Lemmas B.1 and B.2 in hand, we are prepared to prove Theorem B.3.

Theorem B.3 *For any $\alpha > 1$, the probability that any bucket contains more than $\alpha n/p$ keys is at most $ne^{-(1-1/\alpha)^2 \alpha s/2}$.*

Proof: In order to prove that no bucket receives more than $\alpha n/p$ keys, it suffices to show that the distance from any key to the next splitter in the sorted order is at most $\alpha n/p$. We begin by looking at a single key. The distance, l, to the next splitter is larger than $\alpha n/p$ only if fewer than s of the next $\alpha n/p$ keys in the sorted order are candidates. Let T denote this set of $\alpha n/p$ keys. The candidates in this set are chosen according to Method P, where $m = n/b$ and $b = n/sp$. Let Y_P denote the number of candidates in T. Then $\Pr[l > \alpha n/p] \le \Pr[Y_P \le s]$. Thus, we would like an upper bound on $\Pr(Y_P < s)$. By Lemma B.2, any upper bound derived for $\Pr(Y_I \le s)$ also applies to $\Pr(Y_P \le s)$, for $s \le (|T|/b) - 1$. Hence, we will analyze Method I instead.

If the candidates are chosen according to Method I, then the number of candidates in the set T of $\alpha n/p$ keys has a binomial distribution, i.e.,

$$\Pr[Y_I = k] = \binom{r}{k} q^k (1 - q)^{r-k},$$

where $r = \alpha n/p$ is the number of independent Bernoulli trials, $q = 1/b = sp/n$ is the probability of success in each trial, and Y_I is the number of successes. The probability that fewer successes occur than expected can be bounded using the Chernoff-type bound [4]

$$\Pr[Y_I \le \gamma r q] \le e^{-(1-\gamma)^2 r q/2},$$

which holds for $0 \le \gamma \le 1$. Substituting $r = \alpha n/p$, $q = sp/n$, and $\gamma = 1/\alpha$, we have

$$
\begin{aligned}
\Pr[l > \alpha n/p] &\le \Pr[Y_P \le s] \\
&\le \Pr[Y_I \le s] \\
&\le e^{-(1-1/\alpha)^2 \alpha s/2}.
\end{aligned}
$$

To bound the probability that the distance from *any* of the n keys to the next splitter is more than $\alpha n/p$, we simply multiply the bound on $\Pr[l > \alpha n/p]$ by n (we will give a tighter bound in the final version of this paper). $\square$

Acknowledgments

Many people were involved in this project, and we would like to thank all of them. We would particularly like to thank Mark Bromley, Steve Heller, Bradley Kuszmaul and Kevin Oliveau of Thinking Machines Corporation for helping with various aspects of the CM-2, including the implementation of the send that was needed for the sample sort. We would also like to thank John Mucci of Thinking Machines and Rita of Rita's for his support and her inspiration.

References

[1] A. Aggarwal and M.-D. A. Huang. Network complexity of sorting and graph problems and simulating CRCW PRAMs by interconnection networks. In J. H. Reif, editor, *Lecture Notes in Computer Science: VLSI Algorithms and Architectures (AWOC 88)*, vol. 319, pages 339–350. Springer-Verlag, 1988.

[2] M. Ajtai, J. Komlos, and E. Szemeredi. Sorting in $c \log n$ parallel steps. *Combinatorica*, 3:1–19, 1983.

[3] S. G. Akl. *Parallel Sorting Algorithms*. Academic Press, Toronto, 1985.

[4] D. Angluin and L. G. Valiant. Fast probabilistic algorithms for Hamiltonian circuits and matchings. *Journal of Computer and System Sciences*, 18(2):155–193, April 1979.

[5] K. Batcher. Sorting networks and their applications. In *Proceedings of the AFIPS Spring Joint Computing Conference*, volume 32, pages 307–314, 1968.

[6] G. Baudet and D. Stevenson. Optimal sorting algorithms for parallel computers. *IEEE Transactions on Computers*, C–27:84–87, 1978.

[7] G. E. Blelloch. *Vector Models for Data-Parallel Computing*. The MIT Press, 1990.

[8] R. Cole. Parallel merge sort. *SIAM Journal on Computing*, pages 770–785, 1988.

[9] R. Cole and U. Vishkin. Deterministic coin tossing and accelerating cascades: Micro and macro techniques for designing parallel algorithms. In *Proceedings of the 18th Annual ACM Symposium on Theory of Computing*, pages 206–219, 1986.

[10] T. H. Cormen, C. E. Leiserson, and R. L. Rivest. *Introduction to Algorithms*. The MIT Press and McGraw-Hill, 1990.

[11] R. E. Cypher and C. G. Plaxton. Deterministic sorting in nearly logarithmic time on the hypercube and related computers. In *Proceedings of the 22nd Annual ACM Symposium on Theory of Computing*, pages 193–203, May 1990.

[12] E. Felten, S. Karlin, and S. Otto. Sorting on a hypercube. Hm 244, Caltech/JPL, 1986.

[13] W. D. Frazer and A. C. McKellar. Samplesort: A sampling approach to minimal storage tree sorting. *Journal of the ACM*, 17(3):496–507, 1970.

[14] W. Hoeffding. On the distribution of the number of successes in independent trials. *Annals of Mathematical Statistics*, 27:713–721, 1956.

[15] J. S. Huang and Y. C. Chow. Parallel sorting and data partitioning by sampling. In *Proceedings of the IEEE Computer Society's Seventh International Computer Software and Applications Conference*, pages 627–631, November 1983.

[16] F. T. Leighton. Tight bounds on the complexity of parallel sorting. *IEEE Transactions on Computers*, C–34(4):344–354, April 1985.

[17] T. Leighton and G. Plaxton. A (fairly) simple circuit that (usually) sorts. In *Proceedings of the 31st Annual Symposium on Foundations of Computer Science*, pages 264–274, October 1990.

[18] P. P. Li. Parallel sorting on Ametek/S14. Technical report, Ametek Computer Research Division, Arcadia, CA, September 1986.

[19] D. Nassimi and S. Sahni. Parallel permutation and sorting algorithms and a new generalized connection network. *Journal of the ACM*, 29(3):642–667, July 1982.

[20] M. S. Paterson. Improved sorting networks with $O(\log n)$ depth. *Algorithmica*, 5:75–92, 1990.

[21] C. G. Plaxton. Efficient computation on sparse interconnection networks. Technical Report STAN-CS-89-1283, Stanford University, Department of Computer Science, September 1989.

[22] M. J. Quinn. Analysis and benchmarking of two parallel sorting algorithms: hyperquicksort and quickmerge. *BIT*, 29(2):239–250, 1989.

[23] S. Rajasekaran and J. H. Reif. Optimal and sublogarithmic time randomized parallel sorting algorithms. *SIAM Journal on Computing*, 18(3):594–607, June 1989.

[24] J. H. Reif and L. G. Valiant. A logarithmic time sort for linear size networks. *Journal of the ACM*, 34(1):60–76, January 1987.

[25] S. R. Seidel and W. L. George. Binsorting on hypercubes with d-port communication. In *Proceedings of the Third Conference on Hypercube Concurrent Computers*, pages 1455–1461, January 1988.

[26] P. Varman and K. Doshi. Sorting with linear speedup on a pipelined hypercube. Technical Report TR–8802, Rice University, Department of Electrical and Computer Engineering, February 1988.

[27] B. A. Wagar. Hyperquicksort: A fast sorting algorithm for hypercubes. In M. T. Heath, editor, *Hypercube Multiprocessors 1987 (Proceedings of the Second Conference on Hypercube Multiprocessors)*, pages 292–299, Philadelphia, PA, 1987. SIAM.

[28] B. A. Wagar. *Practical Sorting Algorithms for Hypercube Computers*. PhD thesis, Department of Electrical Engineering and Computer Science, University of Michigan, Ann Arbor, MI, July 1990.

[29] Y. Won and S. Sahni. A balanced bin sort for hypercube multicomputers. *Journal of Supercomputing*, 2:435–448, 1988.

Randomized Sorting and Selection
on Mesh-Connected Processor Arrays

(Preliminary Version)

Christos Kaklamanis[*]   Danny Krizanc[†]   Lata Narayanan[†]   Thanasis Tsantilas[‡]

Abstract

We show that sorting an input of size $N = n^2$ can be performed by an $n \times n$ mesh-connected processor array in $2.5n + o(n)$ parallel communication steps and using constant size queues, with high probability. The best previously known algorithm for this problem required $3n + o(n)$ steps. We also show that selecting the element of rank k out of $N = n^2$ inputs on an $n \times n$ mesh can be performed in $1.25n + o(n)$ steps and using constant size queues, with high probability. The best previously known algorithm for this problem involved sorting, and required $3n + o(n)$ steps. Both of our algorithms can be generalized to higher dimensions, achieving bounds better than the known results.

[*]Aiken Computation Laboratory, Harvard University, Cambridge, MA 02138. Supported in part by NSF Grant NSF-CCR-87-04513.

[†]Dept. of Computer Science, University of Rochester, Rochester, NY 14627.

[‡]Dept. of Computer Science, Columbia University, New York, NY 10027. Part of this work was done at Harvard University and supported in part by NSF Grants NSF-DCR-86-00379 and NSF-CCR-89-02500.

1   Introduction

The mesh-connected array has been the object of a great deal of theoretical study as well as the basis for a number of proposed and implemented parallel computers. While its diameter is large in comparison to other well-studied networks (e.g., hypercube, butterfly, shuffle-exchange networks), the simplicity and regularity of its interconnection pattern make it ideal for VLSI implementation. Recent work by Dally [Dal87] suggests that high diameter networks such as the mesh may provide a more efficient communication medium for VLSI-based parallel computers. Furthermore, a large number of efficient algorithms have been designed to run on this architecture.

Sorting and selection (the problem of selecting the element of rank k out of N elements), are important and well-studied problems in computer science. Valiant [Val75] was the first to study the parallel complexity of these and other comparison-based problems and his work has been followed by that of a great many researchers working on different models of parallelism. Reischuk [Rei85] presented a randomized algorithm for sorting N inputs on an N processor parallel random access machine in $O(\log N)$ time, and an algorithm for selection (discovered independently by Meggido [Meg82]) on a N processor parallel comparison tree running in $O(1)$ time, both results holding with high probability. Building upon these results, Reif and Valiant [RV87] gave an optimal randomized $O(\log N)$ time algorithm for sorting on the N-node hypercube (and related networks). Recently, Rajasekaran [Raj90] applied these ideas to achieve processor-time optimal selection in the hypercube. Using new techniques, we are able to adapt these ideas to show bounds for sorting and selection on the mesh which are significant improvements over previously known results.

The problem of sorting on a mesh has a long history starting with Thompson and Kung [TK77], who gave an algorithm which sorts $N = n^2$ inputs into snake-like row major order in $6n + o(n)$ parallel communication steps on a $n \times n$ synchronous SIMD mesh; their algorithm may be adapted to run in $3n + o(n)$ time on a MIMD mesh. Schnorr and Shamir [SS86] gave a second algorithm for sorting on a MIMD mesh running in $3n + o(n)$ time, and they also provide a lower bound, discovered independently by Kunde [Kun89], of $3n - o(n)$ communication steps. The model for the lower bound puts no limit on the power of the processors but requires each processor to hold exactly one packet at all times, which forces, for all steps of an algorithm, the configuration of the packets over the mesh to be a permutation of the input.

In this paper, we consider a model in which a processor is allowed to perform only simple operations, to communicate one packet of information to its neighbors during a single time step and to store a constant number of packets between time steps. (This is the same model used when the problem of routing permutations on the mesh is studied; see for example [RT91], [LMT89] and [Kun88].) In this model we provide a randomized algorithm for sorting $N = n^2$ inputs on a $n \times n$ mesh in $2.5n + o(n)$ steps, with high probability. The inputs are sorted into block snake-like ordering (defined below). It should be noted that a lower bound of $3n - o(n)$ steps for any deterministic algorithms for sorting to this indexing scheme is easily obtained in the Schnorr-Shamir model. Furthermore, Chlebus [Chl89], provides a lower bound of $2.5n - o(n)$ for any randomized algorithm for sorting into snake-like order in the Schnorr-Shamir model which also extends to the block snake-like ordering used here.

A complete description of the problem of selecting the element of rank k out of $N = n^2$ elements on a $n \times n$ mesh must include the identity of the processor where the element is output. Due to the mesh's relatively large diameter, we consider the case where the selected element must reach the middle processor (i.e., the one labeled $(\lceil \frac{n}{2} \rceil, \lceil \frac{n}{2} \rceil)$ in the labeling described below). The sorting result of Schnorr and Shamir immediately implies an $O(n)$ time algorithm for selection in general and a $3n + o(n)$ algorithm for selecting the median (the element of rank $\lceil \frac{N}{2} \rceil$) at the middle processor. The results of Kunde [Kun89] imply a lower bound of $2n - o(n)$ steps for selecting the median at the middle processor in the Schnorr and Shamir model.

We give a randomized algorithm for selection at the middle processor which runs in $1.25n + o(n)$ steps, with high probability. Again the model used for this result is the commonly used model of the mesh described above. The only known lower bound for selection in this model is the distance bound of n steps.

The rest of the paper is organized in the following way. The next section gives some preliminary definitions and facts, including details of the model of the mesh that we use. Sections 3 and 4 contain descriptions of our randomized algorithms for sorting and selection, respectively. We close with some discussion of how our algorithms can be extended to higher dimensional meshes.

2   Preliminaries

The $n \times n$ mesh-connected array of processors (or two-dimensional mesh) contains $N = n^2$ processors arranged in a two-dimensional grid without wrap-around edges. More precisely, it corresponds to the graph, $G = (V, E)$, with $V = \{(x, y) \mid x, y \in \langle n \rangle\}$ and $E = \{((x, y), (x, y + 1)) \mid x \in \langle n \rangle, y \in \langle n - 1 \rangle\} \cup \{((x, y), (x + 1, y)) \mid x \in \langle n - 1 \rangle, y \in \langle n \rangle\}$, where $\langle n \rangle = \{1, \ldots, n\}$. Nodes in the graph correspond to processors and edges to bidirectional communication links. The d-dimensional mesh is the logical extension of the two-dimensional version to higher dimensions.

The input to both of our problems is a set $X = \{x_1, \ldots, x_N\}$, the elements of which may be linearly ordered. An indexing scheme is a bijection from $\langle N \rangle$ to $\langle n \rangle \times \langle n \rangle$. The sorting problem on the mesh is: Given a set X, stored with one element per processor, and an indexing scheme, I, move the element of rank k in X to the processor labeled $I(k)$. The selection problem is: Given a set X, stored with one element per processor, an integer $1 \leq k \leq N$, and a specified processor (i, j), move the element of rank k in X to the processor labeled (i, j). In what follows we will consider only the case where the specified processor is labeled $(\lceil \frac{n}{2} \rceil, \lceil \frac{n}{2} \rceil)$, referred to as the middle processor below. It is generally straightforward how to modify the algorithm for the case of another designated processor.

The computations above are to be performed using the following model of the mesh: During a single parallel communication step, each processor can send and receive a single packet along each of its incident edges, where a packet consists of at most a single element of X along with $O(\log N)$ bits of header information used for routing and counting purposes. Between communication steps, processors can store packets in their local queues, which are of bounded size. Furthermore, they can perform a constant number of simple operations (e.g., copying, addition, comparison) on the elements and the header information of packets.

Our algorithms for sorting and selection are randomized and therefore have some probability of failure. In this paper, *with high probability* means with probability at least $1 - n^{-\beta}$ for some appropriate constant β. To analyze such probabilities, we make extensive use of the following bounds for the tails of the binomial distribution.

Fact 1 (*Bernstein-Chernoff bounds*) *Let $S_{N,p}$ be a random variable having binomial distribution with parameters N and p. Then, for any h such that $0 \leq h \leq 1.8Np$,*

$$P(S_{N,p} \geq Np + h) \leq \exp\left(-h^2/3Np\right).$$

For any $h \geq 0$,

$$P(S_{N,p} \leq Np - h) \leq \exp\left(-h^2/2Np\right).$$

Central to our algorithms is the use of a random sample of the keys in order to determine approximately the rank of each key. More specifically, given N keys and a small constant δ, consider the problem of choosing $N^\delta - 1$ elements which split the keys into buckets of size between $N^{1-\delta}(1 - N^{-2\delta})$ and $N^{1-\delta}(1 + N^{-2\delta})$. Using ideas from [Rei85, RV87] we describe the following randomized algorithm to select these splitters:

SELECT-SPLITTERS(N)

Phase A Select a sample of keys by having each key toss a coin with bias $\alpha N^{5\delta-1} \ln N$, for some constant α.

Phase B Count the actual size S of the sample. Then select $N^\delta - 1$ splitters by picking every $\lceil S/N^\delta \rceil$-th element from the sample to be a splitter.

Notice that the average size of the sample will be $\alpha N^{5\delta} \ln N$ and with high probability the size will not differ from its average value by more than $\alpha N^{5\delta/2} \ln N$. Furthermore, the actual rank of the j-th splitter will be $jN^{1-\delta}(1 \pm N^{-\delta})$. This can be shown with the following lemma:

Lemma 1 *For sufficiently small constant δ, there exists $\alpha > 0$, such that, given N keys, the above algorithm produces $N^\delta - 1$ splitters which split the keys into buckets of size $N^{1-\delta}(1 \pm N^{-2\delta})$; the probability that the algorithm fails is smaller than $N^{-\alpha/5}$.*

Proof. We use fact 1 to analyze the probabilistic behaviour of the above scheme. $\square$

Finally, we present some facts about routing and sorting on one-dimensional and two-dimensional arrays.

Lemma 2 *Consider the problem of routing a number of packets in a one-dimensional array with bidirectional edges. Assume that the packets have distinct priorities that are used to resolve contentions for the same edge. Then the time it takes each packet to reach its destination is at most equal to its origin-destination distance plus* *the number of packets that have priority larger than it. Packets are assumed to be forwarded to the next node whenever this is possible.*

Proof. (Cf. [RT91], Fact 1.) Consider a packet p and assume without loss of generality that it moves from left to right. Consider the set of packets with priority greater or equal to the priority of p (p including), and assume that the cardinality of this set is k. At each given time, consider the sequence whose ith term indicates how many among these packets are at the ith node at that given time. Packets that arrive to their destination stop contributing to any term of this sequence. We can easily prove by induction that after $k-1$ steps the initial sequence will be reduced to a sequence of zeroes and ones. This means that the packets are then free to travel and suffer no more delays (packets with smaller priorities can be ignored). In the worst case, p did not move at all so it needs time equal to its origin-destination distance to complete the routing. □

Lemma 3 *For any $k > 0$, and for any indexing scheme, there is a deterministic algorithm that sorts kn^2 keys in an $n \times n$ array (where initially and finally there are k keys per node) in time $O(kn)$. The maximum number of packets stored at any node is $O(k)$.*

Proof. Use any of the standard algorithms for sorting n^2 keys in an $n \times n$ array (e.g. [TK77, SS86]), where every comparison/exchange of two elements is achieved by merge and split operations on lists of size k. By applying a (fixed) k-k mapping we can sort the packets in any desired indexing scheme. □

Lemma 4 *For any $k > 0$, there is a randomized algorithm for routing any k-relation in an $n \times n$ mesh (i.e., at most k packets originate at each node and at most k packets are destined for any node) in time $O(kL)$ and using queues of size $O(k)$, with high probability, where L is the maximum over all origin-destination distances.*

Proof. A randomized algorithm for routing permutations ($k = 1$) in time $O(L)$ and which

uses $O(1)$ sized queues on the average was presented in [RT91]. Using the redistribution technique from that same paper, we can derive an algorithm that uses $O(1)$ sized queues with high probability. The extension for any k is straightforward. □

Lemma 5 *For any $k > 0$, there is a deterministic algorithm that computes the parallel prefix of kn^2 elements in an $n \times n$ mesh (where initially there are k elements per node) in time $O(kn)$. Tha maximum queue size is $O(k)$.*

Proof. The proof is straightforward and omitted. □

3   Sorting

In this section, we describe an algorithm for sorting $N = n^2$ elements on a $n \times n$ mesh in $2.5n + o(n)$ time and using constant size queues, with high probability.

Let $\delta < 1/6$ be a small constant. Divide the mesh in blocks of processors B_i, $i = 0, 1, \ldots, N^{\delta} - 1$, each of size $b = N^{1-\delta}$ (i.e., the B_i are $\sqrt{b} \times \sqrt{b}$ submeshes). Our algorithm works with any indexing scheme that ranks the blocks so that consecutively ordered blocks are physically adjacent on the mesh, e.g. snake-like; the processors inside each B_i are indexed with indices in the interval $[(i - 1)N^{\delta}, iN^{\delta}]$ in some arbitrary way.

Consider also the natural division of the mesh into four $n/2 \times n/2$ quadrants Q_i. Define the "middle diamond of radius k" to include all processors that lie within distance k from the middle processor (i.e., processor $(\lceil \frac{n}{2} \rceil, \lceil \frac{n}{2} \rceil)$); define D to be the middle diamond of radius $.5n$; D consists of four triangles T_i, where $T_i = D \cap Q_i$. Define the "middle block" B to be the block that contains the middle processor. Note that these definitions do not depend on the indexing scheme.

Before we present the algorithm in detail we give a high level description of it. The idea is to route a copy of each element to each triangle T_i; in the meantime, we select a random sample (the splitters), and then broadcast it to each quadrant, in order to determine approximately the rank of each element. The elements are then routed to the neighborhood of the processor whose index equals the approximate rank of the element as long as this processor is in the same quadrant as the triangle they are in. If not, the elements do not survive, so for each element only one of the four copies will survive. In the meantime, in each quadrant we compute and broadcast the exact global rank of the splitters. Now we can determine the exact global rank of each of the elements, which are finally routed to the correct processor.

3.1 The Algorithm

Our algorithm **SORT(N)** consists of the following 10 steps, some of which are performed simultaneously.

1. Select a random sample of expected size $\alpha N^{5\delta} \ln N$. To do this each processor selects itself with probability $\alpha N^{5\delta-1} \ln N$. Each element that is at a selected processor picks a random destination in the middle block B, and routes itself greedily towards it.

2. Sort the sample elements in the middle block B using a standard algorithm for sorting into snake-like order. Pick exactly $s = N^\delta - 1$ splitters as in lemma 1. Note that this leaves s sorted splitters in the b-sized B.

3. Broadcast the s splitters in the middle diamond D. This is done by greedily replicating B in all B_i that overlap with D.

4. In each quadrant Q_i randomize the elements row-wise.

5. Send a copy of each element to each triangle T_i. This is done by moving "together" the elements that start in each quadrant Q_i, and so that the elements that end at processor (r, c) are the ones that started at processors (r, c) or (c, r) (mod $n/2$). Now each triangle of the middle diamond contains all N elements; on the average there are 8 elements per processor.

6. In each block B_i that overlaps D sort all the elements that were sent there in step 4 along with the splitters sent in step 3. Then in each B_i do a prefix computation so that the elements will know their presumed splitter bucket (and therefore their destination block), and so that the splitters will know their exact rank in B_i. Then kill all element copies (not the splitters) that do not lie in the same quadrant as their presumed destination block.

7. Route all (live) elements to random nodes in their presumed destination blocks. This involves four essentially disjoint routing problems, one for each Q_i.

8. In each Q_i compute and broadcast the exact global rank of the splitters.

9. In each B_i sort the elements; do a prefix computation so that the elements will know their exact rank in B_i; then use the exact global splitter rank (broadcast in step 8) to find for each element its exact global rank.

10. Route each element to its exact final position.

The correctness of the algorithm **SORT(N)** follows from the discussion above. We will next prove it runs in time $2.5n + o(n)$ using queues of size $O(\log n)$, with high probability. This is followed by a discussion of how the queue size can be reduced to a constant.

3.2 Running time of SORT(N)

Lemma 6 *Step 1, routing the sample to B, can be done in time $n+o(n)$ with constant size queues, with high probability.*

Proof. Because of lemma 1, there are $\Theta(N^{5\delta} \log N)$ elements in the sample, with high probability. There are $N^{1-\delta}$ possible destinations in B, and each sample packet selects one of them uniformly at random. Since $\delta < 1/6$ and using fact 1, we can prove that there exists a constant $c > 1/\delta$ such that with high probability, at most

c packets choose the same destination. We will route the sample using a greedy algorithm, where each packet travels to the correct row and then to the correct column. Note that we only need to analyze the sample packets in one quadrant. Clearly no collisions occur while the packets are traveling up the column to the correct row. The queue size can increase only when two packets enter the queue for an edge at the same time, and this means at least one of the packets must have "turned" at the node. Since each packet turns only once, the expected number of packets that turn at any node, over all time is less than one. Consider any column and the half of it that lies in the quadrant. With high probability, the number of sample packets in the column does not exceed $n^{5\delta}$. Each of these packets picks one of the "middle" $n^{1-\delta/2}$ rows rows to turn. By fact 1, with high probability, the number of packets turning into a given node is bounded by a constant. □

Lemma 7 *Step 2, sorting the sample and picking the splitters, can be done in $o(n)$ time, using constant size queues.*

Proof. Follows from lemma 3. □

Lemma 8 *Step 3, broadcasting the splitter information inside D can be done in $.5n + o(n)$ time, with constant size queues.*

Proof. This is done by having each splitter send from its initial position inside B four copies, one in each direction; as they travel along the rows (or columns), these copies leave new copies of themselves every $\sqrt{b}$ columns (or rows); then each new copy similarly propagates itself to the two directions in the column (or row). At the end there is a copy of B at each B_i in D. Note that no more than $o(n)$ splitter elements travel per row or column; the maximum distance any splitter has to travel is $.5n$. □

Lemma 9 *Step 4, row-wise randomization inside each quadrant, takes $.5n$ time, using queues of size $O(\log n)$.*

Proof. This is done the obvious way. Each element picks a random destination in its half-row

and goes there. Because of fact 1, no more that $O(\log n)$ elements are destined for each processor. □

Lemma 10 *Step 5, routing copies of the elements to each triangle T_i, can be done in $n + o(n)$ time, using queues of size $O(\log n)$.*

Proof. Omitted. □

Lemma 11 *Steps 1-2-3 and 4-5 can be done simultaneously in $1.5n + o(n)$ time using queues of size $O(\log n)$.*

Proof. Assign to sample and splitter movement highest priority. Then steps 1-2-3 are clearly done after $1.5n + o(n)$ time. On the other hand steps 4-5 will be done in time $1.5n + o(n) + d$ where d is the maximum delay that any element will experience due to sample and splitter movement; but steps 1 and 3 involve the movement of $o(n)$ packets per row or column, while step 2 takes $o(n)$ time; therefore $d = o(n)$. □

Lemma 12 *Step 6 can be done in $o(n)$ time, using $O(\log n)$ size queues.*

Proof. Step 6 involves sorting and doing prefix computations of $O(b)$ elements over a b-sized mesh, where $b = o(n)$. Because of lemma 3 and lemma 5, this can be done $o(n)$ time. □

Lemma 13 *Step 7, routing each element to its presumed destination block, can be done in $n + o(n)$ time using $O(\log n)$ size queues.*

Proof. This is done separately in each quadrant Q_i. In each Q_i, there will be exactly $N/4$ live elements x_j to be routed (for even number of blocks per row). All x_j start inside T_i and we start with a constant number of elements per processor. The x_j are partitioned into two sets C_i and R_i; R_i contains the x_j that after step 5 were in the same row ($\bmod n/2$) as before step 5; C_i contains the x_j that after step 5 were in the same column ($\bmod n/2$) as the row they were before step 5; because of the randomization done in step 4, the elements in R_i are in random columns, while the elements in C_i are in random rows.

During step 7, each x_j is sent to a random processor somewhere inside its presumed destination block. The routing is done in two phases. In the first phase, elements in R_i are routed greedily along their columns to the row of their destination, while elements in C_i are routed along their rows to the column of their destination; then in the second phase all elements are routed to their destinations, C_i along columns and R_i along rows.

Now, as shown in claim 1 below, the first phase can finish in time $.5n + o(n)$ with $O(\log n)$ size queues, if only the elements in R_i are considered. Almost the same argument applies for the elements in C_i. Then similar arguments apply to phase 2. Therefore, since in each phase the elements in R_i use edges different from the ones the elements in C_i use, step 7 can be done in time $n + o(n)$ using $O(\log n)$ size queues. $\square$

Claim 1 *The elements in R_i can be routed to the rows of their destinations in time $.5n + o(n)$ using $O(\log n)$ size queues.*

Proof. The size of R_i is at most $N/4$. Each element in R_i has picked its column at random during step 4. Therefore (fact 1) no more than $.5n + o(n)$ elements will be routed along each column. Furthermore (fact 1 again), along each column no more than $n^{1-\delta} + o(n^{1-\delta})$ elements are destined for the column segment that overlaps some specific block B_l; note that such segments are of length $n^{1-\delta}$. This means that if a furthest-to-go priority is used, for each element that wants to travel $.5n - h(n)$ along the column, no more than $h(n) + o(n^{1-\delta})$ will have higher priority. Therefore, because of lemma 2, the time required is at most $.5n + o(n)$. Since at the beginning of the phase we start with constant number of elements per processor, it is clear that this routing needs no more than constant queues, except for the accumulation of packets at their destinations along the column. Since each element picks at random the particular processor that it wants to go inside its presumed destination block, we can show that no more than $O(\log n)$ elements are destined for each processor during this phase. So clearly this phase can be done with $O(\log n)$ size queues. $\square$

Lemma 14 *Step 8, computing and broadcasting in each quadrant the exact global rank of the splitters, can be done in $n + o(n)$ time using constant size queues.*

Proof. In step 6 the relative ranks of the splitters were computed inside each block B_i. Since at that time there was exactly one copy of each element per quadrant, adding in each quadrant the splitter partial rank information obtained in step 6 is enough to compute the global rank of the splitters. To do this, we first compact inside each B_i the splitter partial rank information; this is compacted in canonical order in a $\sqrt{s} \times \sqrt{s}$ submesh at the left top corner of B_i. Then this information propagates towards the center of the quadrant in a process similar to the one in lemma 6, but in reverse; during the propagation the partial ranks are added at each B_i. Thus, after $.5n + o(n)$ time, the global ranks of the splitters are computed at the center of each quadrant. Then this information is broadcast back to each block in the quadrant, again as in lemma 6 in time $.5n + o(n)$. $\square$

Lemma 15 *Steps 7 and 8 can be done simultaneously in $n + o(n)$ time using $O(\log n)$ size queues.*

Proof. Assign highest priority to splitter movement; then the argument is similar to lemma 11 above. $\square$

Lemma 16 *Step 9, sorting in each B_i and doing prefix computations to find the exact rank of each element, can be done in $o(n)$ time with $O(\log n)$ size queues.*

Proof. As in lemma 12 above. $\square$

Lemma 17 *Step 10, routing the elements to their final destinations can be done in $o(n)$ time using $o(\log n)$ size queues.*

Proof. No element has to travel more than $O(n^{1-\delta})$ distance because of lemma 1. Therefore we can perform step 10 using the algorithm of lemma 4. $\square$

By combining the lemmas above we get the following theorem:

Theorem 1 *There exists a randomized algorithm that sorts $N = n^2$ elements on a $n \times n$ mesh in $2.5n + o(n)$ time using $O(\log n)$ size queues, with high probability.*

3.3 Reducing the size of the queues to constant

In this section, we briefly describe how the size of the queues can be reduced to constant with high probability. As seen in the lemmas above steps 1, 2, 3 and 8 require only constant size queues; furthermore steps 6, 9 and 10 can be done with constant size queues if they start with constant size queues. Therefore, we only need to deal with this issue in steps 4, 5 and 7. For these steps the size of the queues follows a binomial distribution with a constant mean. However the bounds of fact 1 are not strong enough to give constant size queues with high probability.

Now, instead of considering individual processors we consider sets of processors obtained by dividing the rows and columns into consecutive groups of $\log n$ nodes each. Then the expected number of packets per group at the end of step 4, for example, is $\Theta(\log n)$ and using fact 1 we see that with high probability the number of packets per group is also $\Theta(\log n)$. Hence, the packets in each group can be redistributed so that only a constant number of packets resides in each queue. In other words, a packet is not stored at the targeted node but somewhere in the group in which that node belongs. We refer to [RT91] for one way of implementing this redistribution technique. We use the same technique at the end of both phases of step 7.

Then step 5 can be done exactly as described above; no modification is necessary since it starts and ends with constant queues. Finally, at the beginning of both phases of step 7 the packets start $O(\log n)$ distance from their "real" origins. It can be shown that the extra delay introduced by this discrepancy is $o(n)$. The proof is omitted.

Theorem 2 *There exists a randomized algorithm that sorts $N = n^2$ elements on a $n \times n$ mesh in $2.5n + o(n)$ time using constant size queues, with high probability.*

4 Selection

In this section, we describe our algorithm for selecting on the mesh the element of rank k among $N = n^2$ elements in $1.25n + o(n)$ steps and using constant size queues, with high probability. Reischuk [Rei85] and Megiddo [Meg82] describe parallel algorithms for selection in the parallel comparison tree model which work in expected constant time. Using some of these ideas, we will construct a parallel algorithm on the mesh and prove that it has the properties stated above.

As above, a random sample of the keys is chosen in order to determine an approximation to the key of rank k. Specifically, given N keys, we want to select two splitters u and v which split the set into three buckets, such that the element of rank k falls in the middle bucket, and further, the size of the middle bucket is $O(N^{1-\delta})$, for some sufficiently small constant δ.

We use the **SELECT-SPLITTERS(N)** algorithm from Section 2 to choose these bracketing elements. Sort the $N^\delta - 1$ splitters obtained from Phase B of the algorithm. Let $1 \leq j \leq N^\delta$ be such that $(j-1)N^{1-\delta} < k \leq jN^{1-\delta}$. From lemma 1, with high probability, the element of rank k falls into one of the three buckets determined by the splitters of rank $j-2, j-1, j$, and $j+1$ in the splitter set. We select u and v to be the splitters of rank $j-2$ and $j+1$, respectively. (If $j = 1$ then $u = -\infty$. If $j = N^\delta$ then $v = +\infty$.) Let $M = \{x_i \mid u \leq x_i \leq v\}$. Then it follows from lemma 1 that with high probability, for $\delta < 1/6$, the element of rank k lies between u and v, and $|M| \leq 6N^{1-\delta}$.

As in Section 3, we define B to be the middle block of side $n^{1-\delta}$ and D to be the middle diamond of radius $n/8$. We will now give a high level description of our algorithm for selection. First we move all the elements into the middle diamond D. In the meantime, we select a random sample and route it to the middle block B; there we select the two splitters u and v that bracket the element of rank k with high probability, and we broadcast them inside D. Then all the elements in the middle bucket M are routed to the middle of the mesh. In the meantime, the exact global ranks of u and v are computed and propagated to the middle block B. Finally the element of appropriate rank is selected among the elements in the block B.

4.1 The Algorithm

Our algorithm **SELECT(N, k)** to select the element of rank k out of $N = n^2$ elements, consists of the following seven steps.

1. Select a random sample of size $\alpha N^{5\delta} \ln N$. To do this each processor selects itself with probability $\alpha N^{5\delta-1} \ln N$. Each element that is at a selected processor picks a random destination in the middle block B, and routes itself greedily towards it.

2. Move all the remaining packets into the middle diamond D of radius $n/8$.

3. Sort the sample packets in B using a standard algorithm for sorting into snake-like order. Find the splitters u and v defined above.

4. Broadcast the values of the splitters u and v to all the processors in the middle diamond D. Each processor can calculate for each of the packets it holds, which splitter bucket it belongs to.

5. Compute the exact global ranks of the two splitters u and v. This can be done by finding the number of packets in each of the three buckets created by the splitters.

6. Packets with values in the middle bucket M choose a random destination in B. Route these packets to their chosen destinations.

7. If the element of rank k in X does indeed lie in M, and if $|M| \leq 6N^{1-\delta}$, sort M and find the element of rank $k - rank(u)$ (which

is the element of rank k in the set X), and we are done. Otherwise, broadcast a message to the whole mesh, and restart. Sort the input configuration, so that the element of rank k reaches the middle processor.

The correctness of the algorithm **SELECT(N,k)** follows from the discussion above. We will now prove it runs in the claimed number of steps using queues of size $O(\log n)$. The queue size can be reduced to a constant by using the same technique as described above for the sorting algorithm.

4.2 Running time of SELECT(N,k)

Lemma 18 *Step 1, routing the sample, can be done in $n + o(n)$ steps with constant size queues, with high probability.*

Proof. Similar to lemma 6. $\qquad \Box$

Lemma 19 *Step 2, overlapping the packets into D, the middle diamond of side $n/8$, can be done in $9n/8$ steps, with constant size queues.*

Proof. Consider the portion of the middle diamond of side $n/9$ in a particular quadrant. There are $n/9$ rows and columns entering it. By equally dividing the $n^2/4$ packets of the quadrant among these rows and columns we can maintain a steady stream of $2n/9$ packets entering this diamond and overlap all the packets into this diamond in $9n/8$ steps. However, the corner processors present a problem, as they have either a row edge or a column edge going into the diamond, but are receiving packets from both row and column edges and thus would require nonconstant size buffers. To solve this problem, we buffer the packets in the $n/72$ nodes inside the diamond of side $n/8$ but outside the diamond of side $n/9$. The overlapping can be achieved in such a way that no node buffers more than a constant number of packets. $\qquad \Box$

Lemma 20 *(i) Step 3, sorting the sample and selecting the splitters u and v , takes $o(n)$ steps.*
(ii) Step 4, broadcasting the values of u and v into the middle diamond D, takes $n/8 + 1$ steps.

(iii) Step 5, computing the exact global ranks of u and v, when all the packets are overlapped into the middle diamond D, takes $n/8 + 1$ steps.

(iv) Step 7, sorting the middle bucket M, and selecting the element of rank $k - rank(u)$, takes $o(n)$ steps.

Proof. The proof of (ii) follows from the fact that all the packets are in the middle diamond. We need to send two packets (the values of u and v) to each processor in the inner diamond. These packets travel up and down along all the center column and out along row edges. The two packets can be routed in a pipelined fashion, thus taking $n/8 + 1$ steps. The proof of (iii) is by noting that calculating the size of the three buckets is sufficient to calculate the ranks of u and v. To do this, each packet participates in two summing operations depending on which bucket it lies in. The summing packets proceed in a manner which is exactly the inverse of the operation described in in the proof of (ii). The proofs of (i) and (iv) follow from lemma 3. □

Lemma 21 *Let all the packets be overlapped into the middle diamond D, such that there are no more than a constant number of packets at any node. Then, step 6, routing the elements in M, can be done in time $n/8 + o(n)$ using queues of size $O(\log n)$, with high probability.*

Proof. We adapt the algorithm described in [RT91] for permutation routing.

Algorithm ROUTE

Divide the mesh up into $1/\epsilon$ slices containing ϵn rows each. If packet (i, j) wants to go to (r, s) eventually:

Phase 1: Choose a random row in its own slice, say p and go to (p, j).

Phase 2: Go to (p, s) (correct the column).

Phase 3: Go to (r, s) (correct the row).

Let γ be a bound on the number of packets at any node in the middle diamond. We show that

ROUTE solves the problem of routing $O(N^{1-\delta})$ packets with at most γ packets per origin node and at most $O(\log n)$ packets per destination node in $n/8 + \gamma\epsilon n + o(n)$ steps with queues of size $O(\log n)$ with high probability.

Queue size analysis: In Phase 1, processor (p, j) can receive γ packets from ϵn processors (the ones at the same strip and column as (p, j)), each with probability $1/(\epsilon n)$. Let E_m be the event that more than m packets will be stored at (p, j) at the end of Phase 1. Then, using fact 1, $P(E_m) = B\left(m; \gamma\epsilon n, \frac{1}{\epsilon n}\right) \leq \exp(m \ln \gamma - m \ln m + m - \gamma) = \exp(cm - m \ln m - \gamma)$. Therefore, the probability that any one processor will have more than m packets at the end of Phase 1, is less than $n^2 \exp(cm - m \ln m - \gamma) = \exp(2 \ln n - m \ln m + cm - \gamma)$. By choosing $m = \Theta(\log n)$ we can make this probability smaller than the inverse of some polynomial in n.

Consider a given node (p, s) at the end of Phase 2. With high probability, not more than $n^{1-\delta/2}$ packets will choose destinations in column s. Each of these picks node (p, s) with probability less than $1/\epsilon n$. Using fact 1, we can prove that with high probability at most $O(\log n)$ packets accumulate at any processor. Since the maximum of the queue sizes at the end of each phase is an upper bound on the sizes of queues at any step during the algorithm, we have proven that with high probability the queue size grows to at most $O(\log n)$.

Routing Time Analysis: Phase 1 can be accomplished in $\gamma\epsilon n$ steps, simply by making γ passes to account for γ packets at every node. In Phase 2, we use queuing discipline Q, and using a similar analysis to [RT91], we can show that the probability that the delay is more than n^{α} is at most $\exp(-Cn^{2\alpha-1})$. For Phase 3, we use queuing discipline Q'. Notice that the actual distance traveled by any packet is always less than $n/8 + \epsilon n + n^{1-\delta/2}$. Consider the effect on the running time if the three phases are coalesced. The only possible conflict is between packets doing their Phase 3 and Phase 1. In such a case, the packet doing its Phase 1 is given preference. If a packet q doing its Phase 3 contends for an edge with a packet that is doing its Phase 1, then it needs to go a maximum of $n/8$ steps to get to its destination. Since after $\gamma \epsilon n$ steps, q will only have to contend with packets doing their Phase 3, it will reach its destination in $n/8 + \gamma \epsilon n$ steps. No other packets suffer additional delays due to coalescing the phases.

Taking $\epsilon = 1/\log n$, we have shown that there is a randomized algorithm to route the middle bucket M in $n/8 + o(n)$ steps and using queues of size $\Theta(\log n)$ with high probability. □

We now show that some of the steps in our algorithm for selection can be combined, thus significantly lowering the total time taken by **SELECT(N,k)**.

Lemma 22 *Steps 1, 2, 3, and 4 can be done simultaneously in $n + n/8 + o(n)$ steps, using constant size queues.*

Proof. Give the sample packets priority over overlapping packets. We know from lemma 18 that the sample packets can be routed in n steps. With high probability, the number of sample packets turning into any row is $o(n)$, and therefore the overlapping packets are never delayed more than $o(n)$. The broadcasting packets are traveling in opposite directions to the overlapping packets; there are never any collisions between these. □

Lemma 23 *Step 5, collecting information about the sizes of the buckets as well as step 6, routing of M, can be done simultaneously in $n/8 + o(n)$ steps, using queues of size $O(\log n)$.*

Proof. The packets belonging to M take lower precedence. Then each such packet can be delayed at most 2 extra steps due to the regular pattern of the summing of the information. □

By combining steps 1, 2 and 3 and 4, and steps 5 and 6 of **SELECT(N,k)**, lemmas 20, 22, 23 prove the following theorem:

Theorem 3 *There exists an algorithm for finding the element of rank k out of $N = n^2$ elements on an $n \times n$ mesh that finishes in $1.25n + o(n)$ steps and uses queues of size $\Theta(\log n)$, with high probability.*

Notice that the only point where we may use large queues in our algorithm is in the routing of M. As in the sorting algorithm (see Section 3.3), we are able to apply redistribution techniques to achieve constant size queues. Therefore, we have:

Theorem 4 *There exists an algorithm for finding the element of rank k out of $N = n^2$ elements on an $n \times n$ mesh that finishes in $1.25n + o(n)$ steps and uses queues of size $O(1)$, with high probability.*

5 Extensions

Using similar techniques we can obtain the following results for 3-dimensional meshes:

Theorem 5 *There exists a randomized algorithm that sorts n^3 elements on an $n \times n \times n$ mesh that finishes in $4n + o(n)$ time and uses constant size queues, with high probability.*

Theorem 6 *There exists a randomized algorithm for selecting the element of rank k out of n^3 elements on an $n \times n \times n$ mesh that finishes in $2n + o(n)$ time and uses constant size queues, with high probability.*

Note that the previously known best bound for sorting in the 3-d mesh was $5n + o(n)$ [Kun88] which implied the same bound for selection.

Our techniques can be applied to obtain fast selection algorithms in higher dimensional meshes as well. On the other hand, they do not seem to extend to sorting algorithms for meshes with dimension 5 or higher.

Acknowledgements

We would like to thank Rajeev Raman and Satish Rao for helpful discussions. Also, we would like to thank Michael Rabin and Leslie Valiant for their constant encouragement and support.

References

[Chl89] B. Chlebus. Sorting within distance bound on a mesh-connected arrays. In *International Symp. on Optimal Algorithms. Vol. 401 of Lecture Notes in Computer Science, Springer Verlag, NY*, pages 232–238, 1989.

[Dal87] W. Dally. Wire-efficient VLSI multiprocessor communication networks. In *Advanced Research in VLSI*, pages 391–415, 1987.

[Kun88] M. Kunde. Routing and sorting on mesh-connected arrays. In *Aegean Workshop on Computing: VLSI algorithms and architectures. Vol.319 of Lecture Notes in Computer Science, Springer Verlag, NY*, pages 423–433, 1988.

[Kun89] M. Kunde. l-selection and related problems on grids of processors. Technical report, Institut fur Informatik, Technische Universitat, Munchen, 1989.

[LMT89] T. Leighton, F. Makedon, and I. Tollis. A 2n-2 step algorithm for routing in an n x n array with constant size queues. In *Symposium on Parallel Algorithms and Architecture*, pages 328–335, 1989.

[Meg82] N. Megiddo. Parallel algorithms for finding the maximum and median almost surely in constant time. Technical report, Carnegie-Mellon University, 1982.

[Raj90] S. Rajasekaran. Randomized parallel selection. In *Foundations of Software Technology and Theory of Computation*, 1990. to appear.

[Rei85] R. Reischuk. Probabilistic parallel algorithms for sorting and selection. *SIAM Journal of Computing*, 14(2):396–411, May 1985.

[RT91] S. Rajasekaran and Th. Tsantilas. Optimal routing algorithms for mesh-connected processor arrays. *Algorithmica (to appear)*, 1991. Preliminary version in Proc. AWOC '88, Lecture Notes in Computer Science, vol. 319, Springer-Verlag (1988), pp. 411-422.

[RV87] J. Reif and L. Valiant. A logarithmic time sort for linear size networks. *Journal of the ACM*, 34(1):60–76, 1987.

[SS86] C. Schnorr and A. Shamir. An optimal sorting algorithm for mesh connected computers. In *Symposium on the Theory of Computation*, pages 255–263, 1986.

[TK77] C. Thompson and H. Kung. Sorting on a mesh connected parallel computer. *Communications of the ACM*, 20:263–270, 1977.

[Val75] L. Valiant. Parallelism in comparison problems. *SIAM Journal of Computing*, 4:348–355, 1975.

Large-Scale Sorting in Parallel Memories

(extended abstract)

*Mark H. Nodine** and *Jeffrey Scott Vitter†*

Dept. of Computer Science
Brown University
Providence, R. I. 02912–1910

Abstract. We present several algorithms for sorting efficiently with parallel two-level and multilevel memories. Our main result is an elegant, easy-to-implement, optimal, *deterministic* algorithm for external sorting with P disk drives. This result answers the open problem posed by Vitter and Shriver. Our measure of performance is the number of parallel input/output (I/O) operations, in which each of the P disks can simultaneously transfer a block of B contiguous records. Our optimal algorithm is deterministic, and thus it improves upon the optimal randomized algorithm of [ViS] as well as the well-known deterministic but nonoptimal technique of disk striping.

The second part of the paper broadens our coverage from two-level memories to more general multilevel memories. In particular we consider the blocked uniform memory hierarchy (UMH) introduced by Alpern, Carter, and Feig, and its parallelization P-UMH, along with new variants. We give optimal and nearly-optimal algorithms for a wide range of bandwidth degradations, including a parsimonious algorithm for constant bandwidth. We also develop optimal sorting algorithms for all bandwidths for other versions of UMH and P-UMH, including natural restrictions we introduce called RUMH and P-RUMH, which more closely correspond to current programming languages.

1 Introduction

Sorting is reputed to consume roughly 20 percent of computing resources in large-scale installations [Knu, LiV]. Of particular importance is external sorting, in which the records to be sorted are too numerous to fit in the processor's main memory and instead are stored on disk. The bottleneck in external sorting is the time needed for the input/output (I/O) operations. Typically data are transferred in large units or *blocks*; this blocking takes advantage of the fact that the seek time is usually much longer than the transmission time per record. An increasingly popular (and necessary!) way to avoid the I/O bottleneck is to use many disk drives working in parallel [GHK, GiS, Jil, Mag, PGK, Uni].

In previous work, Aggarwal and Vitter [AgV] presented optimal upper and lower bounds on the number of I/Os needed for sorting and related problems of size N using a two-level memory model in which P physical blocks, each consisting of B contiguous records, can be transferred simultaneously in a single I/O. This model generalized the initial work of Floyd [Flo] and Hong and Kung [HoK]. The lower bounds are based solely on routing concerns and thus hold for an arbitrarily powerful adversary, except for case when M and B are extremely small, in which case the comparison model is used. The model in [AgV] is somewhat unrealistic, however, because in practice secondary storage is usually partitioned into separate disk drives, each capable of transferring only one block per I/O.

Vitter and Shriver considered the more realistic *P-disk model*, in which the secondary storage is partitioned into P physically distinct disk drives [ViS] (see Figure 1). (Note that each head of a multihead drive can count as a distinct disk in this definition, as long as each head can operate independently of the other heads on the drive.) In a single (parallel) I/O operation, each

*Support was provided in part by an IBM Graduate Fellowship and by a National Science Foundation Presidential Young Investigator Award CCR–9047466 with matching funds from IBM Corporation.

†Support was provided in part by a National Science Foundation Presidential Young Investigator Award CCR–9047466 with matching funds from IBM Corporation, by National Science Foundation grant CCR–9007851, by the U.S. Army Research Office under grant DAAL03–91–G–0035, and by the Office of Naval Research and the Defense Advanced Research Projects Agency under contract N00014–83–K–0146 and ARPA order 6320, amendment 1.

of the P disks can simultaneously transfer one block of B records. Thus, P blocks can be transferred per I/O, as in the [AgV] model, but only if no two of the blocks access the same disk. This assumption is reasonable in light of the way real systems are constructed.

The measure of performance is the number of parallel I/Os required; internal computation time is ignored. In practice, though, the algorithms dealt with are also very efficient in terms of internal procesing. This model also applies to the case in which each of the P disks is controlled by a separate CPU with internal memory capable of storing M/P records, and the P CPUs are connected by a network that allows some basic operations (like sorting of the M records in the internal memories) to be performed quickly in parallel. The bottleneck can be expected to be the I/O.

Vitter and Shriver presented a randomized version of distribution sort using two complementary partitioning techniques. Their algorithm meets the I/O lower bound given earlier for the more lenient model of [AgV], and thus the algorithm is optimal. It can outperform the well-known deterministic technique of disk striping by a logarithmic factor in terms of the number of I/Os. They posed as an open problem the question of whether there is an optimal algorithm that is deterministic.

In the next section, we answer the open question posed in [ViS] and present an optimal deterministic sorting algorithm called *Greed Sort*. It performs a merge sort in a greedy way, using a priority scheme during the first part of each merge process to "approximately merge" the runs together. A second part of the merge process completes the merging. Oddly enough, the intuitions of [ViS] suggested that merge sorting with P disks was particularly difficult to do, as opposed to distribution sorting.

In Section 3, we generalize our two-level perspective of Section 2 and consider multilevel hierarchical memories. The levels of memory in many large-scale computer systems progress from very small but very fast registers to successively larger but slower components, such as several layers of cache, primary memory, disks, and archival storage. We consider in particular the uniform memory hierarchy (UMH) proposed recently by Alpern, Carter, and Feig [ACF], as a followup to the elegant HMM and BT models of {Aggarwal, Alpern, Chandra, Snir} [AAC, ACSa]. Level ℓ consists of $\alpha \rho^{2\ell}$ memory locations organized as $\alpha \rho^\ell$ blocks of size ρ^ℓ, for constants α and ρ. Data are transferred between levels ℓ and $\ell + 1$ in units of blocks of size ρ^ℓ, with a communication bandwidth of $b(\ell)$.

A model for parallel hierarchies was introduced by Vitter and Shriver, in which P hierarchies are connected at their base level via an interconnection network. Optimal algorithms were presented for the parallel versions of HMM and BT (which we denote P-HMM and P-BT) [ViS]. The same parallel construction can be applied to UMH; we call the result P-UMH.

We present in Section 3 optimal and near-optimal sorting algorithms for UMH and P-UMH for a wide range of bandwidth rates $b(\ell)$, and we present a parsimonious schedule for merge sort for the case $b(\ell) = 1$. We also introduce a natural and easy-to-program restriction of UMH, called random-access UMH (or RUMH), for which we have optimal upper and lower bounds for all bandwidths and amounts of parallelism. We do the same for a sequential model of UMH called SUMH.

2 Greed Sort

The parameters for our two-level memory model (or disk I/O model) in Figure 1 are

$$
\begin{aligned}
N &= \text{\# records in the file;} \\
M &= \text{\# records that can fit in primary memory;} \\
B &= \text{\# records per block;} \\
P &= \text{\# disk drives;}
\end{aligned}
$$

where $M < N$, and $1 \leq PB \leq \lfloor (M - M^\beta)/2 \rfloor$, for $\beta < 1$. Our measure of performance is the number of parallel I/Os; during a parallel I/O, each disk can simultaneously transfer one contiguous block of data. For purposes of reference, we number the block locations on the P disks a the cyclical way such that Figure 2 represents a sorted list for the case $B = 1$. The B records within each block are numbered contiguously by their relative positions in the block.

Our Greed Sort algorithm is a type of merge sort. We create initial input runs (sorted lists) of size N/M by repeatedly reading in a memoryload, sorting it, and writing it back to the disks. In each subsequent pass, we merge together $R = \sqrt{M/B}/2$ input runs at a time to form larger runs, which are used as input runs for the next pass. Each pass will be shown to take $O(N/PB)$ I/Os, giving us a total I/O bound of[1]

$$
O\left(\frac{N}{PB}\left(1 + \log_{\sqrt{M/B}} \frac{N}{M}\right)\right) = O\left(\frac{N}{PB} \frac{\log \frac{N}{B}}{\log \frac{M}{B}}\right),
$$

which is optimal, by the lower bound of [AgV]. The analysis is presented in Section 2.2.

Theorem 1 *Greed Sort deterministically sorts $N \geq M$ records with $O(\frac{N}{PB} \log \frac{N}{B} / \log \frac{M}{B})$ parallel I/Os, which is optimal.*

The basic idea behind Greed Sort is the following: Let us assume that each of the R runs to be merged is stored consecutively on disk, beginning on disk 1 and cycling through the P disks. In each parallel read operation, the one or two "best" available blocks from each

---

[1] We use the notation $\log x$, where $x \geq 1$, to denote the quantity $\max\{1, \log_2 x\}$.

disk are read into primary memory: the block with the smallest minimum key value and the block with the smallest maximum key value. Treating each of the P disks independently, we sort its $2B$ records in primary memory and write the smallest B to the output list that we're forming; we put the largest B records at the front of the run from which the smallest minimum was taken (note that this run remains sorted after this operation). Figure 3 gives an example of this operation assuming that Run 1 contains the block with the smallest minimum and Run 2 the block with the smallest maximum on disk j. Ties are broken arbitrarily. If the blocks with the smallest minimum and the smallest maximum are the same block, we read only the one block and write it to the output list.

This operation results in an "approximately merged" list. The crucial observation is that the records are within $RPB = P\sqrt{MB}/2$ positions of their correct sorted locations. By an appropriate use of clustering throughout the course of the algorithm, this approximately merged list can be completely merged by a single pass consisting of several applications of the columnsort algorithm of Leighton [Lei] applied to subfiles of size $P\sqrt{MB}$. Then the next merge begins.

Columnsort is easiest to visualize as sorting into column-major order a matrix with r rows and c columns, with the requirement that c divides r and $r > 2(c-1)^2$. It has eight steps, of which the odd-numbered steps are all the same, consisting of sorting the records in each column. Steps 2 and 4 are a transpose operation, and Steps 6 and 8 amount to a cyclical shift by $r/2$.

The pseudocode for the Greed Sort algorithm is given in Figure 4. Since all the records within a run are sorted, consecutive blocks on the same disk from a run are in non-decreasing order. Thus, the block with the smallest minimum (or maximum) on a given disk must be the next unread block on that disk from some run. The collection of next unread blocks, one for each (run, disk) pair, is called the *candidate set* of blocks and is stored in a priority queue. There are P disks and R runs, so the candidate set has cardinality PR.

We assume for convenience that the runs are separated on each disk by blocks containing the key value $+\infty$, that is larger than any key. The algorithm uses $next[i,j]$ to keep track of the next block of run i to be read from disk j. The set of all blocks $next[i,j]$ comprises the candidate set. The maximum and minimum key fields of block $next[i,j]$ are stored in $biggest[i,j]$ and $smallest[i,j]$, respectively. We do our I/O operations into the buffers $b1$ and $b2$, which each consist of P smaller buffers. Buffers $b1[j]$ and $b2[j]$, for $1 \leq j \leq P$, each hold B records from disk j; we denote their maximum and minimum keys by $\max(b1[j])$, $\min(b1[j])$, $\max(b2[j])$, and $\min(b2[j])$. In the pseudocode below, when we use the construct **do in parallel**, we mean that the I/O within the loop should be done in parallel, not that the actual computation needs to be done in parallel.

2.1 Proof of Correctness

The correctness of Greed Sort depends on showing that each merge pass correctly merges the $R = \sqrt{M/B}/2$ runs into a single sorted run.

Theorem 2 *Each sequence of an approximate merge followed by columnsorts in the Greed Sort algorithm correctly merges R runs.*

Theorem 3 below shows that each record in the approximately merged output list formed from the R runs is at most $L = RPB$ locations from its correct sorted location. That the columnsorts on successive overlapping subfiles of size $2L$ complete the sorting is shown in Theorem 4. Together, Theorems 3 and 4 prove Theorem 2.

Theorem 3 *In the approximately merged output list formed from R runs, each record is at most RPB locations from its correct sorted location.*

This theorem is proved using Lemmas 1–3.

Lemma 1 *For any two records $x < y$ written to disk j in the approximately merged output list, x will be located at most $R - 1$ blocks later than y on disk j.*

Proof Sketch: Let record y be written to disk j of the output list at step t. (See Figure 3.) (By step t, we mean the tth time PB records are written to the output list being formed.) In the example given in Figure 3, $y \in \{1, 2, 3, 4\}$. The crucial observation is that at most one block in every run contains values less than y, and that all such values will be written in the next $R - 1$ blocks. □

We need a definition before presenting Lemma 2, which generalizes Lemma 1 by considering all the disks.

Definition 1 *A sequence is called L-regressive if for any two elements $x < y$, y does not precede x by more than L elements in the sequence.*

Lemma 2 *The approximately sorted output list is RPB-regressive.*

Proof: Let y be output on disk j. Then at most one block in any run on disk $i < j$ contains a value less than y as suggested by Figure 5. All elements less than y will either be output at the same time or within the next $R - 1$ time steps, using the same argument as in the proof for Lemma 1. Furthermore, any disk $i > j$ has already written all records with keys less than y. Combining with Lemma 1, which tells about other records on disk j, and noting that each "stripe" on the collection of disks contains PB records, the maximum regression is RPB. □

Lemma 3 *If a list is L-regressive, then every record is at most L locations from its correct sorted location.*

Proof Sketch: For simplicity, let all the records have unique keys. Assume that y is the jth smallest record and occurs at position i where $i < j - L$. We derive a contradiction by showing that there exists an $x < y$ that succeeds y by more than L records and hence the list is not L-regressive. There are $j - 1$ records less than y. In order to meet the L-regressive condition, they must all occur in the range $1, \ldots, i + L$. There are $i + L < j$ locations up to the point that is L records beyond y, of which y is occupying one. At least one record less than y must be out of the desired range, since $i + L - 1 < j - 1$. This same argument also shows that the jth record cannot be at any location $i > j + L$. The case of duplicate keys is more complicated and is covered in the full paper. □

Lemmas 2 and 3 directly prove Theorem 3. Finally, we demonstrate that the final pass of columnsorts finishes the sort.

Theorem 4 *If every element in a list is within a distance of L of its sorted location, then a series of sorts of size $2L$, beginning at every Lth location, will suffice to complete the sort.*

Proof Sketch: Let there be N total records, so that we perform a total of $N/L - 1$ sorts of size $2L$. The proof proceeds by induction on the number of sorts performed. During step t we sort records $tL + 1, tL + 2, \ldots, tL + 2L$. We have the following invariants at the beginning of step t (see Figure 6) and show that each step maintains the invariants:

1. All the records $1, \ldots, tL$ are completely sorted.

2. No record in $tL + 1, \ldots, N$ is more than $2L$ before or L after its final position.

The last step by definition sorts the last $2L$ records, so that at its conclusion, the whole list is sorted. □

2.2 Analysis of the Algorithm

To prove Theorem 1, we first show by a clustering technique that the amount of storage space required for the data structures is small enough.

Theorem 5 *The amount of primary memory space needed for the data structures of Greed Sort is $O(M^\beta)$, for $\beta < 1$.*

Proof Sketch: The number of runs that we must merge together in order to obtain optimal performance is $\sqrt{M/B}/2$. As we pointed out in Section 2, the candidate set requires a total of $P\sqrt{M/B}$ key fields to be kept in primary memory to decide what blocks to read next. At first glance, it seems if $P = O(M)$ and $B = 1$ that $\Omega(M^{3/2})$ storage space will be required in primary memory, which is clearly impossible. However, we can use a partial disk striping method throughout the course of the algorithm. Assume that $P = P(M)$

grows faster than M^α, where $0 < \alpha < 1/2$. We can cluster our P disks into clusters of $P' = M^\alpha$ clusters of $B' = BP/P'$ disks synchronized together. Each of the P' clusters acts like a logical disk with block size B'. Thus, the number of primary storage locations we need is at most

$$P'\sqrt{M/B'} \leq M^\alpha \sqrt{M/B'} = O(M^{\alpha + 1/2}).$$

but the number of I/Os remains the same within a constant factor. We set $\beta = \alpha + 1/2$. □

In order to demonstrate that Greed Sort has an optimal I/O bound, we need to analyze the I/O efficiency of the columnsort subroutine.

Theorem 6 *Columnsort sorts $N \leq P\sqrt{MB}$ records with $O(N/PB)$ parallel I/Os.*

Proof: First we show that columnsort produces a correctly sorted sequence when $N \leq P\sqrt{MB}$. We define the number of rows in the matrix to be $r = M$, so that each column can be sorted internally. We have

$$N \leq P\sqrt{MB} \leq PB\sqrt{M} \leq \frac{M^{3/2}}{2} < \frac{M^{3/2}}{\sqrt{2}},$$

making use of our assumption that $2PB \leq M$. Thus, the number of columns in our application of columnsort is $c = N/r \leq \sqrt{M/2}$, and the columnsort requirement that $r \geq 2(c-1)^2$ is met. Thus, the columnsort works correctly.

Steps 1, 3, 5, 6, 7, and 8 can be done easily with $O(N/PB)$ I/Os. The transpose-like operation in Steps 2 and 4 can be done with $O(N/PB)$ I/Os by a variant of the $p \times q$ matrix transpose algorithm of [ViS], for $p = M$ and $q = N/M \leq P\sqrt{B/M}$, which we omit for brevity. The resulting number of I/Os is also $O(N/PB)$. □

The greedy merge reads each record at most three times (once for updating *biggest* and *smallest* and up to twice for merging) and writes each record at most twice, taking full advantage of parallel block transfer. The columnsort routine is called $2N/k - 1$ times, each time using $O(k/PB)$ I/Os, for a value of k that differs from pass to pass. Thus the total number of parallel I/Os is $O(N/PB)$:

Corollary 1 *Each merging step requires $O(N/PB)$ parallel I/Os.*

By the remarks immediately before Theorem 1, this concludes the proof of Theorem 1.

3 Uniform Memory Hierarchies

Several interesting and elegant hierarchical memory models have been proposed recently to model the many levels of memory typically found in large-scale computer systems. The levels of memory range from very small but very fast registers to successively larger but slower components such as caches, primary memory, disks, and archival storage.

The HMM model of Aggarwal, Alpern, Chandra, and Snir [AAC] allows access to individual location x in time $f(x)$. The BT model of Aggarwal, Chandra, and Snir [ACSa] represents a notion of block transfer applied to HMM; in the BT model, access to the $t + 1$ records at locations $x - t$, $x - t + 1$, ..., x takes time $f(x) + t$. Typical access cost functions are $f(x) = \log x$ and $f(x) = x^\alpha$, for some $\alpha > 0$. A model similar to the BT model that allows pipelined access to memory in $O(\log n)$ time was developed independently by Luccio and Pagli [LuP]. Optimal sorting algorithms for each of these models have been developed [AAC, ACSa, LuP].

For the same reason that multiple disks are useful in overcoming the I/O bottleneck, Vitter and Shriver [ViS] considered the HMM and BT models in a parallel framework. In the P-HMM (respectively, P-BT) model [ViS], there are P HMM (respectively, BT) hierarchies, which can function independently, as shown in Figure 7. Communication between the P hierarchies takes place at the *base memory level* (call it level 0), which consists of location 1 from each of the P hierarchies. The P base memory level locations are interconnected via a network such as the hypercube or cube-connected cycles so that the P records in the base memory level can be sorted in $O(\log P)$ time (perhaps via a randomized algorithm [ReV]). Vitter and Shriver introduced optimal randomized sorting algorithms for P-HMM and P-BT [ViS]. The algorithms were based on their randomized two-level partitioning technique applied to the optimal single-hierarchy algorithms for HMM and BT developed in [AAC, ACSa].

In this section we concentrate on a newer model introduced by Alpern, Carter, and Feig [ACF, ACSb], called uniform memory hierarchies (UMH), which offer an alternative model of blocked multilevel memories. In the $\text{UMH}_{b(\ell)}$ model (for integer constants $\alpha, \rho \geq 2$), the ℓth memory level (as illustrated in Figure 8) consists of $\alpha\rho^\ell$ blocks, each of size ρ^ℓ; it is connected via buses to levels $\ell - 1$ and $\ell + 1$. Each individual block on level ℓ can be randomly accessed as a unit and transferred to or from level $\ell + 1$ at a *bandwidth* of $b(\ell)$; that is, each block transfer takes time $\rho^\ell/b(\ell)$. The CPU resides at level 0. The initial input of N elements resides at level $\lceil \frac{1}{2} \log_\rho \frac{N}{\alpha} \rceil$.

We can consider parallel UMH hierarchies (analogous to P-HMM and P-BT), and we call the resulting model P-UMH. (This is fundamentally different from the parallel type of UMH called UPHM mentioned in [ACF].)

A UMH or P-UMH "program" consists of a schedule of choreographed block transfers and computations. If a RAM program that runs in $T(N)$ steps can be scheduled in UMH in $\sim T(N)$ time, the program is said to be *parsimonious*; note that the constant factor must be 1. If the UMH program runs in time $O(T(N))$, it is said to be *efficient*. A UMH program whose running time is within a constant factor of best possible in the UMH model is said to be *optimal*.

3.1 UMH and its Parallelization

Optimal sorting in $O(N \log N)$ time in UMH is possible only when the bandwidth $b(\ell)$ at level ℓ is $\Omega(1/\ell)$, or else the time required just to access the N records will be greater than $O(N \log N)$. Many buses may be active simultaneously in the UMH model, so conceivably it is possible to sort in $O(N \log N)$ time even with small bandwidth $b(\ell) = 1/(\ell + 1)$.

Recently other authors announced an efficient UMH sorting algorithm for the case $b(\ell) = 1/(\ell + 1)$, based on the optimal two-level distribution sort algorithm of [AgV], but their $\text{UMH}_{1/(\ell+1)}$ algorithm turned out to be inefficient, with a running time of $\Omega(N \log^c N)$, for $c > 3$. Whether or not an $O(N \log N)$-time $\text{UMH}_{1/(\ell+1)}$ algorithm exists is still open.

In this section we give a near-optimal sorting algorithm for the small bandwidth case $b(\ell) = 1/(\ell + 1)$, and optimal sorting algorithms for several other bandwidths. For the special case of constant bandwidth, we present a *parsimonious* algorithm. Since optimal sorting seems to require nonoblivious UMH programs, the oblivious UMH model of [ACF] must be modified in a reasonable way. In Theorem 7, we assume that the ℓth level of the hierarchy can initiate a transfer from the $(\ell + 1)$st level when one of its blocks becomes empty. In Theorem 8, we assume that the CPU can originate the transfer of a block at level ℓ given the address of the block, with suitable delay.

Theorem 7 *A variant of merge sort can be scheduled in UMH_1 parsimoniously, assuming $\alpha \geq 2$ and $\alpha\rho \geq 6$.*

The basic idea is to schedule a systolic binary merge sort in such a way that the CPU is always kept busy (after a small initial delay and with a small final delay for writing the results back). After the initial delay, the CPU (level 0) reads one element from each of the two lists. At every time step after the initial delay, the CPU will write the smaller element to the output list and then read the next element from that list that had the minimum at the previous step. We use a double-buffering scheme so that level ℓ, for $\ell \geq 1$, has two blocks from each of the two lists being merged. It also has two blocks for the output list. When level $\ell - 1$ requests a subblock from one of the lists, and this request causes level ℓ's buffer to be emptied, then level ℓ requests the next block from level $\ell + 1$. In this way, level ℓ always has a sub-block for level $\ell - 1$ available on demand. The output blocks fill up at a known rate, so they can be scheduled in advance (again using double-buffering to keep an empty subblock available for writing from level $\ell-1$). If one list empties before the other, then we immediately begin to send a new list down. The CPU can keep track of how many elements have been read from each list, so that it can know when one list is finished and that it just needs to copy the rest of the other list to the output. While the CPU is processing the rest of this list, we can be filling up our buffers for the next pair of lists to be merged. The number of wasted CPU cycles is only $O(\log N) = o(N \log N)$, so the schedule is parsimonious.

Theorem 8 *Distribution sort algorithms can be scheduled on P-UMH with the following running times. The algorithms for nonconstant P for the first two bandwidth cases are randomized.*

$$
\begin{cases}
\Theta\left(\dfrac{N}{P}\log N\right) & \text{if } b(\ell) = 1; \\[2ex]
O\left(\dfrac{N}{P}\log N \log\left(\dfrac{\log N}{\log P}\right)\right) & \text{if } b(\ell) = 1/(\ell+1); \\[2ex]
\Theta\left(\left(\dfrac{N}{P}\right)^{1+c/2} + \dfrac{N}{P}\log N\right) & \text{if } b(\ell) = \rho^{-c\ell}, \, c > 0.
\end{cases}
$$

The algorithms are optimal, except for the middle $b(\ell) = 1/(\ell + 1)$ case, which is off from the best known lower bound of $\Theta((N/P)\log N)$ by a $\log((\log N)/\log P)$ factor. The proofs are suppressed for brevity. The algorithm that achieves the upper bound for the first case $b(\ell) = 1$ is based on a simulation of the P-BT algorithm for $f(x) = \sqrt{x}$ given in [ViS]. The lower bound follows from the conventional $N \log N$ serial bound for sorting. For the second case $b(\ell) = 1/(\ell+1)$, the upper bound and lower bounds are related to the P-HMM approach for $f(x) = \log x$ [ViS]. The third case $b(\ell) = \rho^{-c\ell}$ makes use of the P-HMM lower bound for $f(x) = x^{c/2}$ and an algorithm based on deterministic merge sort.

We have also scheduled an efficient oblivious sorting algorithm for $\mathrm{UMH}_{1/(\ell+1)}$ corresponding to a nonoptimal RAM sorting algorithm based on columnsort. By oblivious, we mean that that data movement between levels can be prespecified, and thus no extra capabilities of the UMH model are required beyond those of [ACF]. The resulting running time is $O(N \log^c N)$, where $c \approx 3.4$.

3.2 SUMH and RUMH and their Parallelizations

The UMH model can be difficult to program because many buses can be active simultaneously. An earlier version of [ACF] introduced a *sequential* UMH model, appropriately called SUMH, that allowed at most one bus to be active at a time. However, the SUMH restriction can be regarded as too severe.

We introduce the following more natural and less severe restriction that corresponds more closely to fea-

sible and easy-to-use programming languages: We require that the UMH program correspond exactly to a RAM program in which the RAM instruction set is augmented with a block move command that can move t contiguous memory elements in time t, for arbitrary t. Each such block transfer can be implemented in UMH by a coordinated series of transfers in which several buses are simultaneously active but cooperating on that single transfer. We call this natural variant of UMH the *random-access* UMH model, or simply RUMH. For example, a block of $\sqrt{N}$ elements can be moved from the top memory level all the way down to the CPU (or anywhere in between) in $\sim \sqrt{N}$ time in UMH_1 and RUMH_1, but it requires $\Theta(\sqrt{N}\log N)$ time in SUMH_1.

The parallel versions of RUMH and SUMH are called P-RUMH and P-SUMH, respectively. Theorems 9 and 10 give matching upper and lower bounds for sorting in the RUMH and SUMH models and their parallelizations.

Theorem 9 *The running times mentioned in Theorem 8 are matching upper and lower bounds for sorting in P-RUMH. The upper bounds are achieved by the algorithms mentioned in Theorem 8. The algorithms for nonconstant P for the first two bandwidth cases are randomized.*

Theorem 10 *The following bounds are matching upper and lower bounds for sorting in P-SUMH. The algorithms for nonconstant P for the first two bandwidth cases are randomized.*

$$
\begin{cases}
\Theta\left(\dfrac{N}{P}\log N \log\left(\dfrac{\log N}{\log P}\right)\right) & \text{if } b(\ell) = 1; \\[2ex]
\Theta\left(\dfrac{N}{P}\log N \log\dfrac{N}{P}\right) & \text{if } b(\ell) = 1/(\ell+1); \\[2ex]
\Theta\left(\left(\dfrac{N}{P}\right)^{1+c/2} + \dfrac{N}{P}\log N\right) & \text{if } b(\ell) = \rho^{-c\ell}, \, c > 0.
\end{cases}
$$

The structures of the formulas in Theorems 9 and 10 suggest several different relationships between the RUMH and SUMH models on the one hand and the HMM, BT, and two-level models on the other hand (cf. Theorems 5 and 6 in [ViS]); accordingly the upper and lower bounds combine in an interesting way several techniques from [AAC, ACSa, AgV, ViS].

The proofs are suppressed for brevity. The distribution sort algorithms of Theorem 8 are RUMH algorithms. Both sets of algorithms use a distribution sort framework for the higher bandwidths and merge sort for the lower bandwidths. The upper bound for the first two cases $b(\ell) = 1$ and $b(\ell) = 1/(\ell + 1)$ are achieved by an algorithm based on the optimal P-HMM algorithm of [ViS], for access functions $f(x) = \log x$ and $f(x) = \log^2 x$, respectively. The upper bound for the $b(\ell) = \rho^{-c\ell}$ case is achieved by deterministic merge sort. The lower bounds are proved using an approach similar to that of [AAC]. We superimpose on the P-SUMH model a sequence of two-level memories. For $i = 1, 2, 3, \ldots$, the ith two-level memory has P disks, internal memory size $M = P\alpha(\rho^{2(i+1)}-1)/(\rho^2-1)$, and block size $B = \rho^i$. The cost of an I/O in each superposition is B (for $b(\ell) = 1$), $B \log B$ (for $b(\ell) = 1/(\ell+1)$), and B^{1+c} (for $b(\ell) = \rho^{-c\ell}$). The lower bounds follow by applying the lower bounds from [AgV] for the two-level case. The third case also requires the use of the the conventional $N \log N$ serial bound for sorting.

4   Conclusions

We have presented the first optimal, deterministic external sorting algorithm for multiple disks, improving significantly the randomized algorithm of [ViS]. The greed sort algorithm is easy to implement and is efficient in terms of internal computations.

We have also given optimal or near-optimal sorting algorithms for UMH and its parallelization P-UMH, and we have derived tight matching bounds for sorting in the restricted models RUMH and SUMH and their parallelizations. Some parallel versions are randomized. The RUMH model is particularly useful because it is easy to visualize and to extend current programming languages and compilers.

An interesting open problem is whether a distribution-type sort can be implemented deterministically and optimally in terms of the number of parallel I/Os in the two-level model. This could have applications to optimal deterministic sorting in P-HMM, P-BT, P-UMH, P-RUMH, and P-SUMH, for which the current optimal algorithms in several cases are randomized. Another interesting open question is whether it is possible to sort in $O(N \log N)$ time $\text{UMH}_{1/(\ell+1)}$.

References

[AAC] A. Aggarwal, B. Alpern, A. K. Chandra and M. Snir, "A Model for Hierarchical Memory," *Proceedings of 19th Annual ACM Symposium on Theory of Computing* (May 1987), 305–314.

[ACSa] A. Aggarwal, A. Chandra and M. Snir, "Hierarchical Memory with Block Transfer," *Proceedings of 28th Annual IEEE Symposium on Foundations of Computer Science* (October 1987), 204–216.

[AgV] A. Aggarwal and J. S. Vitter, "The Input/Output Complexity of Sorting and Related Problems," *Communications of the ACM* (September 1988), 1116–1127, also appears in *Proceedings of 14th Annual International Colloquium on Automata, Languages, and Programming (ICALP)*, LNCS 267, Springer-Verlag, Berlin, 1987.

[ACF] B. Alpern, L. Carter and E. Feig, "Uniform Memory Hierarchies," *Proceedings of the 31st Annual IEEE Symposium on Foundations of Computer Science* (October 1990), 600–608.

[ACSb] B. Alpern, L. Carter and T. Selker, "Visualizing Computer Memory Architectures," *Proceedings of the 1990 IEEE Visualization Conference Foundations of Computer Science* (October 1990).

[Flo] R. W. Floyd, "Permuting Information in Idealized Two-Level Storage," in *Complexity of Computer Calculations*, R. Miller and J. Thatcher, ed., Plenum, 1972, 105–109.

[GHK] G. Gibson, L. Hellerstein, R. M. Karp, R. H. Katz and D. A. Patterson, "Coding Techniques for Handling Failures in Large Disk Arrays," U. C. Berkeley, UCB/CSD 88/477, December 1988.

[GiS] D. Gifford and A. Spector, "The TWA Reservation System," *Communications of the ACM* 27 (July 1984), 650–665.

[HoK] J. W. Hong and H. T. Kung, "I/O Complexity: The Red-Blue Pebble Game," *Proc. of the 13th Annual ACM Symposium on the Theory of Computing* (May 1981), 326–333.

[Jil] W. Jilke, "Disk Array Mass Storage Systems: The New Opportunity," Amperif Corporation, September 1986.

[Knu] D. Knuth, in *The Art of Computer Programming, Volume 3: Sorting and Searching*, Addison-Wesley, Reading, MA, 1973.

[Lei] T. Leighton, "Tight Bounds on the Complexity of Parallel Sorting," *IEEE Transactions on Computers* C-34 (April 1985), 344–354, also appears in *Proceedings of the 16th Annual ACM Symposium on Theory of Computing*, (April 1983), 71–80.

[LiV] E. E. Lindstrom and J. S. Vitter, "The Design and Analysis of BucketSort for Bubble Memory Secondary Storage," *IEEE Transactions on Computers* C-34 (March 1985), 218–233.

[LuP] F. Luccio and L. Pagli, "A Model of Sequential Computation Based on a Pipelined Access to Memory," *Proceedings of the 27th Annual Allerton Conference on Communication, Control, and Computing* (September 1989).

[Mag] N. B. Maginnis, "Store More, Spend Less: Mid-Range Options Around," *Computerworld* (November 16, 1986), 71.

[PGK] D. A. Patterson, G. Gibson and R. H. Katz, "A Case for Redundant Arrays of Inexpensive Disks (RAID)," *Proceedings ACM SIGMOD Conference* (June 1988), 109–116.

[ReV] J. H. Reif and L. G. Valiant, "A Logarithmic Time Sort on Linear Size Networks," *Journal of the ACM* 34 (January 1987), 60–76, also appears in *Proceedings of the 15th Annual ACM Symposium on Theory of Computing* (April 1983), 10–16.

[Uni] University of California at Berkeley, "Massive Information Storage, Management, and Use (NSF Institutional Infrastructure Proposal)," Technical Report No. UCB/CSD 89/493, January 1989.

[ViS] J. S. Vitter and E. A. M. Shriver, "Optimal Disk I/O with Parallel Block Transfer," *Proceedings of the 22nd Annual ACM Symposium on Theory of Computing* (May 1990), 159–169.

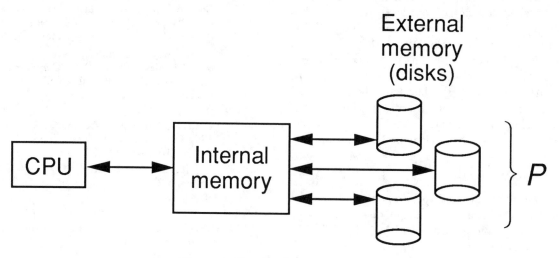

Figure 1: Two-level memory model.

Disk 1	1	26	42	71	83	94
Disk 2	4	29	47	77	85	96
Disk 3	7	31	60	79	89	98
Disk 4	14	32	68	80	91	99

Figure 2: An example of a sorted list with $P = 4$, $B = 1$.

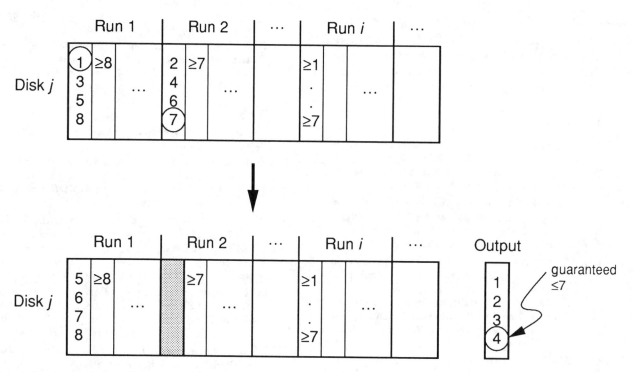

Figure 3: Assume that Run 1 contains the block with the smallest minimum and Run 2 that with the smallest maximum on some disk j. Then this figure shows what the situation will be after the blocks have been processed.

algorithm *Greed Sort*;
{ Create the initial runs }
repeat N/M times
    read the next M records into primary memory, PB at a time
    sort the M records internally
    write the M records back onto disk, PB at a time
end repeat

repeat until only 1 run is left
    { Merge together $R = \sqrt{M/B}/2$ input runs at a time }
    $R := \sqrt{M/B}/2$
    { The output runs of the previous stage become the input runs for this stage }
    repeat until all input runs have been processed
        pick the next R runs to process
        for $i := 1$ **to** R **do**   { Initialize }
            read in parallel the first P blocks of run i into buffer $b1$
            for $j := 1$ **to** P **do**
                $next[i,j] := 1$
                $biggest[i,j] := \max(b1[j])$
                $smallest[i,j] := \min(b1[j])$
            end for
        end for

        { Do an approximate merge of the R runs }
        repeat until all records of the R runs have been processed
            for $j := 1$ **to** P **do in parallel**
                { Find the best one or two blocks to read from each disk }
                $bestrun1[j] := i$ such that $biggest[i,j]$ is a minimum
                $bestrun2[j] := i$ such that $smallest[i,j]$ is a minimum
                read block $next[bestrun1[j],j]$ of run $bestrun1[j]$ from disk j into buffer $b1[j]$
                if $bestrun1[j] \neq bestrun2[j]$ **then**
                    read block $next[bestrun2[j],j]$ of run $bestrun2[j]$ from disk j into buffer $b2[j]$
                    merge $b1[j]$ and $b2[j]$ in place internally
                    write $b2[j]$ to block $next[bestrun2[j],j]$ of run $bestrun2[j]$ on disk j
                endif
                write $b1[j]$ to disk j in the output list
                read block $next[bestrun1[j],j]+1$ of run $bestrun1[j]$ from disk j into buffer $b1[j]$
                { Update data structures }
                $next[bestrun1[j],j] := next[bestrun1[j],j]+1$
                $biggest[bestrun1[j],j] := \max(b1[j])$ { May be $+\infty$ }
                $smallest[bestrun1[j],j] := \min(b1[j])$ { May be $+\infty$ }
                if $bestrun1[j] \neq bestrun2[j]$ **then**
                    $smallest[bestrun2[j],j] := \min(b2[j])$ { The biggest hasn't changed }
                end if
            end for
        end repeat

        { Do a restorative pass to turn the approximate merge into a complete merge }
        $L := RPB$
        $T :=$ total # of records in the R runs
        for $n := 0$ **to** $T/L - 2$ **do**
            use columnsort to sort records $nL+1, nL+2, \ldots, nL+2L$ of the output list
        end for
    end repeat
end repeat

Figure 4: The Greed Sort algorithm.

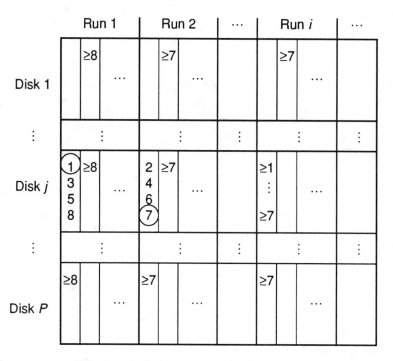

Figure 5: All the records output on disk j at this step are guaranteed to have keys ≤ 7 (in fact the largest key will be 4). Any disk prior to disk j has at most one block per run containing elements less than any key output on disk j, all of which will be written no more than $R-1$ blocks after this one. Any disk after disk j has already output all keys less than those written on disk j. Thus, a smaller key can follow a larger one by at most RPB locations in the approximately merged output list.

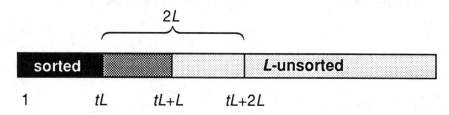

Figure 6: A series of sorts of size $2L$ suffices to fix up an L-regressive list.

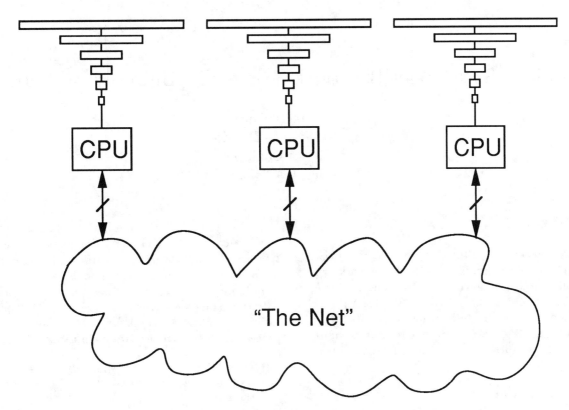

Figure 7: A parallel hierarchical memory. The P individual memory hierarchies are all of the same type, such as HMM, BT, or UMH. The P CPUs can communicate among one another via the interconnection network (which can be a hypercube or cube-connected cycles, for example).

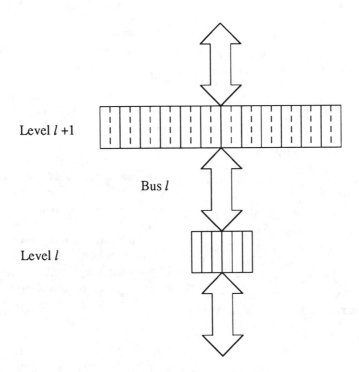

Level $l+1$

Bus l

Level l

Figure 8: The uniform memory hierarchy (UMH), pictured here for the case $\alpha = 3$, $\rho = 2$. The ℓth memory level contains $\alpha\rho^\ell$ blocks, each of size ρ^ℓ. It is connected via buses to levels $\ell - 1$ and $\ell + 1$. Each level ℓ block can be randomly accessed and transferred to level $\ell + 1$ at a *bandwidth* of $b(\ell)$ (that is, in $\rho^\ell/b(\ell)$ time).

Optimal Speedup for Backtrack Search on a Butterfly Network

Abhiram Ranade *
Computer Science Division
University of California
Berkeley, CA 94720

Abstract

We present a generic algorithm for implementing back-track search on an N processor butterfly network. For a backtrack search tree having M nodes and height h, our algorithm requires time $O(\frac{M}{N} + h + \log N)$ with high probability. This is optimal for trees with $M = \Omega(N \log N)$, and is obtained without making assumptions about the shape of the tree being searched.

1 Introduction

Combinatorial optimization problems frequently arise in many areas including operations research, artificial intelligence and VLSI design, e.g. finding a minimum cost tour through a set of cities, or placement of components on a printed circuit board. For many such problems the best known algorithms consist of heuristically enumerating possible solutions and then choosing an optimum. Given that these problems are often very compute intensive, a parallel algorithm for speeding up the search process is very desirable.

It is customary to represent the space of possible solutions to the optimization problem by the leaves of a rooted *search tree*. The tree is not explicitly specified as a part of the input, but is dynamically generated by the algorithm as it executes. Each internal node of the tree represents a partial solution (e.g. a partial placement of components), with its children representing its refinements (e.g. with a few additional components placed). Leaves in the tree either represent complete solutions (e.g. all components placed), or may represent partial solutions which cannot be refined any further to yeild complete solutions. Each leaf is associated with a cost (e.g. printed circuit board area), and the goal of the

algorithm is to find the minimum cost leaf.[1] In the simplest case, the search algorithm explores the entire tree in a depth first manner. After exploring each leaf, it *backtracks* to a previous node and resumes searching from there. This is referred to as *backtrack search*.

In this paper we present a generic parallel implementation of backtrack search on a Butterfly network of processors. This involves two main issues:

1. *Load Balancing:* The task of generating the search tree must be distributed among the processors in the network.

2. *Communication locality:* It is desirable to schedule operations that share data on processors that are closeby in the network, so as to minimize communication delay.

Our implementation addresses both these issues and with high probability guarantees optimal speedup *without making assumptions about the shape of the search tree.*

Many techniques have been developed for balancing load and acheiving communication locality for *static* problems i.e. problems in which the data flow is completely known before hand e.g. matrix multiplication, FFT and others. However, parallelizing backtrack search is considerably more difficult, because the structure of the search tree can be known only during execution. Thus the load balancing algorithm must be able to deal with any tree that may be generated during execution while maintaining communication locality. In fact, to our knowledge, our algorithm is the first example of a provably optimal algorithm for solving a *dynamic* problem on a sparse network.

1.1 Model

Following Karp and Zhang[1], we model a backtrack search problem as a rooted tree H with a cost function over its leaves. The goal is to find the leaf of least cost in H. The input to the algorithm is the root of

*Supported in part by Air Force Office of Scientific Research, Grant # F49620-87-C-0041.

[1] A leaf corresponding a partial solution that cannot be further refined is assigned infinite cost.

H, and the other nodes in H are generated as required during execution by a procedure called *node expansion*. Expanding a node results in generating its children if any, or else in determining the cost if it is a leaf. A node can be expanded only if it is the root, or if it has been generated previously during the expansion of its parent. No other constraints are placed on the order in which nodes are expanded. The number of nodes in the tree is denoted by M and the height of the tree is denoted by h. We assume that the algorithm does not know M or h or the shape of the tree before execution.

Our parallel computer consists of a Butterfly network of $N = n2^n$ processors organized in n levels numbered 0 through $n - 1$, with the processors in each level numbered 0 through $2^n - 1$. Processor x in level i is connected to processors x and $x \oplus 2^i$ in level $i + 1 \mod n$.[2]

In a single time step each processor in our network can perform one node expansion and send or receive a single message from each of its neighbors. We assume that in a single message a processor can send a single tree node to another processor for expansion. The execution of the search algorithm consists of node expansion steps as well as other operations for the purposes of bookkeeping. Our model only charges for node expansion and communication, the bookkeeping operations like maintaining unexpanded nodes in a queue etc. are assumed to take zero time. This is based on the assumption that in real applications the time for node expansion and communication will dominate.

1.2 Main result

Theorem 1 *Let H denote a binary search tree having M nodes, height h, and a cost function on its leaves. The minimum cost leaf in H can be determined in time $O(\frac{M}{N} + h + \log N)$ with probability at least $\left(1 - \frac{1}{N}\right)$ using an N processor butterfly network.*

Note that the time required must be at least $\max(M/N, h) = \Omega(M/N + h)$. This is because (1) any algorithm must expand all the M nodes in H, requiring M/N time using N processors, and (2) the h nodes on the path from the root to the farthest node in H can only be expanded sequentially. The lower bound, or optimal speedup is attained whenever the problem size $M = \Omega(N \log N)$. To obtain linear speedup over a single processor we require $M = \Omega(N(h + \log N))$. Note that both of these conditions will be easily satisfied in practice with modest sized trees.

1.3 Previous and related work

Previously, Karp and Zhang[1, 4] also gave a randomized $O(M/N + h + \log MN)$ time algorithm. However,

their algorithm uses a complete network, or an N processor PRAM. This completely ignores the issue of communication which is vitally important for real machines. One possibility is to use PRAM emulation to implement their algorithm on a sparse network; but this degrades the performance by a $O(\log N)$ factor.

Leighton, Newman, Ranade and Schwabe [2] have considered the related problem of embedding a tree into a Butterfly network as it grows dynamically (used and discussed in section 3). They show that an M node tree can be embedded into an N processor Butterfly network such that each processor receives $O(M/N + \log N)$ tree nodes. Naively using this result gives $O(h(M/N + \log N))$ as the time for backtrack search. Our result however, is much stronger.

Finally, Karp and Zhang's algorithm [1, 3, 4] also applies to branch-and-bound searches. A branch-and-bound search problem is similar to a backtrack search problem, except that the cost function is defined for all nodes in the tree, and further the cost function monotonically increases away from the root. This allows the possibility of pruning the search tree. Extending our algorithm to the branch-and-bound case is an open problem.

1.4 Overview

Section 2 describes the algorithm. Its execution is governed by two randomized policies called the *node placement policy* and the *scheduling policy*, respectively described in sections 3 and 4. Section 5 evaluates the performance of the algorithm and proves the main result.

2 The Algorithm

The algorithm essentially consists of each processor repeatedly expanding one of the nodes allocated to it, and sending the resulting children to its neighboring processors. From time to time all processors execute a termination detection phase, and if termination is detected, the minimum cost leaf is reported. The precise manner in which the children of a node are allocated to neighboring processors is determined by a *node placement policy*. Of the several nodes that a processor may hold at any instant, which one it chooses for expansion is determined by a *scheduling policy*.

More formally, each processor X maintains two data structures in its local memory, a priority queue $q(X)$, and a variable $b(X)$ holding the least cost leaf ever expanded by the processor. The ordering of the priority queue is determined by the scheduling policy, described in section 4. Initially all queues are empty, except for the queue of processor 0 in level 0 which contains the

---

[2] We use $x \oplus y$ to denote the exclusive or of x and y.

41

root. All variables b are initialized to null. The algorithm consists of repeated execution of a loop, each iteration of which consists of $\log N$ invocations of a *node expansion phase* followed by a single *termination detection phase*:

1. Node expansion phase: Each processor X picks the node at the head of its priority queue $q(X)$ and expands it. If the node turns out to be a leaf, the bound $b(X)$ is updated if necessary. Else each resulting child is sent to some neighbor of X, using the node placement policy (section 3). Likewise, X may itself receive nodes from its neighbors, which are entered into $q(X)$. Each node expansion phase executes in a single step.

2. Termination detection phase: The processors first determine if all queues are empty. If all queues are in fact found to be empty, the minimum of $b(X)$ over all X is determined, and the algorithm terminates. Else, the algorithm continues into the next iteration. Each termination detection phase can easily be seen to execute in $O(\log N)$ steps.

For the analysis we shall only consider the node expansion phases, and completely ignore the termination detection phases. This is justified because in every iteration of the loop only a constant fraction of the time is spent in termination detection.

We next describe the node placement and scheduling policies.

3 Node Placement Policy

The nodes of the tree are alloted to processors as soon as they are generated using the dynamic tree embedding technique of Leighton, Newman, Ranade and Schwabe [2]. It is convenient to think of dynamic tree embedding as consisting of a preprocessing step called *stretching*, and a *growth* step. The stretching step dynamically transforms the original tree H into a slightly modified tree $S(H)$, which is then embedded into the butterfly by the growth step. Stretching ensures that the tree nodes get distributed uniformly among the levels in the butterfly, the growth step ensures uniform distribution within each level. Both steps use randomization.

3.1 Growth

The growth step causes the children of a node expanded in a processor in level i to be placed on neighboring processors in level $i + 1 \mod n$. Let A denote processor x in level i, with B and C its neighbors in level $i + 1 \mod n$, i.e. processors x and $x \oplus 2^i$. When A expands a

tree node, the children generated are allocated to B and C. The precise placement is determined by randomly choosing a bit called the *flip* bit. If the flip bit is a zero, then the left child (if any) is placed on B and the right child (if any) is placed on C. If the flip bit is 1, then the left child (if any) is placed on C, and the right child (if any) is placed on B. In either case, both B and C receive at most one child. Flip bits are chosen independently for each node expansion. The random choice guarantees that within any level, all processors will receive roughly the same number of tree nodes.

The growth step does not ensure that tree nodes will be uniformly distributed amongst levels in the Butterfly. For instance, 2^l leaf nodes from a complete binary tree of height l will be placed on Butterfly level $l \mod n$, i.e. a single Butterfly level will receive about half the tree nodes, which is excessive imbalance. So we need the stretching step.

3.2 Stretching

The stretching step randomly stretches edges in the tree by adding dummy nodes into them so as to even out the placement of nodes among levels. While these nodes are added dynamically as the tree grows, for convenience we will describe it as a preprocessing step.

Let $h(v)$ denote the height of a tree node v, i.e. distance from the root, with $h(\text{root}) = 0$. Define a node v of H to be *distinguished* if $h(v) = 0 \pmod{n/3}$.[3] For each distinguished node v in H we pick a random number $S(v)$ between 0 and $n/3$ called the *stretch count*. We insert a single dummy node in each of the edges that connect v to its descendants at heights $h(v) + 1$ through $h(v) + S(v)$. Figure 1 illustrates the transformation.

Notice that the tree $S(H)$ resulting from stretching is embedded into the Butterfly with dilation 1 as a result of the growth step. This in turn gives a dilation 2 embedding of the original tree H.

Random stretch counts ensure that every level i of $S(H)$ has roughly the same number of nodes as its neighboring levels. Let m_j denote the number of nodes in level j of $S(H)$ and define $M(k) = \sum_{j=0}^{n-1} m_{kn+j}$. We shall say that $S(H)$ is ψ-smooth if for all k and $i < n$ we have:

$$m_{kn+i} \leq \psi \left(2^n + \frac{M(k-1) + M(k) + M(k+1)}{n} \right)$$

Lemma 1 *For any constant k_0 there exists a constant ψ independent of H such that with probability $1 - \frac{1}{2}N^{-k_0}$ the tree $S(H)$ is ψ-smooth.*

---

[3] In what follows we may make references like "(mod x)" or "contribution of x nodes" when x may not be integral. This can be dealt with by rounding these quantities to integers, which does not alter the proof idea but does reduces readability. For simplicity, we shall not consider the issue.

The proof is ommitted. It follows simply using the techniques of [2].

4 Scheduling: Assigning ranks to nodes

For the purposes of scheduling execution, we shall directly consider the tree $S(H)$ rather than H. It should be clear that $S(H)$ can be constructed from H as execution proceeds. Each node only needs to know what level of the tree H it belongs to, and the stretch count generated at its nearest distinguished ancestor. This is sufficient information to decide whether or not a dummy node is inserted when a child is spawned.

Each node in $S(H)$ is assigned a *rank*, which is used to order the nodes in the priority queues maintained by the processors. The rank $r(v)$ of a node v is defined to be $r(v) = \text{major}(v) * n + \text{minor}(v)$, where $\text{major}(v)$ and $\text{minor}(v)$ are respectively the major and minor ranks assigned as follows. The major rank of a node v of $S(H)$ is $\lfloor h(v)/n \rfloor$. The minor rank is assigned randomly as follows. Define a node v of $S(H)$ to be a leader if $h(v) = 0$ (mod n). The descendants of v in levels $h(v)+1$ through $h(v) + n - 1$ are called its followers. Each leader is assigned a minor rank by picking an independent random number from $[0, n-1]$. The minor rank of a follower is fixed to be identical to its leader's.

Each queue is ordered in ascending order of the ranks. Within nodes of the same rank, the order is chosen arbitrarily.

Lemma 2 *The rank assignment has two properties: (1) If nodes u and v are expanded in the same processor and $r(u) \le r(v)$, then $h(u) \le h(v)$, and (2) If u is the child of v, then $r(u) \le r(v)$.*

Proof: Obvious. ■

5 Analysis

We shall show that large execution times will occur only if a large number of nodes in the $S(H)$ are mapped onto a short path in the network, and in addition are assigned ranks in a certain order. More formally, we shall show that whenever execution takes long, a delay sequence event (defined below) must occur. Then the probability of large delays is estimated just by counting the number of all possible delay sequences and estimating the probability of each sequence.

What makes delay sequences unlikely is that they involve a large set of *independent* nodes.

Definition 1 *Let nodes u and v in a tree be called related iff (1) the distance between the nodes is less than n and one node is the ancestor of the other, or (2) their closest common ancestor is at a distance less than n from both of them. Else, u and v are said to be independent of each other.*

Definition 2 *A delay-sequence is defined using the following parameters:*

1. *A path P in the butterfly of length h with processors on the path numbered $P_0, \ldots, P_{h-1}$, with P_i in level i mod n of the Butterfly.*

2. *A sequence R of rank intervals numbered $R_1, \ldots, R_h$ where $R_i \subseteq [\lfloor i/n \rfloor n, \lfloor i/n \rfloor n + n - 1]$ for all i, and such that adjacent intervals overlap in exactly one rank i.e. $|R_i \cap R_{i+1}| = 1$.*

3. *An integer δ.*

A (P, R, δ) delay sequence is said to occur during a particular execution iff there exists a set V of δ independent nodes from $S(H)$ such that every $v \in V$ is expanded in some P_i and has rank $r(v) \in R_i$.

Lemma 3 *Suppose the execution time is T, i.e. execution started at step 0 and finished at step $T - 1$. Then some $(P, R, (T-h)/2)$ delay sequence occured.*

We prove the lemma by identifying the delay sequence, and the associated set of nodes V. Initially, we will identify a large set of nodes $W = \{w_0, \ldots, w_{T-1}\}$ which satisfy definition 2 except that the nodes in W may be related. After removing possibly related nodes from W we will be left with a large enough V completing the proof.

The sequence W as well as the path P are identified starting at the end. We begin by choosing w_{T-1} to be the node that is expanded last, i.e. at time $T - 1$. The processor in which w_{T-1} is expanded is chosen as $P_{h(w_{T-1})}$. We will also build up an auxiliary set of nodes W' which will contain nodes that possibly depend upon other nodes in W. Initially W' is empty. In general, given a node w_t expanded in some processor $P_{h(w_t)}$ at time $t > 0$, we can extend W and P as follows. There are three cases:

ancestor-delay: At step $t - 1$, either no node with rank equal to or smaller than $r(w_t)$ was expanded in $P_{h(w_t)}$. Then we know that w_t must have arrived into $P_{h(w_t)}$ at the beginning of step t, with the parent of w_t expanded in step $t - 1$. We then choose the parent as w_{t-1}. The processor in which w_{t-1} is expanded is chosen to be $P_{h(w_{t-1})}$. Note that $h(w_{t-1}) = h(w_t) - 1$. Finally, we additionally label w_t as $w'_{h(w_t)}$ and add it to W'.

queue-delay: At step $t-1$, another node with the same height and equal or smaller rank than that of w_t was expanded in $P_{h(w_t)}$. Then we chose this node as w_{t-1}.

skip-delay: At step $t-1$, another node with height smaller than that of w_t was expanded in $P_{h(w_t)}$. Then we chose this node as w_{t-1}. We choose $P_{h(w_{t-1})}$ to be the same as $P_{h(w_t)}$. Clearly $h(w_t) - h(w_{t-1}) = kn$ for some k. We choose the intervening processors on P to be from any backward path of length kn connecting $P_{h(w_t)}$ to $P_{h(w_{t-1})}$. Finally, we additionally label w_t as $w'_{h(w_t)}$ and add it to W'.

Clearly, some w_{t-1} is always found provided $t > 0$. The construction terminates on reaching w_0 which is the root of $S(H)$.

Lemma 4 *The sequences constructed above has the following properties:*

1. *W has length T, and each w_i is expanded at step i.*

2. *The sequence $P_0, \ldots, P_{h(w_{T-1})}$ is a path in the Butterfly, with P_j in level $j \bmod n$.*

3. *If $i < j$ then $r(w_i) \le r(w_j)$, and also $h(w_i) \le h(w_j)$.*

4. *The number of elements in W' is at most h. Further, if w_i is a parent of w_{i+1}, then $w_{i+1} \in W'$.*

Proof: Obvious. ∎

The rank interval R_i associated with P_i is chosen large enough to cover the ranks of all nodes in the sequence W lying between w'_i (inclusive) and $w'_{(i+1)}$ (exclusive). Since the nodes expanded in P_i all have height i, we have $R_i \subseteq [\lfloor i/n \rfloor n, \lfloor i/n \rfloor n + n - 1]$. Since we know that the ranks of nodes in W form a non decreasing sequence, the rank intervals associated with adjacent processors on P can overlap in at most one rank, i.e. $|R_i \cap R_{i+1}| \le 1$. The rank intervals as well as P can be easily extended to confirm to definition 2.

5.1 Independence of nodes

Clearly, all nodes in W are not independent. For instance, we may have chosen a parent in the construction (ancestor-delay) to be a part of W. Note however, that in each such case, we included the child in W'. So we know that no node in $W - W'$ has a child in $W - W'$. However this does not rule our the possibility that a distant descendant of a node in $W - W'$ is also in $W - W'$, or that $W - W'$ may contain nodes having a close enough common ancestor. Our next two lemmas show that this cannot be the case for nodes having the same major rank.

Lemma 5 *If w_i and w_j have the same major rank and w_i is an ancestor of w_j, then $w_j \in W'$.*

Proof: Let $k = h(w_i)$, $l = h(w_j)$, and let $U_{kl} = \{u_{k+1}, \ldots, u_{l-1}\}$ be the nodes in $S(H)$ on the path from w_i to w_j. Let $W_{ij} = \{w_y | i < y < j\}$. We can assume without loss of generality that W_{ij} and U_{kl} are disjoint. We shall further assume that $w_j \notin W'$ and show a contradiction.

We first show that all the nodes in $U_{kl} \cup W_{ij} \cup \{w_i, w_j\}$ have the same rank, and must have been expanded along the portion of P between P_k and P_l. The nodes w_i and w_j have the same major rank, the same leader, and hence the same minor rank. Thus these nodes, as well as those in U_{kl} have the same rank. The nodes in W_{ij} must also have the same rank, since the ranks never decrease along the sequence W. Since w_i and w_j have the same major rank, $l - k \le n$. Thus, the part of P connecting P_k and P_l is also the unique shortest path between the two processors. Thus we know that u_x was expanded in P_x for $k < x < l$.

Next, we show that u_x is expanded in P_x before w'_x, for $k < x < l$. Consider the base case $x = k + 1$. We know by assumption that w_i is not the parent of w'_{k+1}. Thus w_i was expanded before the parent of w'_{k+1} (see figure 2). Thus, we know that the child u_{k+1} of w_i arrives into P_{k+1} before w'_{k+1}. But note that at the time of expansion of w'_{k+1} no other node of the same rank could have been present in P_{k+1}. Thus u_{k+1} must have been expanded before w'_{k+1}. Thus u_{k+2} arrives into P_{k+2} before w'_{k+2}. Continuing similarly we have w_j expanded in P_l before w'_l, giving a contradiction. ∎

Lemma 6 *Suppose nodes w_i and w_j have the same major rank, and $w_i, w_j \notin W'$. Then w_i and w_j are independent.*

Proof: Suppose the two nodes are related. Assume wlog that $i \le j$. Then there are two possibilities: (1) w_i is an ancestor of w_j. But then by lemma 5 we would have $w_j \in W'$, giving a contradiction. (2) Neither is an ancestor of the other. Let a_{ij} denote their closest common ancestor, and assume wlog that w_i and w_j are respectively on the left and right branches under a_{ij}. Let Q_i, Q_j and Q_{ij} respectively be the processors in which w_i, w_j, and a_{ij} were expanded.

We now identify two distinct forward paths of length less than n connecting Q_{ij} to Q_j and establish a contradiction. First consider the path from Q_{ij} to Q_j along which the right descendants of a_{ij} were expanded. By definition this path is of length $h(w_j) - h(a_{ij}) < n$. Next consider the path from Q_{ij} to Q_i along which the left descendants of a_{ij} were expanded, concatenated with the path from Q_i to Q_j that is a part of P. The length of the first portion is $h(w_i) - h(a_{ij})$. The second portion must have length $h(w_j) - h(w_i)$, since w_i and w_j have the same major rank. Thus the second path has length $h(w_i) - h(a_{ij}) + h(w_j) - h(w_i) = h(w_j) - h(a_{ij})$, i.e. the same as the first. This is impossible in the Butterfly. ■

Lemma 7 *The sequence $W - W'$ contains at least $(T - h)/2$ independent nodes.*

Proof: Call a node v in $W - W'$ odd (even) if $\lfloor h(v)/n \rfloor$ is odd (even). Assume wlog that at least $(T - h)/2$ nodes are even. We shall show that all the even nodes are unrelated.

Consider any two even nodes $w_i, w_j \in W - W'$. If their major ranks are equal, then they are independent by lemma 6. If the major ranks are unequal, then they must differ at least by two, since both major ranks are even. But then their heights must differ at least by n, and hence independence follows by definition. ■

5.2 Probability of a delay sequence

Lemma 8 *Given that $S(H)$ is ψ-smooth, any given (P, R, δ) delay-sequence occurs with probability at most*

$$\left(4\psi e \frac{h/n + 3M/N}{\delta} \right)^{\delta}$$

Proof: We estimate the probability of the given delay sequence by estimating the number of candidates for the set V, and then estimating the probability that the nodes in each candidate actually obey definition 2.

Let V_i denote the subset of nodes in V that are at height i. We can choose a candidate set V as follows. First we choose the sizes $|V_i|$ of each subset. This can be done in $\binom{\delta}{h}$ ways. Next we choose the elements of V_i from the m_i nodes at height i. This can be done in $\prod_i \binom{m_i}{|V_i|}$ ways.

The probability of having a node $v \in V_i$ expanded in P_i is 2^{-n}, since the flip bits in its n most recent ancestors must be chosen appropriately. Further, its rank lies in the interval R_i with probability at most $|R_i|/n$, since its minor rank is chosen randomly in the range 0 through $n - 1$. The probability that v is expanded in P_i and has rank in R_i is $2^{-n}|R_i|/n = |R_i|/N$. Thus the probability that this happens for all nodes in V_i is at most $(|R_i|/N)^{|V_i|}$, since the nodes are all independent. The probability that all nodes from the candidate set V get expanded along P and are assigned the appropriate minor rank is at most $\prod_i (|R_i|/N)^{|V_i|}$.

The probability of the delay sequence occuring is therefore:

$$\binom{\delta}{h} \prod_{i=0}^{i=h-1} \binom{m_i}{|V_i|} \left(\frac{|R_i|}{N} \right)^{|V_i|}$$

$$\leq \binom{\delta}{h} N^{-\delta} \prod_{i=0}^{i=h-1} \binom{m_i |R_i|}{|V_i|}$$

using $\sum_i |V_i| = \delta$, and $\binom{n}{r} a^r \leq \binom{na}{r}$. We evaluate the product by breaking it into h/n pieces:

$$\prod_{i=0}^{i=h-1} \binom{m_i |R_i|}{|V_i|} = \prod_{k=0}^{k=h/n-1} \left(\prod_{i=0}^{i=n-1} \binom{m_{kn+i} |R_{kn+i}|}{|V_{kn+i}|} \right)$$

$$\leq \prod_{k=0}^{k=h/n-1} \left(\frac{\sum_{i=0}^{i=n-1} \mathcal{A}(k) |R_{kn+i}|}{\sum_{i=0}^{i=n-1} |V_{kn+i}|} \right)$$

where $\mathcal{A}(k) = \psi \left(2^n + \frac{M(k-1)+M(k)+M(k+1)}{n} \right) \geq m_{kn+i}$, since $S(H)$ is ψ-smooth; and using $\prod_i \binom{n_i}{r_i} \leq \binom{\sum_i n_i}{\sum_i r_i}$. Because $R_{kn+i} \subseteq [kn, kn + n - 1]$, and because successive rank intervals can only overlap by at most 1, we have $\sum_{i=0}^{i=n-1} |R_{kn+i}| \leq 2n$. Thus we get

$$\prod_{i=0}^{i=h-1} \binom{m_i |R_i|}{|V_i|} \leq \prod_{k=0}^{k=h/n-1} \binom{2n\mathcal{A}(k)}{\sum_{i=0}^{i=n-1} |V_{kn+i}|}$$

$$\leq \binom{\sum_{k=0}^{k=h/n-1} 2n\mathcal{A}(k)}{\delta}$$

noting $\sum_{k=0}^{k=h/n-1} \sum_{i=0}^{i=n-1} |V_i| = |V| = \delta$. But

$$\sum_{\substack{k=0 \\ k=h/n-1}}^{u=h/n-1} 2n A(k)$$

$$= \sum_{k=0} 2\psi(N + M(k-1) + M(k) + M(k+1))$$

$$\leq 2\psi(Nh/n + 3M)$$

Thus the probability of the occurrence of the delay sequence is at most

$$\binom{\delta}{h} N^{-\delta} \binom{2\psi(Nh/n + 3M)}{\delta} \leq \left(4\psi e \frac{h/n + 3M/N}{\delta} \right)^{\delta}$$

using $\binom{n}{r} \leq (ne/r)^r$, and $\binom{n}{r} \leq 2^n$. ■

Lemma 9 *The probability of occurrence of some (P, R, δ) delay sequences is at most*

$$2^{3h} \left(4\psi e \frac{h/n + 3M/N}{\delta} \right)^{\delta}$$

Proof: We only need to count the number of ways of fixing the different parameters. P can be chosen in 2^h ways, since P_0 is fixed to be the node in which the root is expanded, and there are only 2 choices for every subsequent node on the path. R consists of a sequence h

45

sub-intervals covering $[0, h-1]$ and overlapping by one with one another. These can be chosen in at most $\binom{2h}{h}$ ways. The total number is therefore at most $2^h\binom{2h}{h} \leq 2^{3h}$. The result then follows using lemma 8. ■

5.3 Main Theorem

Theorem 2 *Let H denote a binary search tree having M nodes, height h, and a cost function on its leaves. Then for any constant k_0 there exists a constant k_1 independent of H such that with probability $1 - N^{-k_0}$ the minimum cost leaf in H can be determined in time $T = k_1(\frac{M}{N} + h + \log N)$ using an N processor butterfly network.*

Proof: For the given k_0, we use lemma 1 to first fix ψ such that $S(H)$ is ψ-smooth with probability $1 - \frac{1}{2}N^{-k_0}$.

Given that $S(H)$ is ψ-smooth, the probability of occurrence of some (P, R, δ) delay sequence is at most (with $\delta = (T-h)/2$):

$$2^{3h}\left(4\psi e \frac{h/n + 3M/N}{\delta}\right)^{\delta} \leq \left(2^{3h/\delta}4\psi e \frac{h/n + 3M/N}{\delta}\right)^{\delta}$$
$$\leq \left(2^{6h/(T-h)}8\psi e \frac{h/n + 3M/N}{T - h}\right)^{(T-h)/2}$$

This can be made smaller than $\frac{1}{2}N^{-k_0}$ by choosing $k_1 > 4k_0 + 96e\psi$. Thus the probability of having $S(H)$ be ψ-smooth as well as not having any delay sequence is at least $1 - N^{-k_0}$, as required. ■

References

[1] Richard Karp and Yanjun Zhang. A randomized parallel branch-and-bound procedure. In *Proceedings of the ACM Annual Symposium on Theory of Computing*, pages 290–300, 1988.

[2] Tom Leighton, Mark Newman, Abhiram Ranade, and Eric Schwabe. Dynamic Tree Embeddings on Butterflies and Hypercubes. In *Proceedings of the ACM Symposium on Parallel Algorithms and Architectures*, pages 224–234, June 1989.

[3] Abhiram G. Ranade. A Simpler Analysis of the Karp-Zhang Parallel Branch-and-Bound Method. Technical Report UCB/CSD 90/586, University of California, August 1990.

[4] Yanjun Zhang. *Parallel Algorithms for Combinatorial Search Problems*. PhD thesis, University of California, 1989. UCB/CSD 89/543.

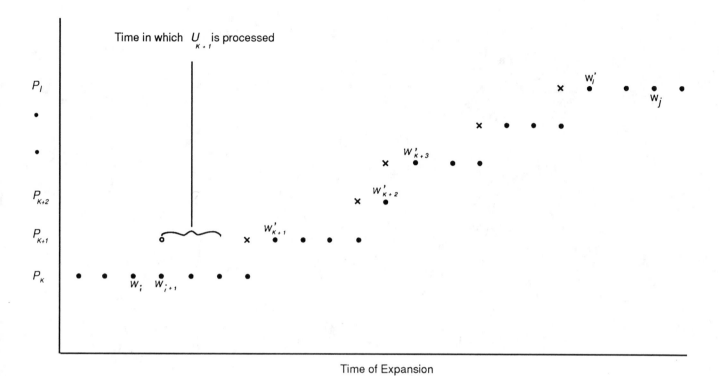

Figure 1: Delay Sequence for Lemma 5

• Node expansion of elements of W

x Processor does not hold node with rank $\leq r(W_i)$

o Arrival of U_{K+1} into P_{K+1} and time at which U_{K+1} is ready to be expanded.

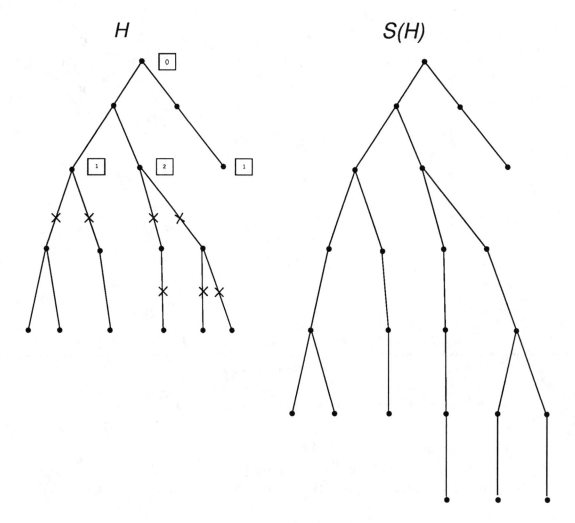

Figure 1: Stretching A Tree H $n = 6$

stretch counts are in squares
crossed edges indicate where dummy nodes will be inserted.

SESSION 2

Fast and Reliable Parallel Hashing

Holger Bast
Fachbereich Informatik, Universität des Saarlandes
W–6600 Saarbrücken, Germany

Torben Hagerup*
Max-Planck-Institut für Informatik
W–6600 Saarbrücken, Germany

Abstract

A *perfect hash function* for a (multi)set X of n integers is an injective function $h : X \to \{1, \ldots, s\}$, where $s = O(n)$, that can be stored in $O(n)$ space and evaluated in constant time by a single processor. We show that a perfect hash function for a given multiset of n integers can be constructed optimally in $O(\log^* n)$ time using $O(n/\log^* n)$ processors. Our algorithm is faster than all previously published methods. More significantly, it is highly reliable: Whereas analyses of previous fast parallel hashing schemes provided bounds on the expected resource requirements only, our algorithm is guaranteed to stay within the bounds given with overwhelming probability.

1 Introduction

While hashing has a long tradition in sequential computing, parallel hashing schemes are of a relatively recent date. We consider in this paper the static version of the problem, where a perfect hash function for a (multi)set of size n fixed in advance is to be constructed. Dietzfelbinger and Meyer auf der Heide (1989) investigated the more general problem of maintaining a dynamically changing dictionary in space proportional to the current number of elements in the dictionary. In particular, their results imply a solution to the static problem that uses $O(n^\epsilon)$ time and $O(n)$ operations (i.e., $O(n^{1-\epsilon})$ processors), for arbitrary but fixed $\epsilon > 0$. While this is perhaps sufficient for practical applications, a quest for theoretical improvements started. Matias and Vishkin (1990a; revised and corrected: 1990b) described an algorithm that uses $O(\log n)$ time and $O(n)$ operations. Gil and Matias (1991) improved the running time to $O(\log \log n)$ without sacrificing optimality. Finally, Matias and Vishkin (1991) have announced an algorithm that uses $O(\log^* n \log(\log^* n))$ time and n processors. The only faster algorithm (Gil, Meyer auf der Heide, and Wigderson, 1990), with a running time of $O(\log^* n)$, is given in a "theoretical" model without a PRAM realization.

All of the resource bounds cited above are bounds on the expected performance of the scheme in question. In a sense, therefore, all these algorithms are quite unreliable: The probability that the resource requirements (e.g., time) of an actual run exceed the bounds given cannot be ignored. Although an algorithm may not actually produce an incorrect answer, we call this probability the *failure probability* of the algorithm. In time-critical applications a constant failure probability may not be acceptable. More satisfactory randomized algorithms have failure probabilities that depend on the input size and tend rapidly to zero as the input size increases. We propose the first fast parallel algorithm of this kind for the hashing problem. When the algorithm runs at maximum speed, its failure probability is $2^{-(\log n)^\alpha}$, where α is fixed but arbitrary. If the algorithm is slowed down to run on fewer than $\Theta(n/\log^* n)$ processors, its probability of failure can be reduced even further. In fact, we believe a sequential version of our algorithm to

* Supported in part by the Deutsche Forschungsgemeinschaft, SFB 124, TP B2, VLSI Entwurfsmethoden und Parallelität, and in part by the ESPRIT II Basic Research Actions Program of the EC under contract No. 3075 (project ALCOM).

be the most reliable sequential algorithm known for the static hashing problem. Moreover, our fastest running time of $O(\log^* n)$ matches a lower bound established by Gil, Meyer auf der Heide, and Wigderson (1990) for an abstract model of computation.

The grandfather of most recent sequential and parallel hashing algorithms is the 2-level scheme introduced by Fredman, Komlós and Szemerédi (1984) (henceforth: the *FKS* scheme), which we briefly sketch. A *primary hash function* f is used to partition the input into n *buckets*, where each bucket is the collection of input keys mapped by f to a particular value. Each bucket is provided with its own space, and for each bucket a *secondary hash function* maps the bucket injectively into its private space. In the following we abbreviate primary and secondary hash functions to *primaries* and *secondaries*, respectively. In order to hash a key x, first the primary is applied to x in order to determine the bucket containing x, and then the secondary for that bucket is applied to x. Let $b_1, \ldots, b_n$ be the bucket sizes induced by a primary f. Fredman, Komlós and Szemerédi proved that if f is chosen at random from a suitable class, then $\sum_{i=1}^{n} b_i^2 = O(n)$ with probability $\Omega(1)$. Furthermore, if a bucket of size b_i is given $2b_i^2$ space, then a random secondary for that bucket is injective with probability $\Omega(1)$. It is easy to see that this leads to a sequential algorithm for static hashing with linear expected running time.

The algorithm of (Matias and Vishkin, 1990a, 1990b) is a straightforward implementation of the FKS scheme: A primary is selected at random and applied to all keys in the input. Then the induced bucket sizes $b_1, \ldots, b_n$ are determined via sorting, $2b_i^2$ space is allocated to the ith bucket, and for each bucket random secondaries are repeatedly tested until an injective secondary is encountered. Although it is possible to improve the running time of the algorithm to $O(\log n / \log \log n)$, the bottleneck of sorting prevents any further speedup through minor modifications. Subsequent faster algorithms therefore had to adopt a different approach, namely to treat all buckets identically, without regard to (and without knowing) their sizes. The rather surprising fact that this works derives from properties of the classes of primaries used. More specifically, the number of large buckets is very small, causing the crude implicit assumption that all buckets are of the same size to be fairly accurate. This very simple "blind" method, however, has its drawbacks. Specifically, as far as we know, it causes the failure probability to be at least $n^{-\alpha}$, for fixed α, since no class of primaries is known to make the number of large buckets sufficiently small with a higher

probability than $1 - n^{-\Theta(1)}$ (allowing nonuniformity, the picture changes; see (Siegel, 1989)). If we want to achieve a still better probability of success, the problem becomes substantially more difficult. It turns out that we must (1) carefully select a primary with certain desired properties, rather than relying on a random choice, and (2) estimate the number of keys in each bucket (since we cannot count them accurately) in order to divide the available resources between buckets accordingly. Our algorithm for (1) is based on several kinds of random sampling, while our solution to (2) is similar to the estimation algorithm described in (Hagerup, 1991).

In many applications hashing must be applied to a sequence of not necessarily distinct integers (equivalently, the input is a *multiset* rather than a simple set). For instance, the applications described by Matias and Vishkin (1990a, 1990b) are of this kind. On the other hand, many hashing schemes require the keys to be distinct. We therefore distinguish between the *simple hashing problem*, whose input is a sequence of pairwise distinct integers, and the *multiset hashing problem*, whose input is a sequence of arbitrary integers. We shall also refer to the multiset problem by saying that *duplicates* are allowed. Observe that the FKS scheme solves the simple hashing problem only: If all keys are equal, any primary with associated bucket sizes $b_1, \ldots, b_n$ will, for trivial reasons, have $\sum_{i=1}^{n} b_i^2 = n^2$. This gives a hint that multiset hashing can be significantly harder than simple hashing. Our basic algorithm solves only the simple hashing problem. However, we describe a preprocessing step that allows all duplicates to be eliminated, thus providing in fact a solution to the multiset hashing problem.

2 Preliminaries

We assume all keys to be hashed to come from a fixed universe U of the form $\{0, \ldots, Q-1\}$, where Q is a known prime. Following Dietzfelbinger and Meyer auf der Heide (1989), for $s, d \in \mathbb{N}$, define

$$\mathcal{H}_s^d = \{h_a : a = (a_0, \ldots, a_d) \in \{0, \ldots, Q-1\}^{d+1}\},$$

where the function $h_a : U \to \{1, \ldots, s\}$ is given by

$$h_a(x) = 1 + \left(\left(\sum_{i=0}^{d} a_i x^i \right) \bmod Q \right) \bmod s.$$

The important properties of the class $\{\mathcal{H}_s^d\}$ are expressed in the following facts.

Fact 2.1: There is a sequence $C_1, C_2, \ldots$ of positive integers such that the following holds for all $n, k, d \in \mathbb{N}$ with $k \leq d + 1$: For every simple set $S \subseteq U$ with $|S| \leq n$, if h is chosen randomly from $\mathcal{H}_n^d$ and $b_i = |\{x \in S : h(x) = i\}|$, for $i = 1, \ldots, n$, then

$$\Pr\left(\sum_{i=1}^n b_i^k \leq C_k n\right) \geq \frac{1}{2}.$$

Fact 2.2: For every $b \in \mathbb{N}$ and for every simple set $B \subseteq U$ with $|B| \leq b$, if h is chosen randomly from $\mathcal{H}_{2b^2}^1$ and $b_i = |\{x \in B : h(x) = i\}|$, for $i = 1, \ldots, n$, then

$$\Pr(h \text{ is injective}) \geq \frac{1}{2}.$$

Below we use $C_1, C_2, \ldots$ in the sense of Fact 2.1. When an input set S and a hash function h can be deduced from the context, define the ith *bucket* as $B_i = \{x \in S : h(x) = i\}$ and let $b_i = |B_i|$, for all i in the range of h. For $k \in \mathbb{N}$, a function $h \in \mathcal{H}_n^d$ is called k-*good* (with respect to an implied input set) if $\sum_{i=1}^n b_i^k \leq C_k n$. Fact 2.1 implies that at least half of the functions in $\mathcal{H}_n^d$ are k-good for a fixed input set of size at most n, provided only that $d \geq k - 1$. Note also that if $h \in \mathcal{H}_n^d$ is k-good, then $\max\{b_i : 1 \leq i \leq n\} \leq (C_k n)^{1/k}$.

In order to make many proofs more readable, we operate extensively with the notion of a *negligible probability*. Is the goal, e.g., to show that the running time of some algorithm is $O(\tau)$ with probability at least $1 - 2^{-(\log n)^\tau}$, then in the proof all probabilities of the form $2^{-(\log n)^{\Omega(\tau)}}$ can be ignored. An event that occurs *with high probability* (w.h.p.) is the complement of an event of negligible probability. We often tacitly assume that such events always occur.

Essential tools for our high-probability analysis are the well-known Chernoff bounds (Hagerup and Rüb, 1990) and a corollary to Azuma's inequality (Bollobás, 1987).

Fact 2.3: For every binomially distributed random variable S,
(a) $\Pr(S \geq 2E(S)) \leq e^{-E(S)/3}$;
(b) $\Pr(S \leq \frac{1}{2}E(S)) \leq e^{-E(S)/8}$;
(c) For every $r > 0$, $\Pr(S \geq r) \leq (er^{-1}E(S))^r$. In particular, if $r \geq 6E(S)$, then $\Pr(S \geq r) \leq 2^{-r}$.

Fact 2.4: Let $Z_1, \ldots, Z_n$ be independent random variables with finite ranges, and let S be an arbitrary function of $Z_1, \ldots, Z_n$ with $E(S) \geq 0$. Assume that S changes by at most c in response to an arbitrary change in a single Z_i. Then
(a) for every $r \geq 2E(S)$, $\Pr(S \geq r) \leq e^{-r^2/(8c^2n)}$;

(b) for every $r \leq \frac{1}{2}E(S)$, $\Pr(S \leq r) \leq e^{-r^2/(2c^2n)}$.

We shall often write "by a martingale argument" rather than "by Fact 2.4". In numerous applications we leave out the details and simply state that a random variable takes on values deviating by no more than a constant factor from its expected value, except with negligible probability.

The model of computation used throughout the paper is the COLLISION CRCW PRAM, except that the elimination of duplicates described in Section 5 needs the stronger COLLISION$^+$ CRCW PRAM. Definitions of these models may be found in (Chlebus *et al.*, 1988).

The following fact is an adaptation of a result due to Ragde (1990, Theorem 1).

Fact 2.5: For all given $m \in \mathbb{N}$ at most m elements placed in an array of size n can be moved to an array of size at most m^5 in constant time using $O(n)$ operations and $O(n)$ space.

Definition: An estimate $\hat{b}$ for a quantity b is *exact* if there is a constant $c \geq 1$ such that $b \leq \hat{b} \leq cb$. For $a \geq 0$, $\hat{b}$ is said to be a-*bad* (for b) if $a\hat{b} < b$.

Definition: For $k \in \mathbb{N}$ and $\epsilon > 0$, a (k, ϵ)-*good estimator* for a sequence $b_1, \ldots, b_n$ of n nonnegative integers is a sequence $\hat{b}_1, \ldots, \hat{b}_n$ of n nonnegative integers such that for some $C \in \mathbb{N}$,
(1) for all a with $1 \leq a \leq \epsilon \log n$,
$$|\{i : \hat{b}_i \text{ is } a\text{-bad for } b_i\}| \leq C \cdot \frac{n}{2^a};$$
(2) for all $i = 1, \ldots, n$, $\hat{b}_i$ is not n^ϵ-bad for b_i;
(3) $\sum_{i=1}^n \hat{b}_i^k \leq Cn$.

For $n, \tau \in \mathbb{N}$ and $\epsilon > 0$, let $\phi(n, \tau, \epsilon) = 2^{-(\log n)^\tau} + 2^{-n^\epsilon}$. Note that this quantity is $2^{-\text{polylog}(n)}$ for τ constant in n and can be as low as $2^{-n^{\Omega(1)}}$ in case $\tau = \Omega(\frac{\log n}{\log\log n})$.

(Graduated) conditional scatterings were introduced in (Hagerup, 1991) as a useful way of estimating certain quantities crudely, but rapidly. The following definitions and facts are taken from that paper.

Definition: For $s \in \mathbb{N}$ and $0 \leq p \leq 1$, a *conditional scattering* with probability p and range s is a random experiment carried out by a set W of elements as follows: Each element $w \in W$, independently of other elements, chooses a random number X_w with $\Pr(X_w = 0) = 1 - p$ and $\Pr(X_w = i) = p/s$, for $i = 1, \ldots, s$. An element $w \in W$ *collides*, if $X_w > 0$ and $X_w = X_{w'}$ for some $w' \in W - \{w\}$. If $\{1, \ldots, s\} \subseteq \{X_w : w \in W\}$, the scattering is said to be *full*.

Definition: For $r, s \in \mathbb{N}$, a *graduated conditional scattering* (GCS) with range $r \times s$ is a collection

$S = \{S_1, \ldots, S_r\}$, where S_i, called the ith *row* of S, is a conditional scattering with probability 2^{-i} and range s, for $i = 1, \ldots, r$. Define the *last full row* of S as 0 if none of $S_1, \ldots, S_r$ is full, and otherwise as $\max\{i : 1 \leq i \leq r \text{ and } S_i \text{ is full}\}$.

Fact 2.6: Let $m, r, s \in \mathbb{N}$ and $a > 0$ and let L be the last full row of a GCS of m elements with range $r \times s$. Then if $M = 2^L s$,

(a) $\Pr(L = r) \leq (2^{-r} em/s)^s$;

(b) $\Pr(M > \max\{s, am\}) \leq (2e/a)^s$;

(c) $\Pr(L < r \text{ and } m > aM) \leq s \cdot 2^{1-a/2}$.

Fact 2.7: For every constant $\delta > 0$, there is a constant $\epsilon > 0$ such that the following holds for all $\tau \geq 1$: If one processor is associated with each of $b = O(n)$ elements, it is possible, using $O(\tau)$ time, $O(n^\delta)$ additional processors and $O(n^\delta)$ space, to compute a nonnegative integer $\hat{b}$ such that with probability at least $1 - \phi(n, \tau, \epsilon)$,

(1) $\hat{b} > 0 \Rightarrow \hat{b}$ is an exact estimate for b;

(2) $b \geq (\log n)^\tau \Rightarrow \hat{b} > 0$.

In case there are $n^{\Omega(1)}$ processors associated with each element, we can always estimate b exactly, except with probability $\phi(n, \tau, \Omega(1))$.

We say that m elements are *scattered over an array A*, if they carry out a conditional scattering with probability 1 and range $|A|$, and each noncolliding element is moved to A at the position corresponding to its chosen number. Some basic combinatorial observations prove the following fact.

Fact 2.8: Let $m, v, s \in \mathbb{N}$ and suppose that v copies of each of m elements are scattered over an array of s cells. Then the probability that all copies of a fixed element collide with other copies is at most $\left(\frac{mv}{s}\right)^v$.

We often need to allocate private blocks of memory cells or groups of consecutively numbered processors to a number of "requesting elements". We make use of the following definitions and facts from (Hagerup, 1991).

Fact 2.9: For every fixed $\epsilon > 0$ and $m = (\log n)^{O(1)}$, given m nonnegative integers $x_1, \ldots, x_m$, it is possible, using constant time, $O(n^\epsilon)$ processors and $O(n^\epsilon)$ space, to compute m nonnegative integers $y_1, \ldots, y_m$ such that

(1) For $i = 1, \ldots, m-1$, $y_{i+1} - y_i \geq x_i$;

(2) $y_m \leq 4 \sum_{i=1}^{m} x_i$.

Definition: For $n \in \mathbb{N}$, the *interval allocation problem* of size n is the following: Given n nonnegative integers $x_1, \ldots, x_n$ (the requested block sizes), compute n nonnegative integers $y_1, \ldots, y_n$ (the offsets of the allocated blocks) such that

(1) For $1 \leq i < j \leq n$, if $0 \notin \{x_i, x_j\}$, then $\{y_i, \ldots, y_i + x_i - 1\} \cap \{y_j, \ldots, y_j + x_j - 1\} = \emptyset$;

(2) For $j = 1, \ldots, n$, if $x_j \neq 0$, then $y_j \neq 0$;

(3) $\max\{y_j : 1 \leq j \leq n\} = O(\sum_{j=1}^{n} x_j)$.

Intuitively (1) means that blocks may not overlap, and (3) says that the requested blocks must be packed optimally, except for a constant factor.

Fact 2.10: For all $\tau \geq \log^* n$, interval allocation problems of size n can be solved in $O(\tau)$ time using $O(n)$ operations and $O(n)$ space with probability at least $1 - \phi(n, \tau, \Omega(1))$.

As an easy corollary we can move at most m elements in an array of size n to an array of size $O(m)$ within the same resource bounds.

Theorem 2.11: For every fixed $\delta > 0$, there is a constant $\epsilon > 0$ such that for all $\tau \geq 1$, interval allocation problems of size n with $O(n^{1-\delta})$ nonzero input numbers can be solved in $O(\tau)$ time using $O(n)$ operations and $O(n)$ space with probability at least $1 - \phi(n, \tau, \epsilon)$.

Proof: Take $\gamma = \delta/2$ and let the input be $x_1, \ldots, x_n$. We begin by mapping $x_1, \ldots, x_n$ randomly to $n^{1-\gamma}$ space. More precisely, allocate an array A of size $n^{1-\gamma}$ and divide it into two halves A_1 and A_2. Scatter $\lceil \frac{2}{\gamma} \rceil$ numbered copies of each element over A_1 and for each element with at least one noncolliding copy, remove all but the lowest-numbered noncolliding copy from A_1. By Chernoff bound (c) making use of Fact 2.8, w.h.p. $O((\log n)^\tau)$ elements are not moved to A_1. W.l.o.g. $\tau \leq \frac{1}{12} \log n / \log \log n$, hence we can move the remaining elements to an array A' of size $(\log n)^{6\tau}$ (Fact 2.5) and can associate $n^{\gamma/2}$ numbered processors with each of them. Now scatter $n^{\gamma/2}$ copies of each of the elements in A' over A_2. Fact 2.8 implies that w.h.p., each element will have at least one associated processor whose copy does not collide with other copies. Move each element in A' to the cell in A_2 chosen by the lowest-numbered such processor associated with the element.

We take $x_1, \ldots, x_n$ to be requests for abstract "resource units". As observed in the proof of Theorem 4.10 in (Hagerup, 1991), we can assume that each nonzero x_j is a power of 2 in the range $2..n$. The problem is hence trivial if $\tau = \Omega(\log n / \log \log n)$. Otherwise, for $i = 1, \ldots, m = \lfloor \log n \rfloor$, let $B_i = \{j : 1 \leq j \leq n \text{ and } x_j = 2^i\}$ and $b_i = |B_i|$, associate n^γ

processors with each element in A and use Fact 2.7 to compute exact estimates $\hat{b}_1, \ldots, \hat{b}_m$ for $b_1, \ldots, b_m$. Then use Fact 2.9 to allocate $C\hat{b}_i \cdot 2^i$ resource units to i, for $i = 1, \ldots, m$ and for a suitable constant C. The remaining task is to divide the resource units allocated to i among the elements of B_i, for $i = 1, \ldots, m$. This is done independently for different values of i. Fix $i \in \{1, \ldots, m\}$ and divide A_1 and A_2 into $s = \lceil \hat{b}_i (\log n)^{-(\tau+1)} \rceil$ equal-sized subarrays each. Since the number of elements of B_i in a fixed subarray is binomially distributed with expected value $\leq (\log n)^{\tau+1}$, w.h.p. no subarray contains more than $2(\log n)^{\tau+1}$ elements of B_i. Divide the resource units allocated to i evenly among the subarrays and divide the resource units allocated to a subarray evenly among the elements of B_i in the subarray by first moving these elements to an array of size $(\log n)^{O(\tau)}$ (Fact 2.5), and then numbering them consecutively (see (Ragde, 1990, Lemma on p.747)). If C is chosen sufficiently large, this will provide each element of B_i with at least 2^i resource units. ∎

Our algorithm is described as follows in the remainder of the paper: Section 3 finds a good primary f, Section 6 estimates the bucket sizes induced by f, and Section 7 uses this information to compute injective secondaries for f. Section 5 eliminates duplicates from the input multiset, a necessary prerequisite for the application of the algorithms in Sections 6 and 7. Section 4, finally, provides a powerful tool for the design of fast randomized algorithms, which allows us to derive concrete algorithms from Sections 5, 6, and 7. Our main result is

Theorem 2.13: There is a constant $\epsilon > 0$ such that for all $\tau \geq \log^* n$, simple hashing problems of size n can be solved on a COLLISION PRAM using $O(\tau)$ time, $O(n)$ operations and $O(n)$ space with probability at least $1 - 2^{-(\log n)^{\tau/\log^* n}} - 2^{-n^\epsilon}$. Multiset hashing problems of size n can be solved on a COLLISION$^+$ PRAM within the same resource bounds.

Clearly this theorem implies a sequential solution for the (multi)set hashing problem using $O(n)$ time and $O(n)$ space with a failure probability of $2^{-n^{\Omega(1)}}$.

3 Finding a good primary

Our task in this section is to find a k-good primary for a given multiset of n integers (keys), where $k \in \mathbb{N}$

is fixed. We first show that if we are given additional space and processors, brute-force techniques can be applied to find a perfect hash function in constant time, even if we are confronted with duplicates in the input set.

Theorem 3.1: For every fixed $\delta > 0$, there is a constant $\epsilon > 0$ such that for all $\tau \geq 1$, multiset hashing problems of size n can be solved in $O(\tau)$ time using $O(n^{1+\delta})$ operations and $O(n^{1+\delta})$ space with probability at least $1 - \phi(n, \tau, \epsilon)$.

Proof: Let $\gamma = \delta/4$ and try out n^γ random primaries from $H_n^{\lceil 3/\gamma \rceil}$. For each bucket of each primary try out n^γ secondaries for each of the range sizes $1, 2, 3, \ldots, n^\gamma$ and attempt to allocate space for the injective secondaries with smallest ranges using Theorem 2.11. Facts 2.1 and 2.2 ensure that w.h.p., at least one perfect hash function will be found. ∎

In the following we will refer to the value of a key as its *color*. All keys with a certain color form a *color class*. The *multiplicity* of a color (or of a key with that color) is the number of all keys with that color. To *eliminate duplicates* in a color class is to remove all except exactly one key in that color class. The next lemma shows that it is easy to eliminate duplicates in large color classes.

Lemma 3.2: For every fixed $\delta > 0$, there is a constant $\epsilon > 0$ such that for every $\tau \geq 1$, duplicates can be eliminated in all color classes of size $\geq n^\delta$ in $O(\tau)$ time using $O(n)$ operations and $O(n)$ space with probability at least $1 - \phi(n, \tau, \epsilon)$.

Proof: Let each key decide with probability $n^{-\delta/2}$ to be active. By Chernoff bounds, the sample of active keys w.h.p. will be of size $\Theta(n^{1-\delta/2})$. Use Theorem 2.11 to move this sample to a block of size $\Theta(n^{1-\delta/2})$ and find a perfect hash function f for it, using Theorem 3.1. With high probability, the sample will contain at least one representative from each color class of size $\geq n^\delta$. Using f one can now eliminate duplicates in all such color classes. ∎

In order to maintain the size of the input set, we do not really remove the duplicates but modify them such that they are different from all other elements in the input set, i.e., we create new dummy color classes.

Theorem 3.3: For all fixed $k \in \mathbb{N}$, there is a constant $\epsilon > 0$ such that for all $\tau \geq 1$, given a multiset X of size n, a k-good primary for X can be found in $O(\tau)$ time using $O(n)$ operations and $O(n)$ space with probability at least $1 - \phi(n, \tau, \epsilon)$.

Proof: We first consider the case where X is a simple set, i.e., all multiplicities are ≤ 1. For all $b, k \in \mathbb{N}$, let $[b]_k = \prod_{j=0}^{k-1}(b-j)$.

Take $\delta = \frac{1}{24(k+1)^2}$ and choose n^δ random primaries $f_1, \ldots, f_{n^\delta}$ from $\mathcal{H}_n^{1/\delta}$. For $j = 1, \ldots, n^\delta$, let $b_1^{(j)}, \ldots, b_n^{(j)}$ be the bucket sizes induced by f_j and take $M_j = \max\{b_i^{(j)} : 1 \leq i \leq n\}$ and $\Sigma_j = \sum_{i=1}^n [b_i^{(j)}]_k$. By Fact 2.1, there is a constant C such that w.h.p. $M_j \leq Cn^{3\delta}$ and $\Sigma_j \leq Cn$ for some $j \in \{1, \ldots, n^\delta\}$. Note that Σ_j is the number of tuples of k distinct keys mapped by f_j to the same value and that it suffices to find a j with $\Sigma_j = O(n)$.

The remaining algorithm consists of two steps detailed below. The aim of Step 1 is to discard all primaries f_j with $M_j \geq n^{5\delta}$, while keeping those with $M_j \leq n^{3\delta}$.

Step 1: Each key chooses with probability $n^{-2\delta}$ to be *active* and each active key assigns itself at random to one of $f_1, \ldots, f_{n^\delta}$.

Let each (active) key x assigned to f_j write to index $f_j(x)$ in an auxiliary array $A[1..n]$. Then allocate n^δ *blocks* of size n^δ (one for each primary) to each index being written to by at least one key.

Finally let each key x assigned to f_j participate in a scattering with probability 1 over the block allocated for f_j at index $f_j(x)$ and discard all primaries with at least one full block.

Analysis of Step 1: By Chernoff bound (a), w.h.p. $O(n^{1-2\delta})$ elements are active, and no more indices in A will be written to. The total space needed is hence $O(n)$, and it can be allocated using Theorem 2.11. By Chernoff bound (b), for every j with $M_j \geq n^{5\delta}$, w.h.p. $\Omega(n^{5\delta-3\delta})$ elements from the largest bucket of f_j will be active and assigned to f_j, and these elements will fill their associated block, causing f_j to be discarded.

Conversely, for every j with $M_j \leq Cn^{3\delta}$, the expected number of keys participating in a fixed scattering is $O(n^{3\delta-3\delta})$. Hence by Chernoff bound (c), w.h.p. no block will be full and f_j is not discarded.

Step 2: Each key chooses with probability $n^{-6k\delta}$ to be *active* and each active key assigns itself at random to one of $f_1, \ldots, f_{n^\delta}$. Furthermore each index i of A assigns itself at random to one of $f_1, \ldots, f_{n^\delta}$. For $j = 1, \ldots, n^\delta$, let $I_j = \{i : 1 \leq i \leq n$ and i is assigned to $f_j\}$. Discarded primaries and all keys or indices assigned to them are excluded in the following.

Now each key x assigned to f_j writes to index $f_j(x)$ of A if $f_j(x) \in I_j$. Allocating n^δ processors and space to each index of A written to by at least one key and n^δ processors to each active key (Theorem 2.11),

use Fact 2.7 to compute for $j = 1, \ldots, n^\delta$ and for all $i \in I_j$ an exact estimate $\hat{r}_i$ of the quantity $r_i = [b'_i]_k$, where $b'_i = |\{x \in X : x$ is assigned to f_j and $f_j(x) = i\}|$. Then allocate $\hat{r}_i n^\delta$ processors to i, for $i = 1, \ldots, n$, and use these to compute an exact estimate $\hat{\Sigma}'_j$ of $\Sigma'_j = \sum_{i \in I_j} r_i$, for $j = 1, \ldots, n^\delta$. Finally discard those primaries f_j with $\hat{\Sigma}'_j > Kpn$, where $p = n^{-(6k^2+k+1)\delta}$ and K is a constant fixed in the analysis below.

Analysis of Step 2: By Chernoff bound (a), w.h.p. $O(n^{1-6k\delta})$ elements will be active. Furthermore, since each primary f_j that survives Step 1 has $M_j \leq n^{5\delta}$, no index i will request more than $n^{(5k+1)\delta}$ processors in the estimation of $\Sigma'_1, \ldots, \Sigma'_{n^\delta}$. It is now clear that Step 2 uses $O(n)$ operations and $O(n)$ space.

Fix $j \in \{1, \ldots, n^\delta\}$ and observe that a tuple of k distinct keys mapped by f_j to the same value is "counted" in Σ'_j exactly if its k elements are active and they and their common image under f_j are all assigned to f_j, which happens with probability $(n^{-6k\delta-\delta})^k n^{-\delta} = p$. It follows that $E(\Sigma'_j) = p\Sigma_j$ and hence that $E(\Sigma'_j + pn) = p(\Sigma_j + n)$. Since $p \geq n^{-1/4}$ and since Σ'_j changes by at most $n^{5k\delta} \leq n^{1/4}$ in response to a change affecting a single key or index of A, a martingale argument shows that w.h.p. $\Sigma'_j + pn$ deviates from $p(\Sigma_j + n)$ by at most a constant factor. Since furthermore $\hat{\Sigma}'_j + pn$ is an exact estimate for $\Sigma'_j + pn$, there are positive constants c_1 and c_2 such that w.h.p.,

$$c_1 p(\Sigma_j + n) \leq \hat{\Sigma}'_j + pn \leq c_2 p(\Sigma_j + n).$$

If we take $K = c_2(C + 1)$, it can be seen that w.h.p., Step 2 discards all primaries f_j with $\Sigma_j > (\frac{c_2}{c_1}(C + 1) - 1)n$, while keeping those with $\Sigma_j \leq Cn$. Hence at least one primary f_j survives Step 2, and it has $\Sigma_j = O(n)$.

We finally show how to reduce the case where X is a multiset to the case above. Let S be the simple set corresponding to X, i.e., containing an element exactly if that element occurs (at least once) in X. The basic idea is now to consider the simple hashing problem for S instead of the multiset hashing problem for X. Let n' denote the cardinality of S. By Lemma 3.2, we can assume that $n' \geq n^{1/2}$. Hence the larger failure probability associated with the smaller problem size is still negligible.

We do not know how to explicitly construct S from X within our time bounds. Fortunately, as can be seen by inspection of our algorithm for the case of simple sets, it suffices to be able to draw a random sample from S by including each element of S in the sample independently of other elements in S and with probability q, where $q = (n')^{-\delta}$, for some fixed $\delta > 0$.

The naive approach would be to include each element of X in the sample with probability q, use Theorem 2.11 and Theorem 3.1 to eliminate duplicates in this "naive" sample, and take the remaining keys as our sample of S. This protocol is not correct, however, since the probability that an element of S occurs in the sample is proportional to its multiplicity in X. In order to remedy this, we virtually select a representative for each color class, say the one with the leftmost position in the input array. We now choose the same naive sample as above, but this time ignore all nonrepresentatives, i.e., only representatives are allowed to be part of a sample. Now all elements in S have the same probability of being chosen for the sample, as desired.

But again, explicitly electing representatives would be more than we really need (and much too hard). Instead, we first choose a naive sample, find a perfect hash function f for it and eliminate for each color all but the leftmost key of that color in the sample (if there is one at all). Using f, all keys not in the sample then compare their position with the position of the key with the same color in the sample, if any. If some key not in the sample is further to the left than a key of the same color in the sample, it causes the latter to be removed from the sample.

Draw such a sample with $q = n^{-1/4}$ in order to compute an exact estimate $\hat{n}'$ for n' (Fact 2.7). Taking $\hat{n}'$ as the new input size, we can now proceed as in the case of simple sets. ∎

4 An abstract approach

Our algorithm employs three different subroutines based on the "log*" technique first used by Raman (1990). Because of the great similarities between these subroutines, in this section we give an abstract formulation of the log* technique that allows us to derive the concrete subroutines with relatively little effort by verifying certain conditions stated in this section in a problem-specific manner. We think of this approach to be of independent interest for the development of very fast algorithms for similar problems too. Because of space constraints and in the interest of readability, we refrain from a formal and rigorous exposition.

In the abstract setting the input consists of a number of *active objects* stored in an array of size n, and

the goal is to *deactivate* all objects. To this end each application must provide a constant-time procedure *Deactivate* that with high probability deactivates most objects. The objects are permanently partitioned into *groups* that can be numbered by integers in a range of size $O(n)$ such that an object can determine the number of its group in constant time, and *Deactivate* operates on a group-by-group basis, either deactivating all objects in a group or leaving them all active. A group is called active when its objects are active.

More precisely, each application is associated with a parameter tuple (v_0, k_0, k, λ) of four positive integer constants with $k \geq k_0 \geq 3$. We require that for all $s \geq 1$, $O(ns^{-\lambda})$ arbitrary groups contain a total of $O(ns^{-1})$ objects (the *group size property*). Intuitively, this means that there are few large groups. The remaining conditions should hold for all sets V_δ of the form $V_\delta = \{v_0, v_0 + 1, \ldots, \delta \log n\} \cup \{n^\delta\}$, where δ is a sufficiently small positive constant. What we basically require of the procedure *Deactivate* is that if it is called with argument $v \in V_\delta$ when the total number of active objects is $O(nv^{-k_0})$, then the probability that a fixed group remains active is at most $2^{-2\lambda kv}$. We do, however, allow $O(n) \cdot 2^{-2\lambda kv}$ *exceptional objects*, whose presence in a group may prevent the deactivation of that group (for $v = n^\delta$ this allows no exceptional objects). While not demanding independence between the deactivation of distinct groups, we require an execution of *Deactivate* to be determined by $O(n)$ independent *elementary events*, a change in one of which affects the number of deactivated objects by $O(n^{1/4})$ (the *bounded differences property*). Finally, we allow *Deactivate* to fail completely with a small error probability, which must be bounded by $\phi(n, \tau', \Omega(1))$ if *Deactivate* is slowed down to run in time $\Theta(\tau')$.

The log* technique provides a subroutine *Allocate* with argument v that may be used a constant number of times during the call of *Deactivate*(v) to allocate resources in the form of consecutively numbered memory cells or processors to requesting active objects. These resources, however, as well as all other resources allocated during a call of *Deactivate*(v), must sum to $O(n/v)$. With small probability, *Allocate* may fail to satisfy the request of an active object; we call such an object *unlucky*. The existence of unlucky objects can be ignored by a concrete application (we deal with it in the general analysis), except that *Deactivate* should treat groups containing unlucky objects as inactive (i.e., such groups remain active).

As a more concrete example, we next sketch how the interval allocation problem defined in Section 2 fits into the framework described above. Let $x_1, \ldots, x_n$

be the input of an interval allocation problem. As in the proof of Lemma 2.11, assume that each nonzero x_j is a power of 2 in the range $2..n$ and for $i = 1, \ldots, m = \lfloor \log n \rfloor$, let $B_i = \{j : 1 \leq j \leq n$ and $x_j = 2^i\}$ and $b_i = |B_i|$. Define an object as an element of $\{1, \ldots, n\}$ and take $j \in \{1, \ldots, n\}$ to be active if and only if $x_j > 0$. When the corresponding request has been satisfied, change x_j to zero and consider j as no longer active. We take each object to form a group by itself, so that the group size property is satisfied with $\lambda = 1$. Also take $v_0 = 1$ and $k_0 = 3$ and let $k \geq k_0$ be arbitrary. In the following we give a realization of $Deactivate(v)$ that runs in time $O(\tau')$ with probability at least $1 - \phi(n, \tau', \Omega(1))$. W.l.o.g. assume that $\tau' \leq \frac{1}{4} \log n / \log \log n$.

(1) For $i = 1, \ldots, m$, use Fact 2.7 to compute an estimate $\hat{b}_i$ for b_i in $O(\tau')$ time with probability at least $1 - \phi(n, \tau', \Omega(1))$. Let $I := \{i : \hat{b}_i > 0\}$ and note that w.h.p., for all $i \in I$, $\hat{b}_i$ is exact for b_i, whereas for $i \notin I$, $b_i \leq (\log n)^{\tau'}$.

(2) For each $i \in \{1, \ldots, n\} - I$, allocate $n^{1/2}$ processors to every object in B_i. Now use Theorem 2.11 to satisfy all requests of such objects in time $O(\tau')$ with probability at least $1 - \phi(n, \tau', \Omega(1))$.

(3) Call $Allocate(v)$ to allocate v processors to every object in $\bigcup_{i \in I} B_i$ and do the following in parallel for all $i \in I$:

   (3.1) Use Fact 2.9 to allocate arrays A_i and R_i of $Kv\hat{b}_i$ and $Kv\hat{b}_i 2^i$ cells, respectively, where $K = 2^{2k}$.

   (3.2) Scatter the processors allocated to elements of B_i over A_i. Place each object with at least one noncolliding processor in the cell chosen by such a processor.

   (3.3) For each cell in A_i occupied by some element of B_i, allocate the corresponding block of 2^i cells in R_i to that element.

We now verify the remaining conditions imposed by the general $\log^*$ technique. The total amount of resources needed is clearly $O(n/v)$. There are no exceptional objects and by Fact 2.8, the probability that a fixed object is not deactivated is at most 2^{-2kv}. The bounded differences property, finally, is satisfied because the actions of single processors in Step 3 are independent, while a change affecting a single processor changes the number of deactivated objects by at most 2.

Consider an application with associated parameter tuple (v_0, k_0, k, λ). For every sufficiently small constant $\delta > 0$ and for every sufficiently large input size n, we define a sequence $v_1, \ldots, v_T$ of arguments such that $v_T = n^\delta$, $v_t = \lceil \log v_{t+1} \rceil$ for all $t = 1, \ldots, T-1$,

and $\log v_1 < v_0 \leq v_1$. Note that for all $t = 1, \ldots, T$, $v_t \in V_\delta$, and the sequence grows exponentially, i.e., $2^{v_t - 1} \leq v_{t+1} \leq 2^{v_t}$, for $t = 1, \ldots, T-1$. Clearly $T = O(\log^* n)$.

Let $Stage\ t$ denote a call of $Deactivate(v_t)$. The calls of $Allocate(v_t)$ may leave some $O(n) \cdot 2^{-2\lambda k v}$ objects unlucky. We consider the procedure $Allocate$ as given for the time being and later provide a realization of it.

We now investigate the performance of Stage t, for $t = 1, \ldots, T$. For $t < T$, the expected number of unlucky or exceptional objects is $O(n \cdot 2^{-2\lambda k v_t})$, and by the group size property, the total size of all groups containing such objects is $O(n \cdot 2^{-2k v_t})$. Each of the remaining groups is deactivated, except with probability $2^{-2\lambda k v_t}$. By a martingale argument making use of the bounded differences property, $O(n \cdot 2^{-2\lambda k v_t})$ groups are not deactivated; consequently $O(n \cdot 2^{-2k v_t})$ objects remain active. Assuming that v_0 is sufficiently large, we may conclude that w.h.p., the number of active objects after Stage t is $\leq n \cdot 2^{-k v_t}$.

In Stage T no objects are exceptional or unlucky, except with negligible probability, and the probabilities for groups to remain active sum to a negligible quantity. Therefore, w.h.p., no objects are active after the last Stage.

We conclude that successively executing Stages 1 through T w.h.p. deactivates all objects. We will call a computational problem $\log^*$-suited if it can be viewed as that of deactivating all active objects as described by means of a suitable procedure $Deactivate$ with the stated properties. Note that the performance of Stage t must not depend on a special selection of active objects but should cope with any $O(nv_t^{-k_0})$ active objects. As can be shown by completing the discussion above, the interval allocation problem is $\log^*$-suited.

Lemma 4.1: For all $\tau \geq \log^* n$, given an instance of size n of a $\log^*$-suited problem $\mathcal{P}$, all objects can be deactivated in $O(\tau)$ time using $O(n)$ processors and $O(n)$ space with probability at least $1 - \phi(n, \tau/\log^* n, \Omega(1))$.

Proof: Let (v_0, k_0, k, λ) be a parameter tuple that can be associated with $\mathcal{P}$, where v_0 is sufficiently large. Choose $\delta > 0$ sufficiently small and consider the associated argument sequence $v_1, \ldots, v_T$. It follows from the discussion above that successively executing Stages 1 through T deactivates all objects with probability $1 - \phi(n, \tau', \Omega(1))$ if each stage is slowed down to run in $\Theta(\tau')$ time, where $\tau' = \tau / \log^* n$.

The time used by this algorithm is clearly $O(T \cdot \tau') = O(\tau)$. In order to be able to allocate resources to active objects, in every stage we need one processor assisting each active object. The amount of working space and other processors used in Stage t is $O(n/v_t)$, for $t = 1, \ldots, T$. We therefore conclude that $O(n)$ space and $O(n)$ processors suffice to deactivate all objects.

To finish the proof, we must describe a procedure *Allocate*, which, when called with argument $v \in V_\delta$, satisfies all but $O(n) \cdot 2^{-2\lambda k v}$ of the requests of $O(nv^{-k_0})$ active objects placed in an array of size n, for which n processors are available. *Allocate* may use $O(n/v)$ space and processors and should not fail, except with probability $\phi(n, \tau', \Omega(1))$ when slowed down to run in $\Theta(\tau')$ time. We consider two cases:

In the first case we describe a very specific procedure for the interval allocation problem $\mathcal{I}$, where all active objects request v processors. For arbitrary $k' \in \mathbb{N}$ let $(v_0', k_0', k', \lambda')$ be a parameter tuple associated with $\mathcal{I}$ and denote by A the array (of size n) in which the active objects are initially placed.

(1) For suitable $K \in \mathbb{N}$, allocate an array B of size $K\lceil n/v^2 \rceil$ and scatter five copies of each active object over B. Now v processors can be allocated to each object with at least one noncolliding copy.

(2) Divide A into *clusters* of size v^6 each. If a cluster contains less than v colliding objects, use Fact 2.5 to move these to an array of size v^5, after which v processors can be allocated to each colliding object in the cluster.

Analysis: If K is chosen sufficiently large (but constant), it can be verified using Chernoff bound (c) that the probability for a fixed cluster to contain more than v colliding objects is less than $2^{-(2\lambda'k'+1)v}$, which is $\leq v^{-6} \cdot 2^{-2\lambda'k'v}$ for sufficiently large v_0. In case $v = n^\delta$ these probabilities sum over all clusters to a negligible quantity. If $v \leq \delta \log n$, a martingale argument shows that the actual number of objects in clusters containing more than v colliding objects is $O(n \cdot 2^{-2\lambda'k'v})$.

We are now ready to give a general allocation procedure for $\mathcal{P}$. Since all of v_0, v_0', k' can be fixed arbitrarily large, we may assume without loss of generality that $v_0' = v_0$ and $k' = k$. Hence, for sufficiently small δ, the argument sequence $v_1, \ldots, v_T$ can be associated with both $\mathcal{P}$ and $\mathcal{I}$.

By naturally identifying the requesting objects of $\mathcal{P}$ with active objects of $\mathcal{I}$, a call of *Allocate*(v_t) simply executes Stage t of the interval allocation procedure, slowed down appropriately to run in $O(\tau')$ time. The analysis above shows that *Allocate* performs as required. ∎

The last lemma is not satisfying in the sense that the resulting algorithm is not optimal, i.e., it uses $\Theta(n)$ processors. To remedy this, we observe that the number of processors needed by *Deactivate* decreases very rapidly (to $O(n/v_t)$ in Stage t), and that the same applies to the number of active objects. This leads us to the following result.

Theorem 4.2: For all $\tau \geq \log^* n$, given an instance of size n of a $\log^*$-suited problem $\mathcal{P}$, all objects can be deactivated optimally in $O(\tau)$ time using $O(n/\tau)$ processors and $O(n)$ space with probability at least $1 - \phi(n, \tau/\log^* n, \Omega(1))$.

Proof: Let (v_0, k_0, k, λ) be a parameter tuple that can be associated with $\mathcal{P}$. In view of Fact 2.10, it suffices to prove that the number of active objects can be decreased as described in the following lemma.

Lemma 4.3: The number of active objects can be decreased to $O(n/(\log^* n)^k)$ in $O(\tau)$ time using $O(n/\tau)$ processors and $O(n)$ space with probability at least $1 - \phi(n, \tau/\log^* n, \Omega(1))$.

Proof: In respect of the readability of the proof, we ignore matters of rounding in the following. Without loss of generality we may assume that there is a $T' \in \{1, \ldots, T\}$ such that $v_{T'} = \sqrt{\log^* n}$ (if neccessary, we can insert an intermediate Stage with argument $\sqrt{\log^* n}$ between Stages T' and $T' + 1$, where $v_{T'} \leq \sqrt{\log^* n} \leq v_{T'+1}$). For $t = 1, \ldots, T'$, instead of Stage t we now consider *Extended Stage t* consisting of a *Deactivation Step t* followed by a *Compaction Step t*. Before Extended Stage t we require the active objects, whose number may be at most $nv_t^{-k_0}$, to be placed in an array of size $v_1 \cdot \frac{n}{v_t}$.

In the Deactivation Step t, we execute Stage t slowed down appropriately to run on $O(n/\tau)$ processors. As follows from the proof of Lemma 4.1, the number of operations needed by *Allocate* in Stage t is the sum of $O(n/v_t)$ and the size of the array containing the requesting objects. Hence, by assumption, the Deactivation Step needs $O(\tau/v_t)$ time and fails with probability at most $\phi(n, \tau/\log^* n, \Omega(1))$.

For $t < T'$, Compaction Step t consists of the following, where A denotes the array into which active objects are placed at the beginning of Extended Stage t and I is the block of size n initially containing all objects. By *putting back* an object we mean placing it at its original position in I. To put back a group is to put back all contained objects.

(1) Allocate a block of $v_1 \frac{n}{v_{t+1}}$ memory cells and divide it into two halves A_1 and A_2.

(2) Scatter all objects which are active after the Deactivation Step over A_1. Divide A into *clusters*

of size $v_1 \cdot \frac{\tau}{v_t}$ and call a cluster *overfull* if it contains more than $v_1 \cdot \frac{\tau}{2v_{t+1}}$ colliding objects. All groups containing objects in overfull clusters are put back and will be ignored in all following Extended Stages.

(3) Use one processor per cluster to copy all remaining objects in A to A_2.

Analysis: By Fact 2.8 an object collides with probability at most 2^{-v_t}. Hence, by Chernoff bound (a), a fixed cluster is overfull with probability $e^{-\Theta(\tau/v_{t+1})}$ which is certainly less than $\tau^{-\lambda k}$ for sufficiently large n. A martingale argument finally shows that w.h.p., $O(n/(v_{t+1}\tau^k))$ objects are put back.

In extended Stage T', less than $n \cdot 2^{-k\sqrt{\log^* n}}$ objects are active after the Deactivation Step. Even if we put back all of these, the total number of objects put back in Extended Stages 1 through T' is $O(n/(\log^* n)^k)$. ∎

For matters of convenience we naturally extend the class of log*-suited problems, by allowing an arbitrary preprocessing procedure to be executed before the argument sequence $v_1, \ldots, v_T$ is fixed and the deactivation process begins. The preprocessing procedure may use $O(n)$ operations and $O(n)$ space with probability at least $1 - \phi(n, \tau/\log^* n, \Omega(1))$, when slowed down to run on $O(n/\tau)$ processors, for $\tau \geq \log^* n$.

5 Eliminating duplicates

This section shows how to eliminate all duplicates in the input set. In this section alone, we use the Collision+ PRAM instead of the weaker Collision PRAM.

Lemma 5.1: The problem of constructing the simple set S corresponding to a multiset $X = \{x_1, \ldots, x_n\} \subseteq U$ is log*-suited.

Proof: Begin by using Lemma 3.2 to eliminate duplicates in all color classes of size $\geq n^{1/12}$ and Theorem 3.3 to compute a primary f which, applied to S, has maximum bucket size $\leq n^{1/12}$. Define a new function $f': U \rightarrow \{1, \ldots, r\}$, where $r = n^{11/12}$, by taking $f'(x) = 1 + \lfloor f(x) \cdot n^{-1/12} \rfloor$, for $x \in U$. Note that f' maps at most $n^{1/4}$ elements of X to the same value.

Now take $\{1, \ldots, n\}$ as the set of objects and let each object form a group by itself, which satisfies the group size property with $\lambda = 1$. The procedure *Deactivate* attempts to write each element of S

exactly once to a designated storage area. An object $j \in \{1, \ldots, n\}$ is deactivated exactly when x_j is written.

Before a call of *Deactivate*(v), let J denote the set of active objects. For $i = 1, \ldots, r$, let $B_i = \{j \in J : f'(x_j) = i\}$ and $b_i = |B_i|$. After calling *Allocate*(v) to allocate $6v$ processors to each active object, *Deactivate*(v) does the following in parallel for $i = 1, \ldots, r$:

(1) Use Fact 2.7 to compute estimates $\hat{b}_1, \ldots, \hat{b}_r$ for $b_1, \ldots, b_r$ such that $\hat{b}_i \geq b_i$, for $i = 1, \ldots, r$, while $\sum_{i=1}^r \hat{b}_i = O(|J| + n^{12/13})$.

(2) Using Theorem 2.11, allocate arrays $A_{i,1}, \ldots, A_{i,6v}$ of $4\hat{b}_i$ cells each to B_i.

(3) Select random hash functions $h_{i,1}, \ldots, h_{i,6v}$ from $\mathcal{H}^1_{4\hat{b}_i}$. For each $j \in B_i$ and each $l \in \{1, \ldots, 6v\}$, attempt to write x_j to position $h_{i,l}(x_j)$ in $A_{i,l}$. This will succeed exactly if x_j is *left alone* by $h_{i,l}$, i.e., if no value different from x_j is mapped by $h_{i,l}$ to the same location. If x_j is left alone by $h_{i,l}$ for at least one value of l, remove all except exactly one occurrence of x_j from the arrays $A_{i,1}, \ldots, A_{i,6v}$ and deactivate all $j' \in \{1, \ldots, n\}$ with $x'_j = x_j$.

Using the techniques of (Fredman, Komlós and Szemerédi, 1984), it is easy to prove that a function chosen at random from $\mathcal{H}^1_{4b}$, when applied to a set B with $|B| \leq b$, leaves a fixed element $x \in B$ alone with probability at least $1/2$. Since *Deactivate*(v) carries out $6v$ independent trials of this kind for each active object, the probability that a fixed object is not deactivated is at most 2^{-6v}. We can hence choose $k = k_0 = 3$. If *Deactivate*(v) is called with $v \leq n^{1/26}$ when the number $|J|$ of active elements is $O(n \cdot v^{-k_0})$, the resources used by the call are $O(v \sum_{i=1}^r \hat{b}_i) = O(n/v)$. Finally, the bounded differences property is satisfied because elements mapped to different values by f' are treated independently. ∎

6 Estimating bucket sizes

Lemma 6.1: Given $l \in \mathbb{N}$ and $\epsilon > 0$, a simple set $S \subseteq U$ of n keys and an $(8l + 2)$-good primary f for S with associated bucket sizes $b_1, \ldots, b_n$, the problem of computing an (l, δ)-good estimator for $b_1, \ldots, b_n$, for some $\delta \leq \epsilon$, is log*-suited.

Proof: Let the buckets associated with f be $B_1, \ldots, B_n$, such that $b_i = |B_i|$, for $i = 1, \ldots, n$.. We consider all keys and buckets as objects and let a group consist of a bucket together with all its keys. The group containing a bucket B_i is deactivated by computing an estimate $\hat{b}_i$ for b_i. Since f is at least 2-good, Schwarz's inequality implies that for every $s \geq 1$, $O(ns^{-2})$ arbitrary groups contain $O(\sqrt{ns^{-2}}\sqrt{\sum b_i^2}) = O(n/s)$ elements. The group size property is hence satisfied with $\lambda = 2$.

In the realization of $Deactivate(v)$ below, the argument v intuitively determines the range of bucket sizes for which "good" estimates are almost certainly found.

> **procedure** $Deactivate(v)$;
>   Call $Allocate(v)$ to allocate a $2v \times v$ array
>   and $2v$ processors to each active bucket
>   **for** each active bucket B_i **pardo**
>   **begin**
>   Let the elements of B_i carry out
>   a GCS $\mathcal{S}_i$ with range $2v \times v$;
> $l_i :=$ last full row of $\mathcal{S}_i$;
>   **if** $l_i < 2v$ ($*$ not entirely full $*$)
>   **then** $\hat{b}_i := 2^{l_i} v^2$;
>   **end**;

Analysis: Let $k_0 = k = 4l + 1$. Then the total amount of resources used by $O(nv^{-k_0})$ active objects is $O(n/v)$. Consider all buckets with size greater than 2^{2v} as exceptional objects. Since h is $(8l + 2)$-good, there are $O(n) \cdot 2^{-4kv}$ such objects. For sufficiently large v_0, the following statements about the quality of the estimates obtained in a call of $Deactivate$ with argument $v \geq v_0$ can be made. Denote by D_i the event that $\hat{b}_i$ is defined during the call.

Lemma 6.2:
  (a) If $b_i \geq v^2$, then $\Pr(D_i \wedge \hat{b}_i > b_i^2) \leq 2^{-4kv}$;
  (b) If $b_i < v^2$, then $\Pr(D_i \wedge \hat{b}_i > v^4) \leq 2^{-4kv}$;
  (c) If $b_i < 2^{2v}$, then $\Pr(\neg D_i) \leq 2^{-4kv}$;
  (d) For all $a \geq 1$, $\Pr(D_i \wedge \hat{b}_i$ is a-bad$) \leq 2^{-a}$.

Proof: For sufficiently large values of v, the following holds: (a) By Fact 2.6(b), $\Pr(D_i \wedge \hat{b}_i > b_i^2 \geq v^4) \leq \Pr(D_i \wedge \hat{b}_i > v^2 b_i) \leq (2e/v)^v \leq 2^{-4kv}$; (b) $\Pr(D_i \wedge \hat{b}_i > v^4 > b_i^2) \leq \Pr(D_i \wedge \hat{b}_i > v^2 b_i)$. Proceed as in part (a); (c) By Fact 2.6(a), if $b_i < 2^{2v}$, then $\Pr(\neg D_i) \leq (2^{-2v} e b_i/v)^v \leq (e/v)^v \leq 2^{-4kv}$; (d) By Fact 2.6(c), $\Pr(D_i \wedge \hat{b}_i$ is a-bad$) \leq v \cdot 2^{1-av/2} \leq 2^{-a}$. ∎

As follows directly from part (c) of the above lemma, the probability that a nonexceptional bucket is deactivated is at most $2^{-2\lambda kv}$. Furthermore, distinct groups are treated independently of each other; hence the bounded differences property is satisfied.

Let $v_1, \ldots, v_T$ be a possible sequence of arguments to $Deactivate$, such that $v_T = n^\delta$, for some $\delta \leq \epsilon$. We finally check that after executing Stages $1, \ldots, T$, the computed sequence $\hat{b}_1, \ldots, \hat{b}_n$ is w.h.p. an (l, δ)-good estimator for $b_1, \ldots, b_n$. We prove that the following holds w.h.p. for $t = 1, \ldots, T$, where I_t denotes the set $\{i : 1 \leq i \leq n$ and $\hat{b}_i$ is defined in Stage $t\}$, from which the claim can be seen to follow.

(1) $\sum_{i \in I_t} \hat{b}_i^l = \sum_{i \in I_t} b_i^{2l} + O(n/v_t)$;
(2) for all a with $1 \leq a \leq \delta \log n$,
    $|\{i \in I_t : \hat{b}_i$ is a-bad for $b_i\}| = O(n/(v_t 2^a))$.
(3) for all $i \in I_t$, $\hat{b}_i$ is not n^δ-bad for b_i.

Stage t estimates b_i well only if approximately $v_t^2 \leq b_i \leq 2^{2v_t}$. Correspondingly, for $i = 1, \ldots, n$ and $t = 1, \ldots, T$, call i *tardy* in Stage t if $\hat{b}_i$ is defined in Stage t or later and $b_i < v_t^2$. Also call B_i *problematic* in Stage t if $i \in I_t$ and one of the following holds:

  (a) i is not tardy in Stage t, and $\hat{b}_i > b_i^2$;
  (b) i is tardy in Stage t, and $\hat{b}_i > v^4$;
  (c) i is tardy in Stage t, and $\hat{b}_i \leq v^4$.

As follows directly from parts (a) and (b) of Lemma 6.2 together with Chernoff bound (c) and Markov's inequality, w.h.p. the number of problematic buckets of type (a) or (b) in Stage t is $O(n) \cdot 2^{-(4l+1)v_t}$, for $t = 1, \ldots, T$. Obviously, the number of buckets of type (c) is $O(n \cdot v^{-k_0})$ w.h.p., since no more objects are active at the beginning of Stage t. Since $\hat{b}_i \leq 2^{4v_t}$ if $i \in I_t$ and $\hat{b}_i \leq v_t^4$ if B_i is problematic of type (c), w.h.p. $\sum_{i \in I_t'} \hat{b}_i^l = O(n/v_t)$, where $I_t' = \{i : B_i$ is problematic in Stage $t\}$. To prove (1), it now suffices to observe that if $i \in I_t - I_t'$, then $\hat{b}_i \leq b_i^2$. Properties (2) and (3) follow directly from Lemma 6.2(d) together with Chernoff bound (c). ∎

7 Finding injective secondaries

This section shows how to find injective secondaries for a 34-good primary using the estimation procedure described in the previous section. Solutions to variants of this problem make up the bulk of previous work on parallel hashing; in particular, our approach in this section is similar to the one taken by Matias and Vishkin (1991).

Lemma 7.1: Given a 34-good primary f, the problem of finding injective secondaries for f is $\log^*$-suited.

Proof: As in the previous section, an object is defined to be either a key or a bucket, a group consists of a bucket together with its elements, and the group size property is satisfied with $\lambda = 2$. Let $k_0 = k = 8$.

We can use the algorithm resulting from Theorem 4.2 applied to Lemma 6.1 in order to compute a $(4, \delta)$-good estimator $\hat{b}_1, \ldots, \hat{b}_n$ for the bucket sizes $b_1, \ldots, b_n$ induced by f, for some sufficiently small $\delta > 0$. Choose v_0 sufficiently large and consider arguments $v \in V_\delta$ to *Deactivate*. *Deactivate*(v) first calls *Allocate*(v) to allocate $32v$ processors to each active key and $32v$ arrays of $2(32v\hat{b}_i)^2$ cells each to each active bucket B_i (by Schwarz's inequality this sums over all active buckets to $O(n/v)$ since our estimator is $(4, \delta)$-good). Then use the allocated resources to try out $32v$ random secondaries for each active bucket. If an injective secondary is found, the corresponding bucket (and all its elements) becomes inactive.

Provided that $b_i \leq 32v\hat{b}_i$, the probability that B_i is not deactivated is bounded by $2^{-2\lambda kv}$ (Fact 2.2). On the other hand, the $(4, \delta)$-goodness of $\hat{b}_1, \ldots, \hat{b}_n$ implies that the number of buckets B_i with $b_i > 32v\hat{b}_i$ is $O(n) \cdot 2^{-2\lambda kv}$, so that we can declare all such buckets to exceptional objects. The bounded differences property, finally, is satisfied because the deactivation of distinct buckets are independent events. ∎

We apologize for all constants greater than 8 appearing in this paper. However, we conjecture that they can be made ≤ 8.

References

BOLLOBÁS, B. (1987), Martingales, Isoperimetric Inequalities and Random Graphs, *in* Colloq. Math. Soc. J. Bolyai 52, pp. 113–139.

CHLEBUS, B. S., DIKS, K., HAGERUP, T., AND RADZIK, T. (1988), Efficient Simulations between Concurrent-Read Concurrent-Write PRAM Models, *in* Proc. 13th Symposium on Mathematical Foundations of Computer Science, Springer Lecture Notes in Computer Science, Vol. 324, pp. 231–239.

DIETZFELBINGER, M., AND MEYER AUF DER HEIDE, F. (1989), An Optimal Parallel Dictionary, *in* Proc. 1st Annual ACM Symposium on Parallel Algorithms and Architectures, pp. 360–368.

FREDMAN, M. L, KOMLÓS, J., AND SZEMERÉDI, E. (1984), Storing a Sparse Table with $O(1)$ Worst Case Access Time, *J. ACM* **31**, pp. 538–544.

GIL, J., AND MATIAS, Y. (1991), Fast Hashing on a PRAM — Designing by Expectation, *in* Proc. 2nd Annual ACM-SIAM Symposium on Discrete Algorithms, pp. 271–280.

GIL, J., MEYER AUF DER HEIDE, F., AND WIGDERSON, A. (1990), Not All Keys Can be Hashed in Constant Time, *in* Proc. 22nd Annual ACM Symposium on Theory of Computing, pp. 244–253.

HAGERUP, T., AND RÜB, C. (1990), A Guided Tour of Chernoff Bounds, *Inf. Proc. Lett.* **33**, pp. 305–308.

HAGERUP, T. (1991), Fast Parallel Space Allocation, Estimation and Integer Sorting, Tech. Rep. no. 03/91, SFB 124, Universität des Saarlandes.

MATIAS, Y., AND VISHKIN, U. (1990a), On Parallel Hashing and Integer Sorting, *in* Proc. 17th International Colloquium on Automata, Languages and Programming, Springer Lecture Notes in Computer Science, Vol. 443, pp. 729–743.

MATIAS, Y., AND VISHKIN, U. (1990b), On Parallel Hashing and Integer Sorting, Tech. Rep. No. UMIACS–TR–90–13 (revised version), University of Maryland, College Park.

MATIAS, Y., AND VISHKIN, U. (1991), Converting High Probability into Nearly-Constant Time — with Applications to Parallel Hashing, preliminary draft. Also *in* Proc. 23nd Annual ACM Symposium on Theory of Computing, to appear.

RAGDE, P. (1990), The Parallel Simplicity of Compaction and Chaining, *in* Proc. 17th International Colloquium on Automata, Languages and Programming, Springer Lecture Notes in Computer Science, Vol. 443, pp. 744–751.

RAMAN, R. (1990), The Power of Collision: Randomized Parallel Algorithms for Chaining and Integer Sorting, *in* Proc. 10th Conference on Foundations of Software Technology and Theoretical Computer Science, Springer Lecture Notes in Computer Science, Vol. 472, pp. 161–175.

SIEGEL, A. (1989), On universal classes of fast high performance hash functions, their time-space tradeoff, and their applications, *in* Proc. 30th Annual Symposium on Foundations of Computer Science, pp. 20–25.

Tight Bounds for the Chaining Problem

Shiva Chaudhuri
Department of Computer Science
Rutgers University
New Brunswick, NJ 08903

Abstract

The *chaining* problem is defined as follows. Given values $a_1, ..., a_n$, $a_i = 0$ or 1, $1 \leq i \leq n$, compute $b_1, ..., b_n$, such that $b_i = \max\{j \mid a_j = 1, j < i\}$. (Define $\max\{\} = 0$.) The chaining problem appears as a subproblem in many contexts. There are algorithms that solve the chaining problem on CRCW PRAMs in $O(\alpha(n))$ time. We study a class of algorithms (called oblivious algorithms) for this problem. We present a simple oblivious chaining algorithm running in $O(\alpha(n))$ time. More importantly, we demonstrate the optimality of the algorithm by showing a matching lower bound. We also provide the first steps towards a lower bound for all chaining algorithms by showing that any chaining algorithm that runs in two steps must use a superlinear number of processors. Our proofs use *prefix graphs* and *weak superconcentrators*. We demonstrate an interesting connection between the two and use this idea to obtain improved bounds on the size of prefix graphs.

1 Introduction

Consider the following problem called *chaining*. Given values $a_1, ..., a_n$, $a_i = 0$ or 1, $1 \leq i \leq n$, compute $b_1, ..., b_n$, such that $b_i = \max\{j \mid a_j = 1, j < i\}$. (Define $\max\{\} = 0$) The chaining problem is a natural problem to consider in the context of database retreival operations; all the records that satisfy a particular predicate correspond to the input bits that have value 1. Apart from this it appears as a subproblem in many contexts and has been studied before in [14], [15]. Parallel integer sorting [2], [12], parallel merging

of integers drawn from a restricted domain [3], parallel subset compaction [16], [11],[14] and circuits for computing threshold functions [13] are examples. It is easy to solve the problem in $O(n)$ time using one processor. Using n processors, very fast parallel algorithms exist, with running times close to constant. For this reason, and because of its simplicity, it is an open question of theoretical interest [3], [14],[15] whether constant time parallel algorithms exist.

Berkman and Vishkin [4] and independently, Ragde [14] have given parallel algorithms that solve the chaining problem in $O(\alpha(n))$ time using n processors, where $\alpha(n)$ is the inverse of Ackerman's function, and is a very slowly growing function. Using algorithms similar to the chaining algorithm, Berkman and Vishkin [5] give algorithms achieving the same bounds for other problems : the lowest-common-ancestor problem, a parenthesis matching problem and merging of integers drawn from a restricted domain [6].

Chandra, Fortune and Lipton [8] showed that a circuit of bounded depth for the prefix-carry problem requires superlinear size, implying a superconstant lower bound on depth for circuits with linear size. We are not aware of any superconstant lower bounds on the PRAM model of computation for problems which have algorithms with running time $o(\log\log n)$.

We study oblivious algorithms for the chaining problem. Informally, an oblivious algorithm is one in which the pattern of memory access depends only on n (the size of the problem), and not on the specific input. This class of algorithms is of interest because the algorithms of Berkman and Vishkin and Ragde can be modified to be oblivious. We present a simple oblivious algorithm for chaining running in $O(\alpha(n))$ time. Further, we show, that for the class of oblivious algorithms, this is optimal, by proving that an oblivious chaining algorithm using n processors requires $\Omega(\alpha(n))$ time. Since all known algorithms for chaining can be made oblivious, this gives evidence of a superconstant lower bound for all chaining algorithms.

We conjecture that the upper bound is optimal. We provide the first steps towards proving this by showing that any chaining algorithm that terminates in 2 steps requires a superlinear number of processors. We believe the techniques developed in this paper will be useful in proving a lower bound for all algorithms.

Our oblivious chaining algorithm uses *prefix graphs*. Upper and lower bounds on the size of prefix graphs of fixed depth were proved in [7, 8]. We demonstrate an interesting connection between prefix graphs and *weak superconcentrators* [9]. Using this idea, we present a simple proof that improves the lower bound, and shows that the construction is optimal.

The model of computation used in this paper is the Concurrent-Read Concurrent-Write Parallel Random Access Machine (CRCW PRAM). In the COMMON model of CRCW PRAM, all processors that simultaneously write to the same memory cell must write the same value. In the more powerful PRIORITY model, each processor has an associated priority and when several processors simultaneously write to the same memory cell, the highest priority processor succeeds. Throughout this paper, the algorithms described run on the COMMON model and the lower bound is proved on the stronger PRIORITY model.

2 Oblivious computation on PRAMs

The input to an algorithm for chaining consists of a value n (the size of the problem), and n bits (called the input vector) representing the problem. At any step, each processor computes, based on its actions so far, a memory address to access and the contents to write (if it is a write step). By an *oblivious* algorithm, we mean one where the address accessed is fixed over all input vectors, i.e. it depends only on the value n. However, whether or not the processor performs any action may depend on the input vector. For example, when $n = 100$, on the fifth write step, p_1, if it writes always writes to c_{15}, but it may or may not write depending on the input vector.

It will be convenient to model the computation of an oblivious algorithm as a graph. Given an algorithm A and an input size n, the directed graph $G_{A,n}$ is defined as follows. The vertices of A are grouped into levels.

Suppose the algorithm solves the chaining problem in k steps. Then the graph $G_{A,n}$ will consist of $2k + 1$ levels of vertices, numbered $0, ..., 2k$.

At even levels we will have a vertex for each cell in the memory that is accessed by the algorithm. These vertices will have the form $(c, 2j)$, $0 \leq j \leq k$ and will be called cell vertices (or just cells). At odd levels we will have a vertex for each processor. These vertices will have the form $(p, 2j + 1)$, $0 \leq j \leq k - 1$, and will be called processor vertices (or just processors). Thus there are k levels of processor vertices and $k + 1$ levels of cell vertices.

Edges of $G_{A,n}$ are defined as follows.
$(c, 2j) \rightarrow (p, 2j + 1)$: if for some input vector, at step $j + 1$, processor p reads cell c;
$(p, 2j + 1) \rightarrow (c, 2(j + 1))$: if for some input vector, at step $j + 1$, processor p writes to cell c;
$(p, 2j + 1) \rightarrow (p, 2(j + 1) + 1)$;
$(c, 2j) \rightarrow c(2(j + 1))$;
Initially, bit i of the input vector is assumed to be in cell i, $1 \leq i \leq n$, and finally, the output value corresponding to bit i is assumed to be in cell i. We shall refer to vertices $(i, 0)$ as x_i and vertices $(i, 2k)$ as y_i.

Let P be the number of processors used by A. The number of cells accessed during the computation is at most $2kP$. There are two kinds of edges in the graph, those adjacent to a processor vertex and others. Since each processor vertex has degree at most 4, the former are at most $4kP$ in number. Since each cell vertex is adjacent to at most one of the latter type of edge there are at most $2kP$ such edges. Hence the number of edges in the graph is at most $6kP$.

Given an input vector D, of length n, we shall associate with each cell vertex a content and with each processor vertex a state. The content associated with $(c, 2j)$ is the content of cell c at step j (just before the $(j + 1)st$ read-write step) in the computation of A on input D. The state associated with $(p, 2j + 1)$ is the state of the processor p after the read step of the $(j + 1)th$ read-write step in the same computation.

A *partial input* $B = b_1 b_2 ... b_n$ is one in which each $b_i \in \{0, 1, *\}$. An input vector $D = d_1 d_2 ... d_n$, each $d_i = 0$ or 1, is consistent with B if $\forall i, 1 \leq i \leq n$, $b_i \neq * \implies b_i = d_i$. X_B will denote the set of inputs consistent with B. For a partial input B and a cell vertex $(c, 2j)$ define
$$S_B((c, 2j)) = \{d \mid \text{cell } (c, 2j) \text{ has content } d \text{ for some } x \in X_B\}.$$

Similarly, for a processor vertex $(p, 2j + 1)$ define $S_B((p, 2j + 1)) = \{e \mid \text{processor } (p, 2j + 1) \text{ has state } e \text{ for some } x \in X_B\}$.

We say a (cell or processor) vertex (x, j) is *fixed* for a partial input B if $\mid S_B((x, j)) \mid = 1$.

2.1 Oblivious COMMON Simulation of PRIORITY

Consider the following problem called the *leftmost-one* problem. Given input $B = b_1, ..., b_n$, $b \in \{0, 1\}$, compute $s = \min\{j \mid b_j = 1\}$. Fich, Ragde and Wigderson [10] show that the leftmost-one problem can be solved in $O(1)$ time on COMMON using n processors and n memory cells. Their algorithm can easily be modified to be oblivious. We shall use this fact to prove the following

Lemma 2.1 *Consider an oblivious algorithm that runs on a PRIORITY PRAM with p processors and M memory cells. in k steps. Then there is an oblivious algorithm solving the same algorithm on a COMMON PRAM with p processors and $M + p$ memory cells in $O(k)$ steps.*

Proof : It suffices to show that one write step of an oblivious PRIORITY algorithm can be simulated on an oblivious COMMON machine in $O(1)$ steps. Suppose The PRIORITY machine writes to r cells $c_1, ... c_r$. Let D_i denote the set of processors that may write to c_i. D_i is fixed over all inputs. Note that some of the processors may choose not to write. It is sufficient for the COMMON machine to find, for each i, the highest priority processor in D_i that chooses to write. This is done by solving a leftmost-one problem of size $\mid D_i \mid$, using $\mid D_i \mid$ cells and $O(1)$ time. The space bound follows from the fact that $\sum_{i=1}^{r} \mid D_i \mid \leq p$. $\square$

Henceforth we shall refer only to PRIORITY algorithms and by the lemma, all the algorithms run on COMMON with the same time bounds. Note that in general, it is not true that one step of a PRIORITY algorithm can be simulated by a COMMON algorithm in $O(1)$ steps. Boppana [1] gives an example of a problem that can be solved in $O(1)$ time on PRIORITY but requires $\Omega(\frac{\log n}{\log \log n})$ time on COMMON.

3 Some useful functions and their properties

In this section we prove inequalities (1)-(7), which are useful later. The reader who is willing to take the inequalities for granted may familiarize himself with them and skip the proofs.

Ackerman's function is defined as follows:
$A(0, 0) = 0$; $A(i, 0) = 1$ for $i > 0$;
$A(0, j) = 2j$ for $j > 0$; and
$A(i, j) = A(i - 1, A(i, j - 1))$.
Ackerman's function grows rapidly, especially as the first argument increases. For example, $A(1, j) = 2^j$ and $A(2, j) = 2^{A(2, j-1)}$.

For a function f let $f^{(1)}(n) = f(n)$; $f^{(i)}(n) = f(f^{(i-1)}(n))$, $i > 1$. Define $I_0(n) = \lceil \frac{n}{2} \rceil$ and $I_k(n) = \min\{j \mid I_{k-1}^{(j)}(n) \leq 1\}$, $k > 1$. The functions I_k are the inverses of the kth level of Ackerman's function, i.e $I_k(n) = \min\{j \mid A(k, j) \geq n\}$. I_1 behaves like $\log n$ and I_2 like $\log^* n$. Define $\alpha(n) = \min\{j \mid I_j(n) \leq j\}$.

Following [9], we define the trees $T_k(l)$, $l \geq 1$. $T_k(l)$ has all its leaves at depth k and each edge is labelled with a power of 2. The out-degree of the root is l and the out-degree of every other vertex is the label of the edge coming into the vertex from its parent. At any depth, the label of the first edge created is 1 and the label of the jth edge created is twice the maximum of the product of labels on a path starting with the $(j - 1)$th edge and ending at a leaf.

Fact: Let v be a non leaf node in the tree $(T_k(l))$ and let w be the next node to its right at the same level. Let c and d be the labels of the edges to v and w from their parent(s) respectively and let e be the label of the edge from v to the rightmost child of v. Then $d > e \geq 2^c$, since v has c children.

Let $B(k, l)$ be the maximum product of labels on a path from the root to a leaf in $T_k(l)$. Define the following auxiliary family of trees $S_k(l)$. The definition of $S_k(l)$ is the the same as $T_k(l)$ except that the first edge created at each level has the label l (instead of 1). Let $C(k, l)$ be the maximum product of labels on a path from the root to a leaf of $S_k(l)$. Then $B(k, l) \leq C(k, l) \leq B(k, 2l)$ since we can find a subtree of $S_k(l)$ such that the labels on each edge are greater than or equal to the labels on the corresponding edges of $T_k(l)$. The second inequality holds for the same reason.

Lemma 3.1 $B(k, l) \leq A(k, 2l)$ *for* $k, l \geq 1$

Proof : The proof is by induction on k and l.

It is easy to see that $\forall i \geq 1$, $B(i,1) \leq A(i,2)$ and $\forall j \geq 1$, $B(1,j) \leq A(1,2j)$.

Assume $B(k,l) \leq A(k,2l)$ $\forall k$ if $l \leq j$ and $\forall l$ if $k \leq i$. We shall show that $B(i+1,j+1) \leq A(i+1,2(j+1))$.

$B(i+1,j+1)$ may be written as the product of the label on the edge to the rightmost child of the root and the maximum product of labels in the subtree below the rightmost child of the root. Hence,

$$
\begin{aligned}
B(i+1,j+1) &\leq 2B(i+1,j)C(i,2B(i+1,j)) \\
&\leq 2B(i+1,j)B(i,4B(i+1,j)) \\
&\leq B(i,6B(i+1,j)) \\
&\leq A(i,12A(i+1,2j)) \\
&\leq A(i,A(i+1,2j+1)) \\
&\leq A(i+1,2(j+1))
\end{aligned}
$$

□

Set $l = \lfloor \frac{I_{k+1}(n)-1}{2} \rfloor \geq \frac{I_{k+1}(n)}{3}$, for n sufficiently large. By Lemma 3.1 the maximum product of labels along a path from the root to a leaf is n. Let H be the set of leaves. For $h \in H$, let $c_1(h), ..., c_k(h)$ be the labels on the edges of the path from the root to h, in that order. Then the following inequalities hold. (Inequalities similar to (1), (2), (4), (5), (6) and (7b) were stated in [9]. For completeness, we give the proofs.)

(1) $\forall h \in H$, $c_1(h) \geq 1, ..., c_k(h) \geq 1$

(2) $\forall h \in H$, $c_1(h)...c_k(h) \leq n$

(3) $\sum_{h \in H} c_k(h) \leq 2n$

(4) $\sum_{h \in H} \frac{1}{c_1(h)...c_k(h)} \leq 2$

(5) $1 \leq j \leq k-1$,
$$\sum_{h \in H, \, c_1(h)...c_k(h)<y} c_1(h)...c_{j-1}(h)c_k(h) \leq 2y$$

(6) $\sum_{h \in H} \frac{1}{c_1(h)...c_{k-1}(h)} \geq \frac{I_{k+1}(n)}{3}$

(7a) $\exists y_0(k), s.t. \forall y > y_0(k)$ and $1 \leq j \leq k-1$,
$$\sum_{h \in H, \, c_j(h)<y \leq c_1(h)...c_k(h)} \frac{1}{c_j(h)...c_{k-1}(h)} \leq 2$$

(7b) $\forall y > 0$, $1 \leq j \leq k-1$,
$$\sum_{h \in H, \, c_j(h)<y \leq c_1(h)...c_k(h)} \frac{1}{c_j(h)...c_{k-1}(h)} \leq y$$

Lemma 3.2 *Inequalities (1) - (5) hold.*

Proof : (1): Obvious.

(2): By Lemma 3.1 and the choice of l, (2) holds.

(3): It is easy to see that the labels on edges to leaves of the tree increase by a factor of two as we move from left to right along the leaves of the tree. Thus the sum is a geometric series with the stated bound.

(4): The sum is dominated term-by-term by the series $\sum_{h \in H} \frac{1}{c_k(h)}$ whose sum is at most 2.

(5): Consider the sum as it is formed by going through the vertices from left to right. Since the last factor in each product increases by a factor of two and the other factors do not decrease, each term is at least twice the previous term. Since the last term is at most y the series has a sum of at most $2y$. □

Lemma 3.3 *Inequality (6) holds.*

Proof : Let $0 \leq i \leq k$, H_i be the set of vertices at level i of the tree and for $h \in H_i$ let $c_1(h), ..., c_i(h)$ be the labels on the unique path from the root to h. Then we have

$$
\begin{aligned}
\sum_{h \in H} \frac{1}{c_1(h)...c_{k-1}(h)} &= \sum_{h \in H_k} \frac{1}{c_1(h)...c_{k-1}(h)} \\
&= \sum_{h \in H_{k-1}} \frac{1}{c_1(h)...c_{k-1}(h)} c_{k-1}(h) \\
&= ... \\
&= \sum_{h \in H_1} 1 = l \geq \frac{I_{k+1}(n)}{3}
\end{aligned}
$$

□

Lemma 3.4 *Let $c_1, ..., c_k$ be the labels on some path from the root to a leaf. Then, $1 \leq i \leq k-1$, $c_i \leq c_{i+1}^2$.*

Proof : Let $h_1, ..., h_{|H|}$ be the leaves of the tree, from left to right. The lemma clearly holds for the path to h_1 (all the labels are 1). Assuming the lemma holds for the path to h_m we shall show that it holds for the path to h_{m+1}.

The paths to h_m and h_{m+1} diverge at some level; call this level r. then $c_1, ..., c_r$ are common to both levels. Let $c_{r+1}, ..., c_k$ and $d_{r+1}, ..., d_k$ be the remaining labels on the paths to h_m and h_{m+1} respectively. Note that each of $c_{r+2}, ..., c_k$ are labels to rightmost children, so $c_{j+1} \geq 2c_j$, for $r+1 \leq j \leq k-1$. By the inductive hypothesis, $\forall j, 1 \leq j \leq r-1$, $c_j \leq c_{j+1}^2$. Since $d_{r+1} > c_{r+1}$ and $c_r \leq c_{r+1}^2$, we have $c_r \leq d_{r+1}^2$. Now,

65

$\forall j,\ r+1 \leq j \leq k-1, d_j = 2c_j...c_k \leq 2 \cdot 2^{c_j}c_{j+1}...c_k \leq 2c_{j+1}^2 c_{j+2}...c_k \leq 4(c_{j+1}...c_k)^2 = d_{j+1}^2$. This completes the proof. □

Lemma 3.5 *There is a function $y_0(k)$ such that the following holds. Let l, y, j be positive integers. Let $1 \leq j \leq k-1$. Let $y > y_0(k)$. Consider the set of paths from the root to a leaf, which have the property that $c_j < y \leq c_1...c_k$. Let $S_j, ..., S_k$ be the set of vertices they pass through at levels $j, ..., k$ respectively. Then $\mid S_j \mid \leq 2$.*

Proof : Let $v_1, ..., v_{|s_j|}$ be the vertices in S_j, from left to right. Consider the leftmost such path, which passes through v_1 and let the labels on this path be $c_1, ..., c_k$.

If $c_j \geq \log y$, then the label of the edge to $v_2 > y$ and we are done. So assume $c_j < \log y$. Then $1 \leq i \leq j-1$, $c_i \leq (\log y)^{2^{j-i}}$, i.e. $c_1...c_{j-1} \leq (\log y)^{2^j} \leq (\log y)^{2^k}$. Since $c_1...c_k \geq y$, we have $c_j...c_k \geq \frac{y}{(\log y)^{2^k}}$. Let $2 \leq i \leq \mid S_j \mid$, d_i be the label of the edge to v_i. We have $d_2 = 2c_j...c_k \geq \frac{2y}{(\log y)^{2^k}}$ and $d_3 \geq 2^{\frac{2y}{(\log y)^{2^k}}}$. Define $y_0(k) = \min\{x \mid 2^{\frac{2x}{(\log x)^{2^k}}} > x\}$ For $y > y_0(k)$, $d_3 > y$, hence $\mid S_j \mid \leq 2$. □

Corollary 3.1 *(Inequality 7) If $y > y_0(k)$;*
$\sum_{h \in H,\ c_j(h) < y \leq c_1(h)...c_k(h)} \frac{1}{c_j(h)...c_{k-1}(h)} \leq 2$
If $y \leq y_0(k)$;
$\sum_{h \in H,\ c_j(h) < y \leq c_1(h)...c_k(h)} \frac{1}{c_j(h)...c_{k-1}(h)} \leq y$

Proof : For v a vertex at level j of $T_k(l)$, let $c_1(v), ..., c_j(v)$ be the labels on the path from the root to v, in that order. Then we have $\sum_{h \in H,\ c_j(h) < y \leq c_1(h)...c_k(h)} \frac{1}{c_j(h)...c_{k-1}(h)} = \sum_{s \in S_k} \frac{1}{c_j(h)...c_{k-1}(h)} \leq \sum_{s \in S_{k-1}} \frac{1}{c_j(h)...c_{k-2}(h)} \leq \cdots \leq \sum_{s \in S_j} 1 = \mid S_j \mid$.

From Lemma 3.5 we have $\mid S_j \mid \leq 2$ if $y > y_0(k)$. On the other hand, since the labels on successive edges at the same level increase by at least a factor of two, there can be at most $\log y \leq y$ edges at level j before the label exceeds y. □

4 The lower bound

We are now ready to prove that an oblivious PRIORITY algorithm that solves the chaining problem with n processors requires $\Omega(\alpha(n))$ time. It suffices to prove the following

Theorem 4.1 *For n sufficiently large, any oblivious PRIORITY algorithm that solves a chaining problem of size n in k steps requires $\Omega(nI_{k+1}(n))$ processors.*

Proof : Fix n. Let $G_{A,n}$ be the graph for algorithm A, which terminates in k read-write steps, and let $x_1, ..., x_n$ and $y_1, ..., y_n$ be the input and the output vertices of $G_{A,n}$. Let H be the set of leaves of $T_k(l)$ defined in the previous section. Fix $h \in H$ and let $p(h) = \frac{1}{c_1(h)...c_k(h)}$. Pick U, a random subset of $[n]$ by picking each element of $[n]$ independently with probability $p(h)$. Consider the partial input $B = b_1...b_n$, $b_i = 0$ if $i \in [n] - U$ and $b_i = *$ if $i \in U$. Fix the values of the input vertices of $G_{A,n}$ as indicated by B. For a vertex v of $G_{A,n}$ let f_v denote the in-degree of v. Let V_j denote the set of vertices at level $2j$, $0 \leq j \leq k$. Call a vertex $v \in V_j$, $1 \leq j \leq k-1$, *high-degree* if $f_v > c_j(h)$.

Consider a high degree vertex $(c, 2j)$ which is not fixed for B, let $(p, 2j-1)$ be the highest priority processor that writes to $(c, 2j)$, over all inputs consistent with B, i.e. there is a setting for the variables $\{b_i \mid i \in U\}$ so that p writes to c at step j. The state of p can be affected only by those input vertices that can reach $(p, 2j - 1)$. Modify B and the input vertex settings so that over all inputs consistent with the new B, $(p, 2j-1)$ writes some fixed value to $(c, 2j)$. Now $(c, 2j)$ is fixed for B, since $(p, 2j - 1)$ will override any other processor that writes. If no processor writes to $(c, 2j)$, then perform the same operation with $(c, 2(j-1))$ and so on. Call this operation *fixing* a vertex.

Carry out the following two step procedure on $G_{A,n}$. (A) For j starting at 1 and going up to $k - 1$, fix all the high-degree vertices in V_j.
(B) For i starting at 1 and going up to n, if $i \in U$, set all the input vertices (with value $*$) that can reach y_i through low-degree vertices to the value 1, except x_i.

We claim that at the end of this procedure all the undefined input vertices are fixed, except possibly one. To see this, suppose more than one input vertex is undefined. Set all to 1 except the leftmost undefined input vertex x_i. Let this partial input be C. Let x_j be the first input vertex to the right of x_i that has the value 1. Clearly, x_j exists and $i, j \in U$. Since x_i was not set in step (B), x_i does not reach y_j through low-degree vertices. However, for the two inputs consistent with C, only vertices reachable from x_i through low degree vertices can have different values, since the high degree vertices are fixed. Hence the state of y_j remains fixed over both inputs, an error.

Thus the expected number of input vertices that are set in this process is at least $E(|U|) - 1 \geq np(h) - 1$. We now obtain an upper bound for this number.

Note that when fixing $v \in V_j$, all the high-degree vertices in V_i, $1 \leq i < j$ have already been fixed. Thus, the only variables that affect the contents of v are the undefined variables that can reach v through low-degree vertices. Hence $D_v = E(\text{number of inputs set to fix } v \in V_j) \leq E(\text{number of undefined inputs that can reach } v \text{ through low degree vertices}) \leq f_v 2c_{j-1}(h) 2c_{j-2}(h)...2c_1(h)p(h)$. At the same time, since we need only fix the state of the highest priority processor that writes to v, we never set more that the number of inputs that can reach this processor, i.e. $D_v \leq 2c_{j-1}(h) 2c_{j-2}(h)...2c_1(h) = 2^{j-1}c_1(h)...c_{j-1}(h)$.

Hence the expected number of inputs set during step (A) is at most

$$\sum_{j=1}^{k-1} \sum_{X(j)} D_v \leq \sum_{j=1}^{k-1} \sum_{X(j)} 2^{j-1}c_1(h)...c_{j-1}(h) \min[f_v p(h), 1]$$

where $X(j) = \{v \in V_j \mid c_j(h) < f_v\}$.

We now upper bound the expected number of inputs set during step (B). Let y_j be an output vertex and let $S = \{x_i \mid x_i \text{ can reach } y_j \text{ through low-degree vertices and } i \in U, i \neq j\}$. As before, $|S| \leq f_{y_j} 2c_{k-1}(h)2...c_1(h)$. For $x \in S$, P(x_i is set while processing y_j in step B)$\leq$ P($i \in U$ and $j \in U$). Since $i \neq j$, the events $i \in U$ and $j \in U$ are independent and P($i \in U$ and $j \in U$) $= p(h)^2$. Hence $E(\text{number of inputs set while processing } y_j \text{ in step (B)}) \leq f_{y_j} 2c_{k-1}(h)2...c_1(h)p(h)^2$. So the expected number of bits set during step (B) $\leq \sum_{v \in V_k} 2^{k-1} f_v c_1(h)...c_{k-1}(h)p(h)^2$. Summing for steps (A) and (B), we have

$$\sum_{j=1}^{k-1} \sum_{X(j)} 2^{j-1} \min\left[\frac{f_v}{c_j(h)...c_k(h)}, c_1(h)...c_{j-1}(h)\right]$$

$$+ \sum_{v \in V_k} 2^{k-1} \frac{f_v}{c_k(h)} p(h) \geq np(h) - 1$$

Multiplying both sides by $c_k(h)$ and summing over $h \in H$ we get

$$\sum_{j=1}^{k-1} \sum_{v \in V_j} \sum_{Y(v,j)} 2^{j-1} \min\left[\frac{f_v}{c_j(h)...c_{k-1}(h)}, \right.$$

$$\left. c_1(h)...c_{j-1}(h)c_k(h)\right] + \sum_{v \in V_k} \sum_{h \in H} 2^{k-1} f_v p(h)$$

$$\geq \sum_{h \in H}\left[\frac{n}{c_1(h)...c_{k-1}(h)} - c_k(h)\right]$$

where $Y(v,j) = \{h \in H \mid c_j(h) < f_v\}$.
Let $Z(v,j) = \{h \in H \mid c_j(h) < f_v \leq c_1(h)...c_k(h)\}$ and $W(v,j) = \{h \in H \mid c_1(h)...c_k(h) < f_v\}$.
Notice that $Y(v,j)$ is the disjoint union of $Z(v,j)$ and $W(v,j)$. Using this observation and rewriting, we get

$$\sum_{j=1}^{k-1} \sum_{v \in V_j} 2^{j-1} \sum_{Z(v,j)} \frac{f_v}{c_j(h)...c_{k-1}(h)} +$$

$$\sum_{j=1}^{k-1} \sum_{v \in V_j} 2^{j-1} \sum_{W(v,j)} c_1(h)...c_{j-1}(h)c_k(h) +$$

$$\sum_{v \in V_k} 2^{k-1} \sum_{h \in H} \frac{f_v}{c_1(h)...c_k(h)}$$

$$\geq \sum_{h \in H}\left[\frac{n}{c_1(h)...c_{k-1}(h)} - c_k(h)\right]$$

or

$$\sum_{j=1}^{k-1} \sum_{v \in V_j, \, f_v \leq I_{k+1}(n)} 2^{j-1} \sum_{Z(v,j)} \frac{f_v}{c_j(h)...c_{k-1}(h)} +$$

$$\sum_{j=1}^{k-1} \sum_{v \in V_j, \, f_v > I_{k+1}(n)} 2^{j-1} \sum_{Z(v,j)} \frac{f_v}{c_j(h)...c_{k-1}(h)} +$$

$$\sum_{j=1}^{k-1} \sum_{v \in V_j} 2^{j-1} \sum_{W(v,j)} c_1(h)...c_{j-1}(h)c_k(h) +$$

$$\sum_{v \in V_k} 2^{k-1} \sum_{h \in H} \frac{f_v}{c_1(h)...c_k(h)}$$

$$\geq \sum_{h \in H}\left[\frac{n}{c_1(h)...c_{k-1}(h)} - c_k(h)\right]$$

For n sufficiently large, $I_{k+1}(n) > y_0(k)$. Using inequalities (1)-(8) and noting that
(C) $\sum_{j=1}^{k-1} \sum_{v \in V_j} f_v \leq e \leq 6kP$ and
(D) $\sum_{j=1}^{k-1} \sum_{v \in V_j} 1 \leq kP$, we get

$$2^{k-1}kPI_{k+1}(n)^2 + 2^{k-1}12kP + 2^{k-1}12kP + 2^{k-1}12kP$$

$$\geq \frac{nI_k(n)}{3} - 2n$$

where the four LHS terms are obtained using, respectively, inequalities (7b) and (D), (7a) and (C), (5) and (C), and finally (4) and (C). The two RHS terms are obtained using inequalities (6) and (3) respectively. Simplifying, we get

$$P = \Omega\left(\frac{nI_k(n)}{2^{k-1}kI_{k+1}(n)^2}\right) = \Omega(nI_{k+1}(n))$$

□

5   Upper bounds

Berkman and Vishkin [4, 3], and independently, Ragde [14] have given algorithms that solve the chaining problem on PRIORITY in ck steps using $nI_k(n)$ processors, where c is a constant ≥ 2. From these algorithms one can construct an algorithm using $O(n)$ processors that takes $O(\alpha(n))$ time. We give simple oblivious algorithms that solve the problem in $2k$ steps on PRIORITY using $nI_k(n)$ processors. Though the performance bounds are the same, we feel our algorithm is intuitively easier.

A *prefix graph* of size n is a directed acyclic graph with n vertices $(x_1, ..., x_n)$ of indegree 0 called input vertices and n vertices $(y_1, ..., y_n)$ of outdegree 0 called output vertices. The level of a vertex in a prefix graph is the length of the longest path from an input to it. The depth of a prefix graph is the length of the longest path from an input to an output. Prefix graphs have the following property: $\forall i, j \in [n]$, there is a directed path from x_i to y_j iff $i < j$. Say a prefix graph is *levelled* if every edge is from a level $i-1$ vertex to a level i vertex. Call such an edge a level i edge. A prefix graph is *contiguous* if for any vertex v the inputs from which v is reachable are of the form x_r, $r \in [i, j]$. It is possible to construct [7] levelled contiguous prefix graphs of size n and depth $2k$ such that $\forall i, 1 \leq i \leq 2k$, the number of level i edges $\leq nI_k(n)$.

The *restricted-domain prefix-maxima* problem is defined as follows: Given an input $a_1, ..., a_n$; $a_i \geq 0$, $1 \leq i \leq n$ and $\forall i, j$, $1 \leq i < j \leq n, a_i, a_j \neq 0 \impliedby a_i < a_j$, compute $b_1, ..., b_n$ where $b_i = max\{a_j \mid j < i\}$. We show how to solve this problem using a prefix graph. Initially set the value at vertex $x_i = a_i$, $1 \leq i \leq n$. At step i, level i edges propagate the values at their tails to their heads and vertices at level i select the largest value propagated to them. It is easy to see that the value at a vertex $v = max\{a_j \mid v$ is reachable from $x_j\}$ and thus the value at $y_i = b_i$, $1 \leq i \leq n$.

Theorem 5.1 $\forall k \geq 1$, *there is an oblivious PRIORITY PRAM algorithm using $nI_k(n)$ processors that solves the chaining problem in $2k$ steps.*

Proof : We show how an oblivious PRIORITY PRAM algorithm can simulate the computation of a levelled, contiguous prefix graph G. Label the edges of G as follows. Let $\{x_r \mid r \in [i, j]\}$ be the set of input vertices

that can reach the vertex at the tail of edge e. Label e with j. Designate a memory cell $m(v)$ to correspond to each vertex v of G. At step i, allocate a processor $p(e)$ to each level i edge of G so that for any two edges e, f such that $label(e) < label(f)$, $p(f)$ has a higher priority than $p(e)$. Such an allocation is easy to do. For e, an edge from v to w, $p(e)$ reads the value in $m(v)$. If the value is 0, then $p(e)$ does nothing otherwise it writes the value to $m(w)$. It is easy to show that the value in $m(w)$ is $max\{a_r \mid w$ is reachable from $x_r\}$, and so $m(y_i) = b_i$, $1 \leq i \leq n$. To solve the chaining problem with input $a_1, ..., a_n$, at first, $1 \leq i \leq n$, p_i writes i into $m(x_i)$ if $a_i = 1$. Then simply solve the restricted-domain prefix-maxima problem with the values in $m(x_i)$, $1 \leq i \leq n$ as input. The stated bounds follow from the bounds on prefix graphs. □

5.1   Lower bounds for Prefix Graphs

In [8], it is proved that a prefix graph of depth $2k$ requires $\Omega(nI_{2k-1}(n))$ edges. We improve the lower bound, showing that the construction is optimal.

A *weak superconcentrator* is a directed acyclic graph with n vertices $x_1, ..., x_n$ of indegree) and n vertices $y_1, ..., y_n$ of outdegree 0, and the property that $\forall k$ and $i_1 < j_1 < i_2 < j_2... < i_k < j_k$, there exist vertex disjoint paths between $\{x_{i_1}, ..., x_{i_k}\}$ and $\{y_{j_1}, ..., y_{j_k}\}$. The depth of a weak superconcentrator is the length of the longest directed path in it. [9] prove that a weak superconcentrator of depth $2k$ requires $\Omega(nI_k(n))$ edges.

Theorem 5.2 *A prefix graph of depth $2k$ requires $\Omega(nI_k(n))$ edges.*

Proof : We show that every prefix graph is a weak superconcentrator. Let $x_1, ..., x_n$ and $y_1, ..., y_n$ be the input and output vertices of a prefix graph G. $\forall k$ and $i_1 < j_1 < i_2 < j_2... < i_k < j_k$ there exist paths from x_{i_m} to y_{i_m}. If they are not all vertex disjoint, then $\exists p, q, 1 \leq p < q \leq k$ such that the paths from x_{i_p} to y_{j_p} and x_{i_q} to y_{j_q} have a common vertex. But then there is a path from x_{i_q} to y_{j_p}, $i_q > j_p$, a contradiction. □

6   Nonoblivious lower bounds

The techniques used in the lower bounds for oblivious algorithms may extend to nonoblivious algorithms. We conjecture similar lower bounds for all algorithms but are able to prove it only for the case $k = 2$. ($k = 1$ is easy.) Although the following theorem may be proved using computations similar to those used in the oblivious case, we use simpler computations that we hope are more illuminating. Specifically, we prove

Theorem 6.1 *Any PRIORITY PRAM algorithm that solves the chaining problem in 2 steps requires $\Omega(n(\log n)^{\frac{1}{2}})$ processors.*

Proof : Associate a graph $G_{A,B}$ with a nonoblivious algorithm A and partial input B. As before, $G_{A,B}$ will have levels of vertices $(c, 2j)$ and $(p, 2j+1)$, $0 \leq j \leq k - 1$. The edges are defined by:

$(c, 2j) \rightarrow (p, 2j+1)$: if for some input vector consistent with B, at step $j + 1$, processor p reads cell c

$(p, 2j+1) \rightarrow (c, 2(j+1))$: if for some input vector consistent with B, at step $j + 1$, processor p writes to cell c

$(p, 2j+1) \rightarrow (p, 2(j+1)+1)$

$(c, 2j) \rightarrow (c, 2(j+1))$

For v a vertex of $G_{A,B}$ define $S_B(v)$ as before.

Let $P \leq \frac{1}{6}n(\log n)^{\frac{1}{2}}$ be the number of processors used by A. Suppose A terminates in 2 steps. $G_{A,B}$ consists of 5 levels (numbered $0,..4$) of vertices. Let $e_{B,i}$, $1 \leq i \leq 4$ be the set of edges between level $i - 1$ and level i in $G_{A,B}$. It is easily seen that for any partial input B, $| e_{B,1} | \leq P$ and $| e_{B,2} | \leq 2P$.

Let, $1 \leq i \leq 2P$, $D_i = \{v \mid v$ is a level 2 vertex with indegree $\geq i\}$, and $d_i = | D_i |$. Then we have $\sum_{i=1}^{2P} d_i \leq 2P \leq \frac{1}{3}n(\log n)^{\frac{1}{2}}$. Let $z = 2^{\frac{\log n}{2}}$. If $\forall i$, $1 \leq i \leq z$, $d_i > \frac{n}{3i(\log n)^{\frac{1}{2}}}$ then $\sum_{i=1}^{z} d_i > \frac{1}{3}n(\log n)^{\frac{1}{2}}$, so $\exists i_0$, $1 \leq i_0 \leq z$ such that $d_{i_0} \leq \frac{n}{3i_0(\log n)^{\frac{1}{2}}}$.

Let $v \in D_{i_0}$ and consider the highest priority processor p that has an edge to v. The state of this processor depends only on one input bit. We set this input bit so that p writes to v. Let B be the partial input so defined. Clearly $| S_B(v) | = 1$, so v is fixed. Similarly fix all the vertices in B_{i_0}, and let C be the partial input obtained by this procedure. The number of bits set in C is at most d_{i_0}.

All the level 2 vertices of $G_{A,C}$ that are not fixed are written to by at most i_0 processors each in at most 2 states, hence $\forall v$, $| S_C((v, 2)) | \leq 2i_0$. Since $\forall p$, $| S_C((p, 1)) | \leq 2$, we have $\forall p$, $| S_C((p, 3)) | \leq 4i_0$.

Let $y_1, ..., y_n$ be the output vertices of $G_{A,C}$. Suppose $r \leq \frac{n}{3i_0(\log n)^{\frac{1}{2}}}$ bits $(c_{i_1}, ..., c_{i_r})$ have been set

in C. Define $i_0 = 0$ and $i_{r+1} = n + 1$. Consider m, j such that $i_j < m < i_{j+1}$. Since all the bits between c_{i_j} and c_m are undefined, y_m may have, as its final value, any one of $i_j, i_j + 1, ..., m - 1$, or 0, so $| S_C((y_m, 4)) | \geq m - i_j + 1$. Thus $\sum_{i_j < m < i_{j+1}} | S_C((y_m, 4)) | \geq \frac{1}{2}(i_{j+1} - i_j + 1)(i_{j+1} - i_j) - 1 \geq \frac{1}{2}(i_{j+1} - i_j)^2$. Since $\sum_{j=1}^{r}(i_{j+1} - i_j) \geq n$, we have $\sum_{j=0}^{r} \sum_{i_j < m < i_{j+1}} | S_C((y_m, 4)) | \geq \frac{n^2}{2(r+1)}$.

For $e \in e_{C,4}$, an edge from $(p, 3)$ to $(c, 4)$, let $g(e)$ be the number of different values that p writes to c over all inputs consistent with C. For any output vertex $(y, 4)$, $S_C((y, 4)) \leq \sum g(e) + S_C((y, 2)) \leq \sum g(e) + 2i_0$, where the summation is over all edges from a processor to $(y, 4)$. Then we have

$$4i_0 P \geq \sum_{e \in e_{C,4}} g(e) \geq \sum_{j=0}^{r} \sum_{i_j < m < i_{j+1}} (| S_C((y_m, 4)) | - 2i_0)$$

$$\geq \frac{n^2}{2(r+1)} - 2i_0 n$$

or

$$P \geq \frac{1}{6}n(\log n)^{\frac{1}{2}}$$

$\square$

7 Conclusion and Open Problems

We have shown that oblivious chaining with n processors is $\Theta(\alpha(n))$ time. This leaves open the question of whether an $O(1)$ time non-oblivious algorithm exists. Clearly, such an algorithm must make use of its non-obliviousness (adaptiveness) in some fundamental way. We conjecture that such an algorithm does not exist.

Using randomization, it is possible that better performance may be achieved. Raman [15] gave a randomized algorithm that runs in $O(1)$ time if the number of 1's in the input is not too large. It is open whether this can be extended to include all inputs.

A related problem, called *nearest-one-extension* in [6] is: given input $a_1...a_n$, $a_i = 0$ or $< 1, j_i >$ where $j_i = \max\{k \mid a_k \neq 0, k < i\}$, compute $b_1...b_n$ such that $b_i = \max\{k \mid a_k \neq 0, k < i\}$. Informally, the information about nearest ones is available with the 1's in the input and has to be extended to the 0's. This problem is no harder than chaining and in [6], is shown to be solvable on a CREW PRAM in $O(\alpha(n))$ time. It is open whether an $O(1)$ CRCW PRAM algorithm exists.

8 Acknowledgements

I am grateful to Ravi Boppana for introducing me to the work in [7] and [9], and for many helpful discussions. I am indebted to Jaikumar Radhakrishnan for the simple proof of the upper bound and for innumerable insightful comments.

References

[1] R. Boppana, "Optimal Separations Between Concurrent Write Parallel Machines", *Proc. of the 21st ACM STOC*, 1989.

[2] P.C.P. Bhatt, K. Diks, T. Hagerup, V.C. Prasad, T. Radzik and S. Saxena, "Improved Deterministic Parallel Integer Sorting", manuscript, Nov. 1989.

[3] O. Berkman, J. Jaja, S. Krishnamurthy, R. Thurimella and U. Vishkin, "Some Triply-Logarithmic Parallel Algorithms", *Proc. of 31st FOCS*, 1990.

[4] O. Berkman and U. Vishkin, "Recursive Star-Tree Parallel Data Structure", *Proc. of 30th FOCS*, 1989.

[5] O. Berkman and U. Vishkin, "Recursive Star-Tree Parallel Data Structure", UIMACS-TR-90-40, March 1990.

[6] O. Berkman and U. Vishkin, "On Parallel Integer Merging", UIMACS-TR-90-15.1, Feb 1990.

[7] A.K. Chandra, S. Fortune and R.J. Lipton, "Unbounded Fan-in Circuits and Associative Functions", *Proc. of the 15th ACM STOC*, 1983.

[8] A.K. Chandra, S. Fortune and R.J. Lipton, "Lower bounds for Constant Depth Circuits for Prefix Problems", *Proc. of the 10th Int. Colloquium on Automata, Languages and Programming*, Lecture Notes in Computer Science, Springer-Verlag, 1983.

[9] D. Dolev, C. Dwork, N. Pippenger and A. Wigderson, "Superconcentrators, Generalizers and Generalized Connectors with Limited Depth", *Proc. of the 15th ACM STOC*, 1983.

10] F.E. Fich, A. Wigderson and P. Ragde, "Simulations Among Concurrent-Write Models of Parallel Computation", Algorithmica 3, 1988.

[11] J. Gil and L. Rudolph, "Counting and Packing in Parallel", *International Conference on Parallel Processing*, 1986.

[12] Y. Matias and U. Vishkin, "On Integer Sorting and Parallel Hashing", *Proc. 17th ICALP*, 1990.

[13] I. Newman, P. Ragde and A. Wigderson, "Perfect Hashing, Graph Entropy and Circuit Complexity", manuscript, 1989.

[14] P. Ragde, "The Parallel Simplicity of Compaction and Chaining", *Proc. 17th ICALP*, 1990.

[15] R. Raman, "The Power of Collision: Randomized Parallel Algorithms for Chaining and Integer Sorting", *10th Foundations of Software Technology and Theoretical Computer Science*, 1990.

[16] L. Rudolph and W. Steiger, "Subset Selection in Parallel", *Proc. of the 1985 Int. Conference on Parallel Processing*, 1985.

PARALLEL CONSTRUCTION OF TREES WITH OPTIMAL WEIGHTED PATH LENGTH

Lawrence L. Larmore   and   Teresa M.Przytycka [†]

Department of Computer Science,
University of California, Riverside, CA 92521

Abstract

This paper deals with the problem of parallel construction of trees with optimal weighted path length. We study both the unordered case, known as the *Huffman coding* problem and the ordered case known as the *optimal alphabetic binary tree* problem. The methods used in both cases are different. We reduce the Huffman coding problem to the *Concave Least Weight Subsequence* and give a parallel algorithm that solves the latter problem in $O(\sqrt{n}\log n)$ time with n processors on a CREW PRAM. This leads to the first sublinear time $o(n^2)$-total work parallel algorithm for the Huffman coding problem. The alphabetic binary tree problem is a special case of the *Optimum Binary Search Tree* problem and can be solved in $O(\log^2 n)$ time with n^4 processors using the dynamic programming technique. We show that an optimal height restricted alphabetic tree can be constructed in $O(L\log n)$ time on a CREW PRAM using only linearly many processors, where L is an upper bound on the height of the tree.

[†] and Instytut Informatyki, Uniwersytet Warszawski.

© 1991 ACM 089791-438-4/91/0007/0071 $1.50

This implies that an alphabetic tree whose cost differs by at most $1/n^k$ from the cost of the optimal tree can be constructed in $O(k\log^2 n)$ time using linear number of processors. To achieve this result we use a parallel version of the *package merge* technique.

1   INTRODUCTION

The *level* of a node in a tree is its distance from the root. The problem of constructing a *Huffman tree* is, given a sequence of n real numbers, $x_1, x_2, \ldots, x_n$, construct a binary tree with n leaves such that the leaves of the tree are in one-to-one correspondence with elements of the sequence, and the following cost function, c, is minimized:

$$(1.1) \qquad c(T) = \sum_{i=1}^{n} x_i \ell_i$$

where ℓ_i denotes the level of the leaf corresponding to the number x_i, not necessarily the ith leaf. The value x_j associated with a leaf v is called the *weight* of v.

In the *optimal alphabetic binary tree* problem we additionally assume that the ith leaf of the tree is assigned weight x_i. Without loss of generality, $\sum_{i=1}^{n} x_i = 1$ and $x_i \neq x_j$ for $i \neq j$. The *height restricted optimal alphabetic tree* problem is given an integer L, where $\log n \leq L \leq n - 1$, construct an alphabetic tree of height at most L that minimizes the cost function c.

Both the Huffman tree problem and the optimal alphabetic tree problem can be solved in $O(n \log n)$ sequential time [8,13]. Yet, despite much effort, neither of the problems has a good parallel algorithm. Currently the best NC algorithm for the Huffman coding problem takes $O(\log^2 n)$ time with roughly n^2 CREW PRAM processors [4]. A close approximation for the solution to the Huffman coding problem can be computed in $O(\log n \log^* n)$ time using linear number of CREW processors [14,22]. In this paper we present the first sublinear time, $o(n^2)$-work parallel algorithm for the Huffman coding problem.

At the heart of our algorithm is the reduction of the Huffman coding problem to the *Concave Least Weight Subsequence* (CLWS) problem. This reduction leads to a brand new linear time (if the input sequence of weights is sorted) sequential algorithm for the Huffman coding problem.

The CLWS problem has a long list of applications, including paragraph breaking. A good parallel algorithm for this problem is thus interesting in its own right. Hirschberg and Larmore [10] define the *Least Weight Subsequence* (LWS) problem as follows: Given an integer n, and a real-valued *weight* function $w(i,j)$ defined for integers $0 \leq i < j \leq n$, find a sequence of integers $0 = \alpha_0 < \alpha_1 < \ldots < \alpha_{k-1} < \alpha_k = n$ such that $\sum_{i=0}^{k-1} w(\alpha_i, \alpha_{i+1})$ is minimized. The *Single Source* LWS problem is to find such a minimal sequence $0 = \alpha_0 < \alpha_1 < \ldots < \alpha_{k-1} < \alpha_k = m$ for *all* $m \leq n$. The LWS problem can be solved in $O(n^2)$ sequential time [10]. This complexity can be reduced by imposing certain restrictions on the weight function. The weight function is *concave* if for all $0 \leq i_0 \leq i_1 < j_0 \leq j_1 \leq n$,

(1.2) $w(i_0, j_0) + w(i_1, j_1) \leq w(i_0, j_1) + w(i_1, j_0)$.

The inequality (1.2) is also called the *quadrangle inequality* [25]. The LWS problem defined by a concave weight function is called the Concave Least Weight Subsequence (CLWS) problem. Hirschberg and Larmore [10] showed that the CLWS problem can be solved in $O(n \log n)$ time. Subsequently, Galil and

Giancarlo [7] showed the $O(n \log n)$ complexity bound for the *convex* least weight subsequence problem (i.e. when the weight function satisfies the reverse of the inequality (1.2)). Later, Wilber [24] proposed an $O(n)$ algorithm for the CLWS subsequence problem. The best known sequential algorithm for the convex case was proposed by Klawe and Kleitman [16]. Their algorithm requires $O(n\alpha(n))$ time.

All of the above algorithms for the LWS and CLWS problems actually solve the single source versions. Henceforth, when we refer to any variant of the LWS problem, we shall mean the single source version.

In the parallel setting, the CLWS problem seems to be more difficult than the corresponding convex problem. Lam and Chan [6] presented an $O(\log^2 n \log \log n)$-time, $n/\log \log n$ - processor CREW PRAM algorithm to solve the convex problem. On the other hand, the best current NC algorithm for the CLWS problem can be obtained using the concave matrix multiplication techniques [2,3,4] and requires $O(\log^2 n)$ time with $n^2/\log n$ processors. In this paper we present an $O(\sqrt{n} \log n)$-time n-processors CREW PRAM algorithm to solve the CLWS problem.

The optimal alphabetic tree problem is a special case of the Optimum Binary Search Tree (OBST) problem. Thus it can be solved using parallel dynamic programming techniques in $O(\log^2 n)$ time with roughly n^4 processors, using the concave matrix multiplication algorithm [4]. An $O(\log^2 n)$-time, n^2-processor algorithm that uses dynamic programming techniques to compute an approximately optimal binary search tree was given in [4]. This algorithm can be used to obtain an approximately optimal alphabetic tree. On the other hand, the best currently known sequential algorithm to construct an optimal alphabetic binary tree does not use dynamic programming. Thus one can ask whether, in the parallel setting of the problem, one can also find a non-dynamic programming algorithm whose complexity is less than the complexity of parallel OBST algorithms that are currently known. In this paper we give a partial answer to the above question. We present an $O(L \log n)$-time n-processor CREW PRAM algorithm which constructs an optimal alphabetic tree subject to height restriction L. The best known sequential algorithm for this problem [17] requires $O(nL \log n)$ time. As a consequence, we obtain an $O(k \log^2 n)$-time, n-processor algorithm that constructs an almost optimal alphabetic tree (more precisely a tree whose cost differs by at most $1/n^k$ from the cost of an optimal tree). Furthermore if the input sequence of weights does not contain two consecutive elements of weight less than $1/n^k$ the algorithm produces an optimal tree. We base our algorithm on the *package-merge* technique introduced in [17] (see also [18,19,20]).

The paper is organized as follows. In the next section, we present a parallel algorithm for the CLWS problem. In the third section, we show the reduction of the Huffman coding problem to the CLWS problem. In the fourth section, we describe briefly the package merge technique. In the fifth section, we outline a parallel implementation of the package merge algorithm.

2 A PARALLEL SINGLE SOURCE CLWS ALGORITHM

Consider an instance of the least weight subsequence problem over $[0, n]$ defined by a weight function w. Let $lws(i, j)$ denote the solution to the least weight subsequence problem on $[i, j]$ defined by the same function w. (This "solution" includes backpointers as well as the values of the minimum weight paths.) Let $g(i, j)$ be the weight of the least weight subsequence on $[i, j]$. We will compute $lws(0, j)$ for all $0 \leq j \leq n$ under the assumption that the weight function satisfies the quadrangle inequality (1.2). Let $f(j) = g(0, j)$ Define

$$pred(j) =$$

$$\begin{cases} undefined & \text{for } j = 0 \\ min\{i | i < j, f(j) = & \\ \quad f(i) + w(i, j)\} & \text{for } 0 < j \leq n \end{cases}$$

Thus $f(j)$ is equal to the weight of the least weight

subsequence for the interval $[0, j]$ and $pred(j)$ is equal to the index of the last but one element of such a sequence (in the case of ties we choose the leftmost). Let $F(j) = (f(j), pred(j))$. To solve the LWS problem it suffices to compute the function $F(j)$ for all $j \in [0, n]$.

Given an interval $I = [i_1, i_2] \subset [0, n]$ we can also consider a restricted version of the LWS problem in which we require that for all $j > i_2$, $pred(j) \in I$ (i.e. for any $j > i_2$ the last but one element of the solution to $lws(0, j)$ belongs to I). To solve this problem it suffices to compute, for all $0 < j \leq n$, functions $f^I(j)$ and $pred^I(j)$ where

$$f^I(j) = \begin{cases} f(j) & \text{for } j \leq i_2 \\ min_{i \in I}(f(i) + w(i, j)) & \text{for } i_2 < j \leq n \end{cases}$$

$$pred^I(j) =$$

$$\begin{cases} pred(j) & \text{for } j \leq i_2 \\ min\{i | i \in I, i < j, f^I(j) = & \\ \quad f(i) + w(i, j)\} & \text{for } i_2 < j \leq n \end{cases}$$

Let $F^I = (f^I, pred^I)$. For any interval $I = [i_1, i_2]$, where $i_2 = i_1 + k$ the function $pred^I$ partitions the interval $[i_2 + 1, n]$ into $k + 1$ subsets $D_0, D_1, \ldots, D_k$, such that $j \in D_t$ if and only if $pred^I(j) = i_1 + t$. Some of the sets D_i may be empty. We say that element i_t *dominates* elements in D_t. This partition of the interval $[i_2 + 1, n]$ *dominance partition yielded by interval I*. If the weight function is concave then the dominance partition satisfies the properties stated by the following lemma:

LEMMA 2.1. *If the weight function w satisfies the quadrangle inequality (1.2) then, for any interval $I = [i_1, i_2] \subset [0, n]$, all nonempty subsets of the dominance partition yielded by I are intervals. Furthermore, if $D_i = [a, b]$ is the set of elements dominated by i and $D_j = [c, d]$ is the set of elements dominated by j, and $i < j$ then $b < c$.*

Assume that $n = m^2$ for some integer m. Let $f^i = f^{[o, im]}$ and $pred^i = pred^{[o, im]}$. The basic idea of our algorithm is to iteratively compute $F^0, F^1, \ldots, F^m = F$

where $F^i = (f^i, pred^i)$. For $0 < i \leq m$, define $I_i = [(i-1)m, im]$. The algorithm can be described as follows:

ALGORITHM 1: Concave Least Weight Subsequence

1. *(preprocessing)* **for all** i, j such that $i < j$ and $j - i \leq m$ **do** compute $lws(i, j)$;

2. *(initialize)* **for all** $0 \leq j \leq n$
   do $f^0(j) = 0, pred^0(j) = 0$ **od** ;
   $D_0 = [1, n]$;

3. **for** $i := 1$ **to** m **do** *(iteratively compute F^i)*

   3.1 **for all** $k \in I_i$ **do** *using the results of Step 1 and F^{i-1} compute* $lws(0, k)$

   3.2 compute F^{I_i};

   3.3 from F^{I_i} and F^{i-1} compute F^i.

LEMMA 2.2. *The algorithm Concave Least Weight Subsequence can be implemented in $O(\sqrt{n}\log n)$ time with n CREW PRAM processors.*

Proof: To prove the lemma we present an implementation of the consecutive steps of the algorithm and discuss their complexity. Some of the implementation details we leave to the reader.

STEP 1. Assign one processor to each element of the sequence. Compute $lws(i, j)$ for all $0 \leq i < n - m$ and $j \leq i + m$ using a linear-time algorithm for one instance, of size m, of the single source CLWS problem for each i. This step requires $O(m)$ time. $\Diamond$

STEP 3.1. Let $pred_{(i,j)}$ be the $pred$ function for the least weight subsequence on the interval $[i, j]$. Then for all $k \in I_i$, we can compute $f(k)$ and $pred(k)$ using the following algorithm:

for all r in the solution of some $lws(j, s)$ where
  $j, s \in I_i$ **do** $pred(r) = pred_{(j,s)}(r)$ **od** ;

for all $k \in I_i$ **do**
  $f(k) = \min_{j \in I_i, j \leq k}(f^{i-1}(j) + g(j, k))$;
  $t := min\{j \mid j \in I_i, j \leq k, f^{i-1}(j) + g(j, k) = f(k)\}$;
  $pred(t) = pred^{i-1}(t).$

To implement this algorithm we assign one processor for each pair $j, k \in I_i, j < k$ and compute, for each such j, k, the value $f^{i-1}(j) + g(j, k)$. This requires $O(1)$ time using n processors (or in $O(\log n)$ time using $n/\log n$ processors). Then we compute the corresponding minima in $O(\log n)$ time using $n/\log n$ processors. $\Diamond$

STEP 3.2. We implement this step by computing the dominance partition yielded by the interval I_i. To do this, for each $j \in I_i$, we compute $left(j)$ and $right(j)$ equal, respectively, to the left and to the right boundary of D_j ($left(j) > right(j)$ signals empty D_j). Assume that $j < k$. Let $boundary(j, k)$ be the leftmost element in the interval $[im + 1, n]$ for which j is a better candidate for $pred^{I_i}$ than k. We compute the dominance partition using the following algorithm:

For $j < k$, $boundary(j, k) = \min\{t | t \in [im + 1, n],$
  and $f(j) + w(j, t) \leq f(k) + w(k, t)\}$;

for all $j \in I_i$ **do**

  $right(j) = \min_{k \in I_i, k > j} boundary(j, k)$;

  $left(j) = \max_{k \in I_i, k < j} boundary(k, j)$;

  if $right(j) < left(j)$ **then** $D_j = \emptyset$.

As in the step 3.1 assign one processor for each pair $j, k \in I_i, j < k$. Then, by Lemma 2.1, for each such pair j, k, where $j < k$, we compute $boundary(j, k)$ using binary search. Since we have one processor per boundary value, for each j, functions $left(j)$ and $right(j)$ can be computed in $O(\log n)$ time. time using n processors. $\Diamond$

STEP 3.3. To compute F^i we simply have to check, for every element $j \in [im + 1, n]$, which of $f^{i-1}(j)$ and $f^{I_i}(j)$ is smaller, using $O(1)$ time with n processors. $\Diamond$

$\square$

3   REDUCTION OF THE HUFFMAN TREE PROBLEM TO CLWS

A binary tree where each internal node has two children can be uniquely described by listing the levels of its leaves, in left to right order. A sequence of n integers $\ell_1, \ell_2, \ldots, \ell_n$ for which there exists a tree with n leaves whose levels when read from the left to the right are $\ell_1, \ell_2, \ldots, \ell_n$ is called a *leaf pattern*. A tree is said to be *left-justified* [4] if its leaf pattern is non-increasing. It can be shown (see for example Hu and Tan [11]) that a Huffman tree can be realized as a tree whose whose leaf pattern is sorted. Thus, by the definition of the cost function, c, we have the following lemma:

LEMMA 3.1. ([4]) *Given an arbitrary input sequence X, a Huffman tree for X can be realized by a left-justified binary tree whose leaf weights form a non-decreasing sequence.*

By the above lemma, sorting reduces our initial problem to that of constructing a left-justified binary tree which minimizes the cost function c. We show that the last problem can be reduced to the CLWS problem. A left-justified tree T of height k can be uniquely described by listing the numbers of internal nodes on each level of the tree. Thus T can be described by a strictly monotone increasing sequence of integers $\overline{\alpha_T} = \alpha_0, \alpha_1, \ldots, \alpha_{k-1}, \alpha_0 = 0, \alpha_k = n - 1$, where, for any $j > 0$, $\alpha_j - \alpha_{j-1}$ is equal to the number of internal nodes on level $k - j$. We call $\overline{\alpha_T}$ the *level sequence* of the tree T. However, not every strictly monotone sequence starting at 0 and ending at $n - 1$ is the level sequence for a left-justified tree.

The main result of this section is stated in the following theorem:

THEOREM 3.1. *Let $s_1, s_2, \ldots, s_n$ be the sequence of prefix sums for a nondecreasing sequence $X = x_1, x_2, \ldots, x_n$ i.e. $s_i = \sum_{j=1}^{i} x_j$ and let $w(i, j)$ be the weight function defined as follows:*

$$w(i, j) = \begin{cases} s_{2j-i} & \text{if } 2j - i \leq n \\ \infty & \text{otherwise} \end{cases}$$

then the LWS problem defined by w is concave and the solution to this problem is equal to the level sequence of the left justified Huffman tree for X.

Proof: (sketch) The fact that w is concave follows easily from the fact that $x_i \leq x_{i+1}$. Let $\overline{\alpha} = \alpha_0 < \ldots < \alpha_k$ be a sequence which is a candidate for being the level sequence of some tree – *i.e.*, $\alpha_0 = 0$, $\alpha_k = n - 1$, and $2\alpha_i - \alpha_{i-1} \leq n$ for all $0 < i \leq k$. We construct a tree $T_{\overline{\alpha}}$ which satisfies the following properties:

a) If $\overline{\alpha} = \overline{\alpha_T}$ for some left-justified binary tree T, then $T_{\overline{\alpha}} = T$ and $weight(\overline{\alpha}) = weight(T)$.

b) Otherwise, $weight(\overline{\alpha}) > weight(T_{\overline{\alpha}})$.

It follows that if $\overline{\alpha}$ has minimum weight, $\overline{\alpha} = \overline{\alpha_T}$, where T is the Huffman tree.

The construction of $T_{\overline{\alpha}}$ is as follows. Start with the ordered forest of n one-element trees. In step i, first take $2(\alpha_i - \alpha_{i-1})$ trees from the left and, for every j such that $2j \leq 2(\alpha_i - \alpha_{i-1})$, create a common parent for the trees which are on positions $2j - 1$ and $2j$ in the forest (counting from the left). □

4   THE PACKAGE MERGE ALGORITHM

First, we introduce a geometric interpretation of binary trees and forests. A more detailed description of the properties of such interpretation is given in [20].

Consider an $n \times n$ square in the plane, divided into n^2 unit squares, which we call *tiles*. (See Figure 4.1) We refer to the tile in the lth row and the ith column as $s_{l,i}$. We refer to l as the *level* of $s_{l,i}$, and to i as its *index*. We adopt the conventions that levels range from 0 to $n - 1$, from the top down, while indices range from 1 to n, from left to right.

The weight, $w(s_{l,i})$, of a tile $s_{l,i}$ is defined to be x_i. The weight of a set of tiles is equal to the sum of the weight of its members.

A tree, or a forest, can be represented as a connected union of "tiles ". Namely, if a $\ell_1, \ell_2, \ldots, \ell_n$ is a leaf-pattern of a tree T then tile $s_{l,i}$ belongs to the geometrical representation of T if and anly if $l \leq \ell_i$. Thus the cost of a tree is equal to weight of its geometric representation.

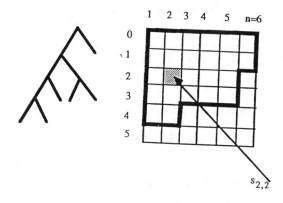

Figure 4.1 A tree and its geometric
representation

We now give a jointly recursive (but still fairly simple) definitions of two concepts: *level i item* and *level i package*. A *level l item* is either a level l package or a level l tile. A *level l package* is a union of two level $l-1$ items. By this recursive definition it follows that a package is a union of tiles.

Two sets of tiles A, B are *tentatively connected* with respect to a set of tiles C (denoted T-C$(A,B;C)$) if and only if for any tile a from A and any tile b from B there exists a path of tiles between a and b which is contained in $A \cup B \cup C$.

An optimal alphabetic tree can be constructed iteratively as a union of certain packages. Let $\log n \leq L \leq n-1$. At each level l, starting from level L, the algorithm receives 0 or more *l-packages* from

previous iteration. These are inserted (merged) into the list of level l tiles; both packages and tiles are called level l-items. These items are paired according to tentative-connectivity rules similar to [12], and resulting *packages* are exported to the next higher level; the odd item, if any is discarded. The set of 0-items defines the optimla tree.

ALGORITHM 2: **Package Merge(L)**

1. $PK_L := \emptyset; IT_L := \{s_{L,1}, s_{L,2}, \ldots, s_{L,n}\};$

comment: PK_l is a set of level l tiles and IT_l is a set of level l items

2. **for** $l := L$ **downto** 1 **do**

   2.1. $IT_{l-1} := \{s_{l-1,1}, s_{l-1,2}, \ldots, s_{l-1,n}\};$ $PK_{l-1} := \emptyset; j := 1;$

   2.2. **while** $|IT_l| \geq 2$ **do**

      2.2.1.   Pick $x, y \in IT_l$ of minimal total weight such that T-C$(x, y; PK_{l-1})$;

      2.2.2. $P_{l-1,j} := x \cup y;$

      2.2.3. $PK_{l-1} := PK_{l-1} \cup P_{l-1,j};$

      2.2.4. $IT_l := IT_l - \{x, y\}; IT_{l-1} := IT_{l-1} \cup \{P_{l-1,j}\};$

      2.2.5. $j := j + 1;$

3. $geom\_repr := PK_0 \cup \{s_{0,1}, s_{0,2}, \ldots s_{0,n}\}$

An $O(nL \log n)$-time sequential implementation of the Package Merge algorithm was presented in [17] (see also [18,19,20]). In the next section we present a new parallel implementation of this algorithm.

5   PARALLEL CONSTRUCTION OF OPTIMAL HEIGHT RESTRICTED ALPHABETIC TREES

In this section we show an efficient parallel implementation of a single iteration of the main loop of the Package Merge algorithm. Let $P_{l-1,j}$ be a package created at some iteration of Step 2.2 and let $s_{k,d}$ be an arbitrary tile in this package. A tile $s_{l-1,d}$ is called the *left dominating tile* of the package $P_{l-1,j}$ if $d = \max_{i<k}\{i|w(s_{l-1,i}) > w(P_{l-1,j})\}$. The left dominating tile may be undefined. Informally, the left dominating tile for a package, P, is the closest to the left (with respect to any tile of the package) level l tile, which has weight greater than $w(P)$. For any l we represent the set of level l items (IT_l) as what we call a *normalized sequence of level l items*. With this representation we can compute efficiently, in parallel, all packages created at one iteration of step 2 of the Package Merge algorithm. Below we give a constructive definition of normalized sequence of level l items:

1. For each level l-package compute its left dominating tile;

2. Sort all packages which have the same left dominating tile according to weight in decreasing order,

3. Insert each (sorted) sequence of packages computed at Step 2. into $s_{l,1}, s_{l,2}, \ldots, s_{l,n}$; after its dominating tile (the sorted sequence of elements which do not have a left dominating tile is inserted before $s_{l,1}$).

LEMMA 5.1. *The normalized sequence for IT_{l-1} can be computed in $O(\log n)$ time with n processors, where n is the length of the sequence.*

Proof: Step 1 of the above construction can be implemented in $O(\log n)$ time with $n/\log n$ processors on a CREW PRAM using a parallel algorithm that for any element in a sequence computes its closest bigger neighbor ([5,15]). An implementation of the remaining steps is routine. □

Our algorithm to construct an optimal height restricted alphabetic tree can be described as follows:

ALGORITHM 3: **Parallel Package Merge**

1. **for** $l := L$ **downto** 1 **do**

    1.1 **package construction:** given a normalized sequence of level l items construct the $l-1$ level packages: $P_{l-1,1}, P_{l-1,2}, \ldots$;

    1.2 **package merge:** insert the set of constructed packages into the sequence $s_{l-1,1}$,

$s_{l-1,2}, \ldots, s_{l-1,n}$ in such a way that the resulting sequence is normalized; these packages and slots become the level $(l-1)$ items.

2. $\quad geom\_repr := P_{0,1} \cup P_{0,2} \cup \ldots \cup P_{0,n-1} \cup \{s_{0,1}, s_{0,2}, \ldots s_{0,n}\}$;

3. Compute the actual alphabetic tree.

We need to show how to implement the package construction step. We base our implementation on the concept of *level tree* introduced in [15,22]. Let $V = v_1, v_2, \ldots, v_m$ be a normalized sequence of level l items. We add to this sequence two elements: $v_0, v_{m+1} = BR$ where BR (Big Real) is a real number greater than the cost of the optimal tree.

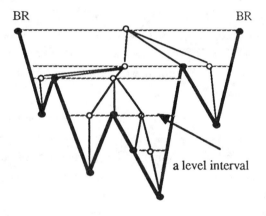

Figure 5.1 Construction of a level tree

Consider the following geometric construction (see Figure 5.1). For every i, there will be an associated point, (i, v_i), in the Cartesian plane. For every $i = 0, \ldots m$ there will be a line segment which connects the points (i, v_i) and $(i+1, v_{i+1})$, forming a polygonal path of $(m + 1)$ segments. For every i such that $v_i < v_{i+1}$ (resp., $v_i > v_{i+1}$), draw a horizontal line going from (i, v_i) to the left (resp.,to the right) until it hits the polygonal path. The intervals defined in this way are called *level intervals*. We also consider the interval $[(0, BR), (m + 1, BR)]$ and the degenerate intervals $[(i, v_i), (i, v_i)]$ to be level intervals. The *level tree* is a binary tree whose nodes are the level intervals. The degenerate intervals are the leaves of the tree, the parent of any level interval is the unique closest level interval which is above it, and $[(0, BR), (m + 1, BR)]$ is the root. A level treee is closely related to the *cartesian tree* introduced in [23]. In the contrasct to a cartesian tree a level tree need not to be binary.

LEMMA 5.2. ([15,22]) *Given a sequence of n weights the level tree can be constructed in $O(\log n)$ time using $n / \log n$ processors on CREW PRAM.*

Let v be a node of a level tree T_{lev}. The *pseudovalley defined by v* is the subsequence of a normalized sequence whose elements are the leaves of the minimal rooted subtree of T_{lev} that contains v. A pseudovalley that has an even (resp., odd) number of elements is called an *even pseudovalley* (resp., an *odd pseudovalley*). If U is a pseudovalley defined by v then $U = W_1 v W_2$ where W_i is a (possibly empty) pseudovalley. An empty pseudovalley is considered to be even.

For any element v of the normalized sequence of level l items we need to find the unique element v' such that v and v' are combined by the algorithm Package Merge into one package. We observe that elements from an even pseudovalley must be paired among themselves. Each odd pseudovalley is responsible for exporting one element which is paired with an element outside this pseudovalley. The "exported element" is the largest element of the valley, thus tis is the element that defines the valley. This observation leads to the following *Package Construction Rules*:

Package Construction Rules:

1. If v defines a pseudovalley $U = W_1 v W_2$ where both W_i are even then U is odd and v is the element exported by U.

2. If v defines a pseudovalley $U = W_1 v W_2$ where one of W_i (say W_1) is odd and the other is even then U is even and v is paired with the element exported by W_1.

3. Assume that v defines a pseudovalley $U = W_1 v W_2$ where both of W_i are odd. Let w_1 (resp. w_2) be the element exported by W_1 (resp., W_2) and $w_1 < w_2$. Then v is paired with w_1 and w_2 is the element exported by U.

LEMMA 5.3. *Given a normalized sequence of level l items, IT_l, the Package Construction Rule defines exactly the same set of level $l - 1$ as it is constructed in step 2 of algorithm Package Merge.*

Proof: We leave the proof to the full version of the paper. The following two observations gives useful hints.

First, two minimal items of any pseudovalley defined by IT_l are tentatively connected with respect to PK_{l-1}. In Step 2. of the Package Merge algorithm, we take the minimal such pair remove it form IT_l, and insert their union into PK_{l-1}. The sequence IT_l remains normalized. Furthermore, two minimal items of any pseudovalley of the modified sequence IT_l are tentatively connected with respect to modified set PK_{l-1}. Thus we can repeat this step iteratively.

Second, the above construction can be performed independently in disjoint pseudovalleys. □

With the Package Construction Rules the package construction step can be implemented in $O(\log n)$ time with $n / \log n$ processors using tree contraction techniques [1,21].

To implement Step 2 of the Parallel Package Merge algorithm we need to identify packages $P_{0,1}, P_{0,2}, \ldots, P_{0,n-1}$ and compute their union. To do this, for each tile we determine whether if belongs to the geometric representation of the optimal tree. This can be done in $O(k \log^2 n)$ time with n processors by a level-by-level computation.

Finally step 3 can be implemented as follows. If tile $s_{i,j}$ belongs to the geometric representation and tile $s_{i+1,j}$ does not, then the jth leaf of the optimal tree has depth i. Given a sequence of leaf depths one can construct the corresponding tree in $O(\log n)$ time with $n/\log n$ processors [15,22].

Thus the algorithm can be implemented in $O(L \log n)$ time with linear number of processors. If L is polylogarithmic this gives immediately a polylogarithmic time algorithm. The algorithm can be also used to find an approximately optimal tree. This observation is made precise in the following theorem.

THEOREM 5.1. *Given a sequence of reals $X = x_1, x_2, \ldots, x_n$ such that $\sum_{i=1}^{n} x_i = 1$, and constant k, an alphabetic tree whose cost differs at most by $1/n^k$ from the cost of an optimal alphabetic tree for X can be constructed in $O(k \log^2 n)$ time with n CREW PRAM processors. Furthermore, if X does not contain two consecutive elements of weight less than $1/n^k$ then the resulting tree is optimal.*

Proof: We use the following lemma, which follows from the results of [9].

LEMMA 5.4. *An optimal alphabetic tree for a sequence of reals $X = x_1, x_2, \ldots, x_n$ such that $\sum_{i=1}^{n} x_i = 1$ and no two consecutive elements are less than $1/n^k$ has height at most $k \lceil \log n \rceil$.*

Let T be an optimal tree for the sequence X. The above lemma leads immediately to an $O(k \log^2 n)$-time n-processor CREW PRAM which computes T if the sequence does not contain two consecutive elements of weight less than $1/n^k$. Thus, assume that X contains one or more subsequences of consecutive elements of weight less than $1/n^k$. We replace each such subsequence with an arbitrary one of its element called the *representative* of the subsequence. By Lemma 5.4, the tree, T', which is optimal for the new sequence, has height at most $k \lceil \log n \rceil$. Now replace every leaf of T' that is a representative of a subsequence of elements of small weight by the full binary tree build on the subsequence. The resulting tree T'' has height at most $(k + 1) \lceil \log n \rceil$. Let T_k be an optimal height $(k + 1) \lceil \log n \rceil$ restricted tree. Observe that

$$c(T_k) \leq c(T'') \leq c(T') + n^2/n^k \leq c(T) + 1/n^{k-2}$$

which together with the parallel implementation of the Package Merge Algorithm implies the theorem. □

6 Open Questions

The best sequential algorithm for the Concave Least Weight Subsequence problem takes $\Theta(n)$ time, and (of course) $\Theta(n)$ work, while every known NC algorithm takes $\Omega(n^2)$ work.

If we define "work-time" to be the product of the time complexity and the work complexity of an algorithm, every known algorithm for the CLWS has $\Omega(n^2)$ "work-time" complexity. The algorithm we have presented in this paper is no exception, having a work-time complexity of $\Theta(n^2 \log^2 n)$.

We conjecture that there should exist a family of parallel algorithms exhibiting various tradeoffs between work and time, ranging between the best sequential and the best known NC algorithms, but all with quadratic times polylog work-time. (Our new algorithm is just in the middle of this hypothetical family.) We also suggest that finding a parallel algorithm whose work-time is less than quadratic will be a very challenging problem.

References

[1] K.Abrahamson, N.Dadoun, D.G.Kirkpatrick, and T.M.Przytycka. A simple parallel tree contraction algorithm, *Journal of Algorithms* 10, (1989) pp. 287–302 also in Proc. 25th Allerton Conference on Communication, Control and Computing (1987).

[2] A.Apostolico, M.J.Atallah, L.L.Larmore, H.S.McFaddin. Efficient parallel algorithms for string editing and related problems, *Proc. 26nd Annual Allerton Conf. on Comm., Control, and Computing*, Monticello IL (Oct. 1988) pp. 253–263. Reprinted as CSD-TR-724, Purdue University (1988), reprinted in *SIAM Journal of Computing*, 19 pp.968–988 (1990).

[3] A.Aggarwal, J.Park. Notes on searching in multidimensional monotone arrays. In *29th Annual Symposium on Foundation of Computer Science* IEEE (1988).

[4] M.J.Atallah, S.R.Kosaraju, L.L.Larmore, G.L.Miller, and S-H. Teng. Constructing trees in parallel, Proc. 1st Symp. on Parallel Algorithms and Architectures (1989) pp. 499–533.

[5] O.Berkman, D.Breslauer, Z.Galil, B.Schieber, and U.Vishkin. Highly parallelizable problems, Proc. 21st ACM Symp. on Theory of Computing (1989) pp. 309–319.

[6] K-F Chan and T-W Lam. Finding Least-Weight Subsequences with Fewer Processors, *Proceedings of the LNCS* pp.318–327. (1990)

[7] Z. Galil and R. Giancarlo. Data Structures and Algorithms for Approximate String Matching, Tech. Report, CS Dept., Columbia University, NY (1987).

[8] M.C. Golumbic. Combinatorial Merging, *IEEE Trans. Comp.* 25, 11 (1976) 1164–1167.

[9] R. Güttler, K. Mehlhorn and W. Schneider. Binary search trees: average and worst case behavior, *Electron. Informationsverarb Kybernet,* 16 (1980) pp. 41–61.

[10] D.S.Hirschberg, and L.L.Larmore, The Least weight subsequence problem, *Proc. 26th Annual Symp. on Foundations of Computer Science,* Portland Oregon (Oct. 1985), pp. 137-143. Reprinted in *SIAM Journal on Computing* 16 (1987) pp. 628–638.

[11] T.C. Hu and K.C. Tan. Path length of binary search trees, *SIAM J. Appl. Math.* 22, pp. 225-234 (1972).

[12] T.C.Hu and C.Tucker. Optimum computer search trees. *SIAM J.Appl. Math.,* 21, 1971, pp 514–532.

[13] D.A. Huffman. A method for the constructing of minimum redundancy codes, Proc. IRE, 40, 1952, 1098–1101.

[14] D.G.Kirkpatrick and T.M.Przytycka. Parallel construction of binary trees with almost optimal weighted path length, Proc. 2nd Symp. od Parallel Algorithms and Architectures (1990).

[15] D.G.Kirkpatrick and T.M.Przytycka. An optimal parallel minimax tree algorithm, Proc. of the 2nd IEEE Symp. of Parallel and Distributed Processing (1990) 293–300.

[16] M.M. Klawe and D.J. Kleitman, An almost linear time algorithm for generalized matrix searching, RJ 6275, IBM - Research Division, Almaden Research Center, (1988)

[17] L.L. Larmore. Length limited coding and optimal height-limited binary trees, TR 88-01 University of California, Irvine (1988).

[18] L.L. Larmore, D.S. Hirschberg. A Fast algorithm for optimal length-limited codes *Journal of the ACM,* (1990) pp. 464–473.

[19] L.L. Larmore, and D.S.Hirschberg. Length-limited coding, *Proceedings of the 1ˢᵗ ACM-SIAM Symposium on Discrete Algorithms* San Francisco, CA. (January 1990) pp. 310–318.

[20] L.L.Larmore, and T.M.Przytycka, A Fast Algorithm for Optimum Height Limited Alphabetic Binary Trees, manuscript.

[21] G.L. Miller and J. Reif. Parallel tree contraction and its application, Proc. 26th IEEE Symp. on Foundation of Computer Science (1985) pp. 478–489.

[22] T.M. Przytycka. *Parallel Techniques for Construction of Trees and Related Problems.* Ph.D thesis, the University of British Columbia, Vancouver (1990).

[23] J.Vuillemin, A unifying look at data structures, *C. ACM,* 23, 4 1980, pp 229–239.

[24] R. Wilber. The concave least weight subsequence problem revisited, *Journal of Algorithms* 9, 3 pp.418–425 (1988).

[25] F.F. Yao, Efficient dynamic programming using quadrangle inequalities, *Proc. of the 12th ACM Symp. on Theory of Computing,* (1980) pp.429–435.

More Time-Work Tradeoffs for Parallel Graph Algorithms*

Thomas H. Spencer
Computer Science Department
Rensselaer Polytechnic Institute
Email: spencert@turing.cs.rpi.edu

Abstract

Some parallel algorithms have the property that, as they are allowed to take more time, the total work that they do is reduced. This paper describes three such algorithms that find the strongly connected components of a directed graph. Two of these algorithms are Las Vegas algorithms that run in $\tilde{O}(t)$ time and do $\tilde{O}(n^3/t^2 + m)$ and $\tilde{O}(mn/t + n^3/t^3)$ work, respectively. The third is a Monte Carlo algorithm that also runs in $\tilde{O}(t)$ time, but does $\tilde{O}(mn + n^3/t^5)$ work. The $\tilde{O}$ notation means to ignore logarithmic factors. It is also possible to solve the single source shortest path problem with edge lengths between 1 and L in $O((n/\rho)\log n \log(\rho L))$ time while doing $O(n\rho^2 \log \rho \log(\rho L)) + \tilde{O}(m + n \log L)$ work. Finally, the problem of finding an ear decomposition of a strongly connected directed graph can be reduced to the problem of finding a spanning tree with a specified root.

1 Introduction.

The complexity of a parallel algorithm is measured by both the time and the number of processors it requires. Equivalently, the complexity can be measured by the time required and the processor-time product or work required. There has been increasing attention paid to designing parallel algorithms that do not do much work. Ideally, in the best case, the work done by a parallel algorithm is proportional to the running time of the fastest known sequential algorithm. Galil

*Supported in part by the National Science Foundation under grants CCR-8810609 and CDA-8805910.

© 1991 ACM 089791-438-4/91/0007/0081 $1.50

calls such an algorithm *optimal* [4]. If the work done by a parallel algorithm is $O(T_s \log^k n)$, where T_s is the sequential time and k is a constant, we call the algorithm *efficient*. However, there are important problems for which no fast efficient parallel algorithm is known. If we try to solve these problems on a parallel computer with sufficiently few processors, it is faster to just run the sequential algorithm than to simulate the parallel algorithm. The question arises "how can parallelism be effectively exploited in these cases?"

One of the reasons that some inefficient parallel algorithms are inefficient is that they compute information on speculation, just in case it happens to be needed. We should expect that as we allow the algorithms to take more time, some of this speculative computation could be eliminated. Thus, the slower the algorithm is allowed to be, the less work it does. We say that such an algorithm exhibits a *time-work tradeoff*.

Karp and Ramachandran [7] have listed six problems that have linear time or nearly linear time sequential algorithms, but that seem to require computing the transitive closure of a directed graph to solve them quickly in parallel. These are:

1. the strongly connected components problem,

2. the cycle detection problem for directed graphs,

3. the directed spanning tree problem,

4. the breadth-first search problem,

5. the single source shortest paths problem with nonnegative edge lengths, and

6. the topological sort problem.

Parallel algorithms that exhibit a time-work tradeoff are known for four of these problems. Ullman and Yannakakis [14] have a probabilistic algorithm that solves the breadth-first search problem and, hence, the directed spanning tree problem, on a graph with n vertices and m edges in $\tilde{O}(t)$ time while doing

$\tilde{O}(m\sqrt{n} + mn/t + n^3/t^4)^1$ work. This algorithm is a Las Vegas algorithm because it can detect when it has made a mistake and try again. Ullman and Yannakakis [14] can also compute the transitive closure of a directed graph in $\tilde{O}(t)$ time while doing $\tilde{O}(mn + n^3/t^2)$ work. Spencer [12] has a deterministic algorithm that solves these problems in $O((n/\rho)\log^2\rho)$ time while doing $O(n\rho^2\log^2\rho)$ work, provided that $\sqrt{m/n} \leq \rho \leq n$. Note that if $\rho = \sqrt{m/n}$, this algorithm is efficient. Spencer [12] also has an algorithm that solves the topological sort and, hence, the cycle detection, problem with the same resources.

In this paper, we consider the two remaining problems from Karp and Ramachandran's list: the strongly connected components algorithm, and the single shortest path problem for graphs with positive edge lengths. We also consider the ear decomposition problem for directed graphs. All three problems have parallel algorithms that exhibit a time-work tradeoff.

Recall that two vertices, u and v, are in the same strongly connected component of a directed graph if and only if there is a path from u to v and from v to u. The strongly connected components partition the vertex set of the graph. In the strongly connected components problem, we are asked to find this partition. There are three different algorithms that solve this problem that are all probabilistic. The first $NSCC$ is based on the breadth-first search algorithm of Spencer [12]. The other two, $SSCC1$ and $SSCC2$, use the sampling ideas of [14]. The algorithm $NSCC$ runs in $O((n/\rho)\log^2\rho\log n)$ time and does $O(n\rho^2\log^2\rho\log n)$ work, provided that $\sqrt{m/n} \leq \rho \leq n$. The algorithms $SSCC1$ and $SSCC2$ run in $\tilde{O}(t)$ time and do $\tilde{O}(mn + n^3/t^5)$ and $\tilde{O}(mn/t + \sqrt{n}m + n^3/t^3)$ work, respectively. All the algorithms are probabilistic; $NSCC$ and $SSCC2$ are Las Vegas algorithms, but $SSCC1$ cannot detect when it has made a mistake, so it is a Monte-Carlo algorithm.

The single source shortest path algorithm $SSSP$ handles graphs where the edge lengths $l(e)$ satisfy $1 \leq l(e) \leq L$. It is a deterministic algorithm that runs in $O((n/\rho)\log n\log(\rho L))$ time and does $O(n\rho^2\log\rho\log(\rho L)) + \tilde{O}(m + n\log L)$ work. Note that $SSSP$ does not require that the edge lengths are integers; it only requires that the ratio of the lengths of the longest and shortest edges is not too huge. Still, it is not a strongly polynomial algorithm.

A solution to the ear decomposition problem is a partition of the edges of G into a list of ears. The first ear E_0 is a simple cycle. Each subsequent ear is a simple path whose endpoints are on previous ears. No vertices in the interior of a path are on a previous ear. The ear decomposition problem can be reduced to the directed spanning tree problem.

Lovász gave a parallel algorithm that finds directed ear decompositions by reducing the problem to that of finding an optimum 0-1 branching. It is not known whether there is a parallel algorithm that finds an optimum 0-1 branching and exhibits a time-work tradeoff. It is possible to reduce the problem to that of finding directed spanning trees. This reduction directly gives a parallel algorithm that exhibits a time-work tradeoff.

Since the new algorithms are based on the algorithm of [14] and [12], these algorithms are described in the next section. The basic ideas behind the new algorithms will be described in the third section. The new algorithms will be described in detail in the next three sections.

All the new algorithms use a subroutine that sorts integers in the range $1, \ldots, n$. Francis and Mathieson have a parallel algorithm that uses p processors and sorts n such integers while doing $O(n\log p)$ work [3].

We will need the following definitions:

Definition: A vertex v *reaches* a vertex u if and only if there is a path from v to u. Conversely, u is *reachable from* v if and only if there is a path from v to u.

Definition: If R is a subset of the vertices of G, $G[R]$ is the subgraph induced on R.

Definition: Two vertices u and v are *identified* by replacing them with a single vertex uv. There is an edge from uv to any vertex at the head of an edge from either u or v, and there is an edge to uv from any vertex at the tail of any edge to u or v.

2   Ideas behind the previous work.

The idea behind the algorithms of [14] is to choose a random sample of the vertices of size $\tilde{O}(\max(n/t, \sqrt{n}))$. If we now choose a specific path from u to v for each pair of vertices (u, v) such that v is reachable from u, then, with high probability, there is no segment of any of these paths of length longer than t that does not contain a sampled vertex. The definition of "high probability" depends on the constants and powers of $\log n$ hidden by the $\tilde{O}$ notation, but "high probability" can be made to mean "with probability at least $1 - n^{-k}$," for any constant k.

---

[1]The $\tilde{O}$ notation means that logarithmic factors are ignored. That is, $f(n) = \tilde{O}(g(n))$ if and only if there are constants c and k such that $f(n) \leq cg(n)\log^k n$ for sufficiently large n.

One way of using this information is to determine which sampled vertices can be reached from each sampled vertex v. This information can be obtained by constructing a graph G_s whose vertices are the sampled vertices. There is an edge in G_s from u to v if and only if there is a path in G from u to v of length t or less. If we now compute the transitive closure of G_s and add the edges of the transitive closure to G, then, with high probability, there is a path of length t or less from u to v if there is a path from u to v of any length. In some cases, it is more efficient to do something more complicated with the sampled vertices. We call these ideas *the sampling approach*.

The approach of [12] is based on a data structure called *nearby lists*. Every vertex v has a nearby list $NL(v)$ and a *nearby radius* $r(v)$. The nearby list $NL(v)$ contains all vertices u such that there is a path from v to u of length at most $r(v)$.[2]

Ideally, every nearby list would contain about ρ vertices. However, this property can not be maintained when vertices are deleted from the graph without doing excessive work. Instead, we maintain the following properties of the nearby lists:

1. $r(v) = 2^k$, for some integer $k \geq 1$;

2. either $r(v) = 1$ or $|NL(v)| \leq \rho^2$; and

3. either $NL(v)$ contains all vertices reachable from v, or there are at least ρ vertices reachable from v with distance at most $2r(v)$.

These properties can be maintained.

THEOREM 2.1. *If there are $O(n/\rho)$ rounds of deletions and $\sqrt{m/n} \leq \rho \leq n$, then the nearby list data structure can be maintained in $O((n/\rho)\log^2 \rho)$ time while doing $O(n\rho^2 \log^2 \rho)$ work.*

Proof. See [12]. ∎

The topological sort algorithm works by considering those vertices v such that $NL(v)$ contains all vertices reachable from v.

Definition: A vertex v is *terminal* if every vertex reachable from v is in $NL(v)$. A vertex v is *totally terminal* if it is terminal and every vertex reachable from v is terminal.

---

[2] If vertices are deleted from the graph, the situation is slightly more complicated. If there was a path from v to u of length at most $r(v)$ in the original graph (before vertices were deleted), but no such path in the current graph, then u may appear in $NL(v)$ but does not have to appear there.

3 The new algorithms

Here the ideas behind the new algorithms will be described. Let us start with the algorithms that find strongly connected components.

The algorithm $NSCC$ uses the nearby list data structure. Essentially, it randomly chooses a vertex v and computes $R(v)$ the set of vertices reachable from v. Then, it generates a new nearby list data structure for $G[R(v)]$ to find $C(v)$ the strongly connected component that contains v. Finally, it calls itself recursively on $G[V - R(v)]$ and $G[R(v) - C(v)]$. It is easy to see that $R(v) - C(v)$ is not likely to be a huge fraction of the whole vertex set V. All the time and work spent computing $R(v)$ counts towards the time required by the recursive call on $G[V - R(v)]$. Thus it does not matter if $V - R(v)$ contains almost all the vertices, unless $|R(v)| \leq \rho$. If $|R(v)| \leq \rho$, then $NSCC$ will not have made sufficient progress for the time expended. In this case, however, there are many totally terminal vertices, and the strongly connected components that contain them can be found directly from their nearby lists. Thus, $NSCC$ first checks to see if there are any totally terminal vertices. If there are, it finds the strongly connected components that the totally terminal vertices belong to and deletes them. Otherwise, it chooses a vertex v at random and uses it to divide the problem in two. Figure 1 shows the basic dividing scheme.

The other two algorithms that find strongly connected components are based on sampling. Both choose a sample of size $\tilde{O}(\max(n/t, \sqrt{n}))$ and construct G_s just like the breadth-first search algorithm of Ullman and Yannakakis described above. The first strongly connected component algorithm $SSCC1$ then calls $NSCC$ to find the strongly connected components of G_s. It then identifies in G all vertices in the same strongly connected component of G_s. This forms the graph G_c. With high probability, if u and v are in the same strongly connected component of G_c then there is a path of length at most t from u to v and from v to u. If this is the case, the strongly connected components of G_c and hence of G can be discovered by a search of length $2t$ from each vertex v of G_c. Note that for some graphs G, it is fairly likely that there are vertices u and v such that there is a path from u to v but no path of length t or less from u to v. This makes it hard to check that $SSCC1$ did compute the correct answer. Therefore, $SSCC1$ is a Monte Carlo algorithm that can make mistakes. The total work done by $SSCC1$ is $\tilde{O}(mn + n^3/t^5)$.

The alternate algorithm $SSCC2$ computes the transitive closure of G_s and add its edges to G. Thus, with high probability, if there is a path from u to v in G

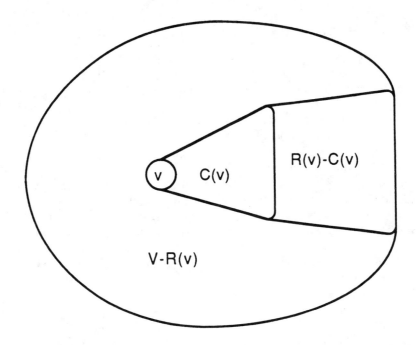

Figure 1: The basic dividing scheme for $NSCC$.

there is a path of length at most t from u to v. Now $SSCC2$ chooses a series of progressively bigger samples S. The last sample contains all the previously unsampled vertices. It processes each sample sequentially, finding the strongly connected component that contains each sampled vertex. It finds these strongly connected components by searching from the sampled vertices. As a result of these searches, $SSCC2$ is able to delete edges from G, while maintaining the property that if there is a path from u to v there is a path of length at most t. The deletion of these edges reduces the expected work done by these searches to $\tilde{O}(m)$. The total work done by $SSCC2$ is $\tilde{O}(mn/t + m\sqrt{n} + n^3/t^3)$.

The algorithm $SSSP$ is a modification of the nearby list approach to breadth-first search. Here when we say that $NL(v)$ contains all vertices reachable from v with distance $r(v)$, the distance is understood to mean the total length of the edges in the path, not the number of edges in the path. This means that we can not assume that $r(v)$ is at least the length of the longest edge from v. Thus, edges from v longer than $r(v)$ must be taken care of separately. Another effect of the edge lengths is that any vertex u in $NL(v)$ may be the penultimate vertex in a shortest path from v to w, a vertex not in $NL(v)$. This fact complicates the procedure for recomputing the nearby lists. A side effect of the mechanism for recomputing the nearby lists is that it is only feasible to require that there be at least ρ vertices with a distance of $4r(v)$ of v. Another effect of the edge lengths is that

the maximum sensible value of $r(v)$ is ρL. One of $\log \rho$ factors in the resources used by the nearby list breadth-first search algorithm is really the number of values of $r(v)$. Thus this factor now becomes $\log(\rho L)$. (Recall that $r(v) = 2^k$, for some integer k.) Therefore, $SSSP$ runs in $O((n/\rho) \log n \log(\rho L))$ time and does $O(n\rho^2 \log \rho \log(\rho L)) + \tilde{O}(m + n \log L)$ work. The factor $\log(\rho L)$ means that $SSSP$ is not a strongly polynomial algorithm.

The first step of the ear decomposition algorithm Ear is to choose an arbitrary vertex r and to find a directed spanning tree rooted at r. At this point, it is possible to identify ears with their last edges. (The other edges in the ears come from the spanning tree.) It is necessary to choose these last edges so that their heads are on previous ears. (The last edge of the first ear must go to r.) These last edges can be chosen by reversing the direction of the edges of G and finding a spanning tree of the resulting graph. The resources required to find the ears are dominated by the resources required to find the spanning trees. These spanning trees can be found by either of the old algorithms mentioned in the previous section.

4 Strongly Connected Components.

The problem of finding the strongly connected components is in some ways more difficult than that of breadth-first search and is in some ways easier. Efforts to develop a deterministic algorithm that exhibits a time-work tradeoff have failed. On the other hand, the nearby list approach and the sampling approach [14] can be combined to give an algorithm that, for appropriate values of t and m, is more efficient than either approach used in isolation. First, we will see how nearby lists can be used to obtain an $O((n/\rho)\log^2 \rho \log n)$ time and $O(n\rho^2 \log^2 \rho \log n)$ work algorithm. Then we will see how the sampling-based transitive-closure algorithm can be modified in two different ways. The first way produces a Monte-Carlo algorithm *SSCC1* that runs in $\tilde{O}(t)$ time and does $\tilde{O}(mn + n^3/t^5)$ work. Unfortunately, there does not seem to be any way to check that all pairs of vertices that *SSCC1* says are in different strongly connected components really are in different strongly connected components without expending substantially more resources. The second modification produces a Las Vegas algorithm that runs in $\tilde{O}(t)$ time and does $\tilde{O}(mn/t + n^3/t^3)$ work. We will call this algorithm *SSCC2*.

4.1 The nearby list approach.

This section describes a probabilistic algorithm *NSCC* that finds the strongly connected components of the input graph G. Suppose that *NSCC* chooses a vertex v and tries to find $C(v)$ the strongly connected component that contains v. The obvious way to find this component is to find $R(v)$, the set of vertices reachable from v, and then determine which vertices in $R(v)$ reach v. Note that no vertex in $R(v)$ is in the same strongly connected component as any vertex not in $R(v)$. This means that *NSCC* can call itself recursively on $G[R(v) - C(v)]$ and $G[V - R(v)]$.

If it happens that neither $R(v) - C(v)$ nor $V - R(v)$ contain more than a constant fraction of the vertices, then the simple divide and conquer algorithm outlined above requires only $O(\log n)$ times as much time and work as it takes to compute $R(v)$ in the first place. Unfortunately, there does not seem to be any way to quickly and deterministically choose a vertex v so that neither $R(v) - C(v)$ nor $V - R(v)$ is too big. Thus, *NSCC* chooses v at random. This is enough to ensure that $R - C(v)$ is not likely to be too big.

LEMMA 4.1. *Let $R(v)$ be the set of vertices reachable from v and let $C(v)$ be the strongly connected component containing v. Then the number of vertices v such that $|R(v) - C(v)| \geq k$ is at most $n - k$.*

Proof. Collapse the vertices in each strongly connected component of the original graphs and do a topological sort on the resulting graph. Now number the vertices in each strongly connected component consecutively, numbering the strongly connected components in the order given by the topological sort. If u is reachable from v and $u \notin C(v)$, then u must

have a higher number than v. The lemma follows. ∎

There is no corresponding bound on the expected size of $V - R(v)$. As long as $R(v)$ is not too small, this does not matter because much of the work done splitting V can be counted towards the work required to split $V - R(v)$. Consider the following outline of *NSCC*:

> procedure $NSCC(G(V, E))$;
> begin
> while $|V| > \rho$ do begin
>   (* stuff to be explained later goes here *)
>   Choose v at random;
>   Compute $R(v)$ the set of vertices reachable from v;
>   Reverse the direction of the edges in $G[R(v)]$;
>   Compute $C(v)$ the strongly connected component containing v;
> $NSCC(G[R(v) - C(v)])$;
> $V \leftarrow V - R(v)$;
>   end;
> Compute the strongly connected components of $G[V]$;
> end;

Suppose that we know that for no v is $|R(v)| < \rho$ and that $R(v)$ is computed using the nearby list breadth-first search algorithm of [12]. Then we can compute the resources required by *NSCC* excluding the recursive calls.

LEMMA 4.2. *If $\sqrt{m/n} \leq \rho \leq n$ and it always happens that $|R(v)| > \rho$, then NSCC runs in $O((n/\rho)\log^2 \rho)$ time on an EREW PRAM with ρ^3 processors, not counting the time required by the recursive calls.*

Proof. The first thing to see is that, aside from the time taken by the recursive calls, *NSCC* runs in $O((n/\rho)\log^2 \rho)$ time. The nearby list breadth-first search algorithm, when searching from v, uses the nearby list data structure described in section 3, where the deleted vertices correspond to vertices that are known to be reachable from v. At least ρ vertices are found each round, to the minimum time required by the search is $O(\lceil |R(v)|\rho \rceil \log^2 \rho) = O((|R(v)|\rho)\log^2 \rho)$, since $|R(v)| \geq \rho$. After the search from v has been completed, the deleted vertices are the ones reachable from v. These are exactly the vertices that need to be deleted to compute $G[V - R(v)]$. Thus, excluding the time required by the recursive calls is $O((n/rho)\log^2 \rho)$. ∎

To compute the total time required by *NSCC* we can construct a call tree with one node for each call to

NSCC. The parent of a node a in this call tree is the call to *NSCC* that called the call represented by node a. We attach to each node the time required by that call, exclusive of the time required by recursive calls. The total size of the problem instances represented by a single level of the call tree is at most n, and each instance has size at least ρ. Thus the total time assigned to a single level of the call tree is at most $O((n/\rho)\log^2 \rho)$.

It remains to estimate the height of the call tree. Lemma 4.1 shows that the probability that $|R(v) - C(v)| > 3/4$ is at most $1/4$, if v is chosen at random. However, it is still possible that there is a significant chance that one of the recursive calls is made on almost all of the vertices. Consider Figure 2, for example.

If the big strongly connected component at the top contains about $\sqrt{n}$ vertices, then *NSCC* will choose a vertex from that component after about $\sqrt{n}$ trials. If the small strongly connected components contain only slightly more than ρ vertices, then one of the recursive calls will be on a graph with about $n - \rho\sqrt{n}$ vertices, which might be nearly n.

To get around this problem, we use two notions of the size of an instance of the strongly connected component problem. The first notion of size is the number of vertices in the graph; the second is the number of edges in the transitive closure of the graph. Note that *NSCC* does not actually compute the transitive closure of any of the graphs; we just reason about its size for the purposes of bounding the running time of *NSCC*.

The key lemma that establishes a logarithmic bound on the height of the call tree is the following

LEMMA 4.3. *With constant probability, all the children of a node in the call tree have either fewer than half as many vertices as the parent or a constant fraction fewer edges in their transitive closures.*

Proof. Suppose that the parent instance has n vertices. Each child instance is on $R(v) - C(v)$ for some randomly chosen vertex v. We call this vertex v the *starting vertex* of the child call. We say that a vertex v is *big* if it reaches more than $n/2$ vertices. If one of the child instances has more than $n/2$ vertices, its starting vertex must be the first big starting vertex chosen. A vertex that is not big is *small*.

Let b be the number of big vertices in the parent instance, and let m^* be the number of edges of the transitive closure of the parent instance. Let v be the first big starting vertex chosen. It turns out that, with constant probability, either the transitive closure of $R(v) - C(v)$ has fewer than $(7/8)m^*$ edges or more than $n/8$ vertices are in previous children.

With probability at least $3/4$, there are $3b/4$ or fewer big vertices in $R(v) - C(v)$. This means that at least $nb/8$ edges of the transitive closure of the parent are not in the transitive closure of the child. If $m^* \leq 2nb$, we're done. If $m^* \geq 2nb$ then there must be many edges of the transitive closure of the parent leaving small vertices. Let m_s be the number of edges of the transitive closure of the parent leaving small vertices just before v is chosen. Then, if we choose a small vertex u at random, the expected number of edges on $r(u)$ is at least m_s/n. The expected number of small vertices chosen before v is chosen is n/b. Thus the expected number of vertices in previous children is m_s/b. We are assuming that $m_s \geq nb$ (otherwise the transitive closure will not have many edges), so the expected number of vertices in previous children is n. With probability at least $7/8$ the number of vertices in previous children is at least $n/8$. Thus, with probability at least $7/8$ all the children either have fewer than $7n/8$ vertices or transitive closures with fewer than $7m^*/8$ edges. ∎

An immediate consequence of the previous lemma is that the expected height of the call tree is at most $O(\log n)$.

Note, however, that if for most (or even all) vertices v it happens that $|R(v)| < \rho$, then the while loop is likely to be executed more than n/ρ times causing *NSCC* to take too long. Thus it is necessary to modify *NSCC* to handle this case.

Consider a vertex v with $|R(v)| < \rho$. It must be terminal. (Otherwise the invariant of the nearby list data structure is violated.) In fact, it must be totally terminal. The strongly connected components that contain totally terminal vertices can be easily computed by sorting the totally terminal vertices' nearby lists to determine which pairs of totally terminal vertices are in each others nearby lists. Thus the stuff to be explained later is:

> while there are totally terminal vertices do
> begin
>> Find the strongly connected components containing these vertices;
>> Delete the totally terminal vertices from G;
>> Update the nearby lists as necessary;
> end;

Since the updates of the nearby lists are due to the deletion of vertices, the work required to do the updates is already accounted for. The work required to find the strongly connected components containing the totally terminal vertices is $O(n\rho^2 \log \rho)$ since each vertex's nearby list contains at most ρ^2 vertices.

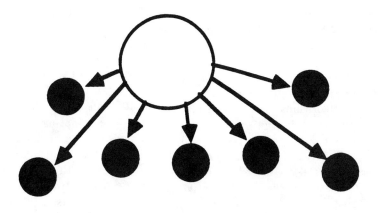

Figure 2: A bad case for *NSCC*.

Thus, it remains to bound the number of times that this inner while loop is executed.

LEMMA 4.4. *The total number of totally terminal vertices found during two consecutive iterations of the inner while loop that occur during the same iteration of the outer while loop is at least ρ.*

Proof. Consider two such iterations; call the first one A and the second one B. Suppose that v was not a totally terminal vertex during iteration A, but that it was removed during iteration B. Since v was not a totally terminal vertex at the beginning of iteration A, there were at least ρ vertices reachable from v at that point. All these vertices must have been totally terminal at the beginning of iteration B or deleted during iteration A, since v was totally terminal at the beginning of iteration B. Therefore, at least ρ totally terminal vertices were deleted during iterations A and B combined. ∎

Putting this all together, we obtain the following:

THEOREM 4.1. *The algorithm NSCC finds the strongly connected components of a graph in $O((n/\rho)\log^2\rho\log n)$ time on an EREW PRAM with ρ^3 processors, provided that $\sqrt{m/n} \leq \rho \leq n$.*

Proof. Lemma B.3 and the proof of Lemma B.2 show that not counting recursive calls, there are $O(n/rho)$ rounds of deletions. Theorem 2.1 shows that the time required, not counting recursive calls is $O((n/\rho)\log^2\rho)$. The proof of Lemma 2.1 shows that the total expected time required is $O((n/\rho)\log^2\rho\log n)$. ∎

4.2 The sampling approach. It is also possible to use the sampling approach of Ullman and Yannakakis [14] to obtain two parallel algorithms that exhibits a time-work tradeoff. Following Ullman and Yannakakis, we will ignore logarithmic factors and use the $\tilde{O}$ notation. Two different algorithms can be obtained in this way. Which one is more efficient depends on the density of the graph and on the amount of time the algorithm is allowed to take. The algorithm $SSCC1$ is a Monte Carlo algorithm that runs in $\tilde{O}(t)$ and does $\tilde{O}(mn + n^3/t^5)$ work. The algorithm $SSCC2$ is a Las Vegas algorithm that runs in $\tilde{O}(t)$ time and does $\tilde{O}(m\sqrt{n} + mn/t + n^3/t^3)$ work. Ignoring the difference between Monte Carlo and Las Vegas algorithms, $SSCC1$ is best on sparse graphs, while $NSCC$ is best on dense graphs and $SSCC2$ is best on graphs of intermediate density. In particular, $SSCC1$ is best when $m < n^2/t^3$; $SSCC2$ is best when $n^2/t^3 < m < n^2/t$ and $m < n^{5/2}/t^2$; and $NSCC$ is best when $m > n^2/t$ or $m > n^{5/2}/t^2$.

Recall how the Ullman-Yannakakis transitive closure algorithm UY works [14]. Basically, UY chooses a sample of $\tilde{O}(n/t)$ vertices at random. Then it creates an auxiliary graph G_s whose vertices are the sampled vertices. The graph G_s that has an edge from u to v if there is a path of length t or less from u to v in the original graph G. Next, UY computes the transitive closure of G_s and adds the edges to G. With high probability, it is now the case that if there is a path from u to v in G there is such a path of length at most t. Thus, UY now just searches for a distance of t from each vertex to compute the transitive closure.

The algorithm UY requires $\tilde{O}(mn + n^3/t^2)$ work. The bottleneck is the last step. The $\tilde{O}(mn)$ term comes from the fact that the search from each vertex might encounter almost all the edges in the original graph. The $\tilde{O}(n^3/t^2)$ term comes from the fact that the search from each vertex might encounter almost all the edges from the transitive closure of G_s. There may be as many as up to $\tilde{O}(n^2/t^2)$ such edges.

The rest of this section describes how to modify UY so that it computes the strongly connected components. Two different algorithms result. The first $SSCC1$ is a Monte-Carlo algorithm that runs in $\tilde{O}(t)$ time and does $\tilde{O}(mn/t + n^3/t^5)$ work. The second $SSCC2$ is a Las Vegas Algorithm that also runs in $\tilde{O}(t)$ time, but it does $\tilde{O}(mn/t + m\sqrt{n} + n^3/t^3)$ work.

It is not necessary to add the edges of the transitive closure of G_s to G. Rather, it is enough to identify the vertices of G_s that are in the same strongly connected component.

LEMMA 4.5. *Suppose that $\tilde{O}(n/t)$ vertices of G are chosen at random and that those vertices in the same strongly connected component are identified. Call the resulting graph G_c. Then, with high probability, if u and v are in the same strongly connected component of G_c there are paths from u to v and from v to u in G_c, each of length at most $2t$.*

Proof. Collapsing vertices does not destroy any paths. Since pairs of vertices that are collapsed together are in the same strongly connected component of G, collapsing the vertices does not add any paths either. For each pair of vertices u and v that are in the same strongly connected component of G choose a path from u to v and another path from v to u. Any paths of length $2t$ or shorter will be preserved or shortened by the collapsing of vertices. If the path P is longer than $2t$, then, with high probability, one of the sampled vertices will be among the first t vertices of P and one of the sampled vertices will be among the last t vertices on P. These sampled vertices must be in the same strongly connected component. Thus, they are collapsed in G_c, so there is a path in G_c from u to v of length $2t$ or shorter. ∎

It is still necessary to compute the strongly connected components of G_s. It is tempting to use $SSCC1$ recursively. However, G_c is dense (at least in the worst case). Thus it is more efficient to use $NSCC$ to compute the strongly connected components of G_s. The call to $NSCC$ requires $\tilde{O}(n^3/t^5)$ work since G_s has $n' = n/t$ vertices and $\rho = \tilde{O}(n'/t)$. The remaining work consists of $\tilde{O}(mn/t)$ work required to compute G_s and $\tilde{O}(mn)$ work required to find the strongly connected components of G_c. Thus we have the following:

THEOREM 4.2. *With high probability, the algorithm $SSCC1$ finds the strongly connected components of the input graph G in $\tilde{O}(t)$ time while doing*

$\tilde{O}(mn + n^3/t^5)$ *work.*

Proof. The theorem follows immediately from Lemma B.4 and from the discussion above. ∎

We would like to improve the algorithm $SSCC1$ in two ways: by converting it to a Las Vegas algorithm so that it can detect when it might have made a mistake, and by eliminating the $\tilde{O}(mn)$ term in the work that it does. If we go back to computing the transitive closure of G_s and adding these edges to G to form G^+, then, with high probability, the shortest path between any two vertices has length at most $\tilde{O}(t)$ or no path exists. This condition can be checked whenever it is relevant, so $SSCC2$ is a Monte Carlo algorithm. Moreover, by not computing the strongly connected components all at once, it is possible to reduce the work required to compute the strongly connected components.

To find the remaining strongly connected components $SSCC2$ again uses the sampling idea. It chooses samples of increasing size and finds the strongly connected components containing the sampled vertices. It also uses information gained from searches from the sampled vertices to delete edges between vertices that cannot be in the same strongly connected component. The deletion of these edges tends to destroy the connectivity of graph and to ensure that with high probability very few edges are searched by very many different searches from sampled vertices. The basic lemma that allows the deletion of these edges is the following:

LEMMA 4.6. *Let S be a subset of the vertices of G and let S_u and S_v be the subsets of S that reach u and v, respectively. If $S_u \neq S_v$, then u and v are not in the same strongly connected component of G.*

Proof. If there is a path from u to v, then $S_u \subset S_v$. If u and v are in the same strongly connected component then $S_u = S_v$. Therefore, u and v are not in the same strongly connected component. ∎

Each sample T_i that $SSCC2$ takes to compute the strongly connected components of G_c consists of vertices chosen independently with probability p_i. Initially, $p_1 = 1/n$. With each subsequent sample, the inclusion probability doubles. That is $p_i = 2p_{i-1} = 2^i/n$. The algorithm $SSCC2$ searches from each sampled vertex to its connected component. Once these components have been found, they are deleted from G_c. In addition, $SSCC2$ keeps track of which sampled vertices can reach each unsampled vertex. It then compares these sets for the endpoints of each edge. If they differ, it deletes the edge. For $SSCC2$ to run in $\tilde{O}(t)$ time, we need to preserve the property that the existence of a path in G implies the existence of a short (length $\tilde{O}(t)$) path in G. The following Lemma shows that $SSCC2$ does this.

Lemma 4.7. *If $SSCC2$ deletes an edge e on a path from u to v, there is no path from u to v after $SSCC2$ is finished processing that sample.*

Proof. Let S_x be the set of sampled vertices that reach x. As x proceeds along a path from u to v vertices are added to S_x, but none are removed. This means that $S_u \neq S_v$. Thus along any path from u to v there is an edge e' whose endpoints are reachable from different sets of sampled vertices. Therefore, after processing the sample, there is no path from u to v in G. ∎

The key lemma in the analysis of the work done by $SSCC2$ is the following:

Lemma 4.8. *The expected number of times $SSCC2$ sees any vertex v in its searches from sampled vertices is $\tilde{O}(1)$.*

Proof. Since there are only $\lceil \log n \rceil$ samples, it is enough to show that the expected number of times that any vertex is seen from any one sample is $\tilde{O}(1)$. The expected size of the first sample is 1, so the expected number of times that any vertex is seen by the first sample is at most 1.

Let $R_i'(v)$ be the set of vertices that reach v just before the ith sample. Then the expected number of times that v is seen by the ith sample is $|R_i'(v)|p_i$. Thus, we want to estimate $|R_i'(v)|$. Let $S_{i-1}(v)$ be the set of vertices of sample $i-1$ that see v. Then $R_i'(v)$ will consist of exactly those vertices of R_{i-1}' that are seen by all the vertices in $S_{i-1}(v)$. Given that $|S_{i-1}(v)| = k$, but that the vertices of $S_{i-1}(v)$ are chosen at random from $R_{i-1}'(v)$, the expected size of $R_i'(v)$ is at most $|R_{i-1}'(v)|/(k+1)$. It turns out that the expected value of $|R_{i-1}'(v)|/|S_{i-1}(v)|$ depends only on p_{i-1}.

Let $n' = |R_{i-1}(v)|$, let $p = p_{i-1}$, and let α be the expected value of $|R_{i-1}'(v)|/|S_{i-1}(v)|$. The probability that $|S_{i-1}(v)| = k$ is $\binom{n}{k}p^k(1-p)^{n-k}$. Thus

$$\alpha = n' \sum_k \frac{\binom{n'}{k}p^k(1-p)^{n'-k}}{k+1}.$$

Some formula manipulation shows that

$$\alpha \leq n' \frac{\sum_k \binom{n'+1}{k+1}p^{k+1}(1-p)^{n'-k}}{(n'+1)p} \leq \frac{n'}{(n+1)p} \leq \frac{1}{p}.$$

Therefore, the expected number of times that v is seen by the ith sample is at most $p_i/p_{i-1} = 2$. ∎

Given this lemma and the previous discussion, the rest of the analysis of $SSCC2$ follows almost immediately.

Theorem 4.3. *The algorithm $SSCC2$ computes the strongly connected components of a graph G in $\tilde{O}(t)$ time while doing $\tilde{O}(m\sqrt{n} + mn/t + n^3/t^3)$ work.*

Proof. Immediate from Lemmas B.5, B.6 and B.7. ∎

5 The Single Source Shortest Path Problem.

In this section we consider the single source shortest path problem with nonnegative edge lengths. We will assume that all edges have length at least 1. If necessary, the edge lengths can be scaled to achieve this property. It can be solved by an algorithm $SSSP$ that is similar to the nearby list algorithm of [12].

The algorithm $SSSP$ also maintains a nearby list $NL(v)$ for each vertex v of the graph. It contains all the vertices within $r(v)$ of v. In this case, distance is measured by the total length of the edges, not by the number of edges. This means that there are $O(\log(\rho L))$ possible ranks, where L is the length of the longest edge. This factor of $O(\log(\rho L))$ appears in both the running time and the work required. This means that $SSSP$ is not a strongly polynomial algorithm.

The major complication in the design and analysis of $SSSP$ comes from the fact that there may be long edges leaving some vertex v. The algorithm $SSSP$ can not afford to insist that $r(v)$ be greater than the length of these edges, since this would allow the nearby lists to become too big and too expensive to compute. The possible presence of long edges means that the procedure for updating nearby lists has to be more complicated. A side effect of the new procedure for updating the nearby lists is that the requirement that there be at least ρ vertices within $2r(v)$ of v must be loosened to require that there be at least ρ vertices within $4r(v)$ of v. Everything else goes through with little change.

Specifically, as before, $SSSP$ maintains for each vertex v a nearby list $NL(v)$ and a nearby radius $r(v)$. In addition, some vertices v have a frontier $F(v)$. If it exists, $F(v)$ contains those vertices u such that there is a path P from v to u of length at most $2r(v)$ such that all the vertices on P (except v and u) are in $NL(v)$. Finally, the edges leaving each vertex v are stored in increasing order of length. Again vertices v whose distances from s, the starting point of the search, are known are considered to be deleted. The algorithm $SSSP$ does not update a nearby list $NL(v)$ unless it can double $r(v)$. Thus $r(v) = 2^k$, for some integer k. If $r(v) = 2^k$, we say that the *rank* of v is k.

When $SSSP$ updates the nearby lists it processes each rank sequentially in increasing order. When it considers a rank k, it first determines which vertices of rank k that do not have frontiers are eligible to obtain them. It finds these frontiers. Then it determines which vertices that have frontiers can double $r(v)$, increasing in rank. When a vertex v's rank increases it does not have a frontier. Of course, when $SSSP$ considers the next rank, it determines if v should acquire a frontier. If v does acquire a frontier, it is considered to see if its rank should increase again, and so on.

Note that if a vertex u is in $NL(v)$, then $SSSP$ knows $d(v,u)$ the length of the shortest path from v to u. If, however, u is only in $F(v)$, $SSSP$ only knows an upper bound on $d(v,u)$.

A vertex v without a frontier obtains a frontier when

1. $|NL(v)| \leq \rho$, and

2. each vertex u in $NL(v)$ is at the tail of ρ or fewer edges of length at most $2r(v)$.

Together these conditions ensure that frontier always contain ρ^2 or fewer vertices.

A vertex v with a frontier increases its rank when

1. $|F(v)| \leq \rho$,

2. each vertex u in $F(v)$ has $r(u) \geq r(v)$, and

3. there are ρ or fewer vertices within $r(v)$ of each vertex in $F(v)$.

Together these condition ensure that nearby lists always contain ρ^2 or fewer vertices.

When $SSSP$ calculates $F(v)$, it does so by considering the edges leaving u of length at most $2r(v)$, for each vertex $u \in NL(v)$. (The vertex v is assumed to belong to $NL(v)$.) It sorts the heads of these edges to remove duplicates, and for each resulting vertex w, it computes the best (least) estimate of $d(v,w)$. Those vertices with an estimate between $r(v)$ and $2r(v)$ become $F(v)$. This calculation requires $O(\log \rho)$ time and $O(\rho^2 \log \rho)$ work.

When $SSSP$ doubles $r(v)$, it must recalculate $NL(v)$. To do this, it considers all vertices u in $F(v)$. For these vertices it finds all vertices w in $NL(u)$ with $d(u,w) \leq r(v)$. It sorts these vertices to remove duplicates, again retaining the least estimate of $d(v,w)$. This calculation also requires $O(\log \rho)$ time and $O(\rho^2 \log \rho)$ work.

LEMMA 5.1. *The procedure outlined above correctly calculates $NL(v)$.*

Proof. Consider a vertex w with $r(v) < d(v,w) \leq 2r(v)$. The shortest path from v to w must go through

a vertex u in $F(v)$. The part of this path after u has length at most $r(v)$. Therefore, the length of this path of $SSSP$'s estimates of $d(v,w)$, and $SSSP$ correctly calculates $NL(v)$. ∎

To see that the nearby list contain enough information, we need to see that either $NL(v)$ contains all vertices reachable from v, or that there are at least ρ vertices within $4r(v)$ of v.

LEMMA 5.2. *After the nearby lists have been updated, either $NL(v)$ contains all vertices reachable from v, or there are at least ρ vertices within $4r(v)$ of v.*

Proof. Let us first consider the case when v has no frontier. Then either $|NL(v)| > \rho$, so there are ρ vertices within $r(v)$ of v; or some vertex u in $NL(v)$ is the tail of more than ρ edges of length at most $2r(v)$. In the second case, the ρ heads of these edges are all within $3r(v)$ of v.

Alternatively, it may be the case that v has a frontier. Again, we need to see why the rank of v was not increased. One possibility is that $F(v)$ contains more than ρ vertices. In this case, there are ρ vertices within $2r(v)$ of v. Another possibility is that a vertex u in $F(v)$ has $r(u) < r(v)$. By induction there are at least ρ vertices within $4r(u) \leq 2r(v)$ of u. Since $d(v,u) \leq 2r(v)$, there are ρ vertices within $4r(v)$ of v. Finally, there may be more than ρ vertices within $r(v)$ of some vertex $u \in F(v)$. These vertices are within $3r(v)$ of v. ∎

Now that we have seen how $SSSP$ maintains the nearby lists, we need to see how $SSSP$ uses them. The algorithm $SSSP$ maintains the following global data structure. Some vertices have been *found*. Their distance from s is known. They are considered to be deleted, so they are never in any vertex's nearby list or frontier. All other vertices are *unknown*. For each unknown vertex w, $SSSP$ maintains $d'(s,w)$ the length of the shortest path from v to w containing no unknown vertices except w. If no such path exists $d'(s,w) = \infty$. In addition, $SSSP$ also maintains for each unknown vertex w the *safe radius* $s(w) = d'(s,w) + r(w)$.

Once the nearby lists have been updated, $SSSP$ finds the minimum safe radius $s(w)$ and all unknown vertices v with $d'(s,v) \leq s(w)$. It puts these vertices into a set C, and examines the nearby list each vertex v of C to find those vertices u with $d'(s,v) + d(v,u) \leq s(w)$. It sorts these vertices to remove duplicates, taking the best estimate of $d(s,u)$. These vertices become found. Finally, $SSSP$ updates the values of $d'(s,v)$ for unknown vertices v. This process is repeated until at least ρ vertices have become found.

At this point, *SSSP* updates the nearby lists, and the whole process is repeated until all vertices have been found.

To maintain the distances $d'(s, w)$ and the safe radii, *SSSP* uses a parallel variant of 2-3 trees where the data are stored in the leaves. In particular, the data structure needs to support the following operations:

1. MassInsert – insert many items in parallel,

2. MassDelete – delete many items in parallel,

3. Min – find the smallest item, and

4. FindSmaller(x, S) – find all elements $\leq x$ that are in S.

Such a data structure was designed by Paul, Vishkin, and Wagner [9]. For the sake of completeness, the ideas behind it will be sketched here. The *min* operation can be done sequentially in $O(\log n)$ time. By treating the 2-3 tree as a concatenable queue [1], the *find_smaller* operation can also be done in $O(\log n)$ time. It remains to see how to do the *mass_insert* and *mass_delete* operations in parallel.

LEMMA 5.3. *The mass_insert and mass_delete operations can be done in $O(\log n)$ time on an EREW PRAM with k processors, where k is the number of items inserted or deleted.*

Proof. Let us consider the case of *mass_delete* first. First, *SSSP* sorts the items to be deleted. Next, it finds the elements to be deleted. (We can assume that this is done by chasing a single pointer.) After finding the deleted elements, and deleting them, *SSSP* identifies all parents of deleted elements. (Because the deleted elements have been sorted, the parents can be uniquely identified in $O(1)$ time.) Those parents with at least two children drop out of further processing, the others find their parents. If the grandparents have at least four grandchildren, they shuffle their grandchildren as necessary, otherwise, they arrange to have at most one child, and they become parents of deleted elements. This process continues up the tree.

Now let us consider *mass_insert*. Again, *SSSP* starts by sorting the items to be inserted. If *SSSP* were using a CREW, it could easily find where to insert each item in $O(\log n)$ time. Since it uses an EREW PRAM, we need to use a pipelined version of binary search. The algorithm *SSSP* starts by comparing the middle inserted element with the root of the 2-3 tree. If the root is less, the right half of the inserted elements can be immediately inserted into the right subtree. With each comparison, either the size of the group that an element is in halves, or the element

moves down one level in the tree. Thus *SSSP* finds the location for all insertions in $O(\log n)$ time. Once, the locations of the insertions have been found, *SSSP* can turn insertions at one level into (usually fewer) insertions at the next level in $O(1)$ time. Therefore, the running time of *mass_insert* is $O(\log n)$. ∎

THEOREM 5.1. *The procedure SSSP described above solves the single source shortest path problem in $O((n/\rho) \log n \log(\rho L))$ time while doing $O(n \log(\rho L)(\rho^2 \log \rho + \log n) + m \log n)$ work.*

Proof. The proof that *SSSP* calculates the correct distances is similar to the proof of Lemma C.1 and is not repeated here.

The work done updating nearby lists is $O(n\rho^2 \log \rho \log(\rho L))$. The nearby lists are updated at most $\lceil n/\rho \rceil$ times, so the time spent updating the nearby lists is $O((n/\rho) \log \rho \log(\rho L))$.

To finish bounding the time required by *SSSP* we need to bound the number of times that $s(w)$ is calculated before the nearby lists are updated. Let $w_1, w_2, \ldots$ be the sequence of vertices of minimum safe radius the *SSSP* finds, and let $r_1, r_2, \ldots$ be the sequence of their ranks. If for some i, $r_{i+1} \geq r_i + 2$, then all the vertices within $4r(w_i)$ have been found. There are ρ such vertices. Similarly, if $r_i = r_{i+1} = r_{i+2} = r_{i+3}$, then after iteration $i + 3$ at least ρ vertices have been found. Finally, if $r_i = r_{i+1} - 1 = r_{i+2}$, then after iteration $i + 2$ at least ρ vertices have been found. Thus, after every element of the sequence r_i, the minimum element seen so far must decrease. Therefore, the length of the sequence is $O(\log(\rho L))$ and the running time of *SSSP* is $O((n/\rho) \log n \log(\rho L))$.

We saw in lemma 5.3 how to use parallel 2-3 trees to calculate the $s(w)$ and the sets C. The value of $d'(s, w)$ changes only when there is an edge (u, w) and u becomes found. This means that it changes $O(m)$ times in all. A safe radius $s(w)$ changes only when $d'(s, w)$ changes or $r(w)$ changes. Thus the total size of the mass inserts and deletes is $O(m + n \log(\rho L))$ and the total work required to do these operations is $O(m \log n + n \log n \log(\rho L))$. Therefore, the total work required is $O(n \log(\rho L)(\rho^2 \log \rho + \log n) + m \log n)$. ∎

6 Ear Decomposition.

This section describes how the ear decomposition of a strongly connected graph G can be computed from a breadth-first search tree of G and a breadth-first search tree of G_r, the graph G with the direction of its edges reversed. A corollary of this result is that the ear decomposition of G can be computed in $O((n/\rho) \log^2 \rho)$ time while doing $O(n\rho^2 \log^2 \rho)$ work, provided that $n\rho^2 \geq m$.

The algorithm *Ear* first computes breadth-first search trees T and T_r of G and G_r, respectively. Both breadth-first searches start from the same vertex r. The tree T divides the edges of G into tree edges and are in T and nontree edges that are not in T. Every ear will contain at most nontree edge. This edge, if present, will be the last edge of the ear. Thus, *Ear* must do two things: order the ears by their last edge, and determine which additional tree edges go with each ear.

The algorithm *Ear* uses the breadth-first search tree of G_r to order the ears. First, it numbers the nodes of T_r in preorder. Then it gives each edge of T_r the number of the child it is incident to. Finally, it subtracts 2 from all of the edge numbers so that the edges are numbered $0, 1, 2, \ldots n - 2$. These edges (actually the reversed versions) are the last edges of the first $n - 1$ ears. All edges that are not in T or in T_r are their own ear. These ears can occur in any order.

It remains to determine which tree edges go with which of the first $n - 1$ ears. Consider an edge (u, v) of T_r. It will occur in some ear as the edge (v, u). This ear must contain a path from some vertex on a lower numbered ear to u. Thus *Ear* gives the vertex u a tail number equal to the number of the edge (u, v). Note that there may be many edges from u in T_r. In this case, the tail number of u is the least number of an edge from u in T_r. The leaves of T_r have no edges coming from them. These vertices have an infinite tail number. Once the tail numbers have been computed, *Ear* computes for each vertex v of T the minimum tail number of any descendant of v. We call this the minimum number of v. The edge of T between the parent of v and v is in the ear with the same number as the minimum number of v.

THEOREM 6.1. *The algorithm Ear described above computes an ear decomposition of a strongly connected graph G in $O(\log n)$ time on an EREW PRAM with $n + m / \log n$ processors once the trees T and T_r have been computed.*

Proof. The bound on the resources used by *Ear* comes from well known techniques such as tree contraction [8] and Eulerian tours of trees [13].

It is less obvious that *Ear* produces an ear decomposition. It follows by induction that the edges of T labeled at most k form a connected subtree of T. This means that the ears are paths that start at a lower numbered path. Moreover, the intermediate vertices are not any lower numbered ear. The first ear ends at r so it is a cycle. Let (u, v) be the last edge of the ith ear. Then it corresponds to the edge (v, u)

in T_r. Thus the edge between u and its parent is on some earlier ear, so u is on an earlier ear, and *Ear* produces an ear decomposition. ∎

COROLLARY 6.1. *An ear decomposition of a strongly connected graph can be computed in $O((n/\rho) \log^2 \rho)$ time on an EREW PRAM with ρ^3 processors, provided that $n\rho^2 \geq m$.*

Proof. Use the nearby list breadth-first search algorithm of [12] to compute T and T_r. ∎

COROLLARY 6.2. *There is a Las Vegas algorithm that computes the ear decomposition of a strongly connected graph in $\tilde{O}(t)$ time while doing $\tilde{O}(mn/t + m\sqrt{n} + n^3/t^3)$ work.*

Proof. Use the sampling breadth-first search algorithm of [14] to compute T and T_r. ∎

7 Further work.

We have seen more examples of algorithms where the work done decreases as the time allowed increases. Finding other algorithms with this property would be interesting. Better algorithms for the problems discussed here would be interesting. Specifically, it would be nice to have a deterministic parallel algorithm that finds strongly connected components, and a strongly polynomial algorithm that solves the single source shortest path problem.

References

[1] A. V. Aho, J. E. Hopcroft, and J. D. Ullman *The Design and Analysis of Computer Algorithms* Addison-Wesley, Reading, Mass. (1974).

[2] R. P. Brent, *The parallel evaluation of general arithmetic expressions*, J. ACM, (1974) pp. 201–208.

[3] R. S. Francis and I. D. Mathieson, *A Benchmark Parallel Sort for Shared Memory Multiprocessors*, IEEE Transactions on Computers, (1988) pp. 1619–1626.

[4] Z. Galil, *Optimal parallel algorithms for string matching*, in Proc. 16th Annual ACM Symposium on Theory of Computing, (1984) pp. 240–248.

[5] H. Gazit and G. L. Miller, *An improved parallel algorithm that computes the BFS numbering of a directed graph*, Information Processing Letters, (1988) pp. 61–65.

[6] T. Hagerup, *Towards optimal parallel bucket sorting*, Information and Computation, (1987) pp. 39–51.

[7] R. M. Karp and V. Ramachandran, *A survey of parallel algorithms for shared-memory machines*, Tech. Report, 88/408, Comp. Sci. Div. (EECS), Univ. California at Berkeley, 1988.

[8] G. L. Miller and J. Reif, *Parallel Tree Contraction and its application*, in Proc. 26th Annual Symposium

on the Foundations of Computer Science, (1985) pp. 478–489.

[9] W. Paul, U. Vishkin, H. Wagner, *Parallel Dictionaries on 2-3 trees*, in *Automata, Languages and Programming* ed. by J. Diaz, (1983), pp. 597–609.

[10] J. Reif, *An optimal parallel algorithm for integer sorting*, in Proc. 26th Annual Symposium on the Foundations of Computer Science, (1985) pp. 496–503.

[11] T. Spencer, *Time-work tradeoffs for parallel algorithms*, Tech. Report, 89-26, RPI, Troy, NY, (1989).

[12] T. Spencer, *Time-work tradeoffs for parallel graph algorithms*, Second Annual Symposium on Discrete Algorithms, (1991), pp. 425–432.

[13] R. Tarjan, U. Vishkin, *An Efficient Parallel Biconnectivity Algorithm*, SIAM J. Comp., **14**, (1985), pp. 862–874.

[14] J. Ullman and M. Yannakakis, *High-probability parallel transitive closure algorithms*, Symposium on Parallel Algorithms and Architectures, (1990) pp. 200–209.

SESSION 3

AN OVERVIEW OF SUPERTOROIDAL NETWORKS

RICHARD N. DRAPER

Supercomputing Research Center

ABSTRACT

The objective of this paper is to define a new class of interconnection networks called supertoroidal networks, to describe their physical layout, scalability, routing, and performance. These networks have topologies which are Cayley graphs of non-commutative groups. The networks are of node degree four and are closely related to k-ary 3-cubes of comparable size. Supertoroidal networks have smaller diameter and average diameter than k-ary 3-cubes of comparable size, thereby providing a design alternative which reduces pin complexity of wide-data-path interprocessor communication in tightly coupled multiprocessor systems.

I. Introduction.

The objective of this paper is to introduce the reader to a new class of interconnection networks which we call supertoroidal networks. These networks are intended to serve as interconnection networks for tightly coupled multiprocessor systems. Properties of the networks seem most appropriate for use in wide-data-path MIMD systems.

A tightly coupled multiprocessor system is connected together by a network. Abstractly, the network consists of a graph commonly called the network topology, an addressing scheme, and a routing scheme. A routing protocol and a layout may also be specified as part of the network. To be of serious practical interest a network must be part of a family of closely related networks of various sizes, a property called scalability. Much of the research into novel networks starts with the topology and then passes on to some or all of the other issues we have listed. The work reported on here is of

this type. We start with a topology, determine an addressing scheme, a routing scheme, a layout, and the scalability of the network. We do not examine routing protocols.

There are three genres of interconnection networks which have been implemented in machines. The most popular is the hypercube or slight variants thereof [Se] [Hi], which we call a 2-ary n-cube following the terminology of [Da]. Other topologies which have been implemented or are under serious consideration are low dimensional meshes, k-ary n-cubes with small n, and multistage networks of low degree. Supertoroidal networks are an intermediate class lying somewhere between k-ary 2-cubes and k-ary 3-cubes. They offer alternatives with tradeoffs which are reasonably well exposed. The underlying concept also can be used in other ways which lead to alternatives to k-ary n-cubes for many values of k and n or to alternatives to n-dimensional meshes. In general supertoidal networks gain reduced node degree at the expense of longer links and more complicated routing. This is the reason that they appear most appropriate for use in wide-data-path systems.

The research leading to the discovery of supertoroidal networks was directed at finding alternative topologies for a particular kind of multiprocessor system. It was a wide-data-path, fine-grained MIMD shared memory architecture much like the architecture now called TERA [Sm]. An architecture of this type imposes constraints on the interconnection network that have been studied in detail by others [PS]. One of these constraints is that the network must be based upon a topology in which the nodes have very low degree. Another is that the network should scale without changing the degree of the nodes. If the multiprocessor is envisioned to have packet switching time equal to CPU operation time, then the network must have a layout with relatively short links and it must be capable of routing packets within the CPU operation time. These constraints lead to networks based upon low-dimensional meshes, k-ary n-cubes for small n, or to multistage interconnection networks. The multistage networks seem to be eliminated from consideration for fully shared-memory

Typeset by $\mathcal{AMS}$-TEX.

systems in which the potential for locality of reference is desired. For these reasons, we focused this research project on finding scalable alternatives to the k-ary n-cube having node degree less than n, high speed routing algorithms and topologies which are simple enough that the network can be built.

Supertoroidal networks belong to a class of networks which are Cayley graphs of groups. The groups used are composed of a pair of cyclic groups by a construction called the semi-direct product [Sco]. The presentation given here supresses this terminology and supposes no familiarity with these concepts. However, it is helpful to introduce this terminology in order to relate this work to other research on interconnection networks.

The idea of using Cayley graphs of groups as sources of interconnection network topologies has been examined by many authors beginning with the work of Akers and Krishnamurthy [AK1]. However, only a few of these investigations have involved Cayley graphs of semi-direct products. Most of the latter investigations have focused on wreath products, a form of semi-direct product in which one of the component groups is a cyclic group $\mathbb{Z}/m$ and the other component group is a power $(\mathbb{Z}/n)^k$ of a cyclic group [Sco]. Commonly $n = 2$, $k = m$ and the network has $k2^k$ nodes. The network topologies based upon wreath products are closely related to the cube connected cycles of Preparata and Vuillemin [PV]. Information about this work can be found in section 7 of [AK2], [CCSW] and [ABR]. The third reference also relates network topologies based upon wreath products to the DeBruijn graph, the shuffle-exchange graph and the butterfly graph.

Recently Shee and Teh [ST] proposed using the Cayley graph of a semi-direct product of a cyclic group of prime order p with its automorphism group, which is a cyclic group of order $p - 1$, as the topology of an interconnection network. This is the only work other than our own to focus on the Cayley graph of the semi-direct product of two cyclic groups as a source of network topologies.

Our research into network topologies is quite distinctive from that referred to above. It differs from the work on wreath products because the networks which we construct belong to the family of k-ary n-cubes and provide useful alternatives when n is small and k is large. Networks based on wreath products belong to the family of cube connected cycles and provide useful alternatives for 2-ary n-cubes when n is large. Our work differs form the work of Shee and Teh because we have found networks which scale gracefully and have simple layouts in 3-space whereas they have not addressed these issues. Furthermore, it is highly unlikely that the networks they found will scale gracefully.

This paper surveys research on supertoroidal networks that is carried out in greater detail in other sources. Three dimensional layout and scalability are

examined in detail in [D1]; a study of the diameter and average diameter, which is joint work with Vance Faber, is in [DF]; and a study of routing algorithms is in [D2]. The reference [D3] is essentially identical to this paper. There remain two major tasks in the study of supertoroidal networks. One is a comprehensive comparative study of network performance and the other is an examination of the mapping of more conventional topologies onto supertoroidal networks.

The remainder of this paper is organized into five sections. Section II describes the logical structure of the network topology, Section III examines the layout of these networks in three space, Section IV discusses routing and Section V discusses scalability. The last section gives conclusions and indicates open questions and areas for future study.

II. General Description of Supertoroidal Networks.

This section contains a description of the address space and connections of a supertoroidal network. A supertoroidal network depends upon parameters k, l and c which are nonnegative integers. The parameter c determines a family of networks parameterized by k and l. A member of the family is denoted $\Gamma(c, k, l)$. It has klc^3 nodes, all of degree four. To simplify the discussion, c is assumed to be even. For the networks to be interesting, $c \geq 4$ so that also is assumed.

The address space for $\Gamma(c, k, l)$ is $[0, ck) \times [0, cl) \times [0, c)$, i.e., representatives of the integers modulo ck, cl and c, respectively. However, the underlying arithmetic of this address space is not arithmetic modulo ck, cl and c, respectively. Let us denote a member of the address space by (x, y, z). The terms y and z are the coordinates of a mixed radix-(cl, c) representation [Hw] of an integer modulo c^2l of the form $y + zcl$ modulo c^2l. The term x is a representative of an integer modulo ck. The product of two addresses (x_1, y_1, z_1) and (x_2, y_2, z_2) is computed by matrix multiplication:

$$
(1) \quad \begin{pmatrix} 1 & y_1 & z_1 \\ 0 & 1 & x_1 \\ 0 & 0 & 1 \end{pmatrix} \begin{pmatrix} 1 & y_2 & z_2 \\ 0 & 1 & x_2 \\ 0 & 0 & 1 \end{pmatrix}
$$
$$
= \begin{pmatrix} 1 & y_1 + y_2 & z_1 + z_2 + x_2 y_1 \\ 0 & 1 & x_1 + x_2 \\ 0 & 0 & 1 \end{pmatrix}.
$$

In a more compact notation

$$
(2) \quad (x_1, y_1, z_1)(x_2, y_2, z_2)
$$
$$
= (x_1 + x_2, y_1 + y_2, z_1 + z_2 + x_2 y_1)
$$

where the coordinate $x_1 + x_2$ is reduced modulo ck and the coordinates $y_1 + y_2$, and $z_1 + z_2 + x_2 y_1$ are taken from the mixed radix-(cl, c) representation of $y_1 + y_2 + (z_1 + z_2 + x_2 y_1)cl$ modulo c^2l. It is a tedious but straightforward exercise to show that this multiplication is well-defined, is associative, has $(0, 0, 0)$ for multiplicative identity, and that the multiplicative inverse of (x, y, z) is $(-x, -y, -z + xy)$. The multiplication is not commutative.[1]

The purpose for introducing this multiplicative law is to use it to determine connections between nodes of $\Gamma(c, k, l)$ as they are represented in the address space. Each node is connected to four other nodes by links or edges labeled $(\pm 1, 0, 0)$ and $(0, \pm 1, 0)$ according to the group law. That is:

(x, y, z) is connected to
(3) $\quad (x, y, z)(\pm 1, 0, 0) = (x \pm 1, y, z \pm y)$
by links labeled $(\pm 1, 0, 0)$, and

(x, y, z) is connected to
(4) $\quad (x, y, z)(0, \pm 1, 0) = (x, y \pm 1, z)$
by links labeled $(0, \pm 1, 0)$.

The links of opposite sign are opposites of one another so the graph has bidirectional links. Because the second coordinate y is taken modulo $c^2 l$, the link labeled $(0, 1, 0)$ generates a cycle of length $c^2 l$ on $\Gamma(c, k, l)$ exactly as would the link labeled $(0, 1)$ on a $ck \times c^2 l$ toroidally connected mesh. That is,

(5) $\quad (0, 1, 0)^{cl} = (0, 0, 1)$ and $(0, 0, 1)^c = (0, 0, 0)$.

Somewhat more obscurely, since the third coordinate z is taken as zcl modulo $c^2 l$ and the first coordinate x is taken modulo ck, the link labeled $(1, 0, 0)$ generates a cycle of length ck on $\Gamma(c, k, l,)$.

The network $\Gamma(c, k, l)$ is closely related to the 2-dimensional $ck \times c^2 l$ toroidally connected mesh, which is also a network of degree four. It is also closely related to the 3-dimensional $ck \times cl \times c$ toroidally connected mesh, a network of degree six. In [DF] the diameter and average diameter of $\Gamma(c, k, l)$ was computed. Table 1 illustrates the relationship of these parameters for the three related networks.

Table 1

$\Gamma(c, k, l)$	dia.
$\Gamma(c, k, l)$	$ck/2 + cl/2$
2-dim. $ck \times c^2 l$ mesh	$ck/2 + c^2 l/2$
3-dim. $ck \times cl \times c$ mesh	$ck/2 + cl/2 + c/2$

$\Gamma(c, k, l)$	ave. dia.
$\Gamma(c, k, l)$	$1/2$ dia. $+ O(\ln(c)/\sqrt{c})$
2-dim. $ck \times c^2 l$ mesh	$1/2$ dia.
3-dim. $ck \times cl \times c$ mesh	$1/2$ dia.

This table is correct for $c \geq 8$. For smaller values of c the diameter of $\Gamma(c, k, l)$ is greater than the value in the table. See [DF] for details. Notice that the diameter and average diameter of $\Gamma(c, k, l)$ behave asymptotically like the diameter and average diameter of a 2-dimensional cross-section of the 3-dimensional $ck \times cl \times c$ mesh. In terms of these metrics, supertoroidal networks get the third dimension (of length c) at no cost. In terms of these metrics it is desirable that k and l be approximately equal. Our table gives an unrealistic value for the 2-dimensional mesh because, with $c^3 kl$ nodes, it would be constructed in a square having diameter $O(c^{3/2})$ instead of $O(c^2)$.

III. Layout of $\Gamma(c, k, l)$.

The address space $[0, ck] \times [0, cl] \times [0, c]$ can be viewed as a rectangular volume of points in the integer lattice $\mathbb{Z}^3$ within Euclidean 3-space. In this section the physical location of the links given by (3) and (4) is examined. We refer to the resulting collection of points or nodes and links in Euclidean 3-space as a layout of $\Gamma(c, k, l)$. A modification of this layout which reduces the length of the longest link required is presented. Lastly a layout for a network prototype project at the Supercomputing Research Center which embraces both the supertoroidal topology and the 3-dimensional mesh is described. This project is called H-net.

Consider a cross-section perpendicular to the x-axis, $x = x_0$. The links labeled $(0, \pm 1, 0)$ connect nodes in this cross-section according to (4) in a manner which is independent of x_0. We observed in the previous section that the nodes in such a $cl \times c$ cross-section are connected into a single cycle by these links. This is pictured in Figure 1 for $\Gamma(4, 1, 1)$. The horizontal axis is the y-axis and the vertical axis is the z-axis.

In a cross-section perpendicular to the y-axis, $y = y_0$, the links labeled $(\pm 1, 0, 0)$ connect nodes according to (3) into cycles of length ck. In this case the role of the third coordinate is more complex. As a result, these links have slopes which are dependent on y_0, the value of the coordinate determining the cross-section. It is very important that the slopes of these links only take

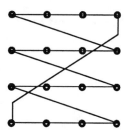

Figure 1. Cross Section x_0 of $\Gamma(4,1,1)$

the values $0, 1, \ldots, c-1$ because $(x, y, z) = (x, y, z+c)$ in the arithmetic defining $\Gamma(c, k, l)$. That is, the slopes of these links are independent of k and l. This observation is fundamental to the scalability of these networks with respect to the parameters k and l. The four distinct cross-sections of $\Gamma(4, 1, 1)$ are pictured in Figure 2. The horizontal axis is the x-axis and the vertical axis is the z-axis.

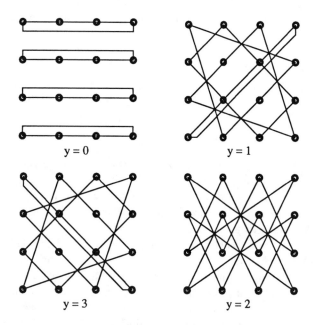

Figure 2. Cross Sections y_0 of $\Gamma(4, 1, 1)$

There are two sources of long links in this layout. One source originates in the behavior of the third coordinate under the action (3) of the link $(1, 0, 0)$. It is intrinsic and imposes links of length proportional to the parameter c. The other source is the wrap-around effect of creating cycles. It leads to links of two different lengths: some of length proportional to cl, as can be seen in a special case by examination of Figure 1, and some of length proportional to ck, as can be seen in the same case in Figure 2. This phenomenon can be eliminated by standard techniques used in laying out toroidally connected meshes. If, for example, the y-axis is laid out as a ring of length cl then the address space becomes a cyclinder and the long links in Figure 1

are reduced. The longest of these links is in the outermost ring of the cylinder and has length proportional to $2\pi ck/cl$. If, in addition, the nodes on the x-axis are interleaved in the pattern $0, ck-1, 1, ck-2, 2, \ldots, ck/2$ then the links connecting the left and right extremes in Figure 2 are reduced so that the longest link has length proportional to c. A more detailed study of these issues has been carried out in [D1]. The conclusion of this analysis is the following result.

Theorem. *If $k/l \leq M$, there exist three dimensional layouts of $\Gamma(c, k, l)$ in a volume proportional to klc^3 having links of maximal length proportional to c.*

The constraint on k/l is compatible with the result on diameter reported in Table 1 of Section II. However, the result on maximal link length is in opposition to the result on diameter in Section II because the advantage in network diameter increases with c but the length of the longest links also increases with c which is a disadvantage.

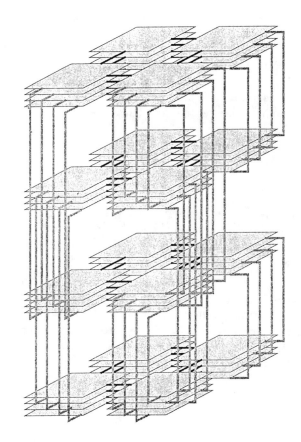

Figure 3. H-Net Layout for $\Gamma(4, 1, 1)$

Figure 3 is a visualization of (part of) the wiring for $\Gamma(4, 1, 1)$ in another layout discussed in [D1]. The relationship between the coordinates used in this paper and the "natural" coordinates of the nodes of the layout in Figure 3 is more complicated than that required in the previous discussion. In the layout in Figure 3 the x-axis is a horizontal ring so the cycles of length four with links labelled $(\pm 1, 0, 0)$ appear as horizontal rings with dark links. The y-axis and the z-axis are interwoven vertically with each group of four horizontal planes constituting a fixed value of y and four values of z. Displacements between these groups of four are exagerated to enhance the clarity of the figure. Each corner column constitutes one of the cycles of length 16 pictured in Figure 1. Only the front right column pictures all of the links labeled $(0, \pm 1, 0)$. The left front and right rear columns picture half of these links and the left rear pictures none of these links. The omissions are made to enhance clarity. The columns have different interconnection patterns which result from the fact that the value of z, being nonconstant along link $(1, 0, 0)$, is not constant on the horizontal planes in this figure. This layout was proposed as part of a project at the Supercomputing Research Center to build a reconfigurable network architecture capable of realizing both $\Gamma(4, 1, 1)$ and a 3-dimensional $4 \times 4 \times 4$ toroidally connected mesh. The mesh can be achieved by linking each group of four nodes in a column into a cycle of length four and appropriately reconnecting the gray links in Figure 3. With this layout both the mesh and $\Gamma(4, 1, 1)$ have maximal links of the same length.[2]

IV. Routing on $\Gamma(c, k, l)$.

We have developed two distributed routing algorithms on $\Gamma(c, k, l)$. Our network model is one in which unit time is required to traverse all links even though some are longer than others in the layouts described earlier. The first algorithm is optimal, in the sense that the algorithm chooses a minimal route from source to destination in the abscence of contention. The second algorithm is suboptimal.

Given a source $S = (x_1, y_1, z_1)$ and destination $D = (x_2, y_2, z_2)$, a distributed routing algorithm $\mathcal{A}$ must choose one of the four links $(\pm 1, 0, 0), (0, \pm 1, 0)$ along which to send a packet. This choice must be based only upon knowledge of S and D. Global knowledge of the network topology can be embedded using the arithmetic structure of the underlying address space of the network. If the link chosen is L and a packet is sent from S on link L, it arrives at node SL. The algorithm $\mathcal{A}$ is recalled with $S' = SL$ and $D' = D$. Clearly, an algorithm $\mathcal{A}$ which examines $D^{-1}S$ in order to choose link L will be called upon to examine $(D')^{-1}S' = D^{-1}SL$ at the node $S' = SL$. Therefore, in the context discussed here, a distributed routing algorithm $\mathcal{A}$ must choose a link L by examination of $D^{-1}S$. As S and D vary over the

address space of $\Gamma(c, k, l)$, $D^{-1}S$ varies over the same space. Therefore, a routing algorithm $\mathcal{A}$ is a function from the address space to $\{(\pm 1, 0, 0), (0, \pm 1, 0), \text{home}\}$. When $D^{-1}S = (0, 0, 0)$, i.e. when $D = S$, the packet is home. That is, it has arrived at its destination. We are tacitly assuming that nodes have the ability to compute $D^{-1}S$ given D and S, that packets carry D in a header and that nodes know their own address S.

We indicated in the Introduction that the address space for $\Gamma(c, k, l)$ together with the multiplicative law (2) defines a group. An optimal routing algorithm $\mathcal{A}$ is a recursive algorithm capable of finding *minimal length representations* for elements of this group. This problem is known to be hard. (See [EG] and [J] for studies of its complexity.) Most network topologies in real machines which are based upon groups are based upon commutative groups where the problem is much easier. The problem is not easy in the group underlying $\Gamma(c, k, l)$.

The only way to achieve optimal routing on $\Gamma(c, k, l)$ is by means of look-up tables. Coupled with the ability to calculate $D^{-1}S$, the look-up tables are identical for all nodes. Assuming that $D^{-1}S = (0, 0, 0)$ is recognized outside the table, these tables require $c^3kl \times 4$ bits. (There are techniques in [CF] for compressing the width of the entries.) This is an acceptable solution to the routing problem provided that the network clock operates at the speed of memory chips. However, if the network clock is to operate at speeds comparable to the logical units, which would be the case in a very fine grained parallel MIMD machine [Sm], this solution is unacceptable.

We have recently discovered a suboptimal routing algorithm for $\Gamma(c, k, l)$ which uses much smaller lookup tables or which can be implemented entirely in logic. The proof that the algorithm is correct and an analysis of the algorithmic diameter of $\Gamma(c, k, l)$ are carried out in [D2]. The principal results of that analysis and the algorithm follow.

Let $D^{-1}S = (x, y, z)$ and $j = y + zcl$ modulo c^2l with the representative j chosen so that $-c^2l/2 \leq j < c^2l/2$. There is a unique representation

$$(6) \qquad j = q(cl - 1) + r$$

with $|r| \leq (cl - 2)/2$ and $|q| \leq c/2$. (See [D2], (3.8) and (3.9).) The supoptimal routing algorithm depends only upon x, r and q. Furthermore, it is like a routing algorithm on a 3-dimensional toroidal mesh in that it only needs to determine whether a coordinate is nonzero and, if so, whether it is greater or less than zero. In terms of look-up tables, this means that a table of length c^2l with two-bit entries specifying whether $r = 0$ and its signature if $r \neq 0$ is required. Since (6) is a form of division algorithm, it can also be implemented in logic rather than ram.

---

[2]This layout was not chosen for that reason, however. It was chosen and later modified slightly because of factors such as power supply, cooling, and dimensions of off-the-shelf components.

Here is the algorithm, which we will denote by $\mathcal{B}$ to distinguish it from the optimal algorithm $\mathcal{A}$.

(7)
$$\mathcal{B}(x,y,z) = \begin{cases} \text{home} & \text{if } (x,y,z) = (0,0,0) \\ (0,-1,0) & \text{if } r > 0, \\ (0,1,0) & \text{if } r < 0, \\ (1,0,0) & \text{if } r = 0 \text{ and } q \neq 0, \\ (-1,0,0) & \text{if } r = 0, \ q = 0 \text{ and } x > 0, \\ (1,0,0) & \text{if } r = 0, \ q = 0 \text{ and } x < 0. \end{cases}$$

Theorem. *The algorithm $\mathcal{B}$ is a distributed routing algorithm on $\Gamma(c,k,l)$. The diameter of $\Gamma(c,k,l)$ with respect to $\mathcal{B}$ is bounded above by $ck/2 + cl/2 + c/2 + 2$.*

This algorithm can be implemented at speeds which compare favorably with routing algorithms on 3-dimensional toroidally connected meshes. Note that the algorithmic diameter has an upper bound which is worse by $+2$ than the diameter of a 3-dimensional mesh and that some of the power of the supertoroidal network has been lost by using this algorithm. (See Table 1 in Section II.) However, the algorithm $\mathcal{B}$ is optimal locally. Specifically, if the distance from S to D is less than three, then $\mathcal{B}$ is optimal. Furthermore, each node has a two dimensional neighborhood, given by $q = 0$, on which $\mathcal{B}$ is optimal.

V. Scalability of $\Gamma(c,k,l)$.

With respect to network topologies, the issues raised by scaling are related to node degree, link length, diameter, address space, node addresses, routing logic and physical layout. For a family of networks to scale gracefully, the logical structure and topology of a small network must be related to that of a large network in a rational and useful way. We claim this to be the case for supertoroidal networks. In fact, large networks can be constructed from smaller networks, provided they share the same value of the parameter c, in a relatively straightforward manner. In this section we examine how this can be done and look fairly closely at changes required in the node addressing, the logic and the network links. For the sake of simplicity, we will discuss the special case of constructing $\Gamma(c,2,1)$ or $\Gamma(c,1,2)$ from two copies of $\Gamma(c,1,1)$.

Because supertoroidal networks have node degree four, which is independent of network dimensions, node degree is not a problem in scaling. Also, link identifiers are identical for all nodes of all of these networks, so no change in port references is needed. Since larger networks require larger address spaces, we will assume that every network in a family has the address space capacity of the largest member of the family. Notice that this means that the node hardware which calculates $D^{-1}S$ for the routing algorithm must be capable of modification because the parameters k and l appear

in the definition of multiplication given in (2). It also means that at least half of the nodes must have their own identifiers changed. These requirements must also be met by a family of k-ary n-cubes if they are to scale gracefully.

In Section III a physical layout is exhibited in which the length of maximal links is proportional to c. The scaling problem will be discussed in terms of this layout because bounding maximal link length for all networks in a family is highly desirable. In this layout the y-axis is a ring and the x-axis is interwoven in the pattern $0, ck-1, 1, ck-2, 2, \ldots, ck/2$.

Let us first examine the construction of $\Gamma(c,1,2)$ from two copies of $\Gamma(c,1,1)$. These copies are cylinders which have the property that nodes with a fixed value of the coordinate x are linked into a cycle of length c^2 by the links $(0, \pm 1, 0)$. (See (4) and the discussion associated with Figure 1.) These nodes must be linked into a single cycle of length $2c^2$ in $\Gamma(c,1,2)$. This can be accomplished easily and gracefully provided the cylinders are flattened into two parallel planes which can by joined at one end. A top view is pictured in Figure 4 where the y-axis is pictured as a cycle and the x-axis is vertical. No change in the links labeled $(\pm 1, 0, 0)$ (see (3)) is required. It is clear that no link has its length increased in this process. This scaling is also relatively graceful with respect to node addresses. The x- and z- coordinates are unaffected. In the two original networks, the y-coordinates are arranged as a cycle in the order $0, 1, 2, \ldots, c-1$. In $\Gamma(c,1,2)$ the y-coordinate is arranged in a single cycle in the order $0, 1, 2, \ldots, 2c-1$. This can be accomplished by adding $c/2$ to the values of the y-coordinate in the second copy of $\Gamma(c,1,1)$ and c to the y-coordinate of the last half of the nodes of the first copy.

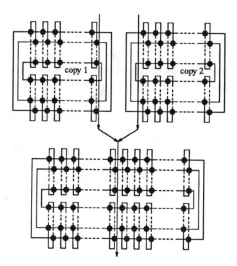

Figure 4. Scaling $\Gamma(c,1,1)$ up to $\Gamma(c,1,2)$

Construction of $\Gamma(c,2,1)$ from two copies of $\Gamma(c,1,1)$ in this layout is somewhat less graceful. Logically, we

100

must join the x-axes of the two networks so, physically, we must place one cylinder inside the other. The top view of this is pictured in Figure 5. With the cylinders flattened as in the above discussion two halves of one copy must be placed on either side of the other copy. As a result, some of the links in the cylindrical direction in the outer copy (copy 2 in Figure 5) will be lengthened in scaling. This is the sense in which this scaling is less graceful.

Recalling the discussion of the links $(\pm 1, 0, 0)$ in Section III, these links have slopes which are determined by the class of the y-coordinate modulo c. As joined, these slopes agree in both copies of the network for each value of y because these values are aligned in both copies. Therefore, reconnecting the links labeled $(\pm 1, 0, 0)$ at the edges of the two copies to create one network is not difficult. Node addressing is handled exactly as above except that in this case it is the x-coordinate which must be modified.

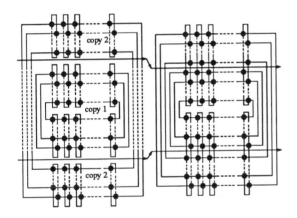

Figure 5. Scaling $\Gamma(c, 1, 1)$ up to $\Gamma(c, 2, 1)$

Alternative physical layouts may alter the relative ease with which scaling with respect to k or l can be achieved. For example, the layout pictured in Figure 3 for H-net scales very gracefully with respect to k. Given two copies of the machine $\Gamma(4, 1, 1)$ as pictured, $\Gamma(4, 2, 1)$ could be built by standing the machines side by side and rewiring the horizontal 4-cycles into 8-cycles.

Routing poses a more challenging problem. The calculation of $D^{-1}S$ is dependent upon k and l as well as c. Therefore, the ability to modify this part of the routing logic must be available in the hardware. If optimal routing based upon lookup tables is used then space for the table for the largest network in the family must be present in the same way that adequate address space must be present. If the suboptimal algorithm is used and scaling is confined to the parameter k, then scaling only effects routing on the x-axis. Either lookup tables or a division algorithm to implement (7) are unaffected. In this case scaling is no more complex than for

any toroidally connected family of meshes. If, however, scaling is done on the parameter l, appropriate modification in the lookup tables or division algorithm which implements (7) must be available in the node logic.

The scaling properties of the family $\Gamma(c, k, l)$ for a fixed value of c are inherent and depend in a fundamental way upon the fact that the coordinate z of the address space is determined independently of k and l.

V. Conclusions and Future Research.

Supertoroidal networks are a new class of networks. A member of the class is denoted $\Gamma(c, k, l)$. It is of degree four and has $c^3 kl$ nodes. For fixed c, the networks form a family which depend on the parameters k and l. The networks in this family are scalable in both concept and physical layout. These networks are closely related to two and three dimensional toroidally connected meshes. They have degree four but have diameter approximating that of 3-dimensional meshes of comparable size. As a result, they offer a design alternative to three dimensional meshes in which pin complexity is traded for routing complexity and wire length. Supertoroidal networks appear to be best suited for use in wide-data-path MIMD multiprocessors.

Two distributed routing algorithms have been presented. One of these is suboptimal but can be implemented in hardware in a manner analogous to implementations of algorithms on k-ary n-cubes for $k > 2$. It is, therefore, capable of much higher speed implementations than the other algorithm, which is optimal but based upon full size look-up tables. The suboptimal algorithm is one of three related algorithms discussed in [D2]. They have some very interesting properties. For example, the path form S to D is not the opposite of the path from D to S. There are "hysteresis loops" in the routing algorithm. What do they mean and do they have any use in managing or analyzing routing congestion? The algorithms are all coset algorithms [SS] so choose two of the links much more frequently as first steps of optimal paths. Therefore, in the presence of random traffic, the frequency count of link traversal is not uniform. This is intrinsic to any coset algorithm, even those on hypercubes. However, coset algorithms have the desirable feature that they are parallel. How does this phenomenon relate to congestion on the network?

In addition to addressing the questions just raised, there are two major tasks remaining in the study of supertoroidal networks. One of these is a comprehensive study of network performance under various loading conditions. Some of this work, using a network simulator, has been done but is not reported in this paper. Additional study using the simulator and a network prototype called H-Net, which is being constructed at the Supercomputing Research Center, will be carried out. The second major task is to examine the emulation of more conventional network topologies on supertoroidal networks.

REFERENCES

[AK1]   Sheldon B. Akers and B. Krishnamurthy, *A Group Theoretic Model for Symmetric Interconnection Networks*, Proc. 1986 International Conf. on Parallel Processing, IEEE Computer Society Press, Washington, D.C., 1986, pp. 216–233.

[AK2]   _____, *A Group Theoretic Model for Symmetric Interconnection Networks*, IEEE Trans. on Comp. **38** (1989), 555–566.

[ABR]   Fred Annexstein, Marc Baumslag and Arnold L. Rosenberg, *Group Action Graphs and Parallel Architectures*, SIAM J. Comp. **19** (1990), 544–569.

[CCSW]   G. E. Carlsson, J. E. Cruthirds, H. B. Sexton and C. G. Wright, *Interconnection Networks Based on a Generalization of Cube-Connected Cycles*, IEEE Trans. on Comput. **C-34** (1985), 769–772.

[CF]   Gene Cooperman and Larry Finkelstein, *New Methods for Using Cayley Graphs in Interconnection Networks*, College of Computer Science, Northeastern University, preprint, J. Discrete and Appl. Math., to appear..

[Da]   William J. Dally, *Performance Analysis of k-ary n-cube Interconnection Networks*, IEEE Trans. on Comp. **39** (1990), 775–785.

[D1]   Richard N. Draper, *Supertoroidal Networks*, Supercomputing Research Center, Technical Report SRC-TR-90-005.

[D2]   _____, *A Fast Distributed Routing Algorithm for Supertoroidal Networks*, Supercomputing Research Center, Technical Report SRC-TR-91-032.

[D3]   _____, *An Overview of Supertoroidal Networks*, Supercomputing Research Center, Technical Report SRC-TR-91-035.

[DF]   _____ and Vance Faber, *The Diameter and Mean Diameter of Supertoroidal Networks*, Supercomputing Research Center, Technical Report SRC-TR-90-004.

[EG]   S.Even and O. Goldreich, *The Minimum-Length Generator Sequence Problem is NP-Hard*, J. Algorithms **2** (1981), 311–313.

[Hi]   W. D. Hillis, *The Connection Machine*, The MIT Press, Boston, Mass., 1986.

[Hw]   Kai Hwang, *Computer Arithmetic: Principles, Architecture, and Design*, John Wiley and Sons, New York, 1979, p. 8.

[J]   M. Jerrum, *The Complexity of Finding Minimum-Length Sequences*, Automata, Languages and Programming; 11th Colloquium, Antwerp, 1984, *Lecture Notes in Comp. Sci.*, vol. 172, Springer-Verlag, Berlin-New York, 1984, pp. 270–280.

[PS]   F. Pittelli and D. Smitley, *Analysis of a 3D Toroidal Network for a Shared Memory Architecture*, Proceedings Supercomputing '88, November 14-18, 1988, Orlando Florida, IEEE Computer Society Press, Washington, DC, 1988, pp. 42–48.

[PV]   F.P.Preparata and J. E. Vuillemin, *The Cube-Connected Cycles: A Versitile Graph for Parallel Computation*, JACM **24** (1981), 300–309.

[Sch]   Walter Schempp, *Neurocomputer Architectures*, preprint, Dept. of Math., Univ. Siegen, Siegen, Germany.

[SS]   Stephen T. Schibell and Richard M. Stafford, *Processor Interconnection Networks from Cayley Graphs*, to appear, Discrete and Appl. Math..

[Sco]   W. R. Scott, *Group Theory*, Prentice Hall, Inc., Englewood Cliffs, N. J., 1964.

[Se]   C. L. Seitz, *The Cosmic Cube*, Communications of the ACM **28** (1985), 22–33.

[ST]   S. C. Shee and H. H. Teh, *An Application of Groups to the Topology Design of Connection Machines*, Group Theory (Singapore, 1987), de Gruyter, Berlin-New York, 1989, pp. 519–529.

[Sm]   Burton Smith, *The Tera Computer System*, Conference Proceedings, 1990 ACM International Conference on Supercomputing, June 11-15, 1990, Amsterdam, The Netherlands, The Association for Computing Machinery, New York, 1990, pp. 1–7.

17100 SCIENCE DRIVE, BOWIE, MD 20715-4300

E-mail: draper@super.org

Architectural Primitives for a Scalable Shared Memory Multiprocessor *

Joonwon Lee   *Umakishore Ramachandran*

College of Computing
Georgia Institute of Technology
Atlanta, Georgia 30332 USA

Abstract

Since large memory latencies are not uncommon for a large scale multiprocessor, researchers have investigated memory models to relax memory access ordering. This paper presents a new memory model, and discusses implementation issues in a cache-based environment. These issues motivate a set of architectural primitives with which software can implement desired memory consistency. For efficient cache management, we propose a cache protocol that allows read-initiated actions for coherence maintenance. For efficient synchronization, we present a cache-based locking scheme that implements queued busy-waiting using cache lines. The scalability of the proposed schemes is explored through analytical modeling and simulation studies.

1 Introduction

Parallel programming based on the shared memory paradigm is a natural progression from sequential programming. Therefore, it is not surprising that shared memory multiprocessors (such as the Sequent and the BBN Butterfly) are popular for developing parallel applications. Message-passing multiprocessors (such as the Intel Hypercube) are intrinsically more scalable than shared memory multiprocessors primarily due to the potential contention for shared memory in the latter [22]. Due to the popularity of programming with the shared memory paradigm, this abstraction is being supported even on message-passing architectures [16]. However,

*This work is supported in part by the NSF PYI Award MIP-9058430

simulating shared memory on message-passing architectures is inherently slower than true shared memory. The main motivation for the research presented in this paper is to understand the issues in realizing scalable shared memory multiprocessors and suggest architectural features that address these issues.

There are two main problems to be solved in realizing scalable shared memory multiprocessors: latency for memory accesses, and network contention generated by these memory accesses. Both these problems are related to the model of memory provided by the architecture. Traditionally, the model assumed by the programmer is that the contents of the shared memory is identical at all times from all the processors. Further, the model assumes that the completion order of the memory references from a single processor is strictly in program order. Both these assumptions restrict the scalability of shared memory multiprocessors. For example, the second assumption prohibits out-of-order completion of memory accesses which is important to enhance performance, especially when the memory latency is high. In parallel applications, it is not unusual to use synchronization operations to ensure the consistency of shared data. In such cases, a temporary inconsistency in the views of the shared data as seen from different processors may be tolerable in certain ranges of the program, e.g., inside a critical section and between barrier synchronization points. This observation leads to weaker consistency models [21, 1, 4] in which updates to shared memory may be delayed until a synchronization point. Using such weaker models of memory is one approach to realizing scalable shared memory multiprocessors.

Another approach to addressing the issues of latency and network contention is to associate private caches with each processor. The effectiveness of this approach depends on an efficient strategy for maintaining the coherence information as well as the choice of the coherence protocol. Snooping cache protocols [2] with distributed directories for maintaining the consistency information have been popular in bus-based shared memory multiprocessors. These protocols exploit the fast broadcast capability of the bus to efficiently implement the coherence protocol. But it is well-known that a bus is not a scalable interconnection network. Unfortunately, more scalable interconnections such as a multistage interconnection network do not usually have such a fast broadcast capability. For this reason, coherence protocols based on a central directory for maintaining the consistency information are usually preferred for scalable shared memory multiprocessors [5, 3].

The coherence protocols define the actions to be taken when a cache line is modified. To maintain consistency on writes to a cache line, the protocol may choose to either invalidate or update copies of this line in other caches. In bus-based systems, it is possible to make a case for either choice depending on the memory reference pattern [2, 9]. In large-scale multiprocessors invalidation is preferred to updates because of the high network transit time [3, 4]. Both these strategies implicitly enforce consistency on writes to a shared location. A dual to this strategy is to explicitly request consistency on reads. In our view such a strategy would reduce the overhead of coherence maintenance especially in large-scale multiprocessors by allowing the consistency requirements to be customized by the software (compiler) instead of blind enforcement.

For performance reason, a cache line usually consists of several words and the cache protocol treats a line as the unit of consistency maintenance. However, program variables may vary in size from a bit to arbitrary length. Since a cache line may contain several words, unless explicit care is taken in writing the parallel program or by the compiler [11], it is quite likely that the same cache line may contain private variables of parallel threads executing on different processors. These cache lines appear shared from the point of view of the cache protocol leading to unnecessary invalidations or updates. This phenomenon is referred to as *false sharing* and limits the line size. From the performance point of view it is important to reduce the effects of false sharing especially for large-scale multiprocessors.

There are two types of memory accesses generated by a parallel program: accesses to normal data, and accesses to synchronization variables. An analysis of the memory reference pattern of parallel programs reveals that the synchronization accesses cause much greater network contention than accesses to normal shared data [18]. A serious limitation to scalability is the fact that the hardware does not distinguish between accesses to synchronization variables and accesses to normal data. Recognizing the importance of making this distinction researchers have proposed hardware primitives for synchronization [23, 8, 10, 13]. An important advantage of making this distinction is that it provides a setting for efficiently supporting the weak consistency model.

This paper presents a new memory consistency model, and discusses implementation issues in a cache-based environment with respect to this model. These issues motivate a machine architecture that provides primitives for addressing the scalability issues raised in this section. The paper concludes with preliminary performance implications of our machine architecture, and directions for future research.

2   A New Consistency Model

In shared memory multiprocessors there is a need for defining a consistency model that specifies the order of execution of memory accesses from multiple processors. Such a consistency model would facilitate reasoning about the correctness of programs written for multiple processors. For simplicity, it is usually assumed that the result of a write operation be immediately observable by other processors. With this assumption, Lamport [12] has proposed *sequential consistency* as the ordering constraint for the correct execution of a multiprocess program: The multiprocessor execution of the program should have the same effect as a sequential execution of any arbitrary interleaving of the operations of all the processes (that comprise the program). The allowed interleavings are those that preserve the program order of operations of each individual process. With the sequential consistency model, read and write operations are sufficient to implement synchronization operations correctly. However, this model is inherently inefficient since it imposes a strong ordering constraint for all memory accesses regardless of the usage of shared data. Further, each memory access has to wait until the previous memory access is completed. Thus large scale shared memory multiprocessors are expected to incur long latencies for memory accesses if this ordering constraint is imposed, leading to poor performance.

In parallel program design, it is not unusual to use synchronization operations to enforce a specific ordering of shared memory accesses. Based on this observation Dubois et al. [7] have proposed *weak ordering* that relaxes the ordering constraint of sequential consistency by distinguishing between accesses to synchronization variables and ordinary data. Their model requires (a) that synchronization variables be strongly consistent, (b) that all global data accesses be globally notified before synchronization operations, and (c) that all global data accesses subsequent to the synchronization operation be delayed until the operation is globally performed. Thus this model requires strong consistency of global data accesses with respect to synchronization variables.

There are several types of synchronization operations: barrier, lock and unlock, and semaphore P and V. While synchronization variables need to be strongly consistent, the consistency requirements for shared data preceding or succeeding accesses to synchronization variables may be different. For example, consider a critical section.

Write operations on shared data performed by a processor prior to entering the critical section need not be globally performed. It is enough if the write operations inside the critical section are globally performed just before exiting it. Therefore, inside the critical section all reads and writes may be treated as entirely operations local to the processor. Similarly, write operations performed after exiting the critical section need not wait for the completion of the synchronization operation that signals the exit.

This observation regarding the consistency requirements and the relative ordering requirements lead to several extensions to the weak ordering model proposed by Dubois et al [7]. *Buffered consistency* is the memory model used in this paper and is defined as follows. There are two types of accesses: synchronization and normal read/write. Synchronization accesses are further subdivided into two classes: consistency preserving (*CP-Synch*), and non-consistency preserving (*NP-Synch*). An NP-Synch operation does not wait for the completion of writes to shared data preceding it. A CP-Synch operation is allowed to be performed only after all writes to shared data preceding it have been globally performed. Writes to shared data issued after a synchronization operation need not be delayed until the synchronization operation is globally performed. Other researchers [4, 1] have proposed weaker models that allow relaxing the consistency requirements within critical sections. Our model allows further weakening of the consistency and ordering requirements even in other synchronization scenarios.

Examples of synchronization operations that belong to the NP-Synch class are: lock, and semaphore P; examples of CP-Synch class of operations include: unlock, semaphore V, and barrier synchronization. Buffered consistency differs from other consistency models including weak ordering [21] and *release consistency* [4] as follows: Consider an NP-Synch operation such as a lock. An implementation of this operation in a cache-based environment may require sending a request to a global directory. An acknowledgment from this directory may signal the acquisition of the lock. However, the global completion of this operation may entail updating cache directories distributed in all the processors. Our model allows the requesting processor to continue with its local computation as soon as the acknowledgment is received without waiting for the operation to be globally performed. Similar arguments apply for CP-Synch operations. In a large-scale shared memory multiprocessor the weakening of the ordering constraint proposed in our model may be crucial to reducing the waiting time for synchronization operations to be globally performed.

3 Issues in Implementing Buffered Consistency

Implementation of weak consistency models requires that either the hardware or the software keep track of updates to shared data so that these updates may be propagated at appropriate points during the execution of the program. To ensure that all the updates inside a critical section be globally performed before the critical section is released, the hardware or the software should be able to detect these pending operations. In this paper we propose efficient hardware primitives for implementing scalable shared memory multiprocessors. The proposed hardware primitives are in the context of a cache-based system implementing the buffered consistency model. In order to implement this model the processor-cache interface should provide the following minimal capabilities:

- local reads and writes

- global writes

- wait until all global writes have been completed

With this interface the model is implemented as follows: Updates to shared data use global writes. Since synchronization variables need to be strongly consistent, the processor uses global writes for updating such variables, and in addition may choose to wait for the completion of such writes depending on the semantics of the synchronization operation. Before performing a CP-Synch operation, the processor waits until all global writes to shared data have been completed.

The above simple interface places the entire burden of implementing our model on the software. For example, the software has to distinguish between shared and private data, has to distinguish between synchronization variables and normal read/write variables, and when to wait for certain writes to be globally performed. From the performance standpoint this burden on the software may prove to be very inefficient.

The rest of this section identifies the issues that need to be addressed by the machine architecture for efficiently supporting this model.

1. There is a delay between the initiation of a global write and its completion. This delay depends on several factors including the number of nodes in the multiprocessor, the size and type of the interconnection network, and the amount of memory contention. Therefore, if there are successive global writes generated by a processor, then it would have to stall unnecessarily unless there is some kind of buffering of the global writes. Such a buffer would help smooth the traffic on the interconnection network as well as allow the local computation to pro-

ceed independent of network latencies (see Section 4.2).

2. In the model there is a necessity to keep track of pending global writes so that a processor may choose to wait on the completion of these writes. Adve and Hill [1] suggest a counter to denote the number of pending global operations. A processor may be stalled until the counter becomes zero when it waits for the completion of global writes. In a software approach [6], the definition and use of shared data are tracked by the compiler, and modified words in the cache are selectively written back and purged depending on the usage pattern of the program. However, this software approach is not practical since shared data may be accessed through pointers, and thus it is impossible to detect all the updates statically. The number of pending operations in the write buffer which we propose in our machine architecture (see Section 4.2) implicitly implements the counter of Adve and Hill [1].

3. The simple interface requires the software to specify each write as local or global. This requirement can be eliminated if the cache distinguishes between shared and private data. The cache would perform the write locally if the data is private and globally if the data is shared. However, this scheme forces all writes to shared objects to be global. In reality, the software is the best judge as to when a shared object has to be globally updated. Thus in our proposed machine architecture (see Section 4.2) the cache does not distinguish between shared and private data. The software is responsible for instructing the cache when writes to shared objects have to be performed globally.

4. As we mentioned in Section 1, there are two approaches to propagating the effect of a global write in a cache-based system: invalidate, and update. Both these schemes are coherence initiated by the writer. Using the buffered consistency model, when a writer updates some shared variables globally, these values may be needed by some readers in the future. If an invalidation approach is used, then such readers would have to request these values again. On the other hand, if an update approach is used, the updates may be sent to readers who may no longer be interested in these values.

In general, it has been observed that in strongly consistent cache-based systems invalidations are less frequent than updates for the same memory reference pattern [2, 9]. In spite of this observation, the performance of write-update schemes has been comparable to that of the invalidation schemes in bus-based systems since invalidations generate more overhead than updates[1]. However, in large-scale multiprocessors employing more scalable interconnects, the network transit time is the dominant cost. In such networks the increased number of network transactions due to updates would make these schemes much less attractive than invalidation-based schemes [4, 3]. However, invalidation cache schemes have their sources of inefficiency as illustrated in Section 4.1. This observation motivates our new reader-initiated coherence protocol.

5. The buffered consistency model assumes that there are two types of accesses: synchronization and normal read/write. The simple interface places the burden of making this distinction on the software. Parallel programs invariably use some form of synchronization for coordinating access to shared data. Efficient synchronization is important to assure good performance. In our machine architecture (see Section 4.3), we propose synchronization primitives that are merged with the coherence protocol.

6. A cache line usually consists of several words and the cache protocol treats a line as the unit of consistency maintenance. Treating a cache line as the unit of consistency maintenance introduces a problem for the buffered consistency model: If two processors update different words in the same cache line and if the writes are delayed the word that is written back to memory first is lost. In the absence of any hardware support, the software is burdened with having to allocate shared variables carefully to avoid such situations. In the extreme, the software may be forced to allocate one shared variable per cache line, which is inefficient both from the point of view of spatial locality as well as usage of cache memory. In our machine architecture, we provide a mechanism to relieve the software of this burden. This mechanism also solves the problem of false sharing encountered in multiprocessor cache protocols.

The software is still responsible for the following:

- determining when to instruct the cache to perform writes globally,

- determining when to stall the processor waiting for global writes to be completed,

- distinguishing whether a synchronization operation belongs to the CP-Synch or the NP-Synch class and taking the appropriate actions, when software-based synchronization is used,

---

[1]An invalidation is usually accompanied by a line transfer.

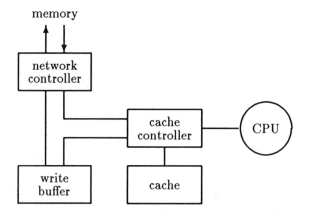

Figure 1: Block diagram of a node

- determining how to exploit the reader-initiated coherence protocol, and the cache-based synchronization primitives from the performance point of view.

4 A Machine Architecture

In this section, we propose a machine architecture that can be utilized by the software for implementing our buffered consistency model. Figure 1 shows the conceptual block diagram of a node in the multiprocessor architecture. Each node is equipped with a cache and a write-buffer. Each cache has a local directory referred to as *cache directory*. An entry in this cache directory contains the state of the associated cache line. The main memory is shared and all the nodes in the multiprocessor are connected to it via their respective network controllers. The main memory maintains a *central directory* for each line of the main memory. The location of the main memory and the interconnection network connecting the processors to the main memory are left intentionally unspecified since the machine architecture to be described does not depend on these details. For example, it is conceivable that the main memory is partitioned and distributed among the nodes in the multiprocessor, and the interconnection network is a multi-stage one. Table 1 summarizes the hardware primitives available to the processor. These primitives may be grouped in the following categories: read/write, buffer management, and synchronization. The next few subsections describe the features of the components in the node architecture.

4.1 Reader-Initiated Coherence

Figure 2, illustrates the structure of an entry in the cache directory and the corresponding entry in the central directory. To address the issues of false-sharing and the shared variables allocation (see Section 3) every entry in the cache directory has dirty bits, $d_1 d_2 \cdots d_k$, for each of the k words in the cache line.

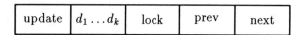

a. An entry in the cache directory

b. An entry in the central directory

Figure 2: Structure of directory entries

When a cache line is replaced, only the dirty words are written back to memory. The *update* bit of cache directory entry and the *queue-pointer* field of the central directory entry are used by the read-update primitive, to be described shortly. The *lock* field is used for cache-based synchronization which will be explained in the next subsection. We chose to use a pointer-based directory structure since it is more scalable than either a full-map or limited directory structures [24].

Read and write requests are deemed for private data, and are treated as would a uniprocessor cache. Read-global bypasses the local cache and retrieves the data from the main memory[2]. The write-global request differs from the write request in that the operation is performed globally. This primitive is similar to the *post* primitive proposed by Cytron et al [6]. Read-update request is similar to read except that it requests future updates for this cache line. This is a dual to the write-update schemes [25, 17] in that the updates are receiver initiated as opposed to sender initiated. A read-update request is serviced locally by the cache if the update bit of the cache line is already set. Otherwise, this bit is turned on and this request is forwarded to the main memory. Processors that issued read-update requests for the same memory block form a doubly-linked list, and the *queue-pointer* field in the central directory contains the address of the head of the list. The linked list is constructed using the *next* and *prev* fields of each cache line corresponding to the requested memory block. When the main memory is updated, the updated block is transferred using this linked-list structure.

The update bit of a cache line is reset when the line is replaced by the node, or by an explicit request, *reset-update* for this line from the node. Subsequent writes to this line would not result in updates being sent to this node. The reset-update request will delete the requesting node from the linked list. Since the read-update request is considered to be mutually exclusive with a lock request for the same memory block, those fields that are used for constructing a linked list can be used for

---

[2]This primitive was motivated by discussions with Richard Huff, Cornell University.

Instruction	Operations
READ	retrieve data without coherence maintenance
WRITE	write data without coherence maintenance
READ-GLOBAL	read data from the main memory, bypassing local cache
WRITE-GLOBAL	write data globally
READ-UPDATE	retrieve data and request the main memory to send updated value
RESET-UPDATE	cancel the request for updated value
FLUSH-BUFFER	stall the processor until all the requests in the write-buffer are globally performed
READ-LOCK	request a shared lock for a data
WRITE-LOCK	request a exclusive lock for a data
UNLOCK	release the lock

Table 1: Hardware primitives

operation	read-update	inv-I	inv-II
initial load	$\lceil n/B \rceil C_B$	$\lceil n/B \rceil C_B$	nC_B
write	$C_W + (n-1)\|C_B$	$\frac{1}{B}(C_R + (n-1)\|C_I) + \frac{B-1}{B}(2C_R + 2C_B)$	$C_R + (n-1)\|C_I$
read	-	$\frac{1}{B}(\lceil n/B \rceil - 1)C_B + \frac{B-1}{B}\lceil n/B \rceil C_B$	$(n-1)C_B$

Table 2: Performance of cache coherence schemes for executing a linear equation solver.

lock operations (see Section 4.3). The *usage bit* in the central directory indicates whether the linked list is for read-update or lock operations. The cache-based lock presented in Section 4.3 also uses the same linked-list structure for processors waiting for a lock.

The read-update scheme differs from a write-update scheme in several ways: In the latter, whenever a read operation is performed it is remembered forever until the line is replaced by the reader. So readers continue to receive updates even if the line is not actively used. In our scheme, readers have to explicitly specify that updates are required using the read-update primitive. Moreover, a smart compiler could selectively determine regions in the program where updates may be needed.

Given these primitives, it would be instructive to analyze their possible usage. We compare our scheme against invalidation-based cache protocols for executing a linear equation solver. A linear equation can be expressed as $Ax = b$ where A is an n by n matrix and x and b are n-element vectors. The algorithm to solve this equation is as follows:

$$x_i^{(k+1)} = (b_i - \sum_{j=1}^{i-1} a_{ij}x_j^{(k)} - \sum_{j=i+1}^{n} a_{ij}x_j^{(k)})/a_{ii}$$

In each iteration, $x^{(k+1)}$ is computed, and the computed x value is used in the next iteration by all the other processors. All the processors are synchronized at the end of each iteration. For simplicity of analysis, we assume dance-hall architecture with n processors.

Furthermore, the analysis is focused only on the global operations of the x vector required in each iteration. Table 2 shows the overhead in terms of network traffic generated by each processor. B denotes the cache line size, and $C_B, C_W, C_I, and C_R$ denote block transfer, word transfer, invalidation, and transaction carrying no data, respectively. To show the effect of false-sharing, two cases for invalidation protocol are considered: one for colocating x vector elements (inv-I) , and another for allocating each x element in separate cache lines (inv-II). When some number of transactions (say p) can be performed in parallel, they are denoted as $p\|transaction\_type$. The costs for initial loading are obvious. With read-update feature, each write of an iteration sends the updated word to the main memory, and the main memory sends the memory block to $n-1$ processors that issued read-update request for that block. For inv-I, there are B writers to the same cache line. The first writer invalidates all the other copies, and the next $B-1$ writers retrieve the cache line from the previous writer. Though separate allocation of the x vector (inv-II) reduces the overhead for write operation, read of the next iteration will incur more overhead than the inv-I scheme. All the schemes perform comparably for write operation. However, read operation of the next iteration results in a significant advantage for the read-update scheme because the invalidation-based schemes have to re-load all the elements of the x vector.

4.2 Buffer Management

Implementation of the buffered consistency model is facilitated by the operation on the write-buffer, namely, *flush-buffer*. As we mentioned earlier, the write-global primitive requires that the operation be performed globally. However, to reduce the latency for global operations such requests are immediately buffered in the write-buffer. Depending on the availability of the interconnection network these writes are performed globally by the write-buffer without stalling the normal operation of the node. As and when an acknowledgment is received from the main memory, the associated buffer entry is deleted from the write-buffer. The flush-buffer primitive stalls the processor until all the buffered writes have been globally performed. This primitive allows the processor to wait for the completion of global operations which may be required by the program before executing a CP-Synch operation.

The read-update primitive combined with the buffered consistency model is a powerful feature. The basic functionality of the read-update primitive is similar to write-update primitive. However the fact that readers can selectively request updates to selected lines is expected to provide a significant performance advantage in implementing several parallel algorithms. For example, in parallel Fast Fourier Transform programs, readers may need access to different regions of a shared data structure during different phases of the computation. In implementing such algorithms, the program may selectively reset the update bit for certain regions of the shared data structure and request the regions to be used in the current computation phase using the read-update primitive.

4.3 Synchronization

Thus far we have proposed a buffered consistency model, and an efficient cache scheme that implements this model to address the two main problems of latency and network contention in the design of large-scale shared memory multiprocessors. An associated problem that also limits the scalability are synchronization operations that are quite heavily used in parallel program design.

For memory-based synchronization, the hardware usually provides some form of an atomic read-modify-write operation that allows higher level primitives to be built. However, such low level primitives could be quite inefficient in large-scale shared memory multiprocessors. The inefficiency caused by synchronization is twofold: wait times at synchronization points and the intrinsic overhead of the synchronization operations. If a busy-wait discipline is used, then the processors generate considerable memory traffic on the busy-wait variable. To reduce this traffic, a busy-wait on the cached copy of the busy-wait variable has been proposed for multiproces-

sors with coherent private caches [20]. However, when a mutual-exclusion lock is released, competition to acquire the lock results in bursty traffic to the same memory location. This contention impedes the useful computation that is being performed by the processor that has acquired the mutual exclusion lock thus prolonging the total execution time of the parallel program. In this section, we propose a cache-based lock scheme (CBL), that reduces the effects of lock contention. This scheme is similar to the one that we proposed in in our earlier work [13].

Exclusive and shared locks are common synchronization abstractions used in parallel programs. This abstraction is quite general and can be used for implementing other synchronization abstractions. In our design we have chosen to support this abstraction. The synchronization primitives provided by the cache are: *read-lock, write-lock,* and *unlock*. Each lock is associated with a cache line, and read-lock gives non-exclusive access to the line, while write-lock gives exclusive access to the line. When a lock request is granted the data associated with this lock is also transferred to the requester thus merging the data transfer with the synchronization request. Similar to the implementation proposed in our earlier work [13], a distributed hardware queue is constructed using participating cache lines.

Figure 3 shows the result of a sequence of lock requests generated by nodes P1, P2, and P3 for a memory location i; P1:read-lock,P2:read-lock, P3:write-lock. Only the cache lines and the memory block that contain the memory location i are shown in the Figure. The memory block is assumed to be of the same size as the cache line. A doubly-linked list is constructed using pointers of the participating cache lines and the central directory as shown in Figure 3. The *prev* and *next* pointers in each cache line denote the previous and the next node in the lock request sequence, respectively. The corresponding central directory entry has a pointer, *queue-pointer*, which points to the last lock requester.

First P1 sends its read-lock request to the main memory. Assuming that the memory block is currently unlocked, P1 is the only outstanding lock requester, and thus the address of P1 is stored in the queue-pointer field of the central directory entry. The memory block is sent to P1. A cache line is selected to store this memory block, the lock field of the associated cache directory entry is set to read-lock, and the prev and next pointers are set to nil. Receiving the read-lock request of P2, the request is forwarded to the current tail (P1), and the queue-pointer field of the central directory is changed to P2. Since the lock types of P1 and P2 are compatible, P1 allows P2 to share the lock. Now, the next pointer of P1 is set to P2 and the prev pointer of P2 is set to P1. Subsequently, when P3 makes a request for an exclusive access to the same memory block, P2 notifies P3 to wait at the tail of the queue. Figure 3

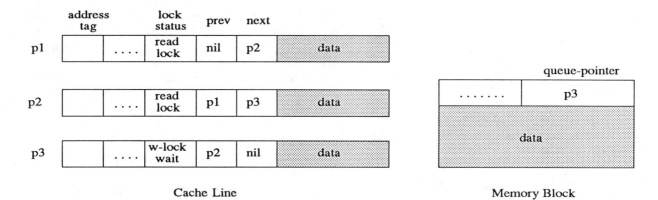

Figure 3: A waiting queue: doubly linked list

shows the final state after all these lock requests have been processed by the central directory[3].

Upon an unlock request, the cache releases the lock to the next waiting processor (if any), and writes the cache line to the main memory (if necessary). When a write-lock is released there could be more than one processor waiting for a read-lock. The lock release notification goes down the linked list until it meets a write-lock requester (or end of the list), and thus, allows granting of multiple read-locks. When a processor unlocks a read-lock and the processor is not the sole lock owner, the list is fixed up similar to deleting a node from a doubly-linked list. Note that the unlocking processor is allowed to continue its computation immediately, and does not have to wait for the unlock operation to be performed globally.

Replacing a cache line that is part of a linked-list may result in breaking the list. The most simple and straightforward solution is to disallow replacement of such cache lines. This solution would require the cache to be fully associatively mapped. Since such a mapping increases the hardware cost and introduces longer delays, this solution is unacceptable. Since a processor holds (or waits for) only a small number of locks at a time, a small separate fully-associative cache for lock variables would be an efficient method to eliminate this restriction. Limited size of the lock cache can be considered as a typical resource management problem, and should be handled as such. The lock cache is a "hardware resource" that can be judiciously used by the system software. Mapping of software locks to hardware locks is a compile time decision that can be made conservatively to ensure that there never will be the case that a hardware lock request cannot be satisfied.

With respect to the buffered consistency model, read-lock and write-lock are NP-Synch class of operations, while unlock is a CP-Synch class of operation. It is appropriate to mention a few usage notes for these primitives. When the size of the data structure to be governed by a lock fits within a memory block, acquiring the lock brings the associated data structure to the requesting processor. If the data structure spans several memory blocks, it is the responsibility of the compiler to associate locks and regulate accesses to the shared data structure. The compiler is also responsible to ensure that multiple lock variables are not allocated to the same memory block. The scheme does not prevent colocating normal read/write data with a lock variable in the same memory block.

5 Performance Implications

Given the issues raised in Section 3, and the architectural features presented in Section 4 there is an interplay of hardware and software that makes the performance evaluation task quite arduous. In this section, we take a first cut at this task. Our preliminary study has two parts: The first part deals with evaluating the advantage of providing synchronization operations in hardware as opposed to simulating them in software. This evaluation is done by both analytical means as well as simulation. Analytical expressions for the cost in terms of time and network messages are developed for implementing standard synchronization scenarios using our primitives and a write-invalidation (WBI) approach. The second part deals with evaluating the performance advantage of buffered consistency as opposed to sequential consistency for processing a memory reference stream. This evaluation is done using simulation. Simulation of a large-scale system at the level of detail needed to evaluate the proposed primitives is a complex task worthy of exposition in its own right. Moreover, such large simulations take considerable computation time.

5.1 Analytical Results

The overhead in executing various synchronization

---

[3]There are several subtle details that are intentionally elided due to space constraints. Detailed algorithms for maintaining the queue can be found in [14]

synchronization operation	WBI		CBL	
	messages	time	messages	time
parallel lock	$6n^2 + 4n$	$nt_{cs} + 10nt_{nw} + n(n+1)/2t_m + 5n(5n-1)/2t_D$	$6n - 3$	$nt_{cs} + (2n+1)t_{nw} + (n+1)t_D + t_m$
serial lock	8	$8t_{nw} + 5t_D + t_m + t_{cs}$	3	$3t_{nw} + t_D + t_{cs}$
barrier request	18	$18t_{nw} + 12t_D$	2	$2(t_{nw} + t_m)$
barrier notify	$5n - 3$	$4t_{nw} + (2n-1)t_D$	n	$2t_{nw} + (n-1)t_D$

Table 3: Cost for executing synchronization scenarios with different cache schemes. Costs for serial lock and barrier request are for one processor.

scenarios are presented in Table 3: n is the number of processors, t_{nw} is the network transit time, t_{cs} is the time inside the critical section, t_D is the time to check the central directory or the cache directory, and t_m is the time for reading a memory block from the main memory. *Parallel lock* is the case when n processors request the same lock simultaneously. *Serial lock* is the other extreme case when all the lock requests occur serially. *Barrier request* is an operation executed by each processor participating in the barrier synchronization while *barrier notify* is an operation executed by the last processor to arrive at the barrier. Note that for a large amount of lock contention (parallel lock) the time and message complexity of our scheme is $O(n)$ while it is $O(n^2)$ for the WBI scheme. Detailed derivation of these cost functions can be found in [15].

5.2 Simulation Results

A new workload model (*work-queue* model), is used in our simulation studies. This model represents a dynamic scheduling paradigm believed to be the kernel of several parallel programs [19]. The basic granularity is a task. A large problem is divided into atomic tasks, and dependencies between tasks are checked. Tasks are inserted into a work queue of executable tasks honoring such dependencies, thus making the work queue non-FIFO in nature. Each processor takes a task from the queue and processes it. If a new task is generated as

Parameters	value
ratio of shared accesses	$0.03, 0.5*$
number of shared blocks	32
cache hit-ratio	0.95
read ratio	0.85
main memory cycle time	4 cache cycles
block size	4 words
cache size	1024 blocks
lock ratio	50%

* 0.03: task execution, 0.5: queue access

Table 4: Summary of parameters used in simulation

a result of the processing, it is inserted into the queue. All the processors execute the same code until the task queue is empty or a predefined finishing condition is met. If there is a need to synchronize all the processors at some point, then a barrier operation is used. In the simulation, the memory modules are distributed among the nodes in the multiprocessor, and the nodes are interconnected via a multistage Ω network with two-way switches. It is assumed that each switching element in the network has infinite buffer capacity. The size of the write buffer is also assumed to be infinite.

To simulate the memory reference pattern of each processor during task execution, a probabilistic model (*sync model*) similar to the one developed by Archibald and Baer [2] is incorporated into our model. Additional features in our model are synchronization primitives, differentiation of synchronization variables from other variables, and different evaluation metrics. The values of the parameters used in the simulation are summarized in Table 4. Another important parameter is the grain size of parallelism. The grain size is decided by the number of data memory references during the execution of a task. The performance metric used is completion time measured in machine cycles. Though processor utilization is measured in [2], synchronization activities may keep the processor busy without performing any useful computation.

The Figures 4 - 7 present simulation results for two different workload models. The lines with the prefix Q denote the results for the work-queue workload model, and the other lines denote the results for the sync workload model. Figures 4 and 5 show the completion time of the WBI scheme and the CBL scheme. WBI denotes the write back invalidation cache scheme. The performance of the WBI scheme with the exponential backoff for acquiring mutual exclusion is also presented (Q-backoff). These tests do not employ buffered consistency. Figure 4 shows that the WBI scheme does not scale well for the work-queue workload model above 16 nodes when the granularity of parallelism is medium-sized. Backoff method eliminates the severe performance loss but it also fails to scale to a large number of processors. The CBL scheme performs comparably with the WBI scheme for the sync workload model (two lines at the bottom). However, for the work-queue workload model, the CBL scheme shows much better performance for a large number of processors. Increasing the task granularity reduces the proportion of time spent in synchronization activity compared to the total computation time. For coarse granularity of parallelism (Figure 5), the WBI scheme shows improved scalability for the work-queue model but its performance degrades as the size of the system increases to more than 32 nodes. These two figures illustrate the effectiveness of implementing synchronization in hardware.

The performance gain due to the buffered consistency model depends on the usage of CP-Synch operations and global writes. In the simulation model, leaving a critical section and barrier synchronization are treated as CP-Synch operations; and writes to shared data are treated as global writes. Further, it is assumed that an unlock operation that follows a lock operation performs any write to the shared data secured by the lock operation globally before relinquishing the lock. The test performed here is a comparison of CBL with buffered consistency (BC-CBL) against CBL with sequential consistency (SC-CBL). The reason why only CBL is considered for the test is because the intent is to measure the performance potential of buffered consistency with respect to sequential consistency, without interference from specific cache coherence strategy. Figures 6 and 7 show the completion times of CBL with the two memory models for the work-queue workload. These results indicate that buffered consistency improves the performance for most tested cases, but the improvement is not very impressive. This can be explained by the fact that buffered consistency reduces memory latency for global writes which happen only with a probability of $sh \times write\_ratio$, i.e., 0.0045 in the tested workload.

6 Concluding Remarks

There are two visible trends in the evolution of multiprocessor architectures, namely, message-passing and shared memory. While the former is intrinsically more scalable than the latter, the latter fits the programming paradigm that is currently popular for developing large parallel applications. In this paper we have shed some light on the issues that affect the scalability of shared memory multiprocessors and have suggested architectural solutions that address these issues. The two main issues are latency for memory accesses and the network contention stemming from these accesses. Private coherent caches alleviate these problems, and their design is well-understood in small shared memory multiprocessor systems (up to about 16 processors). However, the memory model assumed by these designs and the protocols themselves limit their applicability to large-scale

shared memory multiprocessors. Further, such protocols introduce additional problems such as false sharing that hamper the performance potential of such architectures. A new memory model, buffered consistency, was developed in this paper that allows the processor to continue with its local computation without stalling for the completion of global updates. We also identified the hardware support needed for implementing buffered consistency. An important benefit of supporting the buffered consistency model is that false sharing is also eliminated. A new cache protocol based on reader-initiated coherence was proposed. We also extended our earlier work of providing synchronization support in hardware to large-scale shared memory multiprocessors. We feel that the machine architecture we have proposed in this paper has the right blend of features for scaling to large numbers of processors.

In general, evaluation of architectural features is an arduous task. Especially, in our architecture we have identified a division of responsibility between the hardware and the software. This division coupled with the choice of primitives leads to a complex interplay making performance evaluation that much more difficult. We have made some initial attempts at performance evaluation through analytical means and simulation and have presented the results. There are several directions for extending our work. Evaluating the performance advantages of eliminating false sharing, and reader-initiated coherence are important and are being currently pursued. Trace-driven simulation is another alternative to probabilistic simulation and is also being investigated. Our architecture provides a range of primitives for use by the compiler. Investigating compilation techniques, and/or programming language extensions that exploit these primitives are also part of our future research.

References

[1] S. V. Adve and M. D. Hill. Weak ordering - a new definition. In *Proceedings of the 17th Annual International Symposium on Computer Architecture*, pages 2–11, May 1990.

[2] J. Archibald and J. Baer. Cache coherence protocols: evaluation using a multiprocessor model. *ACM Transactions on Computer Systems*, pages 278–298, Nov. 1986.

[3] D. Chaiken, C. Fields, K. Kurihara, and A. Agarwal. Directory-based cache coherence in large-scale multiprocessors. *IEEE Computer*, pages 49–58, June 1990.

[4] K. Characharloo, D. Lenoski, J. Laudon, and A. Gupta. Memory consistency and event ordering

in scalable shared-memory multiprocessors. Technical Report CSL-TR-89-405, Stanford University, Computer Systems Laboratory, Nov. 1989.

[5] D. A. Cheriton, H. A. Goosen, and P. D. Boyle. Multi-level shared caching techniques for scalability in VMP-MC. In *Proceedings of the 16th Annual International Symposium on Computer Architecture*, pages 16–24, June 1989.

[6] R. Cytron, S. Marlovsky, and K. P. McAuliffe. Automatic management of programmable caches. In *Proceedings of the 1988 International Conference on Parallel Processing*, pages 229–238, 1988.

[7] M. Dubois, C. Scheurich, and F. Briggs. Memory access buffering in multiprocessors. In *Proceedings of the 13th Annual International Symposium on Computer Architecture*, pages 434–442, June 1986.

[8] J. Edler, A. Gottlieb, Cl. P. Kruskal, K. P. McAuliffe, L. Rudolph, M. Snir, P. J. Telen, and J. Wilson. Issues related to MIMD shared-memory computers : the NYU Ultracomputer approach. In *Proceedings of the 12th Annual International Symposium on Computer Architecture*, pages 126–135, June 1985.

[9] S. J. Eggers and R. H. Katz. A characterization of sharing in parallel programs and its application to coherency protocol evaluation. In *Proceedings of the 15th Annual International Symposium on Computer Architecture*, pages 373–382, June 1988.

[10] J. R. Goodman, M. K. Vernon, and P. J. Woest. Efficient synchronization primitives for large-scale cache-coherent multiprocessor. Technical Report TR-814, Univ. of Wisconsin at Madison, Jan. 1989.

[11] Mark D. Hill and James R. Larus. Cache consideration for multiprocessor programmers. *Communication of ACM*, 33(8):97–102, August 1990.

[12] L. Lamport. How to make a multiprocessor computer that correctly executes multiprocess programs. *IEEE Transactions on Computers*, C-28(9):690–691, September 1979.

[13] J. Lee and U. Ramachandran. Synchronization with multiprocessor caches. In *Proceedings of the 17th Annual International Symposium on Computer Architecture*, pages 27–37, May 1990.

[14] Joonwon Lee. *Architectural Features for Scalable Shared Memory Multiprocessors*. PhD thesis, College of Computing, Georgia Institute of Technology, 1991.

[15] Joonwon Lee and Umakishore Ramachandran. Architectural primitives for a scalable shared memory multiprocessor. Technical Report GIT-CC-91/10, College of Computing, Georgia Institute of Technology, 1991.

[16] K. Li and R. Schaefer. Shiva: An operation system transforming a hypercube into a shared-memory machine. Technical Report 217-89, Computer Science Dept., Princeton University, 1989.

[17] E. McCreight. *The Dragon Computer System: An early overview*. Xerox Corp., Sept. 1984.

[18] G. F. Pfister and V. A. Norton. Hotspot contention and combining in multistage interconnection network. *IEEE Transactions on Computers*, C-34(10), Oct. 1985.

[19] C. D. Polychronopoulos. *Parallel Programming and Compilers*, pages 113–158. Kluwer Academic Publishers, 1988.

[20] L. Rudolph and A. Segall. Dynamic decentralized cache schemes for MIMD parallel processors. In *Proceedings of the 11th Annual International Symposium on Computer Architecture*, pages 340–347, June 1984.

[21] C. Scheurich and M. Dubois. Correct memory operation of cache-based multiprocessors. In *Proceedings of the 14th Annual International Symposium on Computer Architecture*, pages 234–243, June. 1987.

[22] Charles L. Seitz. The cosmic cube. *CACM*, 28, January 1985.

[23] G. S. Sohi, J. E. Smith, and J. R. Goodman. Restricted fetch-and-ϕ operations for parallel processing. In *International Conference on Supercomputing*, June 1989. Crete, Greece.

[24] Per Stenstrom. A survey of cache coherence schemes for multiprocessors. *IEEE Computer*, 23(6):12–25, June 1990.

[25] C. P. Thacker and L. C. Stewart. Firefly: A multiprocessor workstation. In *Proceedings of the Second International Conference on Architectural Support for Programming Languages and Operating Systems*, pages 164–172, Oct. 1987.

[26] Josep Torrellas and John Hennessy. Estimating the performance advantages of relaxing consistency in a shared memory multiprocessor. In *Proceedings of the 1990 International Conference on Parallel Processing*, pages I:26–33, 1990.

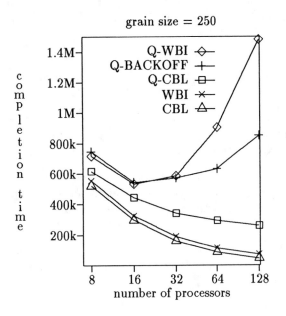

Figure 4: Performance of cache schemes with medium-granularity parallelism

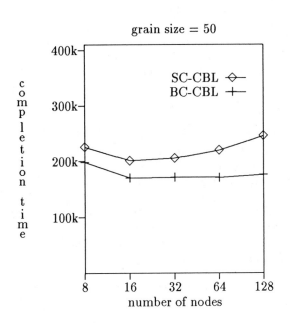

Figure 6: Performance implication of the buffered consistency model for fine-granularity parallelism

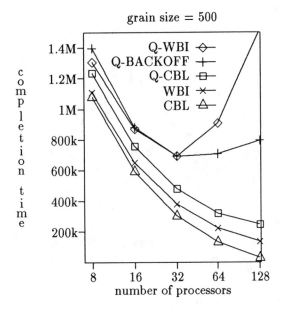

Figure 5: Performance of cache schemes with coarse-granularity parallelism

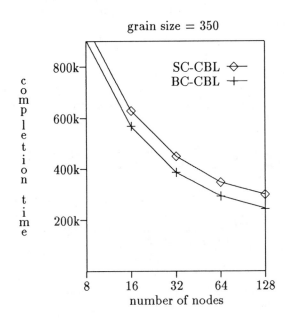

Figure 7: Performance implication of the buffered consistency model for medium-granularity parallelism

Architectural Mechanisms to Support
Three-Dimensional Lattice Gas Simulations

Fung F. Lee   Michael J. Flynn
Computer Systems Laboratory
Stanford University, CA 94305

Abstract

The search for efficient methods of computer simulation of fluid motion is a very important and difficult problem. The lattice gas method has recently emerged as a promising discrete particle simulation method well suited to parallel processing. Application-specific computers can deliver performance a thousand times that of existing supercomputers.

A very high-performance scalable multiprocessor architecture, called ALGE, is proposed for the simulation of a realistic three-dimensional lattice gas model. Several new architectural mechanisms are introduced to resolve various issues of computation and communication in the application context. The synergy of these mechanisms results in 100% utilization of all the processors during the main computation loop; hence true linear speedup is achieved. A 1000-processor configuration of ALGE is expected to deliver over 20 billion node updates per second (NUPS), about 600 times the performance of CRAY-2. A prototype of the key processing element has been implemented.

1   Introduction

High performance computing has become a vital enabling force in the conduct of science and engineering research and development. In particular, simulations based on computational fluid dynamics are less costly and much faster than complex wind tunnel tests. In the past few years, the lattice gas method [4] has emerged as an attractive, robust and promising discrete particle simulation method for fluid flow simulations with complicated boundary conditions, that are difficult or impossible to solve with other methods.

The core computation of a lattice gas model is inherently suitable for execution on scalable parallel computing systems, but requires *no* floating point operations. Much more computing power is needed to solve large scale simulation problems. It is believed that simple and practical application-specific computers can achieve performance orders of magnitude higher than existing "general-purpose" supercomputers, that invariably focus on floating point operations. This belief has been confirmed in the case of two-dimensional simulation, but not in the case of three-dimensional simulation, which is much more important and challenging.

All existing special-purpose lattice gas computers such as CAM-6 [12], RAP1, RAP2 [1], and LGM-1 [7], deal with two-dimensional lattice gas models. Until today, only one other design, CAM-8 [10], proposed by Margolus and Toffoli, attempts to deal with three-dimensional models, but this proposal is limited to 16 or fewer state bits per lattice node. Yet we need to simulate models with 24 bits or more per node in order to achieve realistic results in studying complex phenomena such as turbulent flow [3]. ALGE is the first special-purpose machine proposed to tackle a realistic 3-D lattice gas model.

Conceptually, the core computation of a lattice gas simulation consists of updating the values of all lattice nodes by executing many repetitions of two alternating steps: *collision* and *propagation*. What is preventing the design of a practical large scale parallel lattice gas machine which can handle 24-bit models is that all existing and previously proposed machines use the table lookup approach, that would require a huge lookup table of size at least 384 Mbits (24×2^{24} bits) to compute the collision functions. We have discovered and reported [8, 9] how the underlying symmetry group of a lattice gas model can be exploited to derive compact and high performance single-chip processors to handle a class of collision functions. One of the key concepts behind these architectures is the permutation group representation of the symmetry group of the lattice. The basic techniques can be generalized to handle all

© 1991 ACM 089791-438-4/91/0007/0115 $1.50

allowable collision functions.

With the knowledge that a single chip high performance implementation of a collision function is feasible, we proceed to tackle the system design issues. Implementations [2] of the particle propagation step of a lattice gas model on today's word-addressable computers invariably involve masking, shifting and copying of memory words, given any reasonable data organizations to store the states of the lattice nodes. This kind of data manipulation is relatively time-consuming, given the simple nature of particle propagation, and therefore that of data movement. Can the implementation of propagation be faster on dedicated machines? Whether or not to use buffers is an important issue. Previous architectures such as CAM-6 and LGM-1 use *line buffers* of *fixed* line sizes so that propagation is *implicit* when bits are extracted from nodes in a small neighborhood. The RAP family again use line buffers of fixed sizes matched with special purpose memory — video RAM — chips used to store the states. Adaptation of these techniques to three-dimensional models may lead to the use of *plane buffers* of fixed plane sizes, which would be very large (tens of millions of shift registers) for large problems. Moreover, this kind of buffering strategy, common in some image processing applications, is more or less restricted to a small hardwired neighborhood.

A careful examination of the propagation equation reveals that the bits representing particles in principle do not have to be moved at all in physical memory because of relativity of motion if the particles are observed in the "right" frames of reference. Intuition suggests that, if data do not move physically, then address pointers have to be somehow manipulated to compensate. The number of *bit address pointers* needed is equal to the number of bits per state. Propagation becomes *implicit* and takes zero time when different state bits of a node are addressed by their corresponding address pointers, related to the *rest* frame of reference by *Galilean transformation*. In a distributed memory system, interprocessor communication is a natural consequence of propagation. Therefore, it is expected that interprocessor communication mechanisms are strongly related to addressing mechanisms.

Inspired in part by the conceptual design of CAM-8, we show how a simple and fast memory address translation mechanism, *virtual move*, and a simple and flexible interprocessor communication mechanism can be mathematically derived from the problem definition by using coordinate transformations. These mechanisms are synchronous and require no buffers. A new arithmetic unit, *multi-dimensional modulo adder*, is proposed as the key hardware element in the control unit of our machine: sum bits constitute the translated address; selected carry bits serve as the control lines of the communication switches. The new adder can be easily implemented by slightly modifying a conventional adder, such as a carry lookahead adder. Virtual move implemented with multi-dimensional modulo adders allows variable lengths in each dimension of the lattice space, and a much more flexible neighborhood, which are not possible in previous architectures using buffering strategies.

Pipelining is a common technique to increase system throughput. In general, pipelines are designed with at most one memory access per cycle, and performance is affected by the number of pipeline stages. We propose a robust delay-tolerant pipeline mechanism to sustain the full utilization of the processing elements with a two-way interleaved memory system. The pipeline scheme is delay-tolerant in the sense that it allows one memory read and one memory write per cycle regardless of the number of intervening pipeline stages by appropriately swapping the memory bank pointers if necessary. Because of this robustness, the theoretical peak performance, one node update per cycle per processor, can be achieved even on relatively slow processing elements with deep pipelines.

With CMOS processing units capable of 20 million node updates per second (NUPS), a computing engine consisting of 1000 such units supporting the above proposed mechanisms can achieve over 20 billion NUPS, as this machine is truly scalable. This is about 600 times CRAY-2's performance of approximately 30 million NUPS [11].

2 Lattice Gas Computation

In a lattice gas model, space and time are discretized. Time is divided into a sequence of equal time steps, at which particles reside only at the nodes of the lattice. The evolution consists of two alternating phases: (i) *propagation*: during one time step, each particle moves from one node to another along a link of the lattice according to its velocity; (ii) *collision*: at the end of a time step, particles arriving at a given node collide and instantaneously acquire new velocities. The properties of the lattice not only govern the propagation phase, but also significantly constrain the collision phase, because the *collision rules* must have the same symmetries as the lattice [5].

The *state* of a node can be denoted by the bit vector $\mathbf{b} = (b_1, \ldots, b_n)$, where $b_i = 1$ if a particle with the corresponding velocity $\mathbf{v}^i$ is present [1], and $b_i = 0$ otherwise. Let $\mathbf{b}(\mathbf{x}, t)$, and $\mathbf{b}'(\mathbf{x}, t)$ be the states of

---

[1]In this paper, Roman and Greek indices refer respectively to labels and components.

the node at position **x** and time t before and after the collision respectively. The collision phase specifies that, for all **x** and t,

$$\mathbf{b}'(\mathbf{x}, t) = \mathcal{C}(\mathbf{b}(\mathbf{x}, t)) \tag{1}$$

where $\mathcal{C}$ is a deterministic or non-deterministic n-input n-output boolean collision function. The propagation phase specifies that, for all **x** and t,

$$b_i(\mathbf{x} + \mathbf{v}^i, t + 1) = b_i'(\mathbf{x}, t) \tag{2}$$

An obstacle such as a plate, a wedge or an airplane wing is decomposed into a series of continuous links which approximate its geometrical shape. At nodes which represent an obstacle, particles are either bounced back or undergo specular reflection. This can be handled by adding one or more obstacle bits to the state of a node and adjust the collision function appropriately.

Before simulation, the states of the nodes are initialized according to the initial distribution of particle densities and velocities. After simulation, nodes within a volume of tens of nodes on each side are averaged to compute the macroscopic density and momentum.

There are two types of boundary conditions on the lattice edges we are concerned with. The first type is the *periodic boundary condition*: the particles exiting from one edge are reinjected into the other edge in the same direction. The second type, related to a wind-tunnel experiment, consists in providing a flux of fresh particles on one side of the lattice and allowing an output flux on the other side. In this paper, we focus on the first type of boundary condition, because it is basic: it requires no special treatment for nodes on the *edges*, as there are no edges in a wraparound lattice space. The second type can be dealt with as a simple extension.

2.1 Three-Dimensional Models

The particular lattice we are most interested in is the FCHC lattice used in three dimensional simulations [5, 11]. A FCHC (face-centered hypercubic) lattice consists of those nodes, which are the points with signed integer coordinates $(x_1, x_2, x_3, x_4) = \mathbf{x}$ such that the sum $x_1 + x_2 + x_3 + x_4$ is even. Each node **x** is linked to its 24 nearest neighbors **x**' such that the vector **x**' − **x** corresponds to one of the following 24 values:

$$(\pm 1, \pm 1, 0, 0), \quad (\pm 1, 0, \pm 1, 0), \quad (\pm 1, 0, 0, \pm 1),$$
$$(0, \pm 1, \pm 1, 0), \quad (0, \pm 1, 0, \pm 1), \quad (0, 0, \pm 1, \pm 1). \tag{3}$$

These 24 nearest neighbors form a regular polytope. With time steps normalized to 1, the vectors in (3) are

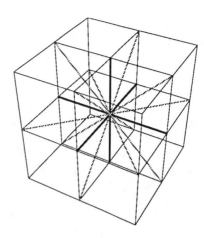

Figure 1: The pseudo-four-dimensional FCHC model. Only the neighbors of one node are shown as connected.

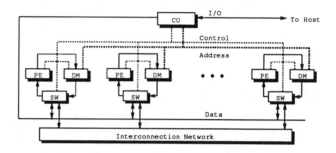

Figure 2: The overall architecture of the array processor

also the 24 possible velocities of the particles arriving at a node or leaving it.

The pseudo four-dimensional FCHC model is derived by projecting the four-dimensional FCHC lattice to three dimension so that the fourth dimension has a periodicity of 1. Each node of a regular cubic lattice is a node in the model. Figure 1 shows the neighborhood of a node: along the gray links, connecting to 12 neighbors, at most one particle can propagate, with component $v_4 = 0$; along the thick black links, connecting to 6 neighbors, up to two particles can propagate, with components $v_4 = \pm 1$.

3 Architectural Mechanisms

3.1 General Organization

The machine is organized as an array processor, serving as a special purpose high performance computing engine to a host computer. The host computer downloads the problem (data) into the engine and offloads the engine-produced solution. The host provides the user interface to the computing engine and performs the pre-processing and post-processing phases of the simulation.

The machine consists of three types of elements: the control unit, the processing units, and the interconnection network (see Figure 2). A large number of processing units are anticipated; a reasonably sized configuration might contain from 10 to 10000 processors. Each processing unit (PU) is identical; it contains its own processing element (PE), data memory (DM) and switch (SW). All the PEs perform the same function synchronously under the control of the control unit (CU). The identity of a PU is loaded in its SW, which may route data differently according to the location of the PU in relation to the interconnection network. The interconnection network may be any D_s-dimensional toroid, because the array can be expanded in any one or more of the D_s dimensions. For three-dimensional simulations, there is really no gain in going beyond $D_s = 3$. For practical reasons, we are particularly interested in 1-D rings and 2-D toroids.

3.2 Collision Rule Processor

The properties of a lattice not only govern the propagation phase, but also significantly constrain the collision phase, because the *collision rules* must have the same symmetry as the lattice [5]. How the underlying symmetry group of a lattice gas model can be exploited to derive compact and high performance processing elements to handle collision functions of potentially exponential complexities ($O(n2^n)$) was posed as a major challenge in this area of research (see the Preface of [4]). The FCHC isometric model proposed by Hénon [6] was the first real 24-bit three-dimensional model with a detailed specification of an optimized non-deterministic collision function. Therefore, it was chosen as our first case study. A VLSI architecture for the FCHC isometric model has been designed and implemented as an ASIC. We have shown that a 4000 gate chip can replace the equivalent of 4.5 billion bits (rather than 384 million bits due to non-determinism) of a lookup table used to solve this problem. Because the architecture is derived by considering the symmetry properties rather than by brute force logic synthesis, it can be generalized to other classes of lattice gas models. We present the main ideas in this paper. (Please see [8, 9] for more details).

Hénon's isometric algorithm [6] shows how the output state of a node is computed as a non-deterministic function of the input state:

1. Compute the momentum of the input state

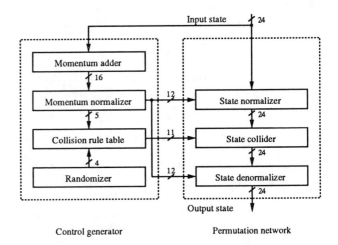

Figure 3: A processor architecture for the FCHC isometric model

2. Normalization: Apply the appropriate isometries (symmetry transformations) to the input state and the momentum, so that the momentum is *normalized*.

3. Collision: Choose at random one of the optimal isometries of the class to which the normalized momentum belongs, and apply this isometry.

4. Denormalization: Apply the isometries applied in step 2 in reverse order to obtain the output state.

The application of an isometry to a state is the most frequent and important operation. An efficient implementation of this operation is thus most crucial. Cayley's theorem states that every group is isomorphic to a permutation group, hence it is not too surprising that conditional application of isometries can be implemented as conditional permutations, which in turn map to simple multiplexers. In essence, the algorithm can be viewed as a description of how to generate the right control signals to permute the input state bits.

The hardware organization (Figure 3) of the first prototype collision rule processor follows classical lines: the *control path* consisting of a momentum adder, a momentum normalizer, a small collision rule table, and a randomizer; the *data path* is a conditional permutation network composed of a state normalizer, a state collider and a denormalizer (inverse-normalizer). The overall feed-forward character of this processor makes it easy to design a *highly pipelined* version with a proportional increase in throughput.

A CMOS field programmable gate array implementation of the processor with a non-pipelined latency of

460 ns has been completed. We are currently looking at a CMOS gate array implementation with an estimated non-pipelined latency below 50 ns. A collision processor capable of 20 NUPS or more is clearly feasible.

3.3 Addressing Generation

Although the FCHC models are our major concerns, the mechanisms described below apply to a larger class of models with other possible velocities. The following section is written with general notations so as to be valid for any D-dimensional space and arbitrary velocity.

3.3.1 Virtual Move

The propagation equation (2) seems to suggest that at every time step, state bits of all the nodes have to be moved. However, a closer examination reveals that the equation actually represents an invariant relationship. If we choose to observe in a *frame of reference* moving at the velocity $\mathbf{v}^i$ with respect to the *rest* frame of the lattice, the particles with velocity $\mathbf{v}^i$ are obviously stationary! Hence, there is no need to actually *move* the bits in memory, as long as we keep track of the *Galilean transformation*. The coordinates $\mathbf{x}^i$ of the moving frame is related to the rest coordinates $\mathbf{x}$ by the transformation:

$$\mathbf{x}^i = \mathbf{x} - \mathbf{v}^i t \qquad (4)$$

Suppose the space-time point $(\mathbf{x}, t)$ corresponds to $(\mathbf{x}^i, t)$, then the point $(\mathbf{x} + \mathbf{v}^i, t+1)$ corresponds to $((\mathbf{x}+\mathbf{v}^i) - \mathbf{v}^i(t+1), t+1) = (\mathbf{x}-\mathbf{v}^i t, t+1) = (\mathbf{x}^i, t+1)$. Hence, (1) and (2) can be written as

$$\mathbf{b}'(\mathbf{x}^i, t) = \mathcal{C}(\mathbf{b}(\mathbf{x}^i, t)) \qquad (5)$$
$$b_i(\mathbf{x}^i, t+1) = b_i'(\mathbf{x}^i, t) \qquad (6)$$

If we interpret $\mathbf{x}^i$ as the *physical address* used to address memory module i, then $\mathbf{x}$ can be treated as the *virtual address*. Equation (6) says that we do not have to move the bits at all in the propagation phase. We refer to this technique as *virtual move*. The cost of implementing virtual move is to have a slightly more complicated address generation scheme. For each *virtual address* $\mathbf{x}$, we need to generate n *physical addresses*, $\mathbf{x}^i$ ($i = 1, \ldots, n$) according to (4).

3.3.2 Multi-dimensional Modulo Adder

The transformation (4) requires D modulo subtractions for each $\mathbf{v}^i$. How can one proceed to implement the address generators in hardware?

Suppose we have a wrap-around lattice space of dimension D, implied by the basic type of periodic boundary condition (see section 2). Equation (4) can be written as

$$
\begin{aligned}
x_\alpha^i &= (x_\alpha - v_\alpha^i t) \bmod n_\alpha \quad (\alpha = 1, \ldots, D) \\
&= (x_\alpha + (-v_\alpha^i t \bmod n_\alpha)) \bmod n_\alpha \\
&= (x_\alpha + d_\alpha^i(t)) \bmod n_\alpha \qquad (7)
\end{aligned}
$$

where n_α is the length of x_α-dimension, and

$$d_\alpha^i(t) = -v_\alpha^i t \bmod n_\alpha \qquad (8)$$

Note that d_α^i has to be recomputed only once per time step by addition:

$$d_\alpha^i(t+1) = (d_\alpha^i(t) + (-v_\alpha^i \bmod n_\alpha)) \bmod n_\alpha \qquad (9)$$

In order to use conventional RAM, we need to map $\mathbf{x}$ ($\mathbf{x}^i$) to a linear address. We choose the conventional one-to-one mapping

$$
\begin{aligned}
A : \{0, 1, \ldots, n_1\} \times \{0, 1, \ldots, n_2\} \times \{0, 1, \ldots, n_D - 1\} \\
\mapsto \{0, 1, \ldots, n_1 n_2 \cdots n_D - 1\}
\end{aligned}
$$

such that

$$
\begin{aligned}
A(\mathbf{x}) &= A((x_1, x_2, \ldots, x_D)) \\
&= x_1 + x_2 n_1 + \ldots + x_D \prod_{\alpha=1}^{D-1} n_\alpha \qquad (10)
\end{aligned}
$$

Assume that all n_α's are powers of 2, such that $m_\alpha = \log_2 n_\alpha$ and $\sum_{\alpha=1}^{D} m_\alpha = m$. The mapping A can then be performed trivially by concatenating the binary representations of $\mathbf{x}$ such that $x_{\alpha+1}$ is on the left of x_α. Similarly, we can obtain the linear address of d^i. Let $a = A(\mathbf{x})$, and $b = A(d^i)$, and define e as

$$e_j = \begin{cases} 0 & \text{if } j = \sum_{\kappa=1}^{\alpha} m_\kappa \text{ for some } \alpha \in [0, D-1] \\ 1 & \text{otherwise} \end{cases}$$
$$(11)$$

The purpose of e is to mark the boundary bits of dimensions so that *carry-out* from lower dimensions would not be propagated to higher dimensions. The value of e does not change during a simulation.

We can calculate all D components of $\mathbf{x}^i$ according to (7) in one step by using a *multi-dimensional modulo adder*, which takes three m-bit inputs, a, b, and e, and computes the sum as $s = A(\mathbf{x}^i)$ (see Figure 4). The adder can be built according to the new definitions of p_i, propagate, and s_i, sum:

$$p_i = (a_i \vee b_i) e_i \qquad (12)$$
$$s_i = a_i \oplus b_i \oplus c_i e_i \qquad (13)$$

119

bit position

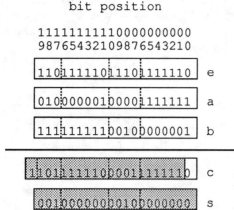

Figure 4: Operation of a multi-dimensional modulo adder. Bits in white areas are inputs; bits in shaded areas are outputs.

and our usual definitions of g_i, generate, and c_i, carry:

$$g_i = a_i b_i \qquad (14)$$
$$c_0 = 0 \qquad (15)$$
$$c_{i+1} = g_i \vee p_i c_i \qquad (16)$$

Hence, this modified adder can be implemented in various ways, such as ripple carry adder, carry lookahead adder, or carry select adder, as it deems appropriate for the system requirement and implementation technology.

3.4 Synchronous Communication

3.4.1 Global and Local Coordinates

In a multiprocessor configuration, updating nodes at the *boundary* requires reading values from neighboring PUs. We want to know when and how to select data bits from which neighbors and the PU itself.

According to (2), we know where the neighboring nodes are in the problem space:

$$b_i(\mathbf{x}, t+1) = b_i'(\mathbf{x} - \mathbf{v}^i, t) \qquad (17)$$

Let us define 3 coordinate systems, namely, the *global*, *processor*, and *local* coordinates such that they satisfy the following relationship:

$$\mathbf{x}^{\mathbf{G}} = \mathbf{P}\mathbf{x}^{\mathbf{P}} + \mathbf{x}^{\mathbf{L}} \qquad (18)$$

where $\mathbf{P}$ is a diagonal matrix with $p_{\alpha\alpha} = n_\alpha$, and the following conditions are satisfied:

$$0 \leq x_\alpha^L < n_\alpha, \quad 0 \leq x_\alpha^P < p_\alpha, \quad 0 \leq x_\alpha^G < n_\alpha p_\alpha \qquad (19)$$

Table 1: Cases of bound

v_α^i	x_α^L	bound$(0, x_\alpha^L - v_\alpha^i, n_\alpha)$
0	$[0, n_\alpha - 1]$	0
> 0	$[0, v_\alpha^i - 1]$	-1
	$[v_\alpha^i, n_\alpha - 1]$	0
< 0	$[0, n_\alpha - |v_\alpha^i| - 1]$	0
	$[n_\alpha - |v_\alpha^i|, n_\alpha - 1]$	1

Alternatively, we can write for any α

$$x_\alpha^G \bmod n_\alpha p_\alpha = n_\alpha(x_\alpha^P \bmod p_\alpha) + x_\alpha^L \bmod n_\alpha \qquad (20)$$

Then we can show that for any α,

$$
\begin{aligned}
& (x_\alpha^G - v_\alpha^i) \bmod n_\alpha p_\alpha \\
= \; & n_\alpha((x_\alpha^P + \text{bound}(0, x_\alpha^L - v_\alpha^i, n_\alpha)) \bmod p_\alpha) \\
& + (x_\alpha^L - v_\alpha^i) \bmod n_\alpha
\end{aligned} \qquad (21)
$$

where bound is defined as

$$\text{bound}(L, k, U) = \begin{cases} -1 & \text{if } k < L \\ 0 & \text{if } L \leq k < U \\ 1 & \text{if } k \geq U \end{cases} \qquad (22)$$

For any given $\mathbf{v}^i$, bound$(0, x_\alpha - v_\alpha^i, n_\alpha)$ is either non-negative or non-positive. Hence, it is only necessary to distinguish whether the value is zero or non-zero. The various cases are shown in Table 1.

3.4.2 Communication Mechanisms

In equation (21), the processor coordinates determines the source module, and the local coordinates determine the bit within a module. Since the machine is synchronous, at any one time, all x_α^L have the same value for all PUs. This exactly matches the requirement implied by (21).

The size of the neighborhood (including itself) of a processing unit $\mathbf{x}^{\mathbf{P}}$ under $\mathbf{v}^i$ is given by

$$|\mathcal{N}(\mathbf{x}^{\mathbf{P}}, \mathbf{v}^i)| = 2^{\sum_{\alpha=1}^{D} |\text{sgn}(v_\alpha^i)| \bmod p_\alpha} \qquad (23)$$

The number of *control* wires used to select the multiplexer input lines for state bit i is given by

$$\sum_{\alpha=1}^{D} |\text{sgn}(v_\alpha^i)| \bmod p_\alpha \qquad (24)$$

We now show how the function bound can be computed as a *carry-out* of the multi-dimensional modulo adder. Let $a = A(\mathbf{x}^{\mathbf{L}})$, $d_\alpha^i = -v_\alpha^i$, and e as defined before, as the inputs to a multi-dimensional modulo

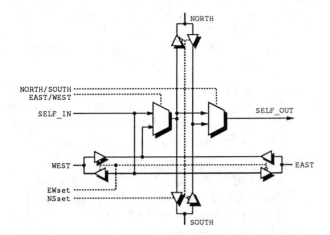

Figure 5: One of the n identical parts of a switch to be used in a two-dimensional toroid interconnection network

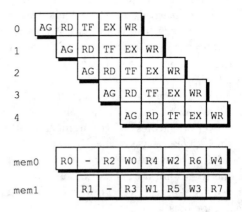

Figure 6: A 5-stage pipeline

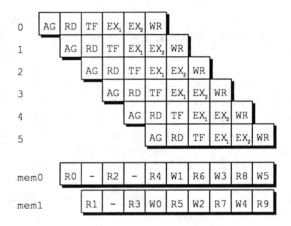

Figure 7: A 6-stage pipeline

adder, then for each α, $|\text{bound}(0, x_\alpha^L - v_\alpha^i, n_\alpha)|$ is exactly the carry-out bit which is to be blocked so that it will not flow across the dimension boundary. The mux select lines are the carry-outs c_j, where $j = \sum_{\kappa=1}^{\alpha} m_\kappa$, and $\alpha \in \{1, \ldots, D_s\}$, where D_s is the number of dimensions of the interconnection network. For practical reasons, we are most interested in the case when $D_s = 1, 2$.

Since in general, j is not fixed when the hardware is designed, we cannot just pull out the bits, instead, we may extract c_j by using some sorts of mask registers.

Figure 5 shows one of the n identical parts of a switch for use with a two-dimensional toroid interconnection network for a n-bit model. During initialization, the bi-directional buffers are configured so that the directions are fixed during simulation, and the number of input wires equal to that of output wires. The switch first routes in the east/west direction (either east or west as dictated by v_i) so that the multiplexer output goes to the north/south direction, and then uses a multiplexer again to select the output. In general, this scheme requires a maximum of $(2D_s + 2)n$ data wires, and $D_s n$ control wires for a n-bit model running on a machine with a D_s-dimensional toroid. However, for the FCHC model, we need only 72 data wires and 12 control wires with the 1-D ring interconnection, if we take into account of individual $\mathbf{v}^i$'s in (3).

3.5 Delay-tolerant Pipelining

Each node update operation can be implemented with five basic steps:

1. AG — address generation

2. RD — memory read

3. TF — data transfer between neighboring PUs

4. EX — collision rule execution

5. WR — memory write

The system is easily pipelined. Each of the steps above becomes a pipeline stage (Figure 6).

Exactly one memory read and one memory write is required every cycle. If one bank of memory can only support one read or write per cycle, then we need two banks of memory. One bank supports the even words, the other supports the odd words.

In Figure 6, there are two, a even number of stages between the RD and WR stages. Suppose for some reasons, the EX stage takes longer, and we decide to break it up into two stages, EX_1 and EX_2. Now there are three, a odd number of stages between the RD and WR stages. The memory interleave scheme in Figure 6

121

no longer works. It has to be modified slightly as in Figure 7. Note that words read from bank 0 are written to bank 1, and words read from bank 1 are written to bank 0. At the end of a time step when a complete scan of the node is performed, we swap the memory bank pointers, and start over again.

The pipeline scheme is delay-tolerant in the sense that it allows one memory read and one memory write per cycle regardless of the number of intervening pipeline stages between the RD and WR stages. Because of this robustness, the theoretical peak performance, one node update per cycle per processor, can be achieved even on relatively slow processing elements with deep pipelines.

4   Conclusions

We have proposed a set of new architectural mechanisms which can work together in a very high performance pipelined array processor dedicated to lattice gas simulation. The architecture is truly scalable in the sense that it achieves linear speedup for both fixed and increasing problem sizes with more processors. It is necessary and possible to take advantage of the special properties of the application and design application-specific computers that are a thousand times more powerful than existing supercomputers.

The major limitation of ALGE is memory bandwidth. This situation becomes more severe as the processing elements run faster and the clock cycle gets shorter.

Current work is going on to resolve finer issues of design and implementation toward building a prototype system.

5   Acknowledgements

This work was supported by NASA Ames Research Center under contract NAGW 419. We thank Martin Morf for his helpful discussions and suggestions.

References

[1] Andre Clouqueur and Dominique d'Humières. R.A.P., A Family of Cellular Automaton Machines for Fluid Dynamics. *Helvetica Physica Acta*, 62:525–541, 1989.

[2] Dominique d'Humières and Pierre Lallemand. Numerical Simulations of Hydrodynamics with Lattice Gas Automata in Two Dimensions. *Complex Systems*, 1(4):599–632, August 1987.

[3] K. Diemer, K. Hunt, S. Chen, T. Shimomura, and G.Doolen. Density and velocity dependence of reynolds numbers for several lattice gas models. *Lattice Gas Methods for Partial Differential Equations*, pages 137–177, 1990.

[4] Gray D. Doolen, editor. *Lattice Gas Methods for Partial Differential Equations*, volume IV of *Santa Fe Institute Studies in the Sciences of Complexity*. Addison-Wesley, 1990.

[5] Uriel Frisch, Dominique d'Humières, Brosl Hasslacher, Pierre Lallemand, Yves Pomeau, and Jean-Pierre Rivet. Lattice Gas Hydrodynamics in Two and Three Dimensions. *Complex Systems*, 1(4):649–707, 1987.

[6] Michel Hénon. Isometric Collision Rules for the Four-Dimensional FCHC Lattice Gas. *Complex Systems*, 1(3):475–494, June 1987.

[7] Steven D. Kugelmass. *Architectures for Two-Dimensional Lattice Computations with Linear Speedup*. PhD thesis, Princeton University, June 1988.

[8] Fung F. Lee, Michael J. Flynn, and Martin Morf. A VLSI Architecture for the FCHC Isometric Lattice Gas Model. Technical Report CSL-TR-90-426, Computer Systems Laboratory, Stanford University, April 1990.

[9] Fung F. Lee, Michael J. Flynn, and Martin Morf. Design of Compact High Performance Processing Elements for the FCHC Lattice Gas Models. *Proceedings of the Fifth SIAM Conference on Parallel Processing for Scientific Computing*, March 1991.

[10] Norman Margolus and Tommaso Toffoli. Cellular Automata Machines. *Lattice Gas Methods for Partial Differential Equations*, pages 219–249, 1990.

[11] Jean-Pierre Rivet, Michel Hénon, Uriel Frisch, and Dominique d'Humières. Simulating Fully Three-Dimensional External Flow by Lattice Gas Methods. *Proceedings of the Workshop on Discrete Kinetic Theory, Lattice Gas Dynamics and Foundations of Hydrodynamics*, pages 276–285, September 1988.

[12] Tommaso Toffoli and Norman Margolus. *Cellular Automata Machines – A New Environment for Modeling*. MIT Press, 1987.

Invited Speaker: Architecture

Burton Smith

Chairman and Chief Scientist
Tera Computer Company

"A Massively Parallel Shared Memory Computer"

SESSION 4

Coding Theory, Hypercube Embeddings, and Fault Tolerance[*]

Bill Aiello
Bellcore
Morristown, NJ 07960

Tom Leighton
Mathematics Department and
Laboratory for Computer Science
Massachusetts Institute of Technology
Cambridge, MA 02139

Abstract

In this paper, we devise a special 1-error-correcting code that enables us to embed the product graph $H_{N/\log N} \otimes K_{\log N}$ in an N-node hypercube H_N with constant load, dilation and congestion. We apply the result to construct improved embeddings of trees and other structures in a hypercube, and to design more efficient and robust algorithms for reconfiguring a hypercube around random or worst-case faults.

1 Introduction

In this paper, we show that the graph formed by taking the cross product of an $N/\log N$-node hypercube $H_{N/\log N}$ and a $\log N$-node complete graph $K_{\log N}$ can be embedded with constant load, dilation and congestion into an N-node hypercube H_N. As a consequence, we find that the hypercube has even stronger structural and algorithmic properties than previously realized.

It is easily seen that the product graph $P_N = H_{N/\log N} \otimes K_{\log N}$ contains the N-node hypercube H_N as a subgraph since $H_N = H_{N/\log n} \otimes H_{\log N}$. In other words, P_N can be formed from H_N by inserting an edge between any pair of nodes whose binary addresses differ only in the last $\log \log N$ bit positions.

The fact that P_N can be embedded in H_N with constant load, dilation and congestion is more surprising, however. Indeed, whereas $H_N = H_{N/\log N} \otimes H_{\log N}$ can be thought of as a hypercube of $\log N$-node hypercubes, $P_N = H_{N/\log N} \otimes K_{\log N}$ is essentially a hypercube of $\log N$-node cliques. And, of course, any constant-load embedding of $K_{\log N}$ into $H_{\log N}$ must have congestion at least $\Omega(\log N)$ and dilation

at least $\Omega(\log \log N)$.

Nevertheless, we show that it is still possible to construct a good embedding of P_N in H_N. The embedding is described in Section 2, and makes use of a special 1-error-correcting code in order to map the cliques of P_N to "stars" in H_N. Roughly speaking, a *star* consists of a node v whose binary address is a codeword together with its neighbors in the hypercube. The fact that hypercubes can be partitioned into stars corresponding to codewords is well-known, and has been exploited in many previous papers [1, 10, 12, 14]. It was not known how to use this fact to embed P_N in H_N, however. In fact, we need to devise a 1-error-correcting code with some special properties in order to guarantee that the embedding has constant dilation and congestion.

As a consequence of proving that P_N can be nicely embedded in H_N, we can resolve several problems concerning hypercubes. For example, an immediate corollary is the fact that a $\log N$-dilated N-node butterfly can be embedded in H_N with constant load, congestion and dilation. (A network is said to be *r-dilated* if every edge is replaced with r parallel edges.[1]) The $\log N$-dilated butterfly is itself a very useful network, particularly for applications involving packet routing [1, 11]. The best previously known embeddings of this network in H_N have dilation $\Omega(\log N)$ [1, 8] or congestion $\Omega(\log N)$.

The embedding of P_N in H_N can also be used to design improved algorithms for embedding trees in hypercubes. In particular, we improve the results of Bhatt, Chung, Leighton and Rosenberg [5], Bhatt and Greenberg [8], and Leighton, Newman, Ranade and Schwabe [12] by showing how to (off-line) embed any $\log N$-dilated M-node binary tree into H_N with $O(M/N + 1)$ load and $O(1)$ congestion and di-

---

[*]This research was supported by the Defense Advanced Research Projects Agency under Contracts N00014-87-K-825 and N00014-89-J-1988, the Air Force under Contract AFOSR-89-0271, and the Army under Contract DAAL-03-86-K-0171.

[1]Note that *r*-dilated and $O(r)$ dilation sound similar, but have very different meanings. An embedding has $O(r)$ dilation if every edge of the embedded graph is stretched across at most $O(r)$ edges by the embedding.

lation, and how to dynamically (on-line) embed any M-node binary tree in H_N with $O(M/N + 1)$ load, $O(M/N \log N + 1)$ congestion and $O(1)$ dilation. The best bounds previously known for embeddings of trees in hypercubes worked only for $M = O(N)$ and/or required greater edge congestion. In particular, the off-line embeddings of undilated trees in [5] require $M = O(N)$, the off-line embeddings of $\log N$-dilated trees in [8] require $M = O(N)$ and have $\Omega(\log \log N)$ congestion and dilation, and the on-line embeddings of trees in [12] have congestion $\Omega(M/N + 1)$. We also prove a general tree contraction lemma in Section 3 that may be of independent interest.

Lastly, we apply our technique to the problem of reconfiguring a hypercube around faults. Previously, Hastad, Leighton and Newman [10] showed that if each component of H_N fails independently with any constant probability $p < 1$, then the functioning parts of the hypercube can be reconfigured to simulate the original hypercube with constant slowdown. The reconfiguration algorithm of [10] is probabilistic and runs in polylogarithmic time. Baumslag [2] later determinized this algorithm, but at a cost of $O(N)$ in the embedding time. In Section 4, we show how to embed P_N in H_N with constant load, congestion and dilation even if the nodes and edges of H_N fail with some small constant probability $p \leq p_0$. The embedding algorithm is deterministic and uses $O(\log N)$ rounds of communication, thereby improving upon the performance of the previously known algorithms for the special case of hypercube reconfiguration.

The reconfiguration algorithm can also be made to work for any faulty hypercube containing up to $\log^{O(1)} N$ worst-case faults. Previously, Bruck, Cypher and Soroker [7] had shown that an N-node hypercube with $\log^{O(1)} N$ worst-case faults can implement certain restricted hypercube computations with constant slowdown. The best previous general simulation was by Becker and Simon [3] and Livingston, Stout, Graham and Harary [13], and can tolerate only $O(\log \log N)$ worst-case faults. We obtain the $\log^{O(1)} N$-fault bound by embedding $P_N^{(r)} = H_{N/\log^r N} \otimes K_{\log N}^r$ in the hypercube (for any constant r) and then proving that $P_N^{(r)}$ can tolerate $o(\log^r N)$ faults. We suspect that even greater numbers of worst-case faults can be tolerated, but have left further improvement on our $\log^{O(1)} N$-fault bound as an interesting subject for future research.

2 Embedding $H_{N/\log N} \otimes K_{\log N}$ into H_N

Let us fix the following notation. Given two graphs, $G = (V, E)$ and $G' = (V', E')$, define the product graph $G \otimes G'$ to have the vertex set which is the cartesian product of V and V' and to have the edge set

$$\{(\langle s, v' \rangle, \langle s, u' \rangle) | (v', u') \in E', s \in V\} \cup$$
$$\{(\langle v, s' \rangle, \langle u, s' \rangle) | (v, u) \in E, s' \in V'\}.$$

We will denote $G \otimes G$ as G^2.

Let $N = 2^n$. The N-node hypercube H_N is a network with vertex set $\{0, 1\}^n$. The edges of the network are between nodes whose labels differ by one bit. In what follows we will use the notation $v(j)$ to denote the jth bit of $v \in \{0, 1\}^n$. For $A \subset \{1, \ldots, n\}$ we define v^A to be the node such that $v^A(k) = \overline{v(k)}$ for $k \in A$ and $v^A(k) = v(k)$ for $k \notin A$. When A has small cardinality we will often omit its brackets, e.g., $v^{\{j\}}$ we be written as v^j, and denotes the node adjacent to v across the jth dimension of the hypercube. The hypercube edges are the set $\{(v, v^j)\}$ where $v \in \{0, 1\}^n$ and $j \in [1, \ldots, n]$. It is well known that $H_N = H_2^n$.

The complete graph on s vertices K_s has vertex set $\{1, \ldots, s\}$ and edge set $\{(i, j) | i \neq j, 1 \leq i, j \leq s\}$. Define the hypercube of cliques as the product graph $H_2^f \otimes K_s$ which we will abbreviate as $H^f K_s$ or $H_{2^f} K_s$. In the special case when $2^f = N/\log N$ and $s = \log N$, we obtain the product graph $P_N = H_{N/\log N} \otimes K_{\log N}$. The edges of $H^f K_s$ are the union of the "complete graph edges" $\{(\langle v, i \rangle, \langle v, j \rangle) | v \in \{0, 1\}^f, 1 \leq i \neq j \leq s\}$, and the "hypercube edges" $\{(\langle v, i \rangle, \langle v^j, i \rangle) | v \in \{0, 1\}^f, 1 \leq i \leq s, 1 \leq j \leq f\}$.

The main result of this section is an embedding of the hypercube of cliques $P_N = H_{N/\log N} \otimes K_{\log N}$ into a hypercube with the same number of nodes H_N. The embedding has constant congestion, constant dilation, and constant load. Hence, the hypercube H_N can simulate the product network P_N with a constant factor slowdown.

By virtue of the embedding, we know that the hypercube of cliques is no more powerful than the hypercube. Nonetheless, several routing, embedding, and robustness problems are conceptually easier to solve when viewed on the hypercube of cliques. These will be dealt with in later sections.

The embedding of P_N into H_N will rely crucially on the notion of a star partition. This in turn will rely on 1-error-correcting codes which were first constructed by Hamming [9] for strings of length $2^k - k - 1$ for some integer k. More specifically, Hamming showed that there are 1-error-correcting perfect mappings g from words m of length $2^k - k - 1$ to codewords $g(m)$ of length $2^k - 1$ such that every string of length $2^k - 1$ has Hamming distance at most 1 from exactly one codeword.

Now suppose that we have a hypercube (or subcube) with $n = 2^k - 1$ dimensions. A node, v, is a *star center* if v is a *codeword*, i.e., if $v \in \{g(m) | m \in \{0,1\}^{2^k-k-1}\}$. Define a *star* to be a star center together with all of its neighbors. The neighbor $g(m)^i$ of $g(m)$ is called the ith *arm* of the $g(m)$ star. If g is a perfect one-error-correcting code, every node in the hypercube is in exactly one star. That is, the stars partition the nodes of the hypercube.

We will now describe the embedding of $H^f K_n$ into H_2^n for the special case when $n = 2^k - 1$, for some integer k, and $f = 2^k - k - 1$. We postpone the general case to the end of the this section.

Theorem 1 *There is a one-to-one embedding of $H^f K_n$ into H_2^n with $O(1)$ dilation and congestion for $n = 2^k - 1$, and $f = 2^k - k - 1$.*

Proof: Intuitively, the n-cliques of $H^f K_n$ will be mapped to stars in H_2^n. Furthermore, cliques which differ in one dimension in $H^f K_n$ will be mapped to stars which are "close" in H_2^n.

To describe the embedding we will need an additional fact about perfect one-error-correcting codes. Let C_k be the k by n matrix where the columns are all the strings of length k except for the all-zeroes string. Consider strings of length n as vectors in the vector space $GF(2)^n$. It is a property of perfect 1-error-correcting codes that $C_k \cdot y = 0$ iff y is a codeword, i.e., $y = g(m)$ for some m. It is well known that the nullspace of C_k has dimension f and hence the nullspace has a basis set $B = \{v_1, \ldots, v_f\}$. Alternatively, we will let B denote the natural n by f matrix formed by the column vectors v_i. Define the map g from strings m of length f to codewords of length n as the linear combination in $GF(2)^n$ of the v_i's weighted by the bits of m, i.e., $g(m) = B \cdot m$. Our map from nodes of $H^f K_n$ to nodes of H_2^n is defined as follows:

$$\langle m, i \rangle \mapsto g(m)^i.$$

Note that each clique is mapped to a unique star and that each node in a clique is mapped to a unique arm in the star to which the clique was mapped. Since the stars partition H_2^n, the embedding is one-to-one.

Embedding the clique edges of $H^f K_n$ is easy. The edge $\langle v, i \rangle \to \langle v, j \rangle$ is mapped to the path $g(v)^i \to g(v)^{i,j} \to g(v)^j$. It is easy to see that a directed

edge of H_2^n is used at most once as the first edge of these paths and at most once as the second edge. Hence, the directed congestion due to the clique edges of $H^f K_n$ is at most 2.

To embed hypercube edges of $H^f K_n$, $\langle m, j \rangle \to \langle m^i, j \rangle$, observe that $g(m)$ and $g(m^i)$ differ by v_i; i.e., $g(m^i) = g(m) \oplus v_i$. This can also be written as $g(m^i) = g(m)^{V_i}$ if we let V_i be the indicies of the bits of v_i which are 1. The edge $\langle m, j \rangle \to \langle m^i, j \rangle$ is mapped to the path which starts at $g(m)^j$ and goes to $g(m^i)^j$ by changing the bits indicated by V_i. More formally if $V_i = \{l_{i_1}, l_{i_2}, \ldots, l_{i_t}\}$ then the path is

$$g(m)^j \to g(m)^{j, l_{i_1}} \to g(m)^{j, l_{i_1}, l_{i_2}} \to \cdots$$
$$\to g(m)^{\{j\} \cup V_i} = g(m^i)^j.$$

To make this path unique assume that $l_{i_1} < l_{i_2} < \cdots < l_{i_t}$ and change the bits of $g(m)^j$ in increasing order. In short, to simulate changing dimension i in $H^f K_n$, change the dimensions in H_2^n indicated in order by the 1s of v_i.

Consider the following measures of the basis set. Let the *size* of a vector be the number of 1s. Let the *height* of the basis be maximum size of any vector in the basis. Let $B(i)$ be the set of basis vectors vectors which have a 1 in dimension i, and set $b(i) = |B(i)|$. Let the *width* of the basis be the maximum of the $b(i)$ over all dimensions i.

Lemma 1 *The embedding of the hypercube edges of $H^f K_n$ into H_2^n based on a basis of the nullspace of C_k with height h and width w has dilation h and congestion $2w$.*

Proof: That the dilation is h follows directly from the embedding above and the definitions of dilation and height.

To bound the congestion of the embedding, consider a directed hypercube edge $u \to u^j$. Let $B(j) = \{v_{j_1}, v_{j_2}, \ldots, v_{j_w}\}$ be the basis vectors with a 1 in dimension j. In conjunction with the edge $u \to u^j$, each v_{j_i} defines a unique directed path in H_2^n. If the first node of this path is the arm of a star, say $g(m)^l$, then $u \to u^j$ is on the image path of the $H^f K_n$ edge $\langle m, l \rangle \to \langle m^{j_i}, l \rangle$. There are no other sources of congestion since any hypercube edge of $H^f K_n$ across a dimension which is not among $j_1, j_2, \ldots, j_w$ cannot be mapped to $u \to u^j$. Hence, the directed congestion across any edge is at most w. $\square$

A basis for the nullspace of C_k with bounded height is well-known in the literature as a length-preserving code. For our applications, we need to construct a basis with constant height *and* width. We describe an algorithm for constructing such a basis for all k in Appendix A.

This finishes the proof of Theorem 1. $\qquad\square$

We next show how to extend the embedding to hypercubes of arbitrary size.

Corollary 1 *For any s, and $f = 2^k - k - 1$, there exists an embedding of $H_2^{f+q} \otimes K_s$ into $H_2^{2^k-1+q}$ for all k and $1 \leq q < 2^k - 1$ with load $\lceil s/(2^k - 1) \rceil$, dilation $O(1)$ and congestion $O(\lceil s/(2^k - 1) \rceil)$.*

Proof: We will write nodes of H_2^{f+q} as $m \circ l$ where m is the first f bits and l is the last q bits: $m_1 \dots m_f \circ l_1 \dots l_q$. The node $\langle m \circ l, i \rangle$ of $H^{f+q} K_s$, $i \in [1, \dots, s]$, is mapped to $g(m)^{i'} \circ l$ in $H_2^{2^k-1+q}$ where $i' = i \bmod 2^k - 1$ (except when $i = 0 \bmod 2^k - 1$, in which case $i' = 2^k - 1$).

Complete graph edges $(\langle m \circ l, i \rangle, \langle m \circ l, j \rangle)$ are mapped nearly as in the previous discussion to the path $g(m)^{i'} \circ l \to g(m)^{i',j'} \circ l \to g(m)^{j'} \circ l$. Hypercube edges of $H^{f+q} K_s$ for the first f dimensions are similarly modified. Hypercube edges of $H^{f+q} K_s$ for the last q dimensions, $(\langle m \circ l, i \rangle, \langle m \circ l^j, i \rangle), j \in [1, \dots, q]$, are mapped to edges across the $(f+j)$th dimension of $H_2^{n+q} : (g(m)^{i'} \circ l, g(m)^{i'} \circ l^j)$. The congestion and dilation analyses are nearly the same as before but the embedding is no longer one-to-one. We have loaded some of the nodes of H_2^{n+q} by a factor of $\lceil s/(2^k - 1) \rceil$. $\square$

For general N, we will set $q = \log N - (2^k - 1)$ and $s = \log N$ where k is the largest integer such that $2^k - 1 \leq \log N$. In this case, $\lceil s/(2^k - 1) \rceil \leq 2$ and thus we can conclude that $P_N = H_{N/\log N} \otimes K_{\log N}$ can be embedded in H_N with load 2, congestion $O(1)$ and dilation $O(1)$.

3 Embedding Trees into Hypercubes

3.1 The Tree Compression Lemma

In what follows, we will show how to compress any M-node binary tree into an N-node binary tree for any $N < M$. The compression will have the important property that at most $O(\frac{M}{N})$ nodes of the M-node tree will be compressed into any node of the N-node tree. In particular, we will prove the following theorem.

Lemma 2 (The Tree Compression Lemma)
For any M-node binary tree T and any positive integer $N < M$, it is possible to partition T into N subtrees by removing $N - 1$ edges so that every subtree has at most $\frac{12M}{N} + 1$ nodes and so that each subtree is incident to at most three removed edges.

Given the partition of an M-node binary tree T into N subtrees as defined in Lemma 2, it is easy to compress T into an N-node binary tree. We simply contract each of the subtrees into a single node. The result is an N-node tree which, by Lemma 2, has maximum node-degree three.

The proof of Lemma 2 has been included in Appendix B.

As our first application of the Tree Compression Lemma we will generalize the result of Bhatt, Chung, Leighton, and Rosenberg[5] who show that any tree of size N can be embedded into H_N with load 1, congestion $O(1)$, dilation $O(1)$, and node congestion $O(1)$.

Theorem 2 *Any M-node tree can be embedded into H_N with load $O(\frac{M}{N} + 1)$, congestion $O(1)$, dilation $O(1)$, and node congestion $O(1)$.*

Proof: When $M > N$, use the Tree Compression Lemma to contract the M-node tree into an N-node supertree where each supertree node is an $O(\frac{M}{N})$ size tree. Now use the theorem of [5] to embed the N node supertree into H_N. This clearly gives $O(1)$ dilation, congestion and node congestion. It also maps 1 supernode onto each hypercube node. Since each supernode consists of $O(\frac{M}{N})$ tree nodes, this gives the desired result. (By node congestion in this context, we mean the number of edges that pass through a node, which may be less than the number of edges contained in a node.) $\qquad\square$

3.2 Embedding Dilated Trees in a Hypercube

Our second application of the Tree Compression Lemma is slightly more difficult. We will show how to embed $\log N$-dilated binary trees in a hypercube with constant dilation and congestion. A tree is said to be r-dilated if every edge is replaced with r edges.

Greenberg and Bhatt[8] studied the problem of embedding N-node, $O(\log N)$-dilated grids and $O(\log N)$-dilated trees into H_N. Their motivation was as follows. If one is simulating a tree or grid algorithm on a hypercube in which the interprocessor messages are large, say $\Omega(\log^2 N)$ length, then one might be able to achieve an $O(\log N)$ speedup by breaking up the messages into $O(\log N)$ pieces and sending each piece on a path which is short and has low congestion. They were able to embed the $O(\log N)$-dilated grid into H_N with $O(1)$ load, congestion and dilation but they were only able to achieve $O(\log \log N)$ dilation and congestion for $O(\log N)$-dilated binary trees. In what follows, we show how to achieve $O(1)$ dilation and congestion for $O(\log N)$-dilated binary trees.

Theorem 3 *Any N-node $O(\log N)$-dilated binary tree can be embedded into H_N with $O(1)$ congestion, dilation, and load.*

Proof: Let T be an $O(\log N)$-dilated tree with N nodes. We will embed T into $H_{N/\log N} \otimes K_{\log N}$ with $O(1)$ congestion, dilation, and load. By our previous embedding of $H_{N/\log N} \otimes K_{\log N}$ into H_N, the theorem will follow.

Apply the Tree Compression Lemma to get an $O(\log N)$-dilated tree T' of $N/\log N$ subtrees each of size $O(\log N)$. Use the result of [5] to map T' into $H_{N/\log N}$ treating each multiedge of T' as a single super edge. In such a case, 1 subtree is mapped to each node of $H_{N/\log N}$ and subtrees which are neighbors in T' are mapped to nodes of $H_{N/\log N}$ within distance $O(1)$. Furthermore, the congestion of $H_{N/\log N}$ edges by super-edges of T' is $O(1)$. Call this embedding Γ.

Now extend Γ to an embedding of T into $H_{N/\log N} \otimes K_{\log N}$ in the following way. Any subtree mapped to a node of $H_{N/\log N}$ by Γ is mapped to the corresponding $K_{\log N}$ of $H_{N/\log N} \otimes K_{\log N}$. Evenly distribute the $O(\log N)$ nodes of the subtree to the nodes of $K_{\log N}$. This ensures that the nodes of $K_{\log N}$ will have load $O(1)$.

Suppose two neighbors a and b in a subtree of T' are mapped to different nodes in $K_{\log N}$, say v_a and v_b. Distribute the $O(\log N)$-multiedge between a and b evenly among the $\log N - 1$ paths of length at most 2 in $K_{\log N}$: $v_a \rightarrow u \rightarrow v_b$, $u \neq v_a$. Since the directed edge $v_a \rightarrow u$ in $K_{\log N}$ is used only to distribute the multiedges originating at the nodes mapped to v_a the congestion on $v_a \rightarrow u$ due to subtree multiedges is $O(1)$. Similarly, the congestion on other clique edges due to subtree edges is at most $O(1)$.

We must also extend the embedding of the super edges of T' into $H_{N/\log N}$ to an embedding into $H_{N/\log N} \otimes K_{\log N}$. Suppose the super edge of T' is between node q of subtree Q and node r of subtree R. Further suppose that the subtree Q is mapped to the $K_{\log N}$ with hypercube address v_Q and node q is mapped to $\langle v_Q, q' \rangle$. Likewise assume R and r are mapped to v_R and $\langle v_R, r' \rangle$ respectively.

We know that $v_R = v_Q^D$ where D is some set of dimensions of size $O(1)$. We distribute the $O(\log N)$ edges of the super edge evenly among the $\log N$ paths between $\langle v_Q, q' \rangle$ and $\langle v_R, r' \rangle$ defined as follows for $1 \leq k \leq \log N$:

$$\langle v_Q, q' \rangle \rightarrow \langle v_Q, k \rangle \rightarrow \langle v_Q^{d_1}, k \rangle \rightarrow \langle v_Q^{d_1, d_2}, k \rangle \rightarrow$$
$$\cdots \rightarrow \langle v_Q^D, k \rangle = \langle v_R, k \rangle \rightarrow \langle v_R, r' \rangle.$$

Recall that in Γ, the edges of $H_{N/\log N}$ have $O(1)$ congestion due to super edges of T'. Hence, hypercube edges of $H_{N/\log N} \otimes K_{\log N}$ will have $O(1)$ congestion due to edges of T. Furthermore, since any given clique is an endpoint for only 3 super edges of T', clique edges of $H_{N/\log N} \otimes K_{\log N}$ will pick up only an additional $O(1)$ congestion due to distributing the super edges of T'. $\square$

We should note that it is easy to modify and combine Lemma 2 and Theorem 3 to obtain an embedding of an M-node $O(\log N)$-dilated tree with load $O(M/N + 1)$, dilation $O(1)$ and congestion $O(1)$.

3.3 Embedding Dynamic Trees

The previous two theorems dealt with off-line embeddings of arbitrary trees. However, for many parallel algorithms with a tree structure, the growth pattern and eventual shape of the tree are dependent on the input. Bhatt and Cai [4] were the first to examine whether dynamic trees could be efficiently simulated on the hypercube. Their results were improved by Leighton, Newman, Ranade, and Schwabe[12] who gave a probabilistic embedding of a dynamic tree of size M into H_N which achieved, with high probability, $O(\frac{M}{N} + 1)$ load, $O(1)$ dilation, and $O(\frac{M}{N} + 1)$ congestion. Their bounds for load and dilation are clearly optimal (and, in fact, they show that a deterministic algorithm cannot simultaneously achieve optimal load and dilation). Using an algorithm similar to theirs we improve the congestion to $O(\frac{M}{N \log N} + 1)$, which is a $\log N$ factor improvement. This is within a $\log(M/N)$ factor of the lower bound $\Omega(M/N \log N \log(M/N))$ on congestion for on-line algorithms implied in the work of Bhatt, Greenberg, Leighton and Liu [6].

Theorem 4 *An arbitrary binary tree T with M vertices can be dynamically grown on an N-processor hypercube with constant dilation such that with high probability the maximum load per processor is $O(\frac{M}{N} + 1)$ and the maximum congestion on any edge is $O(\frac{M}{N \log N} + 1)$.*

Proof: The starting point of our proof is an algorithm by Leighton, Newman, Rande and Schwabe [12] which dynamically embeds an M-node tree into an N by $\log N$ node butterfly with constant dilation such that with high probability the number of tree nodes per column is $O(\frac{M}{N} + \log N)$ and the load is $O(\frac{M}{N \log N} + \log N)$. As another preliminary we should note that $H_{N/\log^2 N} \otimes K_{\log N} \otimes K_{\log N}$ can be embedded into H_N with $O(1)$ load, congestion, and dilation simply by first embedding $H_{N/\log^2 N} \otimes K_{\log N}$ into $H_{N/\log N}$ and then embedding $H_{N/\log N} \otimes K_{\log N}$ into H_N.

The essential idea will be to use the algorithm of [12] on a butterfly of size $N/\log^2 N$ by $\log N$ and then adapt this algorithm to run on $H_{N/\log^2 N} \otimes K_{\log N} \otimes K_{\log N}$. Observe that the algorithm of [12] will dynamically embed an M-node tree on a $N/\log^2 N$ by $\log N$ butterfly with $O(1)$ dilation such that with high probability there are $O(\frac{M}{N/\log^2 N} + \log N)$ nodes per column and $O(\frac{M}{N/\log N} + \log N)$ load.

Call this Algorithm A. Algorithm A' will be the adapted version of this algorithm which runs on $P' = H_{N/\log^2 N} \otimes K_{\log N} \otimes K_{\log N}$.

Let $\langle v, i \rangle$ represent a node of the butterfly and $\langle v, i, I \rangle$ represent a node of P'. When a tree node is at $\langle v, i \rangle$ in Algorithm A it will be at $\langle v, i, I \rangle$, for some I, in Algorithm A' on P'. When Algorithm A embeds an edge across $\langle v, i \rangle \rightarrow \langle v^{i+1}, i+1 \rangle$, Algorithm A' embeds the edge as follows. First choose the edge $\langle v, i, I \rangle \rightarrow \langle v, k, I \rangle$ which has thus far been used the least. The next two edges in the path are uniquely specified to be $\langle v, k, I \rangle \rightarrow \langle v^{i+1}, k, I \rangle \rightarrow \langle v^{i+1}, i+1, I \rangle$. The final edge will be of the form $\langle v^{i+1}, i+1, I \rangle \rightarrow \langle v^{i+1}, i+1, J \rangle$. Pick one of the $\lceil 3 \log N/4 \rceil$ least congested edges of this form such that the endpoint is among the $\lceil 3 \log N/4 \rceil$ least loaded processors. Such an edge is guaranteed to exist.

That the dilation is $O(1)$ is immediate. To argue that the bounds for load and congestion are as stated in the theorem, we will need the following simple lemma.

Lemma 3 *Assume a total of m balls are placed into n boxes one at a time. If at each step a ball is placed in any one of the $\lceil 3n/4 \rceil$ least occupied boxes, then after all balls have been assigned, at most $4m/n$ balls are in any box.*

Proof: Suppose to the contrary that more than $4m/n$ balls are in one box. This implies that there are at least $\lfloor n/4 \rfloor$ other boxes of size at least $4m/n$. So the total number of balls must be more than

$4\frac{m}{n}(\lfloor \frac{n}{4} \rfloor + 1)$ which is more than m. □

Since the load of the embedding on the butterfly is at most $O(\frac{M \log N}{N} + \log N)$, we know that there are at most $O(\frac{M \log N}{N} + \log N)$ tree nodes mapped to the set of nodes $\{\langle v^{i+1}, i+1, J \rangle \mid 1 \le J \le \log N\}$ for every v and i. By virtue of the way in which we assign tree nodes to this set in Algorithm A', we can apply Lemma 3 to conclude that the load on any processor of P' is $O(\frac{M}{N} + 1)$.

Call the first three edges of the paths of length four used in our embedding *partial paths*. Since the load on P' is $O(\frac{M}{N} + 1)$ there are only $O(\frac{M}{N} + 1)$ tree edges originating out of a node of P'. Since A' evenly distributes these edges among $\log N$ disjoint partial paths, the congestion on edges in the partial paths is $O(\frac{M}{N \log N} + 1)$.

The fourth edge in each path is of the form $\langle v^{i+1}, i+1, I \rangle \rightarrow \langle v^{i+1}, i+1, J \rangle, 1 \le J \le \log N$. Since $\langle v, i, I \rangle$ has load $O(M/N + 1)$, there are $O(M/N + 1)$ edges to distribute among these $\log N$ edges. Since the fourth path edge is embedded among the $\lceil 3 \log N/4 \rceil$ least congested edges, Lemma 3 implies that the congestion is $O(\frac{M}{N \log N} + 1)$. □

In the model just analyzed only one node is expanded at a time. It is more natural to allow many tree nodes to expand in one time step. Because the algorithm embeds nodes locally, it is not difficult to adapt the algorithm to run in an on-line fashion with a polylogarithmic slowdown on the hypercube.

4 Reconfiguring Hypercubes Around Faults

In this section, we show how to apply the techniques developed in Sections 2 and 3 to devise improved algorithms for using faulty hypercubes to simulate fault-free hypercubes. We will consider the case of probablistic faults in Subsection 4.1 and the case of worst-case faults in Subsection 4.2.

4.1 Random Faults

Consider an N-node hypercube H_N in which every edge and node is faulty with some constant probability $p < 1$. We will assume that each fault is independent of the location of other faults, and that if a node is faulty, then it cannot be used for any purpose (i.e., no communication can pass through it). In what follows, we will prove that if p is a sufficiently small constant, then with high probability, we can embed

$P_N = H_{N/\log N} \otimes K_{\log N}$ into H_N with constant load, dilation and congestion so that every node of P_N is mapped to a live node of H_N, and so that every edge of P_N is mapped to a path of live nodes and edges of H_N. Since H_N is a subgraph of P_N, we will have thus shown how a faulty hypercube can simulate a functioning hypercube of the same size with constant slowdown.

The result is similar to that proved by Hastad, Leighton and Newman [10], except that the reconfiguration algorithm in [10] is probabilistic and uses a polylogarthmic number of communication steps to achieve the reconfiguration. The only previously known deterministic reconfiguration algorithm requires $\Omega(N)$ steps. The algorithm described in this subsection is simple, deterministic, and uses only $O(\log N)$ local communication steps. The algorithm described in this subsection is limited by the fact that the probability of component failure p must be a small constant, but it should be possible to extend the result to work for all $p < 1$ using the methods of [10] and Section 4.2 of this paper.

The algorithm for embedding P_N into a faulty hypercube is very similar to the fault-free embedding described in Section 2. To economize on space, we will only sketch the aditional steps needed to tolerate faults in what follows. As in Section 2, we will assume that $N = 2^{2^k - 1}$ for some integer k, and that $P_N = H_2^{n-k} \otimes K_n$ where $n = 2^k - 1$. The extension of the result to general N is straightforward.

The first step of the embedding is to map the nodes of each n-clique of P_N to the n nodes of the corresponding star in H_N. Since $n = \log N$ and p is a sufficiently small constant, it is easy to show that with high probability, at least $(1 - \epsilon_1)n$ nodes in each star are alive for any $\epsilon_1 > 0$. (As ϵ_1 gets small, so must p.) Hence, we will map the ith node of a clique to the ith live node of the corresponding star, using wraparound as necessary. In particular, if $\epsilon_1 \leq 1/2$, then at most two nodes of any clique will be mapped to any star node by this process.

We next show how to interconnect the live nodes of each star into a clique. Given any two live nodes v^i, v^j in a star centered at v, we will connect them with the path $v^i \rightarrow v^{ij} \rightarrow v^j$ provided that the path is fault-free. Note that the probability that such a path is faulty is $1 - (1 - p)^3 < 3p$, and that the path for $v^i \rightarrow v^j$ is disjoint from the path for $v^{i'} \rightarrow v^{j'}$ whenever $\{i, j\} \neq \{i', j'\}$. Hence, we can use a simple probabilistic argument to show that with high probability, every live node of every star is connected to at least $(1 - \epsilon_2)n$ live nodes in the same star with live disjoint paths of length two. These connections

can be made in constant time on the hypercube.

We next show how to connect a pair of live nodes in a star v^i, v^j for which the path $v^i \rightarrow v^{ij} \rightarrow v^j$ contains a fault. For each such pair we will find a third live node v^s for which the paths $v^i \rightarrow v^{is} \rightarrow v^s$ and $v^s \rightarrow v^{si} \rightarrow v^j$ are functioning. There are at least $(1 - 2\epsilon_2)n$ choices for s since both v^i and v^j are connected to at least $(1 - \epsilon_2)n$ other live nodes with paths of length two. In order to avoid congestion problems, we will choose intermediate nodes in rounds as follows. In the first round, we will find intermediate nodes for disconnected live pairs v^i, v^j where $j \equiv i + 1 \pmod{n}$. In particular, the processors at node v^i will select a value of s such that both $v^i \rightarrow v^{is} \rightarrow v^s$ and $v^s \rightarrow v^{si} \rightarrow v^j$ are live where $j = i + 1$. This step can be accomplished with $O(1)$ communication steps (where we allow $\log N$ bits to traverse each edge during a step), and can increase the congestion of every edge by at most 2 (due to reconfiguring this star). (Note that every edge in a path of length four is involved in reconfiguring at most 2 stars.) In the rth round ($1 \leq r \leq n$), we will find intermediate nodes for live pairs v^i, v^j where $j \equiv i + r \pmod{n}$. In particular, the processor at node v^i will select a value of s such that every component along the path $v^i \rightarrow v^{is} \rightarrow v^s \rightarrow v^{sj} \rightarrow v^j$ is alive, and so that every edge along the path has congestion (due to reconfiguring this star) at most C where C is a predetermined, sufficiently large constant. We can always find such an s since at most $2\epsilon_2 n$ values of s are eliminated due to faults, and since at most $2n/C$ values are eliminated due to edge congestion. (Hence, it suffices to choose $C > 2/(1 - 2\epsilon_2)$.) Information about whether or not edges are congested can be transmitted in $O(1)$ communication steps, where we are allowed to transmit $O(\log N)$ bits of data at each step. Note that we don't need to coordinate among selections being made in a given round since the congestion of any edge can go up by at most two in a single round.

After n rounds, the previous algorithm will have connected every pair of live nodes in a star with a live path of length at most 4. Moreover, the congestion is bounded by $O(1)$. This completes the embedding of the n-cliques into H_N. We next show how to embed the n parallel paths corresponding to each edge of H_2^{n-k} into the faulty hypercube.

By the analysis in Section 2, we know that the n parallel paths corresponding to an edge e of H_2^{n-k} each have constant length. Moreover, it can be easily shown that at most two of the paths can intersect in a single node of H_N. Hence, these paths collectively use $\Theta(n)$ nodes and edges of H_N. Denote this set of nodes and edges (including the endpoints) by $\mathcal{P}(e)$. If p is a sufficiently small constant, then with high probability, at most $\epsilon_3 n$ of the nodes or edges in $\mathcal{P}(e)$ will be faulty for any e and $\epsilon_3 > 0$. Since each faulty node or edge in $\mathcal{P}(e)$ can destroy at most two of the n parallel paths for e, this means that with high probability, at least $(1 - 2\epsilon_3 n)$ of the n parallel paths for each e will be live. Hence, we embed the ith path along the ith live path (counted with wraparound). Provided that $\epsilon_3 \leq 1/4$, this results in at most a factor of 2 increase in congestion.

Of course, we still have to hook up the n parallel paths to the appropriate end points in each star (clique). This is easily accomplished in the following manner. If e is a dimension t edge of H_2^{n-k} whose path ends at v^j in the star centered at v, but whose clique endpoint has been embedded at v^i, we make the connection by routing the path through the path of length at most 4 from v^j to v^t, and then through the path of length at most 4 from v^t to v^i. Similarly we use a path of length four through the tth arm of the star in which the other endpoint is embedded. Because each v^i contains at most $O(1)$ clique nodes and each v^j contains at most $O(1)$ path endpoints for e in dimension t, this embedding results in only constant congestion.

This completes the proof that P_N can be embedded in H_N with constant load, dilation and congestion with high probability even if every component of H_N fails with constant probability.

4.2 Worst-Case Faults

As an immediate corollary of the reconfiguration result just described, we can conclude that P_N can be embedded in H_N with constant load, congestion and dilation even if H_N has up to $((1 - \epsilon) \log N)/2$ worst-case faults for any constant $\epsilon > 0$. This is because the embedding just described works whenever the fault pattern satisfies three conditions:

1. at least $(1 - \epsilon_1)n$ nodes in any star of H_N are live ($\epsilon_1 < 1/2$),

2. for every live node v^i in any star, there are at least $(1 - \epsilon_2)n$ live nodes v^j in the star such that the path $v^i \rightarrow v^{ij} \rightarrow v^j$ is fault free ($\epsilon_2 < 1/2$), and

3. for every e, the set $\mathcal{P}(e)$ has at most $\epsilon_3 n$ faulty components ($\epsilon_3 < 1/2$).

In fact, we can prove a much stronger result. Namely, we can show how to embed $P_N^{(r)} =$

$H_{N/\log^r N} \otimes K_{\log N}^r$ in H_N with constant load, congestion and dilation for any constant r provided that H_N has at most $c_r \log^{r-1} N$ worst-case faults, where c_r is a sufficiently small constant depending on r. Since $P_N^{(r)}$ is a supergraph of the N-node hypercube, this means that a hypercube with $\log^{O(1)} N$ worst-case faults can simulate a fully functioning hypercube of the same size with only constant slowdown. This result substantially generalizes the work of Bruck, Cypher and Soroker [7] as well as that of Becker and Simon [3] and Livingston, Stout, Graham and Harary [13], as described in the introduction.

The proof of this result is fairly simple given the fact that $P_N^{(r)}$ can be embedded in H_N with constant (depending on r) load, congestion and dilation. If H_N has at most $c_r \log^{r-1} N$ faults, then these faults can induce at most $c_r' \log^{r-1} N$ node faults and $c_r' \log^r N$ edge faults in the embedding of $P_N^{(r)}$, where c_r' is a constant that depends on r and grows linearly with c_r. (Any component of $P_N^{(r)}$ that is mapped to a faulty component of H_N is considered to be faulty.) The proof is concluded by observing that $P_N^{(r)}$ itself can be reconfigured with constant load, congestion and dilation given any set of at most $c_r' \log^r N$ faults provided that c_r' is a sufficiently small constant. Without loss of generality, we will assume that all of the faults induced in $P_N^{(r)}$ are node faults.

In order to reconfigure $P_N^{(r)}$ within itself, we first show how to locally reconfigure each r-dimensional mesh of cliques $K_{\log N}^r$. Since there are only only $c_r' \log^r N$ faults overall, there are at most $c_r' \log^r N$ faults within any $K_{\log N}^r$. The reconfiguration strategy proceeds inductively. If $r = 1$, then at most $c_1' \log N$ of the $\log N$ nodes of $K_{\log N}$ are faulty. For small c_1', this means that the faulty copy of $K_{\log N}^1$ contains a totally healthy subclique of size $(1 - c_1') \log N$ that can handle the workload of the whole clique.

For the inductive hypothesis, we will assume that any copy of $K_{\log N}^{r-1}$ with up to $c_{r-1}' \log^{r-1} N$ worst-case faults can reconfigure itself with constant (depending on r) load, dilation and congestion. Now consider a copy of $K_{\log N}^r$ with $c_r' \log^r N$ worst-case faults. Partition $K_{\log N}^r$ into $\log N$ disjoint copies of $K_{\log N}^{r-1}$, and observe that at least $\frac{2}{3} \log N$ of the copies have fewer than $3 c_r' \log^{r-1} N$ faults each. Set c_r' so that $3 c_r' < \min(c_{r-1}', 1/3)$. Then we can apply the induction to reconfigure $\frac{2}{3} \log N$ copies of $K_{\log N}^{r-1}$. These copies will will do the work of all $\log N$ copies of $K_{\log N}^{r-1}$ in $K_{\log N}^r$. We next build the connections between the copies of $K_{\log N}^{r-1}$ to form $K_{\log N}^r$. This can be done for each pair of copies of $K_{\log N}^{r-1}$ by using the existing good connections (of which there must be $(1 - 6c_r') \log^{r-1} N \geq \frac{1}{3} \log^{r-1} N$) between the pair. To connect the endpoints within each copy of $K_{\log N}^{r-1}$, we route a partial permutation at each end. Overall, we must route $\frac{2}{3} \log N$ partial permuations of paths in each copy of $K_{\log N}^{r-1}$ (one partial permutation for each pair that contains the copy). This can always be done using constant congestion and dilation (assuming that r is constant). The proof is by induction on r, and will be included in the final version of the paper. This completes the reconfiguration of $K_{\log N}^r$.

The reconfiguration of the $\log^r N$ parallel copies of each edge of $H_{N/\log^r N}$ within $P_N^{(r)}$ proceeds similarly. The details will be included in the final version of the paper.

References

[1] W. Aiello, T. Leighton, B. Maggs, and M. Newman. Fast algorithms for bit-serial routing on a hypercube. In *Proceedings of the 1990 ACM Symposium on Parallel Algorithms and Architectures*, pages 55–64, July 1990.

[2] M. Baumslag, 1990. Personal communication.

[3] B. Becker and H. U. Simon. How robust is the n-cube? In *Proceedings of the 27th Annual Symposium on Foundations of Computer Science*, pages 283–291, 1986.

[4] S. N. Bhatt and J. Cai. Take a walk, grow a tree. In *Proceedings of the 29th Annual Symposium on Foundations of Computer Science*, pages 469–478, 1988.

[5] S. N. Bhatt, F. R. K. Chung, F. T. Leighton, and A. L. Rosenberg. Optimal simulations of tree machines. In *Proceedings of the 27th Annual Symposium on Foundations of Computer Science*, pages 274–282. IEEE, Oct. 1986.

[6] S. N. Bhatt, D. Greenberg, F. T. Leighton, and P. Liu. Tight bounds for on-line tree embeddings. In *Proceedings of the 2nd Annual SIAM Symposium on Discrete Algorithms*, pages 344–350, Jan. 1991.

[7] J. Bruck, R. Cypher, and D. Soroker. Running algorithms efficiently on faulty hypercubes. In *Proceedings of the 1990 ACM Symposium on Parallel Algorithms and Architectures*, pages 37–44, July 1990.

[8] D. S. Greenberg and S. N. Bhatt. Routing multiple paths in hypercubes. In *Proceedings of the 1990 ACM Symposium on Parallel Algorithms and Architectures*, pages 45–54, July 1990.

[9] R. W. Hamming. Error detecting and error correcting codes. *Bell System Technical Journal*, 29:147–160, 1950.

[10] J. Hastad, T. Leighton, and M. Newman. Fast computation using faulty hypercubes. In *Proceedings of the 21st Annual ACM Symposium on Theory of Computing*, pages 251–263, May 1989.

[11] R. R. Koch. Increasing the size of a network by a constant factor can increase performance by more than a constant factor. In *Proceedings of the 29th Annual Symposium on Foundations of Computer Science*, pages 221–230. IEEE, Oct. 1988.

[12] F. T. Leighton, M. Newman, A. Ranade, and E. Schwabe. Dynamic tree embeddings in butterflies and hypercubes. In *Proceedings of the 1989 ACM Symposium on Parallel Algorithms and Architectures*, pages 224–234, June 1989.

[13] M. Livingston, Q. Stout, N. Graham, and F. Hararay. Subcube fault-tolerance in hypercubes. Technical Report CRL-TR-12-87, U. of Michigan Computing Research Laboratory, Sept. 1987.

[14] D. Peleg and J. Ullman. An optimal synchronizer for the hypercube. *SIAM Journal on Computing*, 18(2):740–747, 1989.

[15] W. Stahnke. Primitive binary polynomials. *Mathematics of Computation*, 27(124):977–980, Oct. 1973.

Appendix A   Constructing a Good Basis for the Codewords

In what follows we will describe an algorithm for producing a basis for the null space of C_k with height at most 6 and width bounded by a constant to be determined. The basic approach is to take a well defined spanning set S of vectors all of small size and find an arbitrary subset with full rank, i.e., a basis. This basis will have bounded height but potentially unbounded width. Using linear combinations with elements of S, we will show how to reduce the width to a constant while only doubling the height.

Our spanning set S is all vectors of size 3 which are in the nullspace of C_k. An easy counting argument shows that there are

$$\frac{1}{3}\binom{n}{2}$$

such vectors where (once again) we assume that $n = 2^k - 1$ for $k \geq 2$.

S can easily be seen to span the nullspace by induction on the size of vectors. For the base case, all vectors of size 3 in the nullspace are trivially spanned by S (and there are no vectors of smaller size in the nullspace). Suppose y is a vector of size $l + 1$ in the nullspace. There are many s in S such that adding s to y yields a string y' of length l. (Let s be any vector in S that has two 1-bits in common with y.) Clearly, y' is in the nullspace since y and s are. Hence, y' satisfies the inductive hypothesis and so is spanned by S; therefore, y is as well.

Let $S(i)$ be all the vectors in S which have a 1 in the ith dimension. The size of each $S(i)$ is $(n-1)/2$.

Given S, use any of several methods to find a subset B of S of cardinality $f = n - k$ which is a basis of the nullspace. Recall the definitions of $B(i)$ and $b(i)$ from before. Define D as a distribution function for the $b(i)$: $D(l) = \{i \mid b(i) > l\}$ and $d(l) = |D(l)|$.

Using these definitions it is easy to see that only a constant fraction of the dimensions have $b(i)$ larger than a constant. First note that the sum of $b(i)$ over all the dimensions is just the sum of the size of all the vectors in B which is just $3(n - k)$. Using the fact that $b(i) \geq 1$ we can bound the sum of the $b(i)$ in terms of $d(t)$ as follows:

$$\sum_{1 \leq i \leq n} b(i) \geq (t + 1)d(t) + (n - d(t)).$$

Hence, $d(t) \leq (2n - 3k)/t < (2/t)n$.

In what follows, we will show how to transform our current basis into a new basis in such a way that the $b(i)$ for each dimension i in $D(t)$ will be less than $2t$ for some constant t to be determined. In the process we will not increase the $b(i)$ of any dimension not in $D(t)$ by more than t. As a result, all dimensions will have $b(i) \leq 2t$. Our main tool for doing this is the lemma below, for which we will need the following definition. Given a basis $B = \{v_1, \ldots, v_f\}$, and vectors z and z_B such that $z = B \cdot z_B$, we say that v_j *contributes* to z if $z_B(j) = 1$; otherwise we say that it does not contribute.

Lemma 4 *Given any z, a basis vector v_l which contributes to z, and any other basis vector v_j the following holds. If v_j does not contribute to z then replacing v_j with $z \oplus v_j$ and v_l with z results in a new basis. If v_j does contribute to z then replacing v_j with $z \oplus v_l$ and v_l with z results in a basis.*

Proof: Let us examine the first case. Without loss of generality suppose $v_2 = v_l$ contributes to z but

that $v_1 = v_j$ does not. Let B' be the new basis $\{z \oplus v_1, z, v_3, \ldots\}$. We only need to show that if $B' \cdot a = 0$ then $a(i) = 0$ for all i. Rewriting the matrix-vector product in terms of the original basis we see that the coefficients of $v_1, v_2, v_i, i \geq 3$, are respectively $a(1), a(1) \oplus a(2)$, and $a(1)z_B(i) \oplus a(2)z_B(i) \oplus a(i)$, $i \geq 3$. All these coefficients must be zero since the v_i are independent. This implies that all the $a(i)$ are zero.

The proof for the second case follows identical reasoning. □

Observe that for any z and any subset of basis vectors $\{v_{j_1}, v_{j_2}, \ldots\}$ which includes at least one contributing vector, say v_{j_2}, we can use the lemma inductively to replace this subset with one of the form $\{z \oplus v_{j_2}, z, z \oplus v_{j_3}, \ldots\}$ or $\{z \oplus v_{j_1}, z, z \oplus v_{j_3}, \ldots\}$ depending on whether or not v_{j_1} contributes to z. (Note that once z is inserted into the basis, no other vector will contribute to it.)

Recall that $D(t)$ is the set of dimensions with more than t 1s and that $D(t)$ has size at most $2n/t$. Without loss of generality, say $D(t) = \{1, 2, \ldots, d(t)\}$ and say $B(1)$ is $v_1, v_2, \ldots, v_{b(1)}$. Call a vector in $S(1)$ good if both of the other non-zero dimensions are not in $D(t)$. The number of such good vectors is at least $\frac{(n-1)}{2} - \frac{2n}{t}$ since the number of vectors of $S(1)$ with at least one more 1 in a dimension in $D(t)$ is at most the size of $D(t)$. For t large enough a good vector exists. Call it z. Use our lemma to combine z with t of the vectors of $B(1)$. This eliminates t 1s in dimension 1. For each of the new vectors gotten by combining with z we have added a 1 in two dimensions not in $D(t)$. These two dimensions will now have more than t 1's (but at most $2t$). Label these two dimensions as *used*.

Continue using a new good z to eliminate t 1's in the first dimension until the number of 1's drops below $2t$. The number of good z we need to accomplish this is $\lfloor \frac{b(1)-t}{t} \rfloor$. Hence, to finish the first dimension we need $\frac{n-1}{2} - \frac{2n}{t} \geq \lfloor \frac{b(1)-t}{t} \rfloor$. In working on the second dimension we have fewer potential good vectors since we have marked $2\lfloor \frac{b(1)-t}{t} \rfloor$ dimensions as being used in finishing the first dimension. To guarantee we have enough good vectors to finish the second dimension we need

$$\frac{n-1}{2} - \left(\frac{2n}{t} + 2\left\lfloor \frac{b(1)-t}{t} \right\rfloor\right) \geq \left\lfloor \frac{b(2)-t}{t} \right\rfloor.$$

To ensure we have enough good vectors to get all the dimensions of $D(t)$ below $2t$ it, is sufficient that

$$\frac{n-1}{2} - \frac{2n}{t} \geq 2 \sum_{i \in D(t)} \left\lfloor \frac{b(i)-t}{t} \right\rfloor.$$

Let $M = \sum_{i \in D(t)}(b(i) - t)$. The right hand side of the inequality is bounded above by $2M/t$. M itself is at most $2n$ since the sum of the $b(i)$'s is $3(n-k)$, and $t \geq 1$, and each other dimension has at least one 1. Hence, if $\frac{n-1}{2} \geq \frac{6n}{t}$ then there are enough good vectors to reduce the number of 1's in each dimension of $D(t)$ to below $2t$. For example, $t = 14$ is sufficient for $n \geq 7$.

Using the above procedure we have created a basis with width at most $2t$, but now we must check that our height is still bounded. When we eliminated a 1 in a vector in a dimension in $D(t)$ we added two 1's in dimensions not in $D(t)$. We did this at most three times which bounds the size of the resulting vector by six.

An Alternate Construction

In what follows, we will describe a relationship between primitive polynomials and good bases. This will lead to a good basis for C_k for k up to 137. This in turn gives us an alternative method for obtaining good embeddings for hypercubes up to size $2^{2^{137}}$.

Let p be a primitive polynomial of degree k in $GF(2)[x]$. By definition, $x^i \bmod p$, $0 \leq i \leq n-1$, generates all polynomials of degree $k-1$ or less except for the zero polynomial. Any $(k-1)$-degree polynomial can be uniquely associated with a string of length k when the string is regarded as a sequence of coefficients. Let the size of a polynomial be the size of its associated string.

Lemma 5 *If there exists a primitive polynomial of degree k in $GF(2)[x]$ of size s, then there is a basis for the nullspace of C_k of height and width s.*

Proof: Let column i of C_k be x^i reduced modulo p for $0 \leq i \leq n-1$. Now suppose for simplicity that p has three terms: $x^{j'}$, x^j, and 1. It will be clear how the proof generalizes to arbitrary size. Define v_l to be a vector of length n which is zero everywhere except for a 1 in the lth position, a 1 in the $(l+j)$th position, and a 1 in the $l+j'$th position where $j' > j$. Let $\mathcal{V}$ be the set of all v_l with $0 \leq l \leq n-k-1$.

Claim 1 *$\mathcal{V}$ is in the nullspace of S.*

Proof: $C_k \cdot v_l$ is just the sum

$$x^l + x^{l+j} + x^{l+j'} \pmod{p}$$

where addition is in $GF(2)[x]$. But this is just $x^l p \pmod{p}$ which is just 0. □

Claim 2 *$\mathcal{V}$ is a basis for the nullspace of S.*

Proof: Since $\mathcal{V}$ has the correct cardinality we need only show that it spans. Consider a nonzero vector y, and let $\sigma(y)$ be the maximum index i such that $y(i) = 1$. Note that $\sigma(v_l) = l + j'$. We proceed by induction on $\sigma(y)$. For the base case, observe that all vectors in the nullspace have $\sigma \geq k$. This is because columns 0 through $k-1$ of C_k are a permutation of the identity matrix. Futhermore, the unique vector with $\sigma = k$ is v_0.

Suppose we are given a vector y in the nullspace with $\sigma(y) = l > k$. Let $y' = y + v_{l-k}$. It is clear that y' is in the nullspace since both y and v_{l-k} are in the nullspace and $\sigma(y') < l$. Hence, y' satisfies the inductive hypothesis and so is spanned by $\mathcal{V}$. This implies y is spanned as well. □

To finish the proof of the lemma observe that the number of 1s in each v_l is s and that the number of v_l's with a 1 in a given dimension is at most s. □

It is not known whether there is a c such that for all degrees there is a primitive polynomial of size at most c. Nonetheless, small primitive polynomials of degree d in $GF(2)[x]$ have been tabulated for d up to 137 [15]. For each of these degrees there is a polynomial of size 3 or 5.

Appendix B Proof of the Tree Compression Lemma

The proof of Lemma 2 will make use of the following two simple lemmas.

Lemma 6 *Given any M-node binary tree T, it is possible to partition T into two subtrees, each with at least $\frac{M-1}{3}$ nodes, by removing a single edge from T.*

Lemma 7 *Let T be a weighted M-node binary tree for which $d_i + w_i \leq 3$ and $w_i \in \{0, 1, 2\}$ for each i $(1 \leq i \leq M)$, where d_i and w_i are the degreee and weight (respectively) of the ith node in T. Then if $\sum_{i=1}^{M} w_i = 4$, it is possible to partition T into two subtrees each having total weight 2 by removing a single edge from T.*

Proof: If T contains a node with weight 2, then this node has degree 1, and we can form the desired partition by removing the edge incident to this node.

If T does not contain a node with weight 2, then it contains precisely four nodes with weight 1. Define T' to be the subtree of T consisting of the simple paths that interconnect the four weight-1 nodes. Since the weight-1 nodes can have degree at most 2 in T, there are only three possibilities for the homeomorphic structure of T', and it is easy to find the desired partition of T for each possibility. $\square$

We are now ready to prove Lemma 2. The partition is constructed by repeatedly applying Lemma 6 to split T into smaller and smaller subtrees. However, we must be careful not to remove too many edges from the same subtree. In order to keep everything balanced, we will apply the following splitting process to subtrees in the partially-formed partition.

Let T_1 be an M_1-node subtree in the partially-formed partition of T. We will assume for now that T_1 is incident to at most three previously removed edges of T. We start by using Lemma 6 to split T_1 into two subtrees, each having at least $\frac{M_1-1}{3}$ nodes. Since T_1 is incident to at most three removed edges, the two newly formed subtrees are incident to two and three removed edges (respectively) or to one and four removed edges (respectively). In the former case, we quit and repeat the entire process on another subtree in the partially-formed partition. In the latter case, we apply Lemma 7 to further split the subtree that is incident to four removed edges. As a consequence, we will have split T_1 into three subtrees, each incident to at most three removed edges, and at least two of which have at least $\frac{M_1-1}{6}$ nodes.

In order to split T into N subtrees, we repeatedly apply the process just described to the largest remaining subtree until a total of $N-2$ or $N-1$ edges of T have been removed. If $N-2$ edges have been removed, then we apply Lemma 7 once more to a subtree to produce a partition with precisely N subtrees.

By construction, we know that each of the subtrees in the partition is incident to at most three removed edges. In what follows, we show that every subtree has at most $\frac{12M}{N}+1$ nodes. The proof is not difficult. Each time that we apply the splitting process, we remove at most two edges from T, and we replace the largest current subtree with two or three subtrees, at least two of which have size at least $\frac{M_1-1}{6}$, where M_1 is the size of the subtree being split. Thus, after the splitting process is applied s times, at least $s+1$ of the subtrees will have size at least $\frac{x-1}{6}$ where x is the size of the largest subtree at that point in the algorithm. Since the splitting process is applied at least $\frac{N}{2}-1$ times during the formation of the partition, this means that the largest subtree in the partition can have size at most x where

$$\frac{N}{2}\frac{(x-1)}{6} \le M.$$

Hence the largest subtree can have size at most $\frac{12M}{N}+1$, as claimed. This concludes the proof of Lemma 2.

136

Embedding de Bruijn and Shuffle-Exchange Graphs in Five Pages[*]

(preliminary version)

Bojana Obrenić

Computer and Information Science
University of Massachusetts
Amherst, MA 01003

Abstract

We present algorithms for embedding de Bruijn and shuffle-exchange graphs in books of 5 pages with cumulative pagewidth $2^n - 1 + (2/3)(2^{n-1} - 2 + (n \bmod 2))$ and $2^{n-1} + (1/3)(2^{n-1} - 2 + (n \bmod 2))$, respectively.

The book-embedding problem abstracts layout problems encountered in designing fault-tolerant VLSI processor arrays; the pagenumber models the cost of the solution. These results are the first nontrivial and practically optimal bounds on the pagenumber of de Bruijn and shuffle-exchange graphs.

1 Introduction

The *book* of *thickness* p is a set of p half-planes, called *pages*, sharing a common boundary, called the *spine*. A *p-page book-embedding* of a directed graph $G = (V, A)$ is a drawing of G in a book of thickness p so that the nodes of G reside on the spine of the book, while each arc of G is drawn in exactly one page, in such a way that no arcs of G cross. Directions of arcs are immaterial for book-embedding—the graphs we consider are directed just for clarity of presentation. The *pagenumber* of a graph G is the thickness of the smallest (in number of pages) book into which G can be embedded. The *width* of a page in a book-embedding is its maximum cutwidth. The *cumulative pagewidth* of a book-embedding is the sum of the widths of all pages.

The book-embedding problem appears in several formulations and has various origins (cf. [4]); within the

realm of parallel architectures it is relevant for the design of fault-tolerant processor arrays of identical processing elements. The Diogenes approach to the design of such arrays [3] assumes that processing elements are laid in a logical line, while some number of "bundles" of wires runs in parallel with the line. Once the faulty processors are discovered, the fault-free processors are configured to form a desired topology. The configuration is effected by a network of switches connecting processors to the bundles of wires. This network is flexible, yet subject to some implementation constraints such that the switching mechanism behaves as a *stack*, to which wires are entered or from which they are removed as the linear array of processors is scanned during the configuration.

The Diogenes approach yields its best results [13] when applied to the design of linear arrays, or when applied to the design of arrays of identical, relatively large processing elements, whose cost redeems the overhead on the fault-tolerating hardware. However, it is equally interesting in the context of more complex array structures, as it allows for designs that can be easily "programmed" to effect various topologies, even dynamically reconfigured, with high utilization of fault-free elements. Yet, the inherent simplicity and regularity of Diogenes arrays brings advantages akin to those found in systolic designs (cf. [10]): these arrays can be extended as needed, at a cost proportional only to their size; they may be built in modules, as the design and fabrication of processing elements and switching mechanisms does not depend on the structure to which the array is eventually configured.

The most important quality measure of a Diogenes layout [3] of an array is the *number* of bundles of wires, organized in hardware stacks, required to configure it. Second to this cost is the total *width* of these bundles. So, a very important part of a Diogenes design is finding a linearization of nodes of the target array which admits a layout of the edges of its interconnection network in few small stacks. This problem, however, is *equivalent to finding an efficient book-embedding* of the graph under-

---

[*]This research was supported in part by NSF Grant CCR-88-12567.

lying the interconnection network. The pagenumber of a graph equals the required number of stacks, while the cumulative pagewidth equals the required stackwidth; it is, therefore, desirable to achieve embeddings of important graph families, with optimal pagenumber and pagewidth. This task is very hard in general; we know [6] that for a given linearization of the nodes of a graph G and a given integer k, the problem of deciding if the linearization admits a k-page book-embedding of G is NP-complete.

At present, book-embeddings of several graph families are known, though it is less often known that these embeddings are optimal. Exemplifying this fact are the family of complete graphs, whose pagenumber is determined exactly [1], and the family of complete bipartite graphs, where it is not yet established whether the known [12] book-embedding is optimal. Very few efficient algorithms exist for achieving book-embeddings of arbitrary graphs [16] [8].

Optimal (within constant factors, or even absolutely) book-embeddings have been constructed for almost all seriously proposed interconnection networks, including: trees [4], grids [4], X-trees [4], butterfly-like networks [7] and hypercubes [4]. Yet, *no efficient book-embeddings have been found so far for shuffle-like networks*, another very popular class of interconnection networks represented by de Bruijn and shuffle-exchange graphs. The very weak upper bound for the much broader class of bounded-degree graphs applies, but is non-constructive, so it follows from [4] or [11] that there exist book-embeddings of N-node de Bruijn (shuffle-exchange) graphs with pagenumber $O(\sqrt{N})$. This paper presents a construction for embedding these graphs in 5 pages. The best known lower bound on the pagenumber of de Bruijn and shuffle-exchange graphs remains 3, which follows from the graphs' nonplanarity.

It may be interesting to compare our results about shuffle-like networks with the results known about butterfly-like networks. Both families are bounded-degree hypercube-derivative networks; their computational power is a frequent topic of comparative studies (cf. [14]). Both families have small pagenumber: for butterfly-like graphs it is 3, in contrast to hypercubes themselves, whose pagenumber is unbounded (logarithmic) in the size of the network.

We remark that Diogenes can utilize a switching mechanism alternative to stacks of wires; this mechanism consists of *queues* of wires [13], so the success of Diogenes design with queues depends on finding efficient *queue layouts* of graphs. For practically all popular networks the queuenumber is known [9]; for both butterfly-like and shuffle-like graphs it is 2.

In Section 2, we define the bidendral decomposition of de Bruijn graphs, and adduce its relevant proper-

ties. In Section 3 we exploit the decomposition for developing the book-embedding of de Bruijn graphs. We start by embedding separately the partial subgraphs produced by the decomposition; then we compose the partial embeddings into an efficient embedding of the whole graph. In Section 4, we adapt the embedding to shuffle-exchange graphs.

Notation: We denote by Z_2 the set $\{0, 1\}$ and we use letters from the beginning of Greek alphabet $(\alpha, \beta, \gamma, \ldots)$ as variables ranging over Z_2. For integer $k \geq 0$, we denote by Z_2^k the set of all strings of length k over Z_2, and we let lowercase letters of Roman alphabet $(a, b, \ldots, x, y, z, \ldots)$ range over Z_2^k; $Z_2^0 =_{\text{def}} \{\lambda\}$ is the singleton consisting of the designated *empty string* λ. For $x \in Z_2^k$, $|x| =_{\text{def}} k$ is the length of string x. We define $\alpha^k \in Z_2^k$ as the length-k string whose all elements are equal to α. Let $\overline{\beta} =_{\text{def}} 1 - \beta$ and for $y \in Z_2^k$, let $\overline{\beta y} = \overline{\beta} y$. The length-$(k-1)$ suffix of a string $y \in Z_2^k$ is denoted by $\sigma(y)$, so $\sigma(\beta y) =_{\text{def}} y$.

2 Bidendral Decomposition of de Bruijn Graphs

We commence by defining the graphs of interest—de Bruijn graphs and complete binary trees.

The *order-n de Bruijn graph* $D(n)$ [2] has node-set Z_2^n; given $y \in Z_2^{n-1}$, two arcs are incident out of each node βy: the *shuffle* arc that leads to $y\beta$ and the *shuffle-exchange* arc that leads to $y\overline{\beta}$. Let $\mathcal{S}(\beta y) =_{\text{def}} y\beta$ and $\mathcal{E}(\beta y) =_{\text{def}} y\overline{\beta}$. Consequently, $\mathcal{S}(\beta y) = \sigma(\beta y)\beta$ and $\mathcal{E}(\beta y) = \sigma(\beta y)\overline{\beta}$.

The *complete binary tree* $T(h)$ of *height* h has node-set $\bigcup_{0 \leq k < h} Z_2^k$ and arcs leading each $y \in Z_2^k$, $0 \leq k < h$, to its *children* $y0$ and $y1$. The *root* of the tree $T(h)$ is the empty string λ, the *leaves* of $T(h)$ are all nodes $y \in Z_2^h$.

Levels in the tree $T(h)$ are defined naturally: the 2^k nodes $x \in Z_2^k$, for $0 \leq k \leq h$, reside at level $h - k$. So, the root is the only node at level h; the leaves are at level 0.

Within the tree $T(h)$, we define *tree-order* on nodes of $T(h)$ as the lexicographic order of nodes as binary strings: node x precedes node y if either $|x| < |y|$, or $|x| = |y|$ and $x < y$, where the latter order is defined on the integers represented in binary by x and y.

We prepare for our embedding of the de Bruijn graph $D(n)$ by identifying two complete binary trees in $D(n)$ and by determining the structure of partial subgraphs induced by the arcs not contained in these trees.

We partition the nodes of $D(n)$ into four sets. The first set is a singleton containing node 0^n; the second set consists of all nodes, other than 0^n, which start with 0.

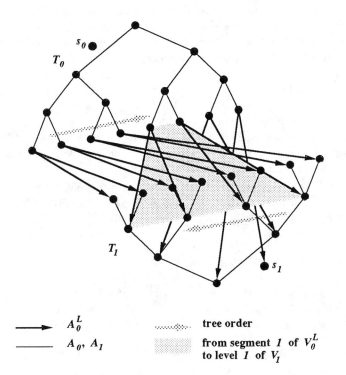

$$\Phi_\gamma(x0) = \sigma(\Phi_\gamma(x))\gamma = \mathcal{S}(\Phi_\gamma(x))$$

$$\Phi_\gamma(x1) = \sigma(\Phi_\gamma(x))\overline{\gamma} = \mathcal{E}(\Phi_\gamma(x))$$

$(|V_\gamma| = |\bigcup_{0 \le k \le n-2} Z_2^k| = 2^{n-1} - 1)$. To show that Φ_γ preserves arcs, note that

whenever $x \in Z_2^k$, $k < n-2$. Call the two arc-sets A_0 and A_1 the *tree arcs* of $D(n)$. Since $T(n-2)$ has $(2^{n-1}-2)$ arcs, there are $2 \times (2^{n-1}-2) = 2^n - 4$ tree arcs in $A_0 \cup A_1$.

Leaf subgraphs: Let V_γ^L, where $\gamma \in \{0, 1\}$, be the set of *leaves* of the tree T_γ. Then the graph $L_\gamma = (V_\gamma^L \cup V_{\overline{\gamma}} \cup S_{\overline{\gamma}}, A_\gamma^L)$ has node-set consisting of the leaves of tree T_γ, all nodes of tree $T_{\overline{\gamma}}$, and singular node $s_{\overline{\gamma}}$. For each $x \in V_\gamma^L$, there is $x' \in Z_2^{n-2}$ such that $x = \gamma\overline{\gamma}x'$, so $\mathcal{S}(x) = \overline{\gamma}x'\gamma \in (V_{\overline{\gamma}} \cup S_{\overline{\gamma}})$ and $\mathcal{E}(x) = \overline{\gamma}x'\overline{\gamma} \in (V_{\overline{\gamma}} \cup S_{\overline{\gamma}})$. We define the arc-set A_γ^L as the arcs incident out of leaves of tree T_γ. As just noted, each such arc leads a node in V_γ^L to some node of tree $T_{\overline{\gamma}}$ or to the singular node $s_{\overline{\gamma}}$. Call the two arc-sets A_0^L and A_1^L the *leaf arcs* of $D(n)$. Since two arcs are incident out of each of the 2^{n-2} leaves of T_γ, there are $2 \times 2^{n-2} \times 2 = 2^n$ leaf arcs in $A_0^L \cup A_1^L$.

Singular subgraphs: There is a self-loop incident to node s_γ, where $\gamma \in \{0, 1\}$, and there is an arc from s_γ to the root of T_γ. Call these the *singular arcs* of $D(n)$. There are 4 singular arcs altogether.

The two trees T_0 and T_1 are node-disjoint, so embedding one of them does not constrain the embedding of the other; however, each arc in both sets of leaf arcs, A_0^L and A_1^L, connects nodes from different trees. The difficulty in embedding $D(n)$ in a small book is in finding a linearization of nodes of the two trees which both accommodates the leaf arcs and respects the relative ordering of nodes within each tree prescribed by the embedding of the tree arcs. The following lemma clarifies the structure of the partial subgraph of $D(n)$ generated by the leaf arcs, thereby making it possible to define the desired linearization. See Fig. 1.

Lemma 1 *Let $a, b \in V_\gamma^L$, where $\gamma \in \{0, 1\}$, be two leaves of T_γ, and let (a, u) and (b, v) be two leaf arcs incident into $T_{\overline{\gamma}}$. Then a precedes b in tree-order of T_γ just when u follows v in tree-order of $T_{\overline{\gamma}}$.*

Proof. We first show that tree-order in T_0 coincides with the lexicographic order on nodes of $D(n)$, while tree-order in T_1 coincides with the reversed lexicographic order on nodes of $D(n)$. Indeed, given nodes x and y of $T(n-2)$ such that x precedes y, we see that

$$\Phi_0(x) = 0^{n-2-|y|}00^{|y|-|x|}1x < 0^{n-2-|y|}01y = \Phi_0(y)$$

Legend (Figure 1):

A_0^L tree order

A_0, A_1 from segment *1* of V_0^L to level *1* of V_1

Figure 1: *Bidendral decomposition of $D(5)$: the trees and leaf arcs A_0^L.*

Analogously, the third set is a singleton containing node 1^n; the fourth set consists of all nodes, other than 1^n, which start with 1. So, for each of the two values of $\gamma \in \{0, 1\}$, the node-set of $D(n)$ has the following two components:

$$S_\gamma = \{s_\gamma\} = \{\gamma^n\}, \qquad \gamma \in \{0, 1\}$$
$$V_\gamma = \{\gamma y \mid y \in Z_2^{n-1} \setminus \{\gamma^{n-1}\}\}, \qquad \gamma \in \{0, 1\}$$

Call the elements of V_0 and V_1 *tree nodes*, and call s_0 and s_1 *singular nodes*. This decomposition induces a partition of the arc-set of $D(n)$ into six subsets, so that $D(n)$ is represented as six arc-disjoint partial subgraphs. So, for each of the two values of $\gamma \in \{0, 1\}$, $D(n)$ contains the following three subgraphs:

Trees: $T_\gamma = (V_\gamma, A_\gamma)$, where $\gamma \in \{0, 1\}$, is the subgraph of $D(n)$ induced on V_γ; it is isomorphic to the complete binary tree $T(n-2)$. The isomorphism Φ_γ of the node-set of $T(n-2)$ to V_γ is defined as follows: For $x \in Z_2^k$, $k \le n-2$,

$$\Phi_0(x) = 0^{n-2-k}01x$$

$$\Phi_1(x) = 1^{n-2-k}10\overline{x}$$

By definition, Φ_γ is injective; it is also surjective by equal cardinality of its domain and its range

139

$$\Phi_1(x) = 1^{n-2-|y|} 11^{|y|-|x|} 0\overline{x} > 1^{n-2-|y|} 10\overline{y} = \Phi_1(y)$$

We complete the proof for the case $\gamma = 0$, the case $\gamma = 1$ being dual. Because $a, b \in V_0^L$, there are $a', b' \in Z_2^{n-2}$ such that $a = 01a'$, $b = 01b'$, $u \in \{S(a), \mathcal{E}(a)\}$ and $v \in \{S(b), \mathcal{E}(b)\}$. We know that a precedes b in tree-order of T_0 just when $a' < b'$, which means that

$$S(a) = 1a'0 < 1a'1 = \mathcal{E}(a) < 1b'0 = \mathcal{E}(b) < 1b'1 = S(b).$$

This chain of relations is true just when $u < v$, meaning that u follows v in tree-order of T_1. $\square$

If we extend tree-order in the two trees, consistently with the lexicographic order in $D(n)$, to cover corresponding singular nodes, then Lemma 1 holds also for the case $v = s_{\overline{\gamma}}$, since $s_{\overline{\gamma}} = \overline{\gamma}^n$ becomes the first node of $T_{\overline{\gamma}}$ in tree-order, while the leaf arc incident into it originates at node $\gamma\overline{\gamma}^{n-1}$, which is the last leaf of V_γ in tree-order.

Consider the leaves V_γ^L of T_γ, linearized so that they appear in tree-order. Partition this sequence into $n-1$ successive contiguous *segments* so that the kth segment, $0 \le k \le n-3$, has 2^{n-3-k} nodes, and the $(n-2)$nd segment has 1 node. Let the singular node $s_{\overline{\gamma}}$ be included in level $n-2$, together with the root of $T_{\overline{\gamma}}$. Our picture of the partial subgraphs L_γ, $\gamma \in \{0, 1\}$, is rendered by the following.

Proposition 1 *Let $\gamma \in \{0, 1\}$, $0 \le k \le n-2$, $0 \le j < 2^{n-3-k}$. The leaf arcs incident out of the jth node, in tree-order, of the kth segment of leaves V_γ^L of T_γ, are incident into the pair of nodes that is the jth pair, in reversed tree-order, of the kth level of $T_{\overline{\gamma}}$.*

3 Embedding de Bruijn Graphs in Five Pages

Our main result is stated as follows.

Theorem 1 *The order-n de Bruijn graph $D(n)$ admits a book-embedding in five pages, with cumulative pagewidth $(5/3)(2^n - 1 - (n \bmod 2)) - (n \bmod 2)$.*

The embedding that establishes Theorem 1 is developed in three stages. In the first stage, we specify the subembedding of the two trees T_0 and T_1. The node-sets V_0 and V_1 are disjoint, so these subembeddings are independent; each requires two pages. So, four pages may be required for the first-stage subembeddings, since we must expect that the node-sets of the trees T_0 and T_1 appear on the spine interleaved in some way dictated by the subembeddings of subsequent stages, thus preventing the pages consumed by one tree from being reused by the other. Four pages are also sufficient, as

the tree-subembeddings do not constrain each other. In the second stage, we show how to embed each set of leaf arcs A_γ^L. The resulting leaf-subembeddings are not mutually independent, as each involves the leaf nodes V_γ^L of one tree and the nodes $V_{\overline{\gamma}} \cup S_{\overline{\gamma}}$ of the other. The consideration of interference between the second-stage subembeddings is deferred until the last stage, so these subembeddings are constructed independently; each requires one page. In the last stage, we exhibit a node layout which is consistent with the four subembeddings of the first two stages. Finally, we identify two pages of the first stage that can be combined into a single page in the complete embedding, thus arriving at the total of five pages.

3.1 Embedding the Trees

We present two varieties of what we term a *spiral embedding* of trees, in particular of $T(h)$. In both spiral embeddings, nodes are laid out by an appropriate alternation of tree levels, while each level is contiguous and ordered. In the *inward* spiral embedding, the outermost levels are the *lowest*-numbered levels, while in the *outward* spiral embedding the outermost levels are the *highest*-numbered levels. See Fig. 2. The following definition makes the layout precise.

Definition 1 *Let $0 \le k \le \lfloor (h-1)/2 \rfloor$ and $0 \le \ell \le \lfloor h/2 \rfloor$.*

*(a) In the **inward spiral embedding** of $T(h)$, the layout of nodes from left to right along the spine is:*

nodes at levels $1, 3, \ldots, 2k+1, \ldots, h-1+(h \bmod 2)$, in that order, each level in reversed tree-order;

followed by:

nodes at levels $h-(h \bmod 2), h-2-(h \bmod 2), \ldots, h-2\ell-(h \bmod 2), \ldots, 0$, in that order, each level in tree-order.

*(b) In the **outward spiral embedding** of $T(h)$, the layout of nodes from left to right along the spine is:*

nodes at levels $h-(h \bmod 2), h-2-(h \bmod 2), \ldots, h-2\ell-(h \bmod 2), \ldots, 0$, in that order, each level in tree-order;

followed by:

nodes at levels $1, 3, \ldots, 2k+1, \ldots, h-1+(h \bmod 2)$, in that order, each level in reversed tree-order.

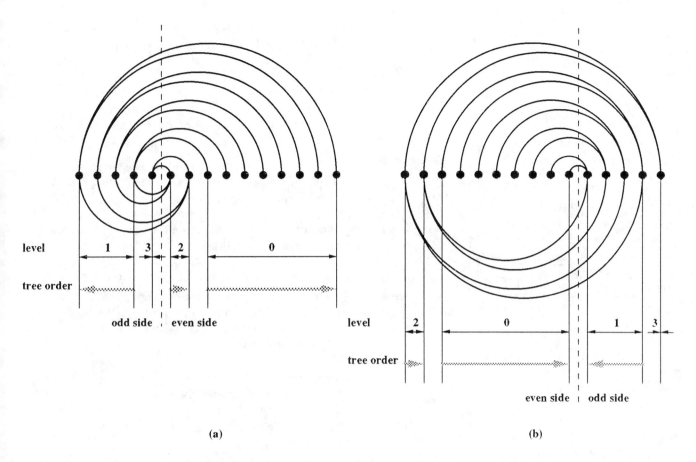

level   1   3   2   0

tree order

odd side   even side

(a)

level   2   0   1   3

tree order

even side   odd side

(b)

Figure 2: *Spiral embeddings of $T(3)$:* (a) *inward,* (b) *outward.*

The spiral embeddings separate odd-numbered tree levels from even-numbered ones, so that all levels of equal parity appear at one side of some point on the spine, while the levels of opposite parity appear at the other side. Call these sides the *even* and the *odd* side of the spine, according to tree levels that occupy them. In the inward spiral embedding the odd side is the left side of the spine, while in the outward spiral embedding the odd side is the right side of the spine. Otherwise, both embeddings place identically the levels of equal parity relative to each other—the odd-numbered ones in the order of increasing level number, the even-numbered ones in the order of decreasing level number. They also place identically the nodes inside each level—in tree-order within even-numbered levels, in reversed tree-order within odd-numbered levels. In summary,

Proposition 2 *The even side of a spiral embedding is laid out in tree-order. The odd side of a spiral embedding is laid out in reversed tree-order.*

We derive now the properties of the arc-assignment.

Lemma 2 *Both outward and inward spiral embeddings of $T(h)$ consume two pages, with cumulative pagewidth $2^{h+1} - 2$.*

Proof. The arcs of $T(h)$ lead from nodes of one level to nodes at the level below, thus each arc leads either from the even side of the spine to the odd side, or vice versa. We assign the arcs that lead from the odd side to the even side to the *upper* page of a spiral embedding, and the arcs that lead from the even side to the odd side to the *lower* page.

Consider two arcs $(x, x\alpha)$ and $(y, y\beta)$, for distinct x, y with $|x|, |y| < h$. Say that these arcs are assigned to the same page of a spiral embedding. Then x precedes y in the tree-order just when $x\alpha$ precedes $y\beta$. However, the even and the odd sides of the spine are ordered oppositely, so $x\alpha$ and $y\beta$ appear on the spine ordered oppositely to x and y; the two arcs, therefore, nest inside one another.

To verify the cumulative pagewidth, note that the total cutwidth of both pages equals the number of arcs in $T(h)$, the maximum occurring at the pivot point between odd and even side. □

Now we are prepared to specify the first stage of the embedding— the layout of the two trees. At this point, we have a "stand alone" embedding for each of the trees, but we cannot yet specify the positions of the trees on the spine relative to each other.

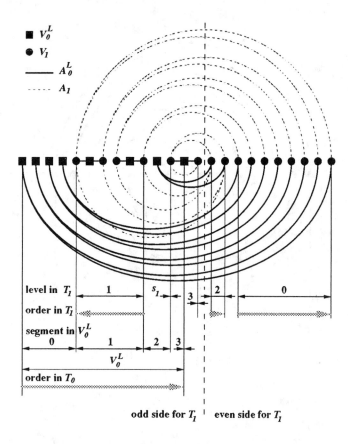

level in T_1 | 1 | s_1 | 3 | 2 | 0
order in T_1
segment in V_0^L 0 | 1 | 2 | 3
V_0^L
order in T_0

odd side for T_1 even side for T_1

Figure 3: *Embedding leaf arcs of A_0^L of $D(5)$.*

Node Layout of the Two Trees T_γ:

- T_0 is laid out by *outward* spiral embedding.

- T_1 is laid out by *inward* spiral embedding.

Recalling that the height of each tree is $n - 2$, Lemma 2 yields:

Corollary 1 *Each of the two component trees T_γ, where $\gamma \in \{0, 1\}$, of $D(n)$ is embedded in two pages, with cumulative pagewidth $2^{n-1} - 2$.*

3.2 Embedding the Leaf Arcs

Our next goal is to embed leaf arcs A_0^L and A_1^L, that lead from V_γ^L to $V_{\overline\gamma} \cup S_{\overline\gamma}$, without violating the *relative* ordering of nodes of $V_{\overline\gamma}$, stipulated by the spiral embedding of $T_{\overline\gamma}$. See Fig. 3.

In the following, we again coopt the singular node $s_{\overline\gamma}$ to level $n - 2$ of $T_{\overline\gamma}$ and place it beside the root $\overline\gamma^{n-1}\gamma$ of $T_{\overline\gamma}$, consistently with the ordering described in Proposition 2.

Node Layout of the Partial Subgraph L_γ Generated by Leaf Arcs A_γ^L:

Lay out the nodes $V_{\overline\gamma}$ as mandated by the spiral embedding of tree $T_{\overline\gamma}$ (inward if $\overline\gamma = 1$, outward if $\overline\gamma = 0$).

Then *interleave* the leaves V_γ^L of tree T_γ with the *odd* side of the spiral embedding of $T_{\overline\gamma}$ so that the following holds:

- Each even-numbered segment of V_γ^L is placed *contiguously, in tree-order*; the kth segment is placed immediately to the *left of the leftmost* node of level $k + 1$ of $T_{\overline\gamma}$.

- Each node of an odd-numbered segment of V_γ^L is placed *between* the two nodes of $T_{\overline\gamma}$ to which it is adjacent via leaf arcs of A_γ^L.

The properties of the second stage embedding are summarized in the following.

Lemma 3 *Each partial subgraph L_γ, where $\gamma \in \{0, 1\}$, generated by arcs A_γ^L that lead leaves V_γ^L of T_γ to nodes of $V_{\overline\gamma} \cup S_{\overline\gamma}$, is embedded in one page of width $(2/3)2^n + (7/3) - (8/3)(n \bmod 2)$. The leaf nodes V_γ^L of T_γ are laid out in tree-order.*

Proof. First, all leaf nodes of odd-numbered segments of V_γ^L are placed immediately beside the corresponding adjacent nodes in the tree $T_{\overline\gamma}$, so these arcs do not cross any other arcs on the page; they contribute 1 to the pagewidth.

To complete the proof for leaf arcs incident out of even-numbered segments of V_γ^L, we invoke Propositions 1 and 2. The odd-numbered levels of $T_{\overline\gamma}$ are placed in increasing order of level numbers, thus compelling the odd-numbered segments of leaves V_γ^L to appear in order of increasing segment numbers. Further, each even-numbered leaf segment, say the kth, is placed between the levels $k - 1$ and $k + 1$ of $T_{\overline\gamma}$, (assuming both levels exist), thus between the segments $k - 1$ and $k + 1$ of leaves V_γ^L. This imposes the order of increasing segment numbers on even-numbered segments. So, all nodes of even-numbered segments appear in tree-order and lie within the odd side, while the even-numbered levels of $T_{\overline\gamma}$ are also in tree-order and lie within the even side. By Proposition 1, this results in opposite orders of sources and destinations of these leaf arcs; therefore, no two leaf arcs cross.

By appealing to Proposition 1 again, we see that the order of nodes within odd-numbered segments of V_γ^L is opposite to the order within odd-numbered levels of $T_{\overline\gamma}$. By Proposition 2, the latter order is reversed tree-order, so the leaves of V_γ^L in odd-numbered segments appear in tree-order. Since leaves in even-numbered segments are in tree-order by construction, and since all segments are laid out in order of increasing segment number, we infer that all leaves V_γ^L are in tree-order.

The contribution of leaf arcs incident out of even-numbered segments of leaves V_γ into even-numbered

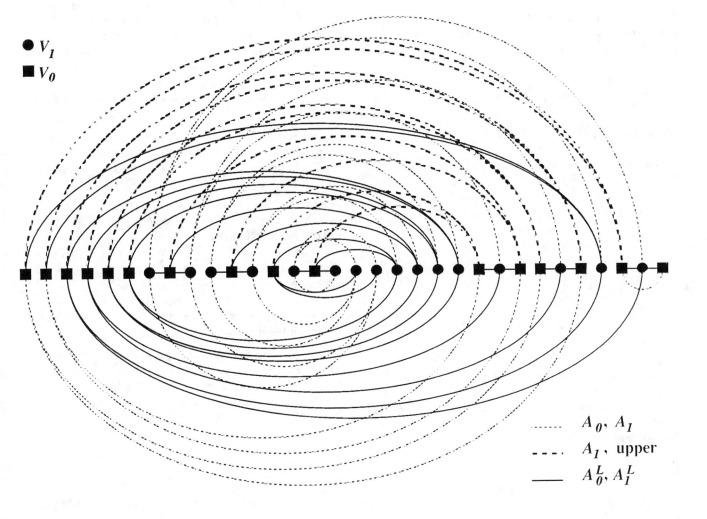

● V_1

■ V_0

.... A_0, A_1

- - - - A_1, upper

———— A_0^L, A_1^L

Figure 4: *Embedding $D(5)$ in five pages*

levels of tree $T_{\overline{\gamma}}$ and, when n is even, into the singular node $s_{\overline{\gamma}}$, is:

$$2 \times ((\sum_{k=0}^{\lfloor \frac{n-1}{2} \rfloor} 2^{2k+(n \bmod 2)}) + 1 - (n \bmod 2)) =$$

$$\frac{2}{3}(2^n + 2 - 4(n \bmod 2))$$

which yields the claimed pagewidth after accounting for the one arc contributed by the leaf arcs incident out of odd-numbered segments. □

3.3 The Complete Embedding

We have to verify now that the partial embeddings defined so far are consistent. The embeddings of the trees in the first stage are trivially so, since they involve disjoint sets of both nodes and arcs. The embedding of each partial subgraph L_γ generated by the leaf arcs is consistent with the corresponding embedding of the tree $T_{\overline{\gamma}}$; it constrains only the leaves V_γ of the other tree T_γ; by Lemma 3, the mandated linearization of the leaves V_γ^L is tree-order; it is, therefore, consistent with the layout of these leaves in the spiral embedding of T_γ. It remains to confirm that each leaf set V_γ^L can be laid out in the odd side of the spiral embedding of the other tree $T_{\overline{\gamma}}$. To that end, we need only recall that the two spiral embeddings have their odd (even) sides in opposite sides of the spine, so the constraint is readily satisfied by identifying the odd side of one spiral embedding with the even side of the other. See Fig. 4.

Finally, the self-loops incident to the singular nodes are embedded easily, and the remaining two singular arcs, each incident out of node s_γ to the root $\gamma^{n-1}\overline{\gamma}$ of T_γ, may be laid out in either of the two pages of the spiral embedding of T_γ, since no other nodes of T_γ are placed between s_γ and $\gamma^{n-1}\overline{\gamma}$.

Corollary 2 *The four partial embeddings of the two trees T_γ, where $\gamma \in \{0, 1\}$, and the two partial subgraphs L_γ generated by the leaf arcs, define an embedding of $D(n)$ in six pages.*

Our final task is to show that two of the six pages can be coalesced.

Lemma 4 *Assume that the lower page of a spiral embedding is the one that accommodates the arcs that lead from the even side to the odd side. Then, the two lower pages of the spiral embeddings of the trees T_0 and T_1 can be coalesced.*

Proof. Let (x_0, y_0) be an arc on the lower page of the outward spiral embedding of T_0, and let (x_1, y_1) be an arc on the lower page of the inward spiral embedding of T_1. We prove that the only possible ordering of the endpoints of these arcs on the spine is x_0, y_1, x_1, y_0, in which ordering the two arcs do not cross. Since the sources of the arcs are in the even sides, and the destinations in the odd sides of the corresponding spiral embeddings, we know that both x_0 and y_1 are to the left of x_1 and y_0, as the left side is even for T_0 and odd for T_1.

To prove that x_0 is to the left of y_1, we find a node which is both to the left of y_1 and to the right of x_0. Indeed, x_0 is in some non-leaf even-numbered level of T_0, so it is to the left of all leaves of T_0, by properties of the outward spiral embedding. However, y_1 is in some odd level of T_1, hence is to the right of segment 0 of the leaves of T_0, by properties of the embedding of leaf arcs. Thus, all nodes in segment 0 of V_0^L are to the left of y_1 and to the right of x_0. Analogously, all nodes in segment 0 of V_1^L are to the left of y_0 and to the right of x_1, whence the claimed ordering. $\square$

We complete the proof of Theorem 1 by noting that the cumulative pagewidths of the component embeddings, as established in Corollary 1 and Lemma 3, combine to yield the claimed cumulative pagewidth.

4 Embedding Shuffle-Exchange Graphs in Five Pages

The order-n *shuffle-exchange* graph $S(n)$ [15] has node-set Z_2^n; given $y \in Z_2^{n-1}$ and $\beta \in Z_2$, the *shuffle* arc leads node βy to node $y\beta$ and the *exchange* arc leads node $y\beta$ to node $y\overline{\beta}$.

It is known [5] that the shuffle-exchange graph $S(n)$ is a subgraph of de Bruijn graph $D(n)$; the book-embedding of Theorem 1, with the appropriate renaming of nodes of $D(n)$, thus contains a book-embedding of $S(n)$. The following announces that this book-embedding of de Bruijn graph $D(n)$ almost contains that of $S(n)$ even without renaming of nodes. See Fig. 5.

Theorem 2 *The order-n shuffle-echange graph $S(n)$ admits a book-embedding in five pages, with cumulative pagewidth $2^n - (1/3)(2^{n-1} - 1 - (n \bmod 2))$.*

Proof. The node layout is identical to that of $D(n)$. All shuffle arcs of $S(n)$ are identified with shuffle arcs of $D(n)$. Each exchange arc of $S(n)$ is incident to nodes $y\gamma$ and $y\overline{\gamma}$, for some $y \in Z_2^{n-1}$. However, one of $\{y\gamma, y\overline{\gamma}\}$ is the immediate successor of the other in the tree-order of one of the trees, say T_γ. There are no nodes of V_γ between $y\gamma$ and $y\overline{\gamma}$, and a new arc between them does not cross any other arc in either of the two pages of the spiral embedding of T_γ.

The claimed cumulative pagewidth is arrived at after removing the shuffle-exchange arcs from the embedding of $D(n)$, and subsequent incrementing by 1 the common width of the pages of the spiral embedding of the two trees. $\square$

5 Conclusion

We have presented algorithms for embedding shuffle-like graphs in books of five pages; our pagenumber results are practically optimal, at least in terms of the cost measures prevailing in the Diogenes design method. Yet, our book-embeddings share the weakness of the majority of the others—their *pagewidths* are greater than optimal, in this case by a factor logarithmic in the size of the graph. It would be very interesting to bring the pagewidths of book-embeddings of popular interconnection networks closer to optimal, while retaining small pagenumbers, or to find some pagenumber-pagewidth tradeoffs. However, we do not consider suboptimal pagewidths as a significant weakness. They reflect the increase in area from which Diogenes layouts suffer, in contrast to the conventional layouts. Nevertheless, this penalty comes with a great advantage of fault-tolerance inherent in the design. Simultaneous optimization of both cost measures would greatly reduce the price of fault-tolerance.

Acknowledgment. The author is greatly indebted to her research advisor Arnold L. Rosenberg, who proposed the problem and supplied many valuable comments from which the presentation has substantially improved.

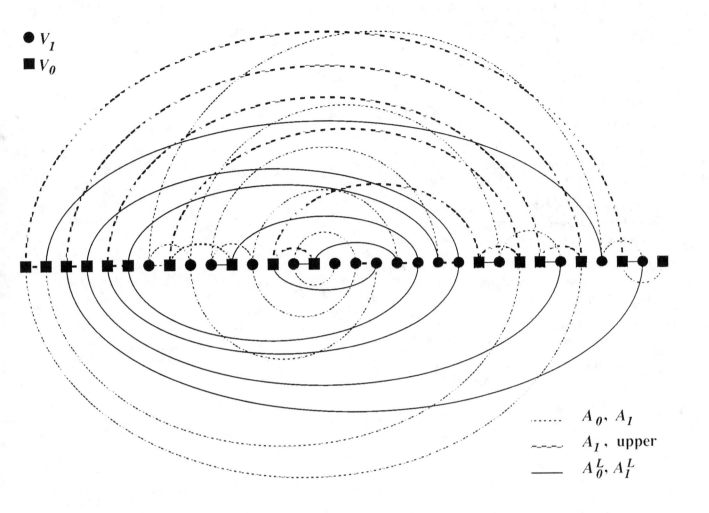

$\bullet\ V_1$

$\blacksquare\ V_0$

$\cdots\cdots\ A_0,\ A_1$

$----\ A_1,\ \text{upper}$

$------\ A_0^L,\ A_1^L$

Figure 5: *Embedding $S(5)$ in five pages*

References

[1] F. Bernhart and P.C. Kainen (1979): The book thickness of a graph. *J. Comb. Th. (B) 27*, 320-331.

[2] N.G. de Bruijn (1946): A combinatorial problem. *Proc. Koninklijke Nederlandsche Akademie van Wetenschappen (A) 49*, Part 2, 758-764.

[3] F.R.K. Chung, F.T. Leighton, A.L. Rosenberg (1983): DIOGENES – A methodology for designing fault-tolerant processor arrays. *13th Intl. Conf. on Fault-Tolerant Computing*, 26-32.

[4] F.R.K. Chung, F.T. Leighton, A.L. Rosenberg (1987): Embedding graphs in books: A layout problem with applications to VLSI design. *SIAM J. Algebr. Discr. Meth. 8*, 33-58.

[5] R. Feldmann and W. Unger (1990): The cube-connected cycles network is a subgraph of the butterfly network. Typescript, Univ. Paderborn.

[6] M.R. Garey, D.S. Johnson, G.L. Miller, C.H. Papadimitriou (1980): The complexity of coloring circular arcs and chords. *SIAM J. Algebr. Discr. Meth. 1*, 216-227.

[7] R.A. Games (1986): Optimal book embeddings of the FFT, Beneš, and barrel shifter networks. *Algorithmica 1*, 233-250.

[8] L.S. Heath and S. Istrail (1990): The pagenumber of genus g graphs is $O(g)$. Tech. Rpt. 90-21, Virginia Polytechnic Inst. see also, *19th ACM Symp. on Theory of Computing*, 388-397.

[9] L.S. Heath and A.L. Rosenberg (1990): Laying out graphs using queues. Tech. Rpt. 90-75, Univ. Massachusetts; submitted for publication.

[10] H.T. Kung (1982): Why systolic architectures? *Computer 15*, 37-46.

[11] S.M. Malitz (1991): Graphs with E edges have pagenumber $O(\sqrt{E})$. *J. Algorithms*, to appear.

[12] D.J. Muder, M.L. Weaver, D.B. West (1988): Pagenumber of complete bipartite graphs. *J. Graph Th. 12*, 469-489.

[13] A.L. Rosenberg (1983): The Diogenes approach to testable fault-tolerant arrays of processors. *IEEE Trans. Comp., C-32*, 902-910.

[14] A.L. Rosenberg (1991): Product-shuffle networks: toward reconciling shuffles and butterflies. *Discr. Appl. Math.*, to appear.

[15] H. Stone (1971): Parallel processing with the perfect shuffle. *IEEE Trans. Comp., C-20*, 153-161.

[16] M. Yannakakis (1989): Embedding planar graphs in four pages *J. Comp. Syst. Sci. 38*, 36-67.

Simulating Binary Trees on X-Trees

(Extended Abstract)

Burkhard Monien*

Dept. of Math. and Computer Science

University of Paderborn

4790 Paderborn, Germany

Abstract

We show how to embed an arbitrary binary tree with dilation 11 and optimal expansion into an X-tree. To our knowledge this is the first result proving that every binary tree can be simulated by a "natural" network of bounded degree with constant dilation and constant expansion. Our construction also leads to a universal graph of bounded degree for binary trees, the degree bound being at most 415.

1 Introduction

A lot of work has been done in recent years studying the properties of interconnection networks for parallel computer systems. An important feature of an interconnection network is its degree of universality, i.e. its ability to simulate programs written for other architectures without a significant time delay. The popularity of the hypercube network is based also on the fact that it can simulate common program structures like grids or trees in a very efficient way.

In this paper we are interested in the simulation of binary trees. Binary trees reflect common data structures and the type of program structure found in common divide-and-conquer algorithms. Bhatt, Chung, Leighton and Rosenberg

[1] show that arbitrary binary trees can be embedded into hypercubes with constant expansion and dilation 10. In [7] Monien and Sudborough improve this result and describe an embedding with constant expansion and dilation 3. They also show that every binary tree can be embedded into its optimal hypercube (i.e. without expansion) with dilation 5.

Hypercubes have many properties distinguishing them as an excellent candidate for an interconnection network. However their vertex degree increases with the number of vertices. Cube connected cycles and butterfly networks are networks of constant degree sharing the topological properties of the hypercube, especially they have a small diameter and a very good routing behaviour. Up to now it is not totally clear up to what extent these networks also have the good universal behaviour of the hypercube. In [3] Bhatt, Chung, Hong, Leighton and Rosenberg give a negative and a positive answer. They show that grids and X-trees cannot be embedded with constant expansion and dilation into cube connected cycles and butterfly networks. The embedding of grids needs dilation $0(\log n)$ and the embedding of X-trees dilation $0(\log \log n)$, where n is the number of nodes. These are the first graphs that are known to be efficiently embeddable into hypercube networks but not into cube connected cycles or into butterfly networks. On the other hand they show that complete binary trees can be embedded with dilation $0(1)$ and expansion $0(1)$. The efficiency of simulat-

*This work was supported by the grant Mo 285/4 from the German Research Association (DFG).

ing arbitrary binary trees is left open. To our knowledge there exists no result showing that arbitrary binary trees can be embedded into some "natural" network of small degree with dilation $O(1)$ and expansion $O(1)$. The existence of such a "universal" network of bounded degree is known ([1,2,6]), but the previous constructions lead to a very large vertex degree which is left unspecified.

In this paper we study embeddings of binary trees into X-trees. An X-tree is a graph that is obtained from a complete binary tree by adding cross edges connecting the vertices of the same level. The X-tree of height 3 is shown in the figure 1 below. An embedding is a mapping of the vertices of the tree into the nodes of the X-tree. Given an embedding, its <u>dilation</u> is the maximum distance in the X-tree between images of adjacent vertices of the tree. Our goal is to minimize the dilation, as the dilation corresponds to the number of clock cycles needed in the X-tree network to communicate between formerly adjacent processors in the tree. It is also important to minimize the size of the host network. The <u>expansion</u> of an embedding is the ratio of the size of the X-tree divided by the size of the tree.

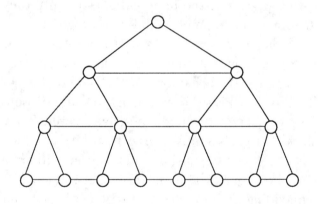

Figure 1: The X-tree of height 3

Often an embedding is not one-to-one. In this case also the <u>load factor</u> measures the quality of an embedding. The load factor is the maximum number of vertices of the tree mapped to any node of the X-tree. For networks of fixed size our goal is to minimize the load factor, as the load factor measures the computation work which has

to be done by a single processor of the X-tree network.

Our main result is the following theorem, which shows that every binary tree can be embedded with dilation 3 and load factor 16 into its "optimal" X-tree.

Theorem 1: Let $T = (V, E)$ be an arbitrary binary tree with n nodes, $n = 16 \cdot (2^{r+1} - 1)$ for some r. Then there exists an embedding of T into the X-tree of height r with dilation 3 and load factor 16.

From Theorem 1 we can easily derive the following two theorems

Theorem 2: Let $T = (V, E)$ be an arbitrary binary tree with n nodes, $n = 16(2^{r+1} - 1)$ for some r. Then there exists an injective embedding of T into the X-tree of height $r + 4$ with dilation 11.

Theorem 3: Let $T = (V, E)$ be an arbitrary binary tree with n nodes, $n = 16 \cdot (2^r - 1)$ for some r. Then there exists an embedding of T into the hypercube Q_r with load factor 16 and dilation 4.

It had to be expected that the embedding into the hypercube found in theorem 3 by using the embedding from theorem 1 cannot match the specialized technique from [7] for embedding binary trees directly into the hypercube (with dilation 3 and constant expansion, and with dilation 5 without expansion, respectively). However, theorem 3 gives some new information. It shows that every binary tree can be embedded into its optimal hypercube with dilation 4 if we allow non-injective mappings with constant load factor.

A graph U with n nodes is said to be <u>universal</u> for a family G of n-node graphs if every graph in the family is a subgraph of U. This is a very strong simulation property since every computation on a network belonging to the family G can be simulated by U in real time. The problem of constructing minimal graphs for the family of all trees with the fewest number of edges has found considerable attention. In [4] and [5] it was shown that $0(n \cdot \log n)$ edges are necessary and sufficient. This result can be improved if we restrict ourselves to the family of binary trees. In [1], [2] and [6] it is shown how to construct a universal graph of bounded degree d, d being very large and left unspecified. We extend our embedding into the X-tree and construct a universal graph of "small" degree. This way we get a universal graph if the number of nodes is equal to $n = 2^i - 16$ for some i. We have no doubt that one could generalize this result to hold also for arbitrary n, but we have not done so in this paper.

Theorem 4: For every $n \in N$, such that $n = 2^i - 16$ for some i, there exists a graph G_n of degree bounded by 415 such that every binary tree with n nodes is a spanning tree of G_n.

Theorem 1 is proved in section 2 and the other results are proved in section 3.

2   The Proof of Theorem 1

In this section we will prove theorem 1. We start with a few definitions and two helpful lemmas about the separation of trees. The proofs of these lemmas are rather straightforward and a similar approach was used already in [7], but there are some details which are different from the formulation in [7] and which are important for the proof of theorem 1. This, we think, justifies to state the proofs also in this paper.

Let us recall the definition of an X-tree from [8].

Definition: The X-tree of height r, denoted by $X(r)$, is the graph whose nodes are all binary strings of length at most r and whose edges connect each string x of length $i(0 \leq i < r)$ with the strings xa, a in $\{0, 1\}$, of length $i + 1$ and, when $\text{binary}(x) < 2^i - 1$, also connects x with $\text{successor}(x)$, where $\text{binary}(x)$ is the integer x represents in binary notation and $\text{successor}(x)$ denotes the unique binary string of length i such that $\text{binary}(\text{successor}(x)) = \text{binary}(x) + 1$. (For completeness let $\text{binary}(\epsilon) = 0$, where ϵ is the empty string).

Note that if we have given some tree $T = (V, E)$

and some set $S \subset V$ of nodes, then the graph $T_S = (S, \{\{u, v\} \in E; u, v \in S\})$, induced by S and T, is a forest. Let us denote this forest by $F(S, T)$.

Definition: S is called <u>collinear</u> <u>with</u> <u>respect</u> <u>to</u> $\underline{T}$, or just <u>collinear</u> if T is understood, if any tree from $F(V - S, T)$ is connected by at most two edges to nodes from S.

Lemma 1: Let $T = (V, E)$ be an n node binary tree with two designated nodes r_1 and r_2. Let Δ be some natural number with $n > 4\Delta/3$. Then we can find two sets $S_1, S_2 \subset V$ with the following properties.

(1) $\{r_1, r_2\} \subset S_1 \cup S_2$

(2) $|S_1| \leq 4, |S_2| \leq 2$

(3) The deletion of the edges connecting nodes from S_1 with nodes from S_2 splits T into two forests T_1, T_2 with n_1, n_2 nodes, respectively, such that T_i contains all nodes from S_i for $i = 1, 2$ and $|n_2 - \Delta| \leq \lfloor \frac{\Delta+1}{3} \rfloor$.

(4) S_i is collinear in T_i for $i = 1, 2$.

Proof: Let T and Δ be as described above. For convenience we replace T with a directed tree T', containing the same vertices, but replace each edge $\{x, y\}$ of T by an edge connecting x and y and directed away from the designated node r_1. (In our proof, for ease of reading, T will denote the directed tree T'.) With directed edges we can refer without loss of generality, for any node z in T, to the subtree of T with root z, denoted by $T(z)$. Also, by $T(z, y)$ we denote the largest subtree of $T(z)$ that does not contain the vertex y.

First we consider the procedure find 1 which will find a node u with

$$(\lceil 4\Delta/3 \rceil - 1)/2 \leq |T(u)| \leq 4\Delta/3.$$

procedure find1 (u);
    while $|T(u)| > 4\Delta/3$ do
    let u be the child of u of maximal cardinality;

It is not difficult to verify that $||T(u)| - \Delta| \leq \lfloor (\Delta+1)/3 \rfloor$ holds. Furthermore $r_1 \neq u$, since we have assumed that $n = |T(r_1)| > 4\Delta/3$ holds. Therefore we will define S_1, S_2 in such a way that $T_2 = T(u), T_1 = T(r_1, u)$ holds. We have to guarantee that S_1 and S_2 are collinear and we consider two cases. Let x be the father of u in T.

If $T(u)$ contains r_2 then we set $S_1 = \{r_1, x\}, S_2 = \{u, r_2\}$. If $T(r_1, u)$ contains r_2 then there exists some node y in $T(r_1, u)$ such that the path from r_1 to u and the path from r_1 to r_2 part at node y. Of course y may be equal to r_1 or equal to r_2, but in general y is a node different from r_1, r_2 and x.

In this case we set $S_1 = \{r_1, r_2, x, y\}, S_2 = \{u\}$. It is obvious that S_1 and S_2 are collinear. $\square$

Lemma 2: Let $T, n, r_1,$ and r_2 be as in Lemma 1 and let Δ be some natural number, $\Delta \le n$. Then we can find two sets $S_1, S_2 \subset V$ which fulfill conditions (1) and (4) from lemma 1 and additionally,

(2') $|S_1|, |S_2| \le 4$

(3') The deletion of the edges connecting nodes from S_1 with nodes from S_2 splits T into two forests T_1, T_2 with n_1, n_2 nodes, respectively, such that T_i contains all nodes from S_i for $i = 1, 2$ and

$$|n_2 - \Delta| \le \lfloor \frac{\Delta + 4}{9} \rfloor$$

Proof: As in the proof of lemma 1 we assume that we have directed the edges in T away from the node r_1. Note that we can find a partition fulfilling condition (3') by applying procedure find1 twice. But we have to be a little bit more careful than in the proof of lemma 1 in order to guarantee the other conditions. First we assume that $|T| = n > 4\Delta/3$ holds. We start our algorithm by calling the following procedure find 2 with the argument v set to the designated node r_1:

procedure find 2 (v);
    while $|T(v)| > 4\Delta/3$ and $v \ne r_2$ do
    let v be the child of v on the path from r_1 to r_2;

This call computes a node v on the path from r_1 to r_2 such that either $|T(v)| \le 4\Delta/3$ or $|T(v)| > 4\Delta/3$ and $v = r_2$. We consider three cases. In all these cases the condition $n > 4\Delta/3$ remains invariant during the computation.

1. $v = r_2$ and $|T(v)| > 4\Delta/3$
   In this case the designated nodes r_1 and r_2 are placed both into the set S_1. We find our partition by applying procedure find1 twice starting from node r_2.

2. $|T(v)| < \Delta$
   Let x be the father of v in the tree T. In this case the nodes r_1 and x are placed into set S_1 and the nodes r_2 and v into set S_2. We find our partition by applying procedure find1 twice in $T(x, v)$ starting from node x.

3. $\Delta \le |T(v)| \le 4 \cdot \Delta/3$.
   Let again x be the father of v in the tree T. The nodes r_1 and x are placed into the set S_1 and then the partition is used which is found in lemma 1 with the entries $T' = T(v), \Delta' = |T'| - \Delta$ and designated nodes $r_1' = v$ and $r_2' = r_2$.

We still have to consider the case $\Delta \le n \le 4\Delta/3$. In this case we solve the problem with $\Delta_1 = n - \Delta \le \Delta/3$ and interchange the roles of S_1 and S_2 and of T_1 and T_2 afterwards. Note that $n \ge \Delta \ge 4 \cdot \Delta_1/3$ and therefore we can apply the algorithm described above. Furthermore $|n_2 - \Delta| = |n_1 - \Delta_1| \le \lfloor (\Delta_1 + 4)/9 \rfloor \le \lfloor (\Delta + 4)/9 \rfloor$. $\square$

Now, we proceed to describe our embedding of an arbitrary binary tree into an X-tree with load factor 16, dilation 3 and optimal expansion. Note that any graph that is embeddable into an X-tree of height r with load factor 16 and optimal expansion has at most $16 \cdot (2^{r+1} - 1)$ nodes.

Theorem 1: Let $T = (V, E)$ be an arbitrary binary tree with n nodes, $n = 16 \cdot (2^{r+1} - 1)$ for some r. Then there exists an embedding into the X-tree of height r with dilation 3 and load factor 16.

Proof: The main idea of our construction is not very difficult, but we have to be very careful in describing it.

We define iterative partial embeddings $\delta_i : D_i \to X_i, D_i \subset V$, for $i = 1, \ldots, r$. For every i these embeddings will have the following properties:

(1) δ_i is an extension of δ_{i-1}; i.e. $D_{i-1} \subset D_i$ and $\delta_i(u) = \delta_{i-1}(u) \ \forall u \in D_{i-1}$.

(2) If $i < r$, then δ_i has load factor 16 and $|D_i| = 16 \cdot (2^{i+1} - 1)$; i.e. if $i < r$, then exactly 16 nodes of T are mapped onto every node of the X-tree X_i.

(3) δ_i has dilation 3; i.e. if $u, v \in D_i$ and $\{u, v\} \in E$, then there exists a path of length at most 3 connecting $\delta_i(u)$ and $\delta_i(v)$.

(4) If two nodes $u, v \in V$ are neighbors in T, then the levels of their images in the X-tree differ at most by an additive constant of two. I.e. let $u, v \in V$ with $\{u, v\} \in E$. Assume $u \in D_i$ and let $\delta_i(u)$ be a vertex in the X-tree on level j, $j \leq i - 2$. Then $v \in D_i$ holds and the level of the vertex $\delta_i(v)$ is some number j' with $|j - j'| \leq 2$.

First we will describe the construction informally. Let $R_i = V - D_i$ be the set of nodes of T not laid out so far. We attach every node from R_i to some leaf of X_i, i.e. we define a mapping $\rho_i : R_i \to \{0, 1\}^i$. To every vertex α of the X-tree X_i we associate all the nodes of T which are mapped or attached to itself or to one of its successors in the X-tree, i.e. we set

$$A_i(\alpha) = \delta_i^{-1}(\alpha) \cup \rho_i^{-1}(\alpha) \quad \text{for } \alpha \in \{0, 1\}^i$$
$$A_i(\alpha) = \delta_i^{-1}(\alpha) \cup A_i(\alpha 0) \cup A_i(\alpha 1)$$
$$\text{for } \alpha \in \{0, 1\}^j, j < i.$$

Let us set $n_i = 16 \cdot (2^{i+1} - 1)$ for $i \in N$, i.e. n_i is the maximum number of nodes which can be embedded onto an X-tree of height i with load factor 16. In the final embedding δ_r we have of course $|A_r(\alpha)| = n_{r-|\alpha|}$ for all α. This is not true for values $i < r$, but our aim is to define the mappings δ_i and the attachments ρ_i in such a way that the differences $|n_{r-|\alpha|} - |A_i(\alpha)||$ get smaller and smaller for increasing values of i. We will try to get better approximations by going from the embedding δ_i to the embedding δ_{i+1}

and we will use the horizontal edges on level $i+1$ of the X-tree X_{i+1} to obtain this improvement.

Furthermore we have to split $A_i(\alpha)$, $|\alpha| = i$, into the sets $A_{i+1}(\alpha 0)$, $A_{i+1}(\alpha 1)$, and we will use the edge $\{\alpha 0, \alpha 1\}$, to get good values for $|A_{i+1}(\alpha 0)|$ and $|A_{i+1}(\alpha 1)|$. Thus we use every horizontal edge on level $i + 1$ for one such adjustment.

To describe this construction more formally, let us consider $R_i = V - D_i$. Let F_i be the forest induced by R_i and T. Since T is connected, every tree from F_i is connected by at least an edge to some node from D_i. δ_i will have the following additional properties:

(5) D_i is collinear.

(6) If for some tree $\tilde{T} = (\tilde{V}, \tilde{E})$ from F_i there exist two different nodes $u, v \in D_i$ and $w_1, w_2 \in \tilde{V}$ with $\{u, w_1\}, \{v, w_2\} \in E$, then u and v are mapped by δ_i to the same vertex, i.e. $\delta_i(u) = \delta_i(v)$.

Thus, for every tree $\tilde{T} = (\tilde{V}, \tilde{E})$ from F_i the value $\delta_i(u)$ for any node $u \in D_i$ with $\{u, w\} \in E$ for some $w \in \tilde{V}$ is determined uniquely and will be denoted by $\alpha(\tilde{T})$. We will call $\alpha(\tilde{T})$ the <u>characteristic address</u> of $\tilde{T}$. Note that because of property (4) the characteristic address is a vertex on level $i - 1$ or on level i of the X-tree X_i.

As above, let $\tilde{T} = (\tilde{V}, \tilde{E})$ be a tree from F_i. Nodes $w \in \tilde{V}$ with $\{u, w\} \in E$ for some $u \in D_i$ are called <u>designated nodes</u> of $\tilde{T}$. Note that every tree from F_i contains at least one designated node and (because of property (5)) at most two designated nodes. Following the notation from [7] we call a tree with two designated nodes an <u>interval</u>. Furthermore we are building pairs of trees with the same characteristic address containing only one designated node. Such a pair of trees will also be called an <u>interval</u>. Note that this way to every vertex of X_i on levels $i - 1$ or i there are associated at most 16 intervals, since every node from D_i has at most 2 neighbors in R_i.

We will now use the characteristic addresses to define the attachment $\rho_i : R_i \to \{0, 1\}^i$. All nodes of some tree $\tilde{T}$ are attached to the same vertex. If $\alpha(\tilde{T}) \in \{0,1\}^i$, then we set $\rho_i(u) = \alpha(\tilde{T})$ for all nodes u of $\tilde{T}$. If $\alpha(\tilde{T}) \in \{0,1\}^{i-1}$, then we set $\rho_i(u) = \alpha(\tilde{T})\beta(\tilde{T})$ for all nodes $u \in \tilde{T}$ and for some $\beta(\tilde{T}) \in \{0,1\}$.

Thus in order to define the attachment we need a mapping $\mu_i : \tilde{R}_i \to \{0,1\}$, where $\tilde{R}_i$ is the set of all nodes $u \in R_i$ for which there exists some node $v \in D_i$ with $\{u,v\} \in E$ and $|\delta_i(v)| = i-1$.

μ_i will fulfill the following properties:

(7) If two nodes $u,v \in \tilde{R}_i$ are neighbors of the same node $w \in D_i, |\delta_i(w)| = i-1$, then $\mu_i(u) \neq \mu_i(v)$.

(8) If two nodes $u,v \in \tilde{R}_i$ belong to the same tree in F_i then $\mu_i(u) = \mu_i(v)$.

The mappings δ_i and μ_i determine the embedding and the attachment and therefore also the sets $A_i(\alpha)$ for all $\alpha \in \{0,1\}^j, 0 \leq j \leq i$. In order to measure the quality of embedding and attachment we introduce the notations $nh(j,i), nl(j,i)$ and $\Delta(j,i)$ for $0 \leq j \leq i \leq r$.

Let $nh(j,i)$ and $nl(j,i)$, respectively, denote the maximal (and minimal, respectively) cardinalities of the set of nodes associated to any node on level j of the X-tree after i rounds. $\Delta(j,i)$ measures the maximal number of nodes which still have to be shifted between vertices on level j after i rounds. I.e.

$$
\begin{aligned}
nh(j,i) &= \max\{|A_i(\alpha)|; |\alpha| = j\} \\
nl(j,i) &= \min\{|A_i(\alpha)|; |\alpha| = j\} \\
\Delta(0,i) &= 0 \\
\Delta(j,i) &= \tfrac{1}{2}\max_{|\alpha|=j-1}||A_i(\alpha 0)| - |A_i(\alpha 1)|| \\
&\quad \text{for } j > 0.
\end{aligned}
$$

We are now ready to describe the construction of the embeddings $\delta_i, 0 \leq i \leq r$.

We start by defining δ_0. We choose some subtree $D_0 \subset V$ of 16 nodes and set $\delta_0(u) = \epsilon$ for all $u \in D_0$. All nodes from $R_o = V - D_o$ are attached to the vertex ϵ, i.e. $\rho_o(u) = \epsilon$ for all $u \in R_o$.

Now the embeddings $\delta_i, 1 \leq i \leq r$, are defined by the iterative algorithm X-TREE which is defined below.

algorithm X-TREE

for $i := 1$ to r do
begin
    for $j := 0$ to $i - 2$ do
        for all $\alpha \in \{0,1\}^j$ do
            $ADJUST(\alpha 0, \alpha 1, i)$;
        for all $\alpha \in \{0,1\}^{i-1}$ do $SPLIT(\alpha, i)$
end;

The procedures $ADJUST$ and $SPLIT$ are described in detail later. They determine which nodes from R_{i-1} are mapped to the leaves $\alpha, |\alpha| = i$, of X_i. Note that during round i we don't change the layout performed in the previous rounds and therefore δ_i is an extension of δ_{i-1}, i.e. condition (1) holds.

Both procedures $ADJUST$ and $SPLIT$ use the partition lemmas 1 or 2, respectively. The call $ADJUST(\alpha 0, \alpha 1, i), 0 \leq |\alpha| \leq i-2$, shifts one or two subtrees attached to the node $\alpha 01^{i-|\alpha|}$ to the node $\alpha 10^{i-|\alpha|}$ (or vice versa). Note that every vertex attached to node $\alpha 01^{i-|\alpha|}$ is also attached to $\alpha 0$ and every vertex attached to $\alpha 10^{i-|\alpha|}$ is also attached to $\alpha 1$ and therefore we can obtain this way values for $|A(\alpha 0)|$ and $|A(\alpha 1)|$ with a better balance. The call $SPLIT(\alpha, i), |\alpha| = i - 1$, partitions the set of trees attached to α into two sets which are attached now to $\alpha 0$ and $\alpha 1$. During these calls all the designated nodes defined by using the partitions from lemma 1 or lemma 2 are laid out. Also, during the call of procedure $SPLIT$ all nodes are laid our which are children of nodes laid out at level $i - 2$ (if this has not been done before).

Note that this way 16 nodes are associated to every vertex of the X-tree. 4 nodes result from applying procedure $SPLIT$, 4 nodes from applying procedure $ADJUST$ and there may be 8 nodes which are children of nodes laid out in the grandparent vertex. Note that also 16 nodes are laid out in the grandparent vertex, which may have 32 children which are distributed among 4 vertices.

We can show that for $0 \leq j \leq i \leq r$

$$\Delta(i,i) \le 2^{r+2-i} \quad \text{, if } i < r$$
$$\Delta(j,i) \le 2^{r+j+1-2i} \quad \text{, if } j < i \text{ and}$$
$$2i \le r+j+1$$
$$\Delta(j,i) = 0 \quad \text{, if } 2i \ge r+j+2$$

This implies that $\Delta(j,r) = 0$ for $j \le r-2$ and the final embedding (i.e. $\Delta(j,r) = 0$ for all $0 \le j \le r$) can be obtained by some simple rearrangement in the last two levels.

The details, will be described in the following subsections:

(i) The procedure $ADJUST$

(ii) The procedure $SPLIT$

(iii) Estimations of $\Delta(j,i), nh(j,i), nl(j,i)$

(iv) Revision of the procedure $ADJUST$

(v) The final embedding

Because of lack of space the subsection (iv) and some details in (ii) and (iii) will not be described in this extended abstract.

While describing the procedures $ADJUST$ and $SPLIT$ we will also show that the embedding computed by our algorithm X-TREE fulfills conditions (2),...,(8). Instead of conditions (3) and (4) we will prove the slightly stronger condition (3').

(3') Let $u,v \in D_i$ with $|\delta_i(u)| \le |\delta_i(v)|$. Then $\{u,v\} \in E$ implies that $\delta_i(v) \in N(\delta_i(u))$.

Here for each vertex α of the X-tree X_i let $N(\alpha)$ be the set of all vertices from X_i which can be reached from α by following a path in X_i consisting of at most three horizontal edges or of at most two downward edges followed by at most two horizontal edges. For the case $|\alpha| \le i-2$, $\alpha \ne 00\ldots0, \alpha \ne 11\ldots1$, the set $N(\alpha)$ is shown in figure 2.

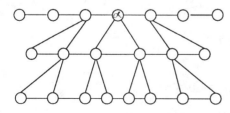

Figure 2: Some vertex α and its set $N(\alpha)$

It is clear, that condition (3) and condition (4) follow directly from condition (3').

(i) The procedure $ADJUST$

In the i-th loop of the algorithm the procedure $ADJUST$ is called with the parameters $(\alpha 0, \alpha 1, i)$ for all $\alpha \in \{0,1\}^j$ and (in this successive order) for all $j = 0,1,\ldots,i-2$. Consider now some fixed j and some $\alpha \in \{0,1\}^j$. Let $A(\alpha 0)$ and $A(\alpha 1)$ be the sets of nodes associated to $\alpha 0$ and $\alpha 1$, respectively, when the algorithm calls $ADJUST(\alpha 0, \alpha 1, i)$.

Let $\Delta = \lfloor \frac{1}{2}(|A(\alpha 0)| - |A(\alpha 1)|) \rfloor$ be half the difference between $|A(\alpha 0)|$ and $|A(\alpha 1)|$ and assume w.l.o.g. that $|A(\alpha 0)| > |A(\alpha 1)|$ holds. Using lemma 2 we will now "shift" some nodes from $A(\alpha 0)$ to $A(\alpha 1)$ such that afterwards half the difference between $|A(\alpha 0)|$ and $|A(\alpha 1)|$ is at most $\lfloor (\Delta + 4)/9 \rfloor$. In doing so we consider the sets of trees in F_{i-1} which are attached by ρ_{i-1} to the leaves $\alpha 01^{i-2-|\alpha|}$ and $\alpha 10^{i-2-|\alpha|}$.

First let us assume that in the set of trees attached to $\alpha 01^{i-2-|\alpha|}$ there exists some interval $\tilde{T}$ which has at least Δ nodes.

From the definition of the attachment we know that the characteristic address β of $\tilde{T}$ is either equal to $\alpha 01^{i-2-|\alpha|}$ or to the parent of $\alpha 01^{i-2-|\alpha|}$ in X_{i-1}. Now consider the two trees T_1 and T_2 obtained by splitting $\tilde{T}$ by using lemma 2.

We add the nodes from $S_1 \cup S_2$ to the domain of the embedding δ_i (which we are constructing during this loop) and we set

$$\delta_i(v) = \alpha 01^{i-1-|\alpha|} \quad \forall v \in S_1$$
$$\delta_i(v) = \alpha 10^{i-1-|\alpha|} \quad \forall v \in S_2$$

Now let us assume, that all intervals from the set of intervals attached to $\alpha 01^{i-2-|\alpha|}$ have cardinality less than Δ, but that there exist two intervals I_1, I_2 with $|I_1| + |I_2| \ge 4\Delta/3$. Let $|I_1| \ge |I_2|$. Then $2\Delta/3 \le |I_1| < \Delta$ holds. Let r_1, r_2 be the two designated nodes of I_1. First we shift the whole interval from $\alpha 01^{i-2-|\alpha|}$ to $\alpha 10^{i-2-|\alpha|}$. This is done by adding r_1 and r_2 to the domain of δ_i and by setting $\delta(r_1) = \delta(r_2) = \alpha 10^{i-1-|\alpha|}$. Afterwards half the difference between $|A(\alpha 0)|$ and $|A(\alpha 1)|$ is equal to $\Delta_1 = \Delta - |I_1| \le \Delta/3$.

Now we apply lemma 1 with the interval I_2 and the value Δ_1. We can do the partition according to lemma 1 with a set S_2 of at most 2 elements. We add the elements from $S_1 \cup S_2$ to the domain of δ_i and set again

$$\delta_i(v) = \alpha 01^{i-1-|\alpha|} \quad \text{for} \quad v \in S_1$$
$$\delta_i(v) = \alpha 10^{i-1-|\alpha|} \quad \text{for} \quad v \in S_2$$

In this way we guarantee that $\lfloor \frac{1}{2}(|A_i(\alpha 0)| - |A_i(\alpha 1)|) \rfloor \leq \lfloor (\Delta + 4)/9 \rfloor$ holds and we have mapped at most 4 nodes from R_i to $\alpha 01^{i-1-|\alpha|}$ and 4 nodes to $\alpha 10^{i-1-|\alpha|}$

Note that $\Delta - \lfloor (\Delta + 4)/9 \rfloor \leq |T_2| \leq \Delta + \lfloor (\Delta + 4)/9 \rfloor$ and therefore after these shifts $\lfloor \frac{1}{2}(|A_i(\alpha 0)| - |A_i(\alpha 1)|) \rfloor \leq \lfloor (\Delta + 4)/9 \rfloor$ holds.

This call of $ADJUST$ laid out a few more nodes and we have to show that all the conditions remain valid. Conditions (2), (7) and (8) are not influenced by a call of $ADJUST$. Condition (5) remains valid since S_i is collinear in T_i for $i = 1, 2$, and condition (6) remains valid since all nodes from S_1 and from S_2, respectively, are mapped to the same vertex.

We still have to show that condition (3') is not affected by a call of $ADJUST$. Let us consider first the case where $\tilde{T}$ has at least Δ nodes.

Edges inside $S_1 \cup S_2$ connect nodes which are laid out at the same vertices or at adjacent vertices of the X-tree. So we have to consider only edges connecting nodes from $S_1 \cup S_2$ with nodes laid out earlier. Condition (5) holds and therefore at most 2 edges are connecting $\tilde{T}$ with D_{i-1}. These edges connect two nodes which are laid out at the characteristic address β of $\tilde{T}$ with the designated nodes of $\tilde{T}$. We just laid out these designated nodes (at the vertices $\alpha 01^{i-1-|\alpha|}$ or $\alpha 10^{i-1-|\alpha|}$) and since β is equal to $\alpha 01^{i-2-|\alpha|}$ or to the parent of $\alpha 01^{i-2-|\alpha|}$ in X_{i-1}, also these edges do not affect condition (3').

The second case, where there exist two intervals I_1, I_2 with $|I_1| + |I_2| \geq 4\Delta/3$ can be studied now easily. First the designated nodes of I_1 are mapped to a leaf of the X-tree and this does not affect condition (3'). Afterwards lemma 1 is used and we can see just in the same way as above that condition (3') remains valid. $\square$

(ii) The procedure SPLIT

In the i-th loop of the algorithm the procedure SPLIT is called with the parameters (α, i) for all $\alpha \in \{0, 1\}^{i-1}$. Note that during the previous computations in this loop (i.e. by the calls of the procedure $ADJUST$) some extension of δ_{i-1} has been computed already and at most 4 nodes from R_{i-1} were mapped to each of the addresses $\alpha 0$ and $\alpha 1$. Then $A_i(\alpha)$ is the set of nodes associated to α during this previous computation.

Note that $A_i(\alpha)$ is given by the 16 nodes from D_{i-1} mapped already to α and by at most 28 intervals from F_{i-1}. These 28 intervals can be divided into three sets. There are at most 8 intervals whose characteristic address is equal to the father of α. Let S_1 be the set of these intervals. Their designated nodes have to be mapped now to $\alpha 0$ or $\alpha 1$, respectively. There are at most 16 intervals whose characteristic address is equal to α. Let S_2 be the set of these intervals. These intervals have to be attached now to $\alpha 0$ or $\alpha 1$, respectively. Finally there are 4 intervals which have been mapped provisionally to $\alpha 0$ or $\alpha 1$, respectively, during the computation of the procedure $ADJUST$. Let S_3 be the set of these intervals. These intervals may be shifted again from $\alpha 0$ to $\alpha 1$ or vice versa by the algorithm described below.

Let us consider again the set S_2. Note that the children of the designated nodes of an interval form one interval and two trees.

These two trees are combined logically to define a new interval. Now let I be any interval whose designated nodes have been mapped to the vertex α. Then one of its children will be attached to $\alpha 0$ and the other one to $\alpha 1$.

We perform the following algorithm in order to split $A_i(\alpha)$ into two sets M_0 and M_1.

$M_0 = M_1 = \emptyset$;
while $S_1 \cup S_2 \cup S_3 \neq \emptyset$ do
begin
    take two intervals I_1, I_2 from the same set S_1
    or S_2 or S_3;
    $w.l.o.g.$ $|I_1| \geq |I_2|$;
    add I_2 to the larger one of the two sets M_0

or M_1 and I_1 to the smaller one end.

Here we can assume that each of the sets S_1, S_2, S_3 contains an even number of intervals. Otherwise we add an empty interval. If in S_2 there are still two intervals which are children of the same interval then choose one of them as I_1 and the other one as I_2.

In this way we guarantee that each one of the sets M_o and M_1 contains

- at most 4 intervals from S_1

- at most 8 intervals from S_2

- at most 2 intervals from S_3

and furthermore

- $\Delta = \frac{1}{2} \cdot (|M_o| - |M_1|)$ is bounded by the cardinality of the largest interval in $S_1 \cup S_2 \cup S_3$.

In order to get good estimations we have to associate the sets M_0 and M_1 to the vertices $\alpha 0$ and $\alpha 1$ in such a way, that the calls of $ADJUST$ in the next round of our algorithm are influenced in a positive way. We will see in (iii) that we have to take special care about the call $ADJUST\ (\alpha 0, \alpha 1, i + 1), |\alpha| = i - 1$. Note that in the $(i+1)$st round each pair of vertices $\alpha 0, \alpha 1$ (except the special cases $\alpha = 0^{i-1}, \alpha = 1^{i-1}$) is influenced by exactly three calls of $ADJUST$. One of these calls is $ADJUST\ (\alpha 0, \alpha 1, i + 1)$ and for each of $\alpha 0, \alpha 1$ there is one further call influencing it.

If we consider the case $\alpha = \hat{\alpha} 10^p, \hat{\alpha} \in \{0,1\}^*$, $p > 0$, then these two calls are $ADJUST\ (\alpha, successor(\alpha), i+1), ADJUST\ (\hat{\alpha} 0, \hat{\alpha} 1, i+1)$. The first of these calls influences $\alpha 1$ and the second one influences $\alpha 0$.

Likewise if $\hat{\alpha} = \hat{\alpha} 01^p, \hat{\alpha} \in \{0,1\}^*, p > 0$, then these two calls are $ADJUST\ (predecessor(\alpha), \alpha, i + 1)$ and $ADJUST(\hat{\alpha} 0, \hat{\alpha} 1, i+1)$.

Let Δ_0, Δ_1 be the two differences existing between the two pairs of trees that are adjusted.

Then we associate M_0 and M_1 to $\alpha 0$ and $\alpha 1$ in such a way that the larger difference affects the larger set of nodes. I.e. in our first case $\alpha = \hat{\alpha} 10^p$ these two differences are

$$\Delta_0 = \frac{1}{2}(|A_i(\hat{\alpha} 1)| - |A_i(\hat{\alpha} 0)|),$$
$$\Delta_1 = \frac{1}{2}(|A_i(\alpha)| - |A_i(successor(\alpha))|)$$

and M_0 is associated to $\alpha 0$ iff $\Delta_0 \geq \Delta_1$ and $|M_0| \geq |M_1|$ or $\Delta_0 < \Delta_1$ and $|M_0| < |M_1|$.

The nodes from S_1 and S_3 are laid out now. Note that at most 12 nodes are mapped to each of $\alpha 0$ or $\alpha 1$. The trees from S_2 are attached to $\alpha 0$ or $\alpha 1$, respectively, and in this way the mapping μ_i is defined.

The 4 free places in $\alpha 0$ and $\alpha 1$ are used now to reduce the difference between $A(\alpha 0)$ and $A(\alpha 1)$. Note that there exists a tree $\tilde{T}$ with at least Δ nodes. Therefore $\Delta \leq nh(i - 1, i)$ and we can reduce the difference to $\Delta(i, i) \leq \lfloor (nh(i-1, i) + 4)/9 \rfloor$ by applying lemma 2.

If the number of nodes mapped to $\alpha 0$ (or $\alpha 1$, respectively) is smaller than 16 then the free places are filled by taking iteratively nodes which are attached to $\alpha 0$ (or $\alpha 1$, respectively) and which are not laid out so far, but which have at least one neighbour which has been laid out already.

Note that therefore condition (2) is fulfilled if the numbers $|A_i(\alpha 0)|, |A_i(\alpha 1)|$ of nodes attached to $\alpha 0$ and $\alpha 1$, respectively, are not smaller than 16. We will show in (iii) that for every $\beta \in \{0,1\}^i$

$$|A_i(\beta)| \geq nl(i, i) \geq n_{r-i} - a(i, i)$$

$$\geq 16(2^{r-i+1} - 1) - 2^{r+2-i} - 2^{r-i}$$
$$\geq 16(2^2 - 1) - 2^3 - 2 \geq 16$$

holds for $i < r$. Therefore condition (2) is fulfilled for $i < r$.

Because of lack of space we omit the proof that also the other conditions hold.

(iii) Estimations of $\Delta(j, i), nh(j, i), nl(j, i)$

We will show that for $0 \leq j \leq i \leq r$
$$\begin{aligned}
\Delta(i, i) &\leq 2^{r+2-i} && \text{, if } i < r \\
\Delta(j, i) &\leq 2^{r+j+1-2i} && \text{, if } j < i \text{ and } 2i \leq r + j + 1 \\
\Delta(j, i) &= 0 && \text{, if } 2i \geq r + j + 2
\end{aligned}$$

155

and $nh(j,i) \leq n_{r-j} + a(j,i)$,
$nl(j,i) \geq n_{r-j} - a(j,i)$,

where

$a(i,i) \leq 2^{r+2-i} + 2^{r-i}$, if $i < r$
$a(j,i) \leq 3 \cdot 2^{r+j-2i}$, if $j < i$ and $2i \leq r+j$
$a(j,i) \leq 1$, if $2i = r+j+1$
$a(j,i) = 0$, if $2i \geq r+j+2$

We will prove this assumption by induction on i. The assumption is true for $i = 0$, since

$$\Delta(0,0) = 0, \quad nh(0,0) = nl(0,0) = n_0 = n$$

Now let us assume $i \leq r$ and let the assumption be true for $0 \leq j \leq i-1$ and let us consider the i-th run of the algorithm.

First $A_{i-1}(0)$ and $A_{i-1}(1)$ are adjusted using lemma 2, therefore $\Delta(1,i) \leq \lfloor \frac{\Delta(1,i-1)+4}{9} \rfloor \leq \frac{\Delta(1,i-1)}{4}$.

Applying the procedure Adjust shifts some nodes between the forests $A_{i-1}(0)$ and $A_{i-1}(1)$. This influences also the trees $A_{i-1}(01), A_{i-1}(10), A_{i-1}(011), A_{i-1}(100)$, etc.

The cardinality of the forests associated to 01, 10, 011, 100, ... and therefore also the differences of brothers on the levels $j, 2 \leq j \leq i-1$, can be changed this way. Since half the difference between $A_{i-1}(0)$ and $A_{i-1}(1)$ before applying Adjust is at most $\Delta(1,i-1)$ and afterwards at most $\Delta(1,i)$, the cardinalities of the trees $T(01), T(10), ...$ are changed at most by $\Delta(1,i) + \Delta(1,i-1)$.

Note that in general every node in depth j can be influenced by at most one application of Adjust in some depth smaller than j. Since the differences $\Delta(j,i-1)$ are increasing in j, we know that after having applied the procedure Adjust to all vertices on levels smaller then j, the actual difference $\tilde{\Delta}(j,i-1)$ between siblings on level j is at most

$\tilde{\Delta}(j,i-1) \leq \Delta(j,i-1) + \frac{1}{2}(\Delta(j-1,i) + \Delta(j-1,i-1)$
$+\Delta(j-2,i) + \Delta(j-2,i-1))$.

We now apply the procedure Adjust and get

$$\Delta(j,i) \leq \lfloor (\tilde{\Delta}(j,i-1)+4)/9 \rfloor.$$

We have to compute $\tilde{\Delta}(j,i-1)$.

By the induction hypothesis, if $j < i-1$ and $2i \leq r+j-1$ then

$\tilde{\Delta}(j,i-1) \leq 2^{r+j+3-2i} + \frac{1}{2} \cdot (2^{r+j-2i} + 2^{r+j+2-2i}$
$\qquad\qquad +2^{r+j-1-2i} + 2^{r+j+1-2i})$
$\qquad\qquad \leq 2^{r+j+3-2i} + \frac{1}{2} \cdot 2^{r+j-1-2i} \cdot (15)$
$\qquad\qquad \leq 3 \cdot 2^{r+j+2-2i}$

Note that $\lfloor (6x + 4)/9 \rfloor \leq x$ holds for all real numbers $x \geq 1$ and therefore $\Delta(j,i) \leq 2^{r+j+1-2i}$ follows for $1 \leq j < i-1$ and $2i \leq r+j-1$.

We have to consider also the remaining cases for $j < i-1$.

	$\tilde{\Delta}(j,i-1)$	$\Delta(j,i)$
$2i = r+j$	$\leq 8 + \frac{1}{2}(4+2+1) \leq 12$	$\leq \lfloor \frac{16}{9} \rfloor = 1$
$2i = r+j+1$	$\leq 4 + \frac{1}{2}(2+1) \leq 6$	$\leq \lfloor \frac{10}{9} \rfloor = 1$
$2i \geq r+j+2$	$\leq 2 + \frac{1}{2}(1) \leq 3$	$\leq \lfloor \frac{7}{9} \rfloor = 0$

The estimations of $\Delta(j,i)$ for $j = i-1$ and for $j = i$ and the estimations of the $a(j,i)$ cannot be described here because of lack of space.

(v) The final embedding

The mapping δ_r fulfills the following properties:

1. δ_r has dilation 3.

2. δ_r has mapped 16 nodes to any inner vertex of the X-tree X_r, and for every $\alpha \in \{0,1\}^r$ it has mapped 16 nodes to α iff $|A_r(\alpha)| \leq 16$ holds.

3. δ_r fulfills the estimations from (iii), especially $\Delta(j,r) = 0$, if $j \leq r-2$.

Therefore for every $\alpha \in \{0,1\}^{r-2}$ (defining a subtree of height 2), we can now distribute the nodes not laid our so far to free places among the leaves $\alpha 00, \alpha 01, \alpha 10, \alpha 11$. This embedding has still dilation 3 and therefore we have proved theorem 1. $\qquad\square$

3 Proofs of Theorems 2,3,4

We can transform the embedding with load factor 16 from Theorem 1 in a straightforward way into an injective embedding.

Theorem 2: Let $T = (V, E)$ be an arbitrary binary tree with n nodes, $n = 16(2^{r+1} - 1)$ for some r. Then there exists an injective embedding of T into the X-tree of height $r + 4$ with dilation 11.

Proof: Let δ be the embedding into the X-tree X_r described in Theorem 1. δ has dilation 3 and load factor 16. We define an injective embedding χ into the X-tree X_{r+4} in such a way that for every $u \in V$

$$\chi(u) = \delta(u) \circ \mu$$

for some $\mu \in \{0, 1\}^*, |\mu| = 4$.

For every address $\alpha, |\alpha| \leq r$, of the X-tree X_r there are exactly 16 nodes from T mapped onto α by δ. It is clear that we get an injective mapping χ if we use the 16 different addresses $\alpha\mu, |\mu| = 4$, as images of these 16 nodes. We do not have to specify this further in order to show that χ has dilation 11. Of course we have to use that δ has dilation 3.

Let $\alpha, \beta, \gamma, \omega$ be some nodes from X_r forming a path of length 3. Let μ and ν be some strings of length 4. We have to show that in X_{r+4} there exists a path of length at most 11 between $\alpha\mu$ and $\omega\nu$. Note that α and $\alpha\mu$ (and ω and $\omega\nu$, respectively) are connected by a path of length 4. Therefore $\alpha\mu - \ldots - \alpha - \beta - \gamma - \omega - \ldots - \omega\nu$ is a path in X_{r+4} of length 11. $\qquad \square$

It is wellknown that a complete binary tree B_r can be embedded into its optimal hypercube Q_{r+1} with dilation 2 (see [8]). One way to establish this is the so called "inorder embedding", which is formally defined by

$$\delta_{io} : \cup_{i \leq r} \{0, 1\}^i \to \{0, 1\}^{r+1},$$

$\delta_{io}(\alpha) = \alpha 10^{r-|\alpha|}$ for $\alpha \in \{0, 1\}^*, |\alpha| \leq r$. δ_{io} has dilation 2, since $\delta_{io}(\alpha 0) = \alpha 010^{r-1-|\alpha|}$, $\delta_{io}(\alpha 1) = \alpha 110^{r-1-|\alpha|}$ and therefore the image of the edge $\{\alpha, \alpha 0\}$ has dilation 2 and the image of the edge $\{\alpha, \alpha 1\}$ has dilation 1. Furthermore δ_{io} has the property that for any natural number λ, if α and β are nodes in B_r with distance λ, then $\delta_{io}(\alpha)$ and $\delta_{io}(\beta)$ have distance at most $\lambda + 1$ in Q_{r+1}.

The proof is straightforward. Let α and β have distance λ in B_r. Then there exists some $\gamma \in \{0, 1\}^*$ and $\omega_1, \omega_2 \in \{0, 1\}^*$ such that $\alpha = \gamma\omega_1, \beta = \gamma\omega_2$ and $\lambda = |\omega_1| + |\omega_2|$. Note that $\delta_{io}(\alpha) = \gamma\omega_1 10^{r-|\gamma|-|\omega_1|}$ and $\delta_{io}(\beta) = \gamma\omega_2 10^{r-|\gamma|-|\omega_2|}$ and therefore the distance between $\delta_{io}(\alpha)$ and $\delta_{io}(\beta)$ in Q_{r+1} is at most $\max\{|\omega_1|, |\omega_2|\} + 1$.

In a similar way X-trees can be embedded into hypercubes (see [8]). This construction has not been stated explicitly before and therefore we formulate it here as a lemma. Furthermore we need a special result for the construction we described in section 2.

Lemma 3: For any natural number r there exists an injective embedding δ of the X-tree X_r into the hypercube Q_{r+1} with the property that if α and β are nodes in X_r with distance λ, then $\delta(\alpha)$ and $\delta(\beta)$ have distance at most $\lambda + 1$ in Q_{r+1}.

Proof:
Our mapping $\delta : \cup_{i \leq r} \{0, 1\}^i \to \{0, 1\}^{r+1}$ is defined by $\delta(\alpha) = \chi(\alpha) 10^{r-|\alpha|}$, where for any $\alpha \in \{0, 1\}^*, \alpha = a_1 \ldots a_i, a_u \in \{0, 1\}$ for $1 \leq u \leq i$, $i \leq r$, we set

$\chi(\alpha) = b_1 \ldots b_i, b_u \in \{0, 1\}$ for $1 \leq u \leq i$ with $b_1 = a_1$ and for $2 \leq \nu \leq i$: $b_\nu = a_\nu$ iff $a_{\nu-1} = 0$. Note that $|\chi(\alpha)| = |\alpha|$ for all α.

We show first that if α and β are siblings in X_r, then $\delta(\alpha)$ and $\delta(\beta)$ are neighbors in Q_{r+1}. We assume w.l.o.g., that $\alpha \neq 1^{|\alpha|}$ and $\beta = successor(\alpha)$, i.e. $\alpha = \tilde{\alpha}01^p$ with some $\tilde{\alpha} \in \{0, 1\}^*, 0 \leq p < r$ and $\beta = \tilde{\alpha}10^p$. We will see that $\chi(\alpha)$ and $\chi(\beta)$ differ from each other exactly in the $(|\tilde{\alpha}| + 1)$st bit. If $p = 0$, then $\chi(\alpha) = \chi(\tilde{\alpha})b, \chi(\beta) = \chi(\tilde{\alpha})\bar{b}$, where $b \in \{0, 1\}$ fulfills $b = 0$ iff the last bit of $\tilde{\alpha}$ is equal to 0. If $p > 0$, then $\chi(\alpha) = \chi(\tilde{\alpha}0)10^{p-1}, \chi(\beta) = \chi(\tilde{\alpha}1)10^{p-1}$.

Now, let λ be some natural number and let α, β

two nodes in X_r of distance λ. Consider the
th between α and β in X_r. Let λ_0 be the
mber of horizontal edges on this path and let
lenote the highest level reached on this path,
$p = \min\{|\gamma|; \gamma$ is a node on the path$\}$. Then
ere exist $\gamma_1, \gamma_2, w_1, w_2 \in \{0,1\}^*$ with $|\gamma_1| =$
$| = p, \alpha = \gamma_1 w_1, \beta = \gamma_2 w_2, \lambda = \lambda_0 + |w_1| +$
$_2|$ and γ_1 can be reached from γ_2 by a path
nsisting of λ_1 horizontal edges, $\lambda_1 \leq \lambda_0$.

ite that $\delta(\alpha) = \chi(\gamma_1)\tilde{w}_1 10^{r-p-|w_1|}, \delta(\beta) =$
$\gamma_2)\tilde{w}_2 10^{r-p-|w_2|}$ with some $\tilde{w}_1, \tilde{w}_2 \in \{0,1\}^*$,
$_1| = |w_1|, |\tilde{w}_2| = |w_2|$.

ice $\chi(\gamma_1)$ and $\chi(\gamma_2)$ differ in at most λ_1 bits
d since $\lambda_1 \leq \lambda_0$ holds, we see that $\delta(\alpha)$ and
$\beta)$ differ in at most $\lambda_0 + \max\{|w_1|, |w_2|\} + 1$
s. □

om Lemma 3 and Theorem 1 the following the-
em follows immediately.

heorem 3: Let $T = (V, E)$ be an arbitrary
iary tree with n nodes, $n = 16 \cdot (2^r - 1)$ for
ne r. Then there exists an embedding of T
o the hypercube Q_r with load factor 16 and
ation 4.

is again a simple corollary from Theorem 3
at every binary tree with at most $2^r - 16$ nodes
n be injectively embedded into the hypercube
with dilation 8.

ir result about universal graphs follows also
sily from Theorem 1. For $\alpha \in \{0,1\}^j, 0 \leq$
$\leq i$ let $N(\alpha)$ again be the set described in
ure 2. Note that for very vertex α of an X-
e the set $N(\alpha) - \{\alpha\}$ has at most 20 vertices
d there exist at most 5 vertices β such that $\alpha \in$
$\beta)$ and $\beta \notin N(\alpha)$. Since our embedding from
eorem 1 fulfills condition (3') it leads directly
a universal graph of degree $25 \cdot 16 + 15 = 415$.

heorem 4: For every $n \in N$, such that $n =$
$- 16$ for some i, there exists a graph G_n of
gree bounded by 415 such that every binary
e with n nodes is a spanning tree of G_n.

Acknowledgement:

The author wants to thank I.H. Sudborough for
many helpful discussions and R. Klasing for a
careful reading of this paper.

References:

1. S.N. Bhatt, F.R.K. Chung, F.T. Leighton,
   and A.L. Rosenberg, "Optimal Simulation
   of Tree Machines", Proc. 27th Annual
   IEEE Symp. Foundations of Computer Science, Oct. 1986, pp. 274-282.

2. S.N. Bhatt, F.R.K. Chung, F.T. Leighton,
   and A.L. Rosenberg, "Universal Graphs for
   Bounded-Degree Trees and Planar Graphs",
   SIAM J. Disc. Math. Vol. 2, 1989, 145-155.

3. S.N. Bhatt, F.R.K. Chung, J.-W. Hong,
   F.T. Leighton, and A.L. Rosenberg, " Optimal Simulations by Butterfly Networks",
   Proc. 20th Annual ACM Theory of Computing Symp., 1988, 192-204.

4. F.R.K. Chung and R.L. Graham, "On universal graphs", Proc. 2nd. Int. Conf. on
   Combin. Math., (A. Gerwirtz and L. Quin-
   tas, Eds.); Ann. N.Y. Acad. Sci. vo. 319,
   1979, 136-140.

5. F.R.K. Chung and R.L. Graham, " On universal graphs for spanning trees", Journal
   London Math. Soc., 27, 1983, 203-211.

6. J. Friedman, N. Pippenger, "Expanding
   graphs contain all small trees", Combinatorica 7, 1987, 71-76.

7. B. Monien and I.H. Sudborough, "Simulating Binary Trees on Hypercubes", Proc.
   AWOC 88, LNCS 319, 1988, 170-180.

8. B. Monien and I.H. Sudborough, "Embedding one Interconnection Network in Another", Computing Supp. 7, 1990, 257-282.

158

An Approach to Emulating Separable Graphs[*]

(preliminary version)

Bojana Obrenić

Computer and Information Science
University of Massachusetts
Amherst, MA 01003

Abstract

We present an *embedding technique* for bounded-degree guest graphs that have *sublinear separators* (multicolor recursive bisectors).

A straightforward application of our approach to *shuffle-like* hypercube-derivative networks as hosts yields new embeddings with constant expansion, having both dilation and congestion logarithmic in the size of the multicolor bisector. The *congestion* of these embeddings is *exponentially better* than previously known, thereby exponentially speeding up the emulations of bounded-degree separable graphs by shuffle-like networks. When applied to *hypercubes* as hosts, our technique also produces new embeddings, whose expansion constants are better than those known so far.

Our approach is *constructive* in that it provides, together with the embedding, a communication schedule with *queue-size 1* (*no dynamic congestion*), thus producing emulations with the slowdown proportional to the sum of dilation and congestion.

1 Introduction

Motivation. The first results on efficient emulations of arbitrary bounded-degree graphs with sublinear node separators (multicolor recursive bisectors, cf. Section 2.1) appeared in [4], where it was proved that such graphs can be embedded into butterflies with *dilation logarithmic* in the size of their multicolor recursive bisectors and with constant expansion. These embeddings

essentially relied on the embedding of complete binary trees into butterflies (with dilation 6 and expansion 8); the embeddings in [4] were actually a composition of this embedding and embeddings of guests graphs into complete binary trees. However, emulations of [4] incurred slowdown as great as *linear* in the size of the multicolor bisector, since the *congestion* of these embeddings was of that order (cf. Sections 1.1, 2.1). This deficiency was subsequently remedied, by proving that *every* embedding of a bounded-degree graph in a butterfly which has good dilation (cf. Section 2.1) can be transformed into an embedding with good dilation *and* good congestion (details of this proof are available in [3]). Since emulation slowdown is proportional to the sum of dilation and congestion ([11], cf. Section 1.1), these results provided emulations of bounded-degree graphs by butterflies with slowdown logarithmic in the size of their multicolor bisectors.

When it comes to emulating bounded-degree separable graphs by *shuffle-like networks* (cf. Section 4), the approach of [4] is not as useful as it is for butterfly-like hosts. Although it is known from [4] how to embed such graphs into complete binary trees, and although shuffle-like graphs practically contain like-sized complete binary trees, *no way has been found to control congestion* of embeddings in shuffle-like graphs, which have been able to emulate bounded-degree graphs with slowdown exponentially worse than their butterfly relatives.

Our results. In this paper, we present a *new technique* for emulating bounded-degree separable graphs. To this end, we devise a notion of *cell trees* (cf. Section 2) which play the part of *generic hosts* for these guests. By cell trees, however, we do not propose new interconnection topologies—cell trees abstract the ability of hosts to emulate efficiently bounded-degree separable graphs; indeed cell trees are host graphs *organized* to emulate these guests. Our organization is based on three parameters (cell slowdown, transfer fraction, and transfer slowdown, cf. Section 2.2). On the one hand, we express the emulation slowdown in terms of these general parameters; on the other hand, we show how to

---

[*]This research was supported in part by NSF Grant CCR-88-12567.

obtain these parameters for cell trees constructed in hypercubes (Section 3) and shuffle-like graphs (Section 4) as hosts. The upper bounds that we obtain for shuffle-like graphs match those known for butterflies [4, 3] and provide the desired optimal speedup. The embeddings in hypercubes that we have obtained are also new and differ from the previously known [4] by having improved expansion constants.

Advantages of our approach are that we have *divided* the task of embedding bounded-degree separable graphs into two tasks: the first is a powerful decomposition of the guest graph (Section 2.1), and the second is a suitable organization of the host graph (Section 2.2). By formalizing the notion of suitable in an *intermediate structure* of the cell tree, we have *reduced* the problem to an easier one: determining the cell tree parameters for specific hosts, which in turn reduces to efficient *deterministic routing* of a *small class* of *specific permutations*. The role of the cell tree can be thought to be analogous to that of the tree of meshes in [10, 8]: The efficient layout for the tree of meshes parallels the construction of an efficient cell tree; reducing the problem of laying out an arbitrary (bounded-degree separable) graph to the problem of laying out the tree of meshes parallels our reducing the problem of emulating an arbitrary (bounded-degree separable) graph to the problem of emulating the cell tree.

Our computation model is *strict* and *general*; thus the upper bounds that we obtain hold easily for the widest range of problems. We review the computation model in the following subsection. Section 2 presents the general technique; Sections 3 and 4 apply it to specific networks.

Conventions. We denote by $|G|$ the number of nodes of graph G. We let $\lg x =_{\text{def}} \lfloor \log_2 x \rfloor$. $Z_2 =_{\text{def}} \{0, 1\}$. The *complete binary tree* $T(h)$ of *height* h has nodeset $\bigcup_{0 \le k \le h} Z_2^k$ and edges connecting each $y \in Z_2^k$, $0 \le k < h$, to its *children* $y0$ and $y1$. The *root* of the tree $T(h)$ is the empty string λ; the *leaves* of $T(h)$ are all nodes $y \in Z_2^h$. The 2^k nodes $x \in Z_2^k$, for $0 \le k \le h$, reside at *level* k.

1.1 Computation Model, Emulations, and Embeddings

We study *arrays* of *identical processing elements*, each associated with a *local memory* module, connected by an *interconnection network*. The computation of such a processor array develops as a sequence of *pulses*; each pulse is either a *computation* or a *communication* step. Computation steps involve only local memories of processing elements; during communication steps each processing element may send a *message* to its neighbor(s). As is customary, (cf. [4]), we represent processor arrays as undirected *graphs*, whose *nodes* stand for processing

elements, and whose *edges* stand for *interprocessor communication links*. It is possible to (consistently) extend our interpretation so as to allow us to view the graphs we study as dependency graphs of parallel computations; this view gains significance when our conclusions address arbitrary graphs.

We investigate and compare the powers of processor arrays by determining how efficiently each array can *emulate* the other. To explain our emulation setup, we recall its core formal notion: *embedding* one graph in another [12].

An embedding of *guest* graph G in *host* graph H comprises two mappings: an injective *assignment* of the *nodes* of G to *nodes* of H, plus a *routing* that assigns to each *edge* of G a *path* in H connecting the images of the edge's endpoints. Efficiency of an embedding is described in terms of its:

- *dilation* — the length of the longest path in H that routes an edge of G,

- *congestion* — the maximum number of edges of G routed over any single edge of H,

- *expansion* — the ratio $(|H|/|G|)$.

In the course of emulation each host processor in H emulates the guest processor which is its preimage in G; this assignment between processors is fixed throughout the emulation. For every step of a processor in G, its image in H executes a sequence of one or more steps. At any time, all processors of the host array emulate the same step of the guest array; the emulation of the next guest step may begin only after all the host sequences emulating the current guest step have ended. This correspondence between steps in the guest computation and sequences in the host computation is also fixed: we neither allow host processors to perform any other computation nor we require any component of the state of any guest processor at any time to be made available (unless mandated by the guest computation itself) to any host processor other than one assigned to it. This uniformity of assignment preserves our upper bounds in cases where the computation state is construed to include the contents of each processor's *unbounded* local memory and its *simultaneous I/O* stream.

We assume that processors of G and H have equal power; computation steps, therefore, incur no slowdown, as one host computation step is sufficient to emulate one guest computation step. Guest communication steps are emulated by sequences of host communication steps, that take messages for the guest over the paths in H that route edges of G. The communication *schedule* specifies the host communication sequences by naming the links of H which are crossed at every step of these sequences. The emulation *slowdown* is determined by the length of the longest communication sequence. When there is an embedding of graph G into graph H with dilation Δ and congestion K, then it is straightforward to construct a schedule with slowdown $O(\Delta K)$; [11] established existence of a schedule with slowdown $O(\Delta + K)$. We *construct* communication schedules with slowdown of this order for our embeddings, thereby also proving that there is *no space overhead* for organizing communication (no additional queues need be maintained).

Our emulation requires that each *host* processor at any communication step can send a message to only *one* of its neighbors. Still, our upper bounds on communication slowdown hold for the case where each *guest* processor in a single step may send a message to *all* of its neighbors. This conservative assumption obviates the variations within the standard model as to the number of communication links that may be active at any step.

2 Emulations by Cell Trees

We commence by elaborating on two structures central to our approach: *guest-oriented* bucket-trees and *host-oriented* cell-trees.

2.1 Preliminaries on Decomposing Guest Graphs

We use two decomposition mechanisms to achieve the desired representation of our guest graphs: the recursive decomposition into like-sized subgraphs based on node-separation, and the decomposition into matchings via edge-coloring. We start by reviewing the more subtle of these mechanisms, the recursive bisection.

Remark. Although we phrase our argument in terms of graph *separators*, it is the balanced decomposition that is essential, not the instrument used to effect it. This means that nothing precludes substitution of *bifurcators* [8] for separators, when convenient.

Definition 1 *Let α be a real such that $0 < \alpha \leq 1/2$, and let S be a nondecreasing integer function. The graph G has an α-**separator** function S either if $|G| \leq 1$ or there is a set of no more than $S(|G|)$ nodes whose removal partitions G into subgraphs, each having no more than $(1 - \alpha)|G|$ nodes and the separator function S. If G has the separator function S, then we say that $S(|G|)$ is the **size** of the separator of G.*

Definition 2 *Let k be a positive integer and let R be a nondecreasing integer function. The graph G has a k-**color recursive bisector** function R either if $|G| \leq 1$, or for every k-coloring of the nodes of G there exists a*

set of no more than $R(|G|)$ nodes whose removal partitions G into subgraphs G_1 and G_2, each having no more than $\lceil(|G|/2)\rceil$ nodes and the recursive bisector function R, while $|(|G_1'| - |G_2'|)| \leq 1$, where $1 \leq \ell \leq k$ and $|G_i'|$ is the number of nodes of the subgraph G_i colored by color ℓ. If G has the k-color recursive bisector function R, then we say that $R(|G|)$ is the **size** of the k-color recursive bisector of G.

All graphs having a separator function have also a k-color recursive bisector function of similar order. The proof of this fact employs the well known techniques of [8]; we just state the fact as the following.

Proposition 1 *For any integer k, any graph G that has a $(1/3)$-separator of size $S(|G|)$ has a k-color recursive bisector of size $R(|G|) = O(k \sum_i S(|G|/2^i))$. Therefore, $R(|G|) = O(kS(|G|)\log(|G|))$; when $S(|G|) = |G|^{\Omega(1)}$, then $R(|G|) = O(kS(|G|))$.*

The bucket tree originates in [5]; it has been successfully used in [4, 6, 7].

Definition 3 *Let graph G have maximum degree d and a $(d + 1)$-color recursive bisector function R. The **bucket tree** $B^{(b)}$ for G is a complete binary tree of height $\lg(|G|/(bR(|G|)))$, each of whose level-ℓ nodes has **bucket capacity***

$$V(\ell) = bR(|G|/2^\ell)$$

*for some constant b. Nodes of $B^{(b)}$ are called **buckets**.*

The bucket capacity is meant to be interpreted as the number of nodes of G assigned to the bucket by some mapping. We denote by $B_x^{(b)}$ the nodes of G thus mapped to bucket x. Where the value of the constant b is implied by the context, we write B for $B^{(b)}$. The role of the bucket tree becomes clear from the following fact [4].

Proposition 2 *Let graph G of maximum degree d have a $(d + 1)$-color recursive bisector function R. There exists a bucket tree $B^{(b)}$ for G such that the nodes of G can be mapped to the buckets of the bucket tree $B^{(b)}$ while:*

(a) the number of nodes mapped to each bucket equals the bucket capacity;

(b) nodes that are adjacent in G are mapped to buckets that are at most distance d apart in the bucket tree, one of them being an ancestor of the other.

The upper bounds in [4] on the cost of embedding bounded-degree separable graphs into butterflies are obtained via a two-step algorithm. In the first step, the bucket tree B of graph G is embedded into the complete binary tree $T(\lg |G| + 1)$, with dilation $O(\lg R(|G|))$, expansion 2, and congestion $O(dR(|G|))$. In the second step, T is embedded into the butterfly with dilation 6, expansion 8, and congestion 1. The obstructive congestion inherited from embedding B into T is removed *within* the butterfly by means of the following property of butterflies [3]:

> Given a dilation-Δ embedding of a graph G with maximum degree d into the butterfly, there is an edge routing (for the same node assignment) with simultaneous dilation $O(\Delta)$ and congestion $O(d\Delta)$.

No equivalent to this property of reducing congestion via rerouting is known for shuffle-like graphs. Therefore, even though T can be embedded into shuffle-like graphs at virtually no cost, the congestion inherited from embedding B into T precludes emulations as efficient as those obtained with butterflies as hosts. At this point we give up the complete binary tree for the cell tree.

2.2   Cell Trees in Host Graphs

Cell trees capture those emulation capabilities of hosts that we deem essential for emulating separable graphs. We proceed by defining cell trees.

Definition 4 *Let H be a graph, c and h integer constants, and C a subset of nodes of H. Partition C into $2^{h+1} - 1$ equal-size parts, called **cells**, each of cardinality c, and label the parts by distinct names from the set of nodes of the complete binary tree $T(h)$. The triplet (C, h, c) is the **cell tree** of **height** h and **cell capacity** c in H.*

Where no ambiguity may arise, we refer to the cell tree (C, h, c) by name of its node set C; a cell labeled by node x of the complete binary tree $T(h)$ is denoted by C_x.

The following two definitions put forward essential parameters of cell trees; these are the parameters that determine how successful hosts are while emulating separable guests.

Definition 5 *For graph H with cell tree (C, h, c), let the set of **cell permutations** $\mathcal{P}$ consist of the permutations of nodes of H that fix cells setwise. The **cell slowdown** of cell tree (C, h, c) in H is the maximum slowdown required to route any permutation in $\mathcal{P}$.*

Definition 6 *For graph H with cell tree (C, h, c), and a real $f \leq 1/2$, let $\mathcal{T}(f)$ be the set of all permutations of nodes of H that map at least (fc) nodes of each cell (other than the root cell) into nodes of its parent cell.*

*The f-**transfer slowdown** of cell tree (C, h, c) in H is the minimum slowdown required to route some permutation in $\mathcal{T}(f)$. Call the permutation for which this minimum occurs the f-**transfer permutation**, call f the **transfer fraction**, and call the (fc) nodes in each cell mapped by the f-transfer permutation to the parent cell the f-**transfer nodes**.*

The rest of this Section is devoted to establishing our general result on the cost of emulating separable graphs of bounded degree. We express the emulation slowdown solely in terms of cell tree parameters—the cell slowdown and the f-transfer slowdown, for some transfer fraction f. Translating this cost into measures that refer to specific hosts requires constructing efficient cell trees in these hosts and computing cell tree parameters. Sections 3 and 4 present examples of such translation.

Theorem 1 *Let graph G of maximum degree d have a $(d+1)$-color recursive bisector of size $R(|G|)$ and bucket tree $B^{(b)}$. Let (C, h, c) be a cell tree in graph H, where $h = \lg(|G|/(bR(|G|))) + 1$ and $c = bR(|G|)$. Let C have cell slowdown p and f-transfer slowdown t. Then H can emulate G with slowdown $(d^2 + d)(\lceil 1/f \rceil)(2p + t)$, queue-size 1, and expansion $\lceil 2(|H|/|C|) \rceil$.*

We prove Theorem 1 by constructing the embedding of G into H, along with the specification of a routing regimen that achieves the claimed cost. First, we assign nodes of G to nodes of H.

Lemma 1 (Assignment Lemma) *Let G be a graph of maximum degree d, with a $(d+1)$-color recursive bisector of size $R(|G|)$ and bucket tree B. Let (C, h, c) be a cell tree in graph H, as in Theorem 1. Then nodes of G can be mapped into C so that nodes adjacent in G are mapped into cells at distance at most d apart, one of these cells being an ancestor of the other.*

Proof. By Proposition 2, G can be mapped to its bucket tree B so that every edge of G is stretched along a path between a node of B and its ancestor; no such path has more than d edges. We prove the Lemma by showing that bucket tree B can be mapped to cell tree C in a way that preserves the dilation of the embedding of G in its bucket tree B.

Recall that R is sublinear. By a simple inductive argument, one verifies that bucket capacities slowly decrease with level in the bucket tree. We have chosen b so that the cell capacity c equals the capacity of the root bucket B_λ, which is the largest in B.

The assignment of buckets of B to cells of C is as follows:

Step 0:

    assign B_λ to C_λ;

    assign B_0 to C_0;

    assign B_1 to C_1.

Step k: $(1 \leq k < \lg |G|)$

    At this step, every bucket B_x has already been assigned to some cell C_y, for $|y| \leq |x| = k$.

If	available capacity r of C_y suffices to receive both B_{x0} and B_{x1}
then	assign B_{x0} and B_{x1} to C_y;
else	assign $\lfloor (r/2) \rfloor$ nodes of B_{x0} to C_y;
	assign $\lfloor (r/2) \rfloor$ nodes of B_{x1} to C_y;
	assign remaining nodes of B_{x0} to C_{y0};
	assign remaining nodes of B_{x1} to C_{y1}.

The following observations establish the claim about the height h of the cell tree and the dilation of embedding G into it:

Since every bucket other than the root is smaller than the cell, no bucket can span more than two cells. Also, a child of a bucket can be only assigned either to the same cell as its parent, or to a child of the cell of its parent, or to both. At each step of the procedure, one level of the bucket tree is assigned, while at most one level of the cell tree is consumed. At most one node of C per bucket of B is left unoccupied, accounting for the factor of 2 in the expansion. $\square$-Lemma 1

Our next task is defining the edge routing of the embedding. We simplify this task by appealing to the following well known result [15].

Proposition 3 *Every graph G of maximum degree d can be decomposed into at most $d+1$ partial subgraphs, each of maximum degree 1.*

Let $G_1, \ldots, G_{d+1}$ be the partial subgraphs resulting from decomposing G by Proposition 3. Our next step is computing the slowdown of emulating such a partial subgraph, say G_1, by graph H with its cell tree (C, h, c). The slowdown of emulating the entire graph G is then $(d+1)$ times greater, since the emulation proceeds in $(d+1)$-step phases, one for each partial subgraph G_i.

Lemma 2 (Routing Lemma) *Let (C, h, c) be a cell tree in graph H, with cell slowdown p and f-transfer slowdown t. Let G_1 be a graph of maximum degree 1, whose nodes are assigned to C so that nodes adjacent in G_1 are assigned to cells at distance at most d apart, one of these cells being an ancestor of the other. Then H can emulate G_1 with slowdown $d(\lceil 1/f \rceil)(2p + t)$ and queue-size 1.*

Proof. The specification of the routing has two parts. The first part, *macrorouting*, specifies only the *cells* that

the routing paths visit; the second part, *microrouting*, specifies paths *within* cells. Our task is to define both parts of the routing and to schedule traversal of edges along the paths so as to achieve the claimed cost.

Macrorouting. Given an edge e, let C_x and C_y be the cells (not necessarily distinct) to which the endpoints of e are assigned. Assume that C_x is m levels below C_y in the cell tree, where $0 \leq m \leq d$. (Note that $m = 0$ just when $C_x = C_y$.) We route e via a *macropath* comprising m *macrolinks*, each macrolink connecting two adjacent cells on the shortest path of m macrolinks, starting at the source cell C_x and ending at the destination cell C_y.

All edges of G_1 are macrorouted by a single orchestrated regimen. The orchestration mandates d *stages*. At stage j, where $1 \leq j \leq d$, active macrolinks are those that lead to cells which are exactly $d-j$ macrolinks away from the destination cell of the macropath to which they belong. In other words, at stage 1 we cross the first macrolink of each macropath of length d; at stage 2 we cross the second macrolink in each such macropath, as well as the first link in each macropath of length $d-1$; at stage j, we cross the $(j-k)$th macrolink in each macropath of length $d-k$, where $0 \leq k < j$. Our macrorouting regimen, therefore, crosses macrolinks in the correct order.

Given a cell C_u, let the *macrocongestion* of C_u at stage j be the ratio of the number of macropaths departing from C_u at stage j and the number of nodes of C_u (which is the cell capacity c). To assess the macrocongestion of C_u at stage j, we appeal to the Assignment Lemma. It grants that the macropaths departing from C_u at stage j are just those macropaths that end at the ancestor cell of C_u which is exactly $d - j$ macrolinks above C_u; call this ancestor C_v. Since G_1 is of maximum degree 1, the maximum number of macropaths whose destination is C_v cannot exceed the cell capacity c of C_v; in particular, at most c such links can depart from C_u at step j. Thus the macrocongestion of any cell at any stage does not exceed one macropath per node of the cell.

Microrouting. First, we request that the macrolinks leaving cell C_u at stage j depart from f-transfer nodes of C_u and arrive at those nodes of the parent cell C'_u to which the f-transfer permutation maps f-transfer nodes of C_u. (Likewise, the macrolinks that arrive to cell C_u at stage $j-1$ end at nodes of C_u to which the f-transfer permutation maps f-transfer nodes of children cells of C_u.)

Since the macrocongestion of cell C_u at stage j is not greater than one, at most a total of c macropaths pass through C_u or start at C_u. Therefore, we can associate a node in C_u with each macropath that leaves C_u at stage j as follows: if there is a macropath of length $d - j + 1$ starting at the node, then associate that macropath with the node; otherwise associate with the node one of the macropaths that pass through v. In such an association, call the node the *home* of the macropath. At stage d, choose for home nodes the very nodes on which macropaths end; note that home nodes chosen this way are guaranteed to be distinct from endpoints of edges whose both endpoints reside in the same cell, since G_1 is of maximum degree 1.

To arrange the microrouting with small congestion, we partition the nodes of cell C_u into (fc) *transfer groups*, of size $\lceil 1/f \rceil$ or $\lfloor 1/f \rfloor$ each, so that each group contains exactly one f-transfer node. Furthermore, we require that every group contains at most one node from each of the two disjoint sets of nodes to which the f-transfer permutation maps f-transfer nodes of each of two children cells. We then associate each group with the unique f-transfer node that it contains; call this node the *leader* of the group.

Now, let us focus on the first stage of the macrorouting, when $j = 1$, in cell C_u. The microrouting sequence at this stage consists of $\lceil 1/f \rceil$ repetitions of a cycle of three elementary components: two turns and one push. A *turn* occurs by routing paths *within* cells. A *push* occurs by routing paths *between* cells. The whole of $\lceil 1/f \rceil$ repetitions of this cycle are needed to remove congestion from f-transfer nodes:

1. First, we route one turn. This turn routes the paths from exactly one node in each transfer group to the leader of the group. Each turn defines a permutation on nodes of C_u by defining a transposition between a node of C_u and the leader of its group. This permutation obviously fixes cells setwise, so the cost of routing a turn in *all* cells simultaneously is the cell slowdown p.

2. After the first turn, we route one push. The push is the f-transfer permutation sending each leader to its matching node in the parent cell C_u'. The cost of one push in the *entire* cell tree simultaneously is the transfer slowdown t.

3. After the push, we route one more turn in the parent cell C_u' from destinations of the f-transfer permutation to home nodes of stage-2 macropaths. The cost of this turn in *all* cells simultaneously is again the cell slowdown p.

After $\lceil 1/f \rceil$ repetitions of this cycle of two turns and one push, all length-d macropaths have advanced one macrolink, so that the length of the longest portion of a macropath that has yet to be routed is $d - 1$; moreover, the macropaths departing from every cell at stage 2 touch the cell at distinct home nodes, thereby preparing the next-stage turn. A straightforward inductive

extension verifies that the following invariant is maintained as the macropaths contract through all d stages: after stage j the macropaths reside with their distinct stage-$(j + 1)$ home nodes; the length of the longest portion to be routed on any macropath is at most $d - j$ macrolinks. The very last turn accommodates those edges of G_1 whose both endpoints reside in a single cell, along with macropaths whose destinations are in that cell. We thus arrive to the total emulation cost of $d(\lceil 1/f \rceil)(2p + t)$. $\square$-Lemma 2

The Assignment Lemma and the Routing Lemma justify the claim of Theorem 1.

Notes on Possible Refinements. Our routing regimen requires *queues of size exactly* 1. This means that at any time during emulation, at most one message can be waiting to be communicated at any processing element. While it is desirable to achieve emulations with such a negligible space (memory) overhead, we note that the emulation can be speeded up at the cost of increasing the number of messages simultaneously waiting at the destinations of the f-transfer permutation. If we allow messages to be queued up at the destination nodes of the f-transfer permutation, then, at the cost of maintaining queues of size $\lceil 1/f \rceil$ at these nodes, we can dispense with the turns that route macropaths to their home nodes. Such turns account for roughly half of all turns, so the result is reducing the last factor in the slowdown of the Routing Lemma from $(2p+t)$ to $(p+t)$. This tradeoff may be welcome when the cell slowdown is large while the transfer fraction f is some positive fraction, since queue-size, though increased, still remains constant. When the transfer fraction f is some sublinear function of the cell size, then the price for this speedup is unbounded growth of the queue-size with the size of the host.

Our regimen of alternating turns and pushes may admit several refinements, so as to exploit the specifics of host networks. It is possible that several efficient transfer permutations with various transfer rates exist for a given host. Also, the set of cell permutations may be further characterized to reflect that the turns are more specific than general cell permutations: some turns fix transfer groups (which are expected to be much smaller than cells) setwise; all turns are bipartite matchings where all transfer nodes have the same color. Also, a many-one mapping may be employed instead of the f-transfer permutation. This tuning of the general approach to specific networks sometimes improves performance. Central to the approach is identifying the cell tree in the host and identifying permutations that enable efficient communication within each cell and between adjacent cells.

From the proof of the Assignment Lemma, one immediately infers another simple yet important point: the cells of the cell tree may be chosen to be larger than the buckets in the bucket tree of the guest; such cells may be filled to capacity without consequences for dilation of those edges of the guest whose endpoints are in distinct buckets. Cell and transfer slowdowns are determined by the properties of the cell tree, not by the properties of the guest. We soon see that this minor observation becomes relevant when the topology of the host requires that (efficient) cell trees have cells of some specific size (e.g., that the size must be a power of 2).

3 Application to Hypercubes

The n-dimensional hypercube $Q(n)$ is the graph whose nodes comprise the set Z_2^n and whose edges connect each node $x\beta y$ to node $x\bar{\beta}y$, where $\beta \in Z_2$ and $xy \in Z_2^{n-1}$.

Theorem 2 *Let graph G of maximum degree d have a $(d+1)$-color recursive bisector of size $R(|G|)$. Then G can be emulated by a hypercube with slowdown $O(d^2 \lg(R(|G|)))$, queue-size 1, and expansion 3.*

Proof. We have to find a cell tree (C, h, c) in the hypercube and to compute its slowdown factors.

Cells. Recall that order-n hypercube $Q(n)$ is a direct product $Q(h+1) \times Q(k)$ of two hypercubes whenever $n = (h+1) + k$. Choose k so that $c = 2^k$ nodes of $Q(k)$ are sufficient as cell capacity; this yields $k = O(\lg(R(|G|)))$, by the Assignment Lemma. Let each cell be an instance of $Q(k)$ in $Q(n) = Q(h+1) \times Q(k)$. Choose the height h so that the cell tree is large enough. It is well known (cf. [7]) that the complete binary tree $T(h)$ can be embedded in $Q(h+1)$ with dilation 2; a witnessing embedding assigns node x of $T(h)$ to node $x10^{h-|x|}$ of $Q(h+1)$. Label each cell, that is each instance of $Q(k)$ in $Q(n)$, by the name of the node of $T(h)$ which is assigned to the node of $Q(h+1)$ associated with that instance of $Q(k)$ in the product $Q(n) = Q(h+1) \times Q(k)$. We thus define the cell C_x as the following subset of nodes of $Q(n) = Q(h+1) \times Q(k)$.

$$C_x = \{(x10^{h-|x|}, y) \mid y \in Z_2^k\}$$

One node of $Q(h+1)$ remains unoccupied by this assignment, thus giving rise to the small increase in expansion over that coming from embedding the bucket tree into the cell tree C.

Given a non-root cell C_u, which is an instance of $Q(k)$ in $Q(n) = Q(h+1) \times Q(k)$, let C_{u_1} be the parent cell of C_u, so that $u = u_1\xi$, for some $\xi \in Z_2$.

Cell slowdown. Within each cell, that is within each instance of $Q(k)$ in $Q(n)$, cell permutations can be routed with cell slowdown $p = 2k - 1 = O(\lg(R(|G|))$ (cf. [2]).

Transfer fraction. $f = (1/2)$.

(1/2)-transfer nodes. In cell $C_{u_1\xi}$, we define the set $F(u_1\xi)$ of $(1/2)$-transfer nodes as the half of cell nodes which have ξ in the leftmost bit position of their second, k-bit component.

$$F(u_1\xi) = \{(u_1\xi 10^{h-|u_1|-1}, \xi z) \mid z \in Z_2^{k-1}\}$$

(1/2)-transfer groups in cell $C_{u_1\xi}$ consist of pairs of nodes, each pair comprising the leader $(u_1\xi 10^{h-|u_1|-1}, \xi z)$, for some $z \in Z_2^{k-1}$, and node $(u_1\xi 10^{h-|u_1|-1}, \bar{\xi}z)$, which differs from its leader only in the leftmost bit of its second, k-bit component.

(1/2)-transfer permutation. The $(1/2)$-transfer permutation is the map $(u_1\xi 10^{h-|u_1|-1}, \xi z) \mapsto (u_1 10^{h-|u_1|}, \xi z)$, where $z \in Z_2^{k-1}$.

(1/2)-transfer slowdown. $Q(h+1)$ can emulate the tree $T(h)$ with slowdown 2; note that the $(1/2)$-transfer permutation is effected by traversing a subset of tree-edges of the embedded $T(h) \times Q(k)$, so $t = 2$ is the required $(1/2)$-transfer slowdown.

The claim follows from Theorem 1, instantiated with the f, p and t that we have just computed. $\square$

The expansion of Theorem 2 should be compared with expansion-16 embedding of separable graphs into hypercubes, derived from their embedding into butterflies in [4].

4 Application to de Bruijn Graphs

The *order-n de Bruijn graph* $D(n)$ [9] has node-set Z_2^n; each node βx, where $\beta \in Z_2$ and $x \in Z_2^{n-1}$, is connected by the *shuffle* edge to node $x\beta$, and by the *shuffle-exchange* edge to node $x\bar{\beta}$. Let $\mathcal{S}(\beta y) =_{\text{def}} y\beta$ and $\mathcal{E}(\beta y) =_{\text{def}} y\bar{\beta}$.

Theorem 3 *Let graph G of maximum degree d have a $(d+1)$-color recursive bisector of size $R(|G|)$. Then G can be emulated by a de Bruijn graph with slowdown $O(d^2 \lg(R(|G|)))$, queue-size 1, and expansion 3.*

Proof. Identifying a cell tree (C, h, c) in the de Bruijn graph is just a little bit more involved than in the hypercube. Consider a host de Bruijn graph of order $n = h + k + 1$.

Cells. Choose k so that $c = 2^k$ nodes are sufficient as cell capacity; this yields $k = O(\lg(R(|G|)))$, by the Assignment Lemma. Choose height h so that the cell tree is large enough. Given tree node $x \in Z_2^j$, $0 \le j \le h$, we define its cell as the following subset of $c = 2^k$ nodes of $D(n)$.

$$C_x = \{x^R 10^{n-k-1-j} y \mid y \in Z_2^k\}$$

where string x^R is the reversal of x. So, all $c = 2^k$ nodes in cell C_x are equal in their first $h + 1 = n - k$ bits, and have distinct k-bit suffixes. Note that c nodes of $D(n)$ of the form $0^{n-k}y$, $y \in Z_2^k$ do not belong to any cell, thus giving rise to the small increase in expansion over that imposed by embedding the bucket tree into the cell tree.

Cell slowdown. Every cell permutation in $D(n)$ can be routed with slowdown $p = 2k$ [1].

Transfer fraction. $f = (1/2)$.

(1/2)-transfer nodes. In cell C_u, we define the set $F(u)$ of $(1/2)$-transfer nodes as the half of cell nodes which have 0 in the leftmost bit position of their k-bit suffix.

$$F(u) = \{u^R 10^{n-k-1-|u|} 0z \mid z \in Z_2^{k-1}\}$$

(1/2)-transfer groups in cell C_u consist of pairs of nodes, each pair comprising the leader $u^R 10^{n-k-1-|u|} 0z$, for some $z \in Z_2^{k-1}$, and node $u^R 10^{n-k-1-|u|} 1z$ which differs from its leader only in the leftmost bit of its k-bit suffix.

(1/2)-transfer permutation is the map $x \mapsto \mathcal{S}(x)$. To verify that it indeed takes $(1/2)$-transfer nodes to their parent cell, let $x \in F(u)$ be a $(1/2)$-transfer node in cell C_u and let C_{u_1} be the parent cell of C_u, so that $u = u_1\xi$, $u^R = \xi u_1^R$, for some $\xi \in Z_2$. Note that the k-bit suffix of x is of the form $0z$ for some $z \in Z_2^{k-1}$. Then

$$x = u^R 10^{n-k-1-|u|} 0z = \xi u_1^R 10^{n-k-1-|u|} 0z$$

$$\mathcal{S}(x) = u_1^R 10^{n-k-1-|u-1|} z\xi \in C_{u_1}.$$

(1/2)-transfer slowdown. Since the $(1/2)$-transfer permutation amounts to crossing shuffle edges, the $(1/2)$-transfer slowdown is $t = 1$.

The claim follows from Theorem 1, instantiated with the f, p and t that we have just computed. $\square$

The expansion of Theorem 3 should be compared with expansion-16 embedding of separable graphs into butterflies in [4].

Theorem 3 extends directly to hypercube-derivative relatives of de Bruijn graphs: to the closely related shuffle-exchange graphs (cf. [14]), and to product-shuffle graphs [13], as these graphs can emulate equal-sized de Bruijn graphs with slowdown 2.

5 Conclusion

We have presented *cell trees* as a general technique for emulating arbitrary bounded-degree separable graphs.

We have instantiated the technique for two families of hosts, thereby obtaining two new emulations, one of them dramatically better than previously known. Further applications and refinements of the technique would be interesting to obtain.

Acknowledgment. The author is greatly indebted to her research advisor Arnold L. Rosenberg, who proposed the problem and supplied many valuable comments and suggestions during the development of the solution.

References

[1] F.S. Annexstein (1989): Fault tolerance in hypercube-derivative networks. *1st ACM Symp. on Parallel Algorithms and Architectures*, 179-188.

[2] M. Baumslag and F.S. Annexstein (1990): A unified approach to global permutation routing on parallel networks. *2nd ACM Symp. on Parallel Algorithms and Architectures*, 398-406. *Math. Syst. Th.*, to appear.

[3] S.N. Bhatt, F.R.K. Chung, J.-W. Hong, F.T. Leighton, B. Obrenić, A.L. Rosenberg, E.J. Schwabe (1991): Optimal emulations by butterfly-like networks. Tech. Rpt. 90-108, Univ. Massachusetts; *J. ACM*, to appear.

[4] S.N. Bhatt, F.R.K. Chung, J.-W. Hong, F.T. Leighton, A.L. Rosenberg (1988): Optimal simulations by butterfly networks. *20th ACM Symp. on Theory of Computing*, 92-104.

[5] S.N. Bhatt, F.R.K. Chung, F.T. Leighton, A.L. Rosenberg (1986): Optimal simulations of tree machines. *27th IEEE Symp. on Foundations of Computer Science*, 274-282.

[6] S.N. Bhatt, F.R.K. Chung, F.T. Leighton, A.L. Rosenberg (1989): Universal graphs for bounded-degree trees and planar graphs. *SIAM J. Discrete Math. 2*, 145-155.

[7] S.N. Bhatt, F.R.K. Chung, F.T. Leighton, A.L. Rosenberg (1991): Efficient embeddings of trees in hypercubes. *SIAM J. Comput.*, to appear.

[8] S.N. Bhatt and F.T. Leighton (1984): A framework for solving VLSI graph layout problems. *J. Comp. Syst. Sci. 28*, 300-343.

[9] N.G. de Bruijn (1946): A combinatorial problem. *Proc. Koninklijke Nederlandsche Akademie van Wetenschappen (A) 49*, Part 2, 758-764.

[10] F.T. Leighton (1983): *Complexity Issues in VLSI: Optimal Layouts for the Shuffle-Exchange Graph and Other Networks*. MIT Press, Cambridge, Mass.

[11] F.T. Leighton, B. Maggs, S. Rao (1988): Universal packet routing algorithms. *29th IEEE Symp. on Foundations of Computer Science*, 256-269.

[12] A.L. Rosenberg (1981): Issues in the study of graph embeddings. In *Graph-Theoretic Concepts in Computer Science: Proceedings of the International Wkshp. WG80* (H. Noltemeier, ed.) *Lecture Notes in Computer Science 100*, Springer-Verlag, N.Y., 150-176.

[13] A.L. Rosenberg (1991): Product-shuffle networks: toward reconciling shuffles and butterflies. *Discr. Appl. Math.*, to appear.

[14] H. Stone (1971): Parallel processing with the perfect shuffle. *IEEE Trans. Comp., C-20*, 153-161.

[15] V.G. Vizing (1964): On an estimate of the chromatic class of a p-graph (in Russian). *Diskret. Analiz 3*, 25-30.

SESSION 5

Constructing Arrangements Optimally in Parallel

(Preliminary Version)

Michael T. Goodrich*

Department of Computer Science
The Johns Hopkins University
Baltimore, MD 21218-2686

Summary of Results

We give two optimal parallel algorithms for constructing the arrangement of n lines in the plane. The first method is quite simple and runs in $O(\log^2 n)$ time using $O(n^2)$ work, and the second method, which is more sophisticated, runs in $O(\log n)$ time using $O(n^2)$ work. This second result solves a well-known open problem in parallel computational geometry, and involves the use of a new algorithmic technique, the construction of ϵ-pseudo-nets, which may be of interest in its own right. Our results immediately imply that one can optimally construct the arrangement of n hyperplanes in $\Re^d$ in $O(\log n)$ time using $O(n^d)$ work, for fixed d. Our algorithms are for the CREW PRAM.

1 Introduction

A geometric structure of recognized importance in computational geometry is the arrangement defined by n hyperplanes in $\Re^d$, i.e., the combinatorial structure describing the cells of $\Re^d$ determined by the hyperplanes, as well as the adjacency information for these cells [13, 21, 32, 33] (see Figure 1 for a 2-dimensional example). Indeed, in his highly-regarded book on algorithms in combinatorial geometry, Edels-brunner argues that "arrangements of hyperplanes are at the very heart of computational geometry" [21]. Even in the plane, where one has an arrangement of lines (which is a planar graph), there are many applications for this structure (see [21, 32, 33]). Moreover, by a well-known duality between hyperplanes and points, the arrangement can also be used to solve a number of problems dealing with points in $\Re^d$ [14, 21, 33, 23]. We are interested in the parallel complexity of constructing arrangements.

The first optimal sequential algorithms for constructing line arrangements were developed independently by Chazelle, Guibas, and Lee [14] and by Edelsbrunner, O'Rourke, and Seidel [23]. The main idea behind these methods is to incrementally construct the arrangement one line at a time. By an interesting "zone lemma" [14, 23], one can show that only $O(n)$ time is needed to insert each line; hence, the entire line arrangement can be constructed in $O(n^2)$ time. Moreover, this approach can be generalized to constructing the arrangement of hyperplanes in $\Re^d$ in $O(n^d)$ time. This is of course optimal, since the arrangement has $\Omega(n^d)$ size. Incidentally, one can also construct a line arrangement in $O(n^2)$ time by sweeping the plane with a vertical *pseudo-line*, i.e., a line that is "topologically" equivalent to a vertical line [22], reducing the working space for the construction to $O(n)$.

The main obstacle to designing an optimal parallel algorithm for line arrangement construction is that these paradigms, which led to efficient sequential algorithms, seem inherently sequential. There is, of course, a trivial par-

*This research was supported by the National Science Foundation under Grants CCR-8810568 and CCR-9003299, and by the NSF and DARPA under Grant CCR-8908092. Author's Email address: goodrich@cs.jhu.edu.

allel algorithm analogous to a brute-force sequential method, where one computes the intersections determined by each line and then sorts the intersections along each line. If one implements this algorithm using any optimal sorting algorithm [17], then it runs in $O(\log n)$ time using $O(n^2)$ processors. Unfortunately, it is not at all clear how one might apply any of the known parallel techniques for deriving improved processor bounds to this algorithm, including Brent's theorem [11], the "sequential subsets" method [24], and the "accelerating cascades" paradigm [18]. This has prompted a number of researchers to pose as an open problem the existence of an $O(\log n)$ time CREW PRAM line-arrangement algorithm that uses $O(n^2/\log n)$ processors [3, 4, 25, 28]. Such an algorithm is said to be *optimal*, because the product of its time and number of processors matches the sequential lower bound for this problem. In this paper we show that one can in fact optimally solve this problem in $O(\log n)$ time.

The previous best deterministic parallel algorithm for this problem is due to Anderson, Beame, and Brisson [4], and runs in $O(\log n \log^* n)$ time using $O(n^2/\log n)$ processors in the CREW PRAM model. There is also a randomized parallel algorithm, due to Hagerup, Jung, and Welzl, that runs in $O(\log n)$ expected time using $O(n^2/\log n)$ processors [28].

There has also been some previous work on solving the related problem of constructing the arrangement of n line segments in parallel, as well. For example, Chow [15] shows how to determine all the pair-wise intersections of n axis-parallel segments in $O((1/\epsilon)\log n + k_{\max})$ time using $O(n^{1+\epsilon})$ processors [15], where $\epsilon > 0$ is a small constant and $k_{\max}$ is the maximum, taken over all input segments s, of the number of intersections on s. In [25] the author shows how to construct the arrangement of such segments in $O(\log n)$ time using $O(n + k/\log n)$ processors in the CREW PRAM model, and

how to construct a general segment arrangement in $O(\log n)$ time using $O(n \log n + k)$ processors. Of course, when applied to the line arrangement problem this is no better than the trivial brute-force method.

In this paper we present two optimal parallel algorithms for line-arrangement construction. The first is quite simple and runs in $O(\log^2 n)$ time using $O(n^2/\log^2 n)$ processors. The main idea of this algorithm is to apply the parallel divide-and-conquer paradigm using a data structures of Anderson, Beame, and Brisson [4] to efficiently perform the "marry" step. The second method is more sophisticated and runs in $O(\log n)$ time using $O(n^2/\log n)$ processors. This algorithm is based on the efficient construction of a structure we call the ϵ-pseudo-net, which is a decomposition of the plane into pseudo-trapezoids (i.e., trapezoids whose top and bottom edges are defined by pseudo-lines) such that each pseudo-trapezoid intersects only a "few" lines.

2 A Simple Method

We begin with some definitions. Suppose we are given a set S of n lines in the plane. For simplicity of expression we assume that there are no vertical lines in S (it is easy to modify our algorithm for the more general case). The *arrangement* for S, denoted $A(S)$, is the planar graph $G = (V, E)$ such that V is the set of intersections formed by the lines in S and E is the set of edges defined by consecutive intersections along lines in S. The *depth* of an edge e in $A(S)$ is the number of lines of S that are directly above e, i.e., the number intersected by a vertical ray emanating upward from a point on e (other than one of e's endpoints). The k-*level* in $A(S)$ is the set of edges at depth k [21]. Clearly, the k-level is a monotone chain of edges in $A(S)$, i.e., a chain that is intersected only once by any vertical line. In general, a k-level can have has many as $\Omega(n \log k)$ edges, but will always have no more than $O(n\sqrt{k})$ edges [21]. Of course, the total size of all k-levels in $A(S)$ is $\Theta(n^2)$.

Our algorithm description, which follows, makes considerable use of k-levels, and builds upon the approach of Anderson, Beame, and Brisson [4]. We describe our algorithm assuming we have $O(n^2/\log n)$ processors at our disposal, and then show how to apply Brent's Theorem [11] to reduce the number of processors to $O(n^2/\log^2 n)$.

Step 1. Divide the set S into two equal-sized sets S_1 and S_2, such that the lines in S_1 all have slope smaller than the lines in S_2. This can easily be done in $O(\log n)$ time using $O(n/\log n)$ processors, assuming the lines in S are pre-sorted by slope [17].

Step 2. Recursively construct the arrangements $A(S_1)$ and $A(S_2)$ in parallel.

Step 3. Construct arrays that store each of the levels in $A(S_1)$ and $A(S_2)$ ordered left to right. This can be done in $O(\log n)$ time using $O(n^2)$ work by the list ranking algorithm of Anderson and Miller [5] or Cole and Vishkin [19]. Distinguish the k-levels such that k is a multiple of $\lceil \log n \rceil$ as *super levels* in the arrangement.

Comment: Anderson, Beame, and Brisson make an interesting observation about sets of lines that are separated by their slopes. In particular, they observe the following:

Observation 2.1 [4]: *If l is a line in S_i, then l intersects each level of $A(S_j)$, $i \neq j$, exactly once.*

As they show, this observation can be used to build a parallel data structure for efficiently finding the intersection of a line l in S_1 with $A(S_2)$. One simply stores each super level of $A(S_2)$ in an array (as above). To intersect $l \in S_1$ with $A(S_2)$ one assigns $O(n/\log n)$ processors and finds l's intersection with each super level by a binary search. This cuts l into $n/\log n$ segments. Then, for each such segment s, one performs the sequential search method

of Chazelle [12] to iteratively crawl around the faces s intersects[1] to discover all the intersections of s with $A(S_2)$. In [25] the author shows that such a sequential search will take $O(\log n)$ time. Thus, the entire computation can be performed in $O(\log n)$ time using $O(n/\log n)$ processors.

Step 4. For each line l in S_1, compute the ordered list of its intersections with $A(S_2)$ using the method outlined above. Also perform the similar computation for each line in S_2. One can then construct $A(S)$ by merging, for each line l, l's sorted lists of intersections in $A(S_1)$ and $A(S_2)$, respectively. This takes $O(\log n)$ time using $O(n/\log n)$ processors for each line l, or $O(n^2/\log n)$ overall, by the list merging method of [5, 19]. This completes the construction.

The time complexity of this method is characterized by the recurrence, $T(n) = T(n/2) + b\log n$, for some constant b. Thus, this method runs in $O(\log^2 n)$ time. Even though we described our algorithm so as to use $O(n^2/\log n)$ processors, we can in fact implement it in $O(\log^2 n)$ time using only $O(n^2/\log^2 n)$ processors. This is because the work complexity is characterized by the recurrence,

$$W(n) = 2W(n/2) + cn^2,$$

where c is a constant. This implies that this method uses $O(n^2)$ work. By an easy application of Brent's Theorem, then, we can therefore derive the following theorem:

Theorem 2.2: *One can construct the arrangement of n lines in the plane in $O(\log^2 n)$ time using $O(n^2/\log^2 n)$ processors in the CREW PRAM model.*

---

[1]The iterative crawling method of Chazelle requires that each edge on a face f store a pointer to the right-most point on f. This can be computed (e.g., in Step 3) using a list ranking procedure [5, 19] for each face in parallel, which requires $O(\log n)$ time using $O(n^2/\log n)$ processors.

In the next section we show how to extend this approach to construct an ϵ-pseudo-net for S, the main structure employed by our optimal $O(\log n)$-time method.

3 ϵ-Pseudo-Nets

Recent developments on the theory of ϵ-nets have proven useful for solving a number of problems in computational geometry (see [1, 27]). The general paradigm is that, given a set X of n "objects" and a set $R \subseteq 2^X$ of "ranges" with finite Vapnik-Chervonenkis dimension (see [16, 27]), one can construct a small-sized subset $N \subset X$ such that, for any range $\rho \in R$ such that $|\rho| > \epsilon|X|$, ρ intersects N. In the context of this paper, the important example is the range space (S, R) where S is a set of n lines and R is the collection of subsets of S that intersect a given triangle, taken over all combinatorially distinct triangles. Agarwal [1] shows that, given a parameter r, one can efficiently construct a collection of r^2 triangles such that no triangle intersects more than $O(n/r)$ lines in S. There are also a number of randomized methods [16, 27] for efficiently constructing a collection of r^2 triangles such that no triangle intersects more than $O((n \log r)/r)$ lines in S. Unfortunately, none of the previous algorithms translate into an efficient deterministic parallel algorithm running in $O(\log n)$ time (which is what we require for our arrangement construction procedure).

In this section we show how to construct a collection Q of r^2 pseudo-trapezoids (i.e., trapezoids with top and bottom edges that are pseudo-lines) such that each pseudo-trapezoid intersects at most $O((n \log \log r)/r)$ lines in S. In particular, by *pseudo-lines* we mean piecewise linear curves that are x-monotone and such that any two intersect each other at most once. (See Figure 2.) Our method runs in $O(\log n)$ time using $O(n^2 \log \log n/ \log \log r + nr)$ work, and extends the approach of the previous sec-

tion.

Step 1. Sort the lines in S by slope. Divide this sorted list into $\lceil \log \log r \rceil$ groups $S_1, S_2, ..., S_{\lceil \log \log r \rceil}$ of size $O(n/ \log \log r)$ each, so that each line in S_i has smaller slope than every line in S_j if $i < j$. By using a slightly different implementation of the method of Anderson, Beame, and Brisson [4] we can construct each $A(S_i)$ in $O(\log n)$ time using $O(n^2 \log \log n/ \log \log r)$ work (where one stops their iterative process after 2 iterations). Also, for each $A(S_i)$, we construct an array representation of each level of $A(S_i)$. Using the list ranking algorithm of Anderson and Miller [5] or that of Cole and Vishkin [19] this can be done in $O(\log n)$ time using $O(n^2/ \log \log r)$ work. We define each k-level of $A(S_i)$ such that k is a multiple of $\lceil n/r \rceil$ (including the first and last levels) to be a *super level* in $A(S_i)$. Note that there are $O(r/ \log \log r)$ super levels per arrangement $A(S_i)$.

The following lemma expresses a property concerning levels that is crucial to our construction.

Lemma 3.1: Let $\mathcal{L}$ and $\mathcal{M}$ be two levels with $\mathcal{L} \subset A(S_i)$ and $\mathcal{M} \subset A(S_j)$, $i \neq j$. Then $\mathcal{L}$ and $\mathcal{M}$ intersect at most once.

Proof: Suppose not. Then there exists points p and q such that (i) $\{p, q\} \subset \mathcal{L} \cap \mathcal{M}$, (ii) p and q are consecutive intersections along $\mathcal{L}$ (resp., $\mathcal{M}$) with $x(p) < x(q)$, and (iii), without loss of generality, $\mathcal{M}$ "dips below" $\mathcal{L}$ at p and dips above $\mathcal{L}$ at q. Let s and t be the lines that define p, and let s' and t' be the lines that define q, with $s, s' \in \mathcal{L}$ and $t, t' \in \mathcal{M}$. Then $slope(s) > slope(t)$ and $slope(s') < slope(t')$. But this contradicts the fact that S_i and S_j are separated by slope. $\square$

Comment: Therefore, by this lemma, the intersections between $A(S_i)$ and $A(S_j)$ can be viewed as the intersections defined by two sets of parallel pseudo-lines, i.e., they define a "pseudo-grid".

Step 2. For each $i \in \{1, ..., \lceil \log\log r\rceil\}$ and for each line $l \in S_i$ intersect l with the super levels in $A(S_j)$, for $j \neq i$. Using the method as in Step 4 of the previous method, this takes $O(\log n)$ time using $O(nr)$ work (n lines $*$ $r/\log\log r$ super levels per group $*$ $\log\log r$ groups). This gives us $\lceil \log\log r\rceil$ sorted lists of intersections for each line l. We distinguish two kinds of intersections with $l \in S_i$: *proper intersections*, which are formed between l and a super level in some $A(S_j)$, $j \neq i$, and *segment intersections*, which are formed between l and the super levels in $A(S_i)$. This step requires $O(\log n)$ time using $O(nr)$ work.

Step 3. Construct the arrangement A' of super levels. By Lemma 3.1, A' is an arrangement of pseudo-lines; hence, each super level has $O(r)$ intersections with other super levels. First, for each l, we sort the list of proper intersections along l. This amounts to merging $\log\log r$ sorted lists each of size $O(r/\log\log r)$; hence, can be implemented in $O((\log\log r)^2)$ time using $O(r)$ processors [10] per line (for $O(nr(\log\log r)^2)$ work overall). We then merge the list of segment intersections along l with this list of proper intersections along l, and "throw away" each proper intersection that does not fall on a segment intersection for l. Finally, we construct the proper intersections along each super level by performing a list-ranking procedure, to link up the proper intersections that fall along each edge in the super level. This requires $O(\log n)$ time and $O(n^2/\log\log r)$ work.

Comment: There are r^2 faces in A', which are defined by r^2 intersection points. Moreover, each face has at most $2\lceil \log\log r\rceil$ pseudo-edges on its boundary. As we show in the following lemma, we almost have the required decomposition.

Lemma 3.2: *The number of proper intersections along the boundary of each face of A' is $O((n\log\log r)/r)$.*

Proof: Let f be a face of A'. By construction,

f lies between two super levels in each $A(S_i)$. Also, since each pseudo-edge on f's boundary is x-monotone, f's boundary can be decomposed into two chains: an upper chain and a lower chain. Index each edge e on f by the index of the group S_i such that e is in a super level of $A(S_i)$. As a simple corollary of Lemma 3.1, it is easy to show that the edges in a left-to-right listing of the lower chain (resp., upper chain) have strictly increasing (resp., decreasing) indices. Suppose, for the sake of contradiction, that a level $\mathcal{L}$ of $A(S_i)$ has more than two proper intersections with f. Let a, b, and c be the indices of the first three proper intersections $\mathcal{L}$ has with f. That is, $\mathcal{L}$ enters f at a, exits at b, and enters again at c. Since $\mathcal{L}$ is x-monotone, b and c most both be on the lower chain of f or both on the upper chain. Without loss of generality, suppose they are both on the lower chain. Then $i < b$ and $c < i$. But this contradicts the fact that the indices on the lower chain of f have increasing indices. Therefore, each $A(S_i)$ can contribute at most $O(n/r)$ proper intersections to the boundary of f. The lemma follows, then, since there are $\lceil \log\log r\rceil$ groups. $\square$

Thus, the only types of intersections that could cause a cell to intersect more than $O((n\log\log r)/r)$ lines are segment intersections (see Figure 3). The next step in our method deals with this problem.

Step 4. To complete the construction, we extend two vertical rays (one up and one down) from each of $O(r^2)$ distinguished points on the pseudo-edges of A' to the first points of A' that the rays intersect, respectively. This forms a decomposition of A' into pseudo-trapezoids with the desired "ϵ-pseudo-net" property for S. The points we distinguish in this way include each point defined by the intersection of two super levels and every (n/r)-th point on a super level (when listed left to right). This implies that we will have $O(r^2)$ pseudo-trapezoids, each of which intersects at most $O((n\log\log r)/r)$

lines. It is an easy matter to complete the construction by listing the lines intersecting each pseudo-trapezoid. This step can be implemented in $O(\log n)$ time using $O(nr \log \log r)$ work, using the arrangement searching method described in the previous algorithm, and completes the construction.

Theorem 3.3: *Given a set S of n lines in the plane, one can construct a decomposition of the plane into r^2 pseudo-trapezoids such that pseudo-trapezoid intersects at most $O(n/r)$ pseudo-trapezoids of S. This construction can be implemented in $O(\log n)$ time using $O(n^2 \log \log n / \log \log r + nr(\log \log r)^2)$ work.*

Before we can present our method for optimal arrangement construction, we have one more algorithmic tool that we must present, that of computing the number of intersections in a pseudo-trapezoid.

4 Counting Intersections in a Disk

This problem is topologically equivalent to the problem of simply counting intersections in a disk. That is, we suppose we are given a collection S of n chords in a disk D and wish to determine the number of chord intersections in D. The method we describe actually does more than simply determine the total number of intersections; it also determines, for each chord c, the number, $k(c)$, of intersections determined by c. Our method is by divide-and-conquer.

1. Imagine cutting the boundary of D at some specified point so as to define a curve, C. This defines a total ordering of chord endpoints based on their rank in a counter-clockwise listing along C. Sort the left endpoints by this ordering (for any chord c, we define c's *left* endpoint to be c's first endpoint in this ordering). This can be done in $O(\log n)$ time using $O(n)$ processors [17], and provides the preprocessing for our divide-and-conquer scheme.

2. Divide the Curve C into two curves A and B by cutting C at x, the median left endpoint of the curves in S. Divide S into 3 groups: S_{AA}, S_{AB}, and S_{BB}, where $S_{\alpha\beta}$ denotes the set of all chords whose "left" endpoint is on α and whose right endpoint is on β. Note that $|S_{AA}| + |S_{AB}| + |S_{BB}| = |S|$, and $|S_{\alpha\beta}| \leq |S|/2$ for $\alpha\beta \in \{AA, AB, BB\}$. Recursively solve the problem for S_{AA}, S_{AB}, and S_{BB} in parallel (we associate the curve A with S_{AA}, the curve B with S_{BB}, and the curve C with S_{AB}).

Comment: Having recursively computed all the intersections between chords in S_{AA}, S_{AB}, and S_{BB}, respectively, we have only to compute the intersections determined by chords in different sets. Note, however, that no chord in S_{AA} can intersect with a chord in S_{BB}. Thus, we need only consider intersections determined by chords in S_{AA} and S_{AB} (resp., S_{AB} and S_{BB}). Since these two cases are symmetric, let us restrict our attention to those intersections determined by chords in S_{AA} and S_{AB}. The following observation establishes the easy, but important, property we exploit to efficiently compute the number of such intersections.

Observation 4.1: *Let s and t be two chords with $s \in S_{AA}$ and $t \in S_{AB}$. The chords s and t intersect if and only if the left endpoint of t occurs between the endpoints of s in a counter-clockwise listing.*

3. Let T be a sorted listing of the left endpoints of chords in S_{AB}. Let U be a sorted listing of the left and right endpoints of chords in S_{AA}. Merge T and U. Given this merge we can immediately compute the number of chords in S_{AB} intersecting a particular chord c in S_{AA}. In particular let $a(c)$ (resp., $b(c)$) be the rank in T of c's left (resp., right) endpoint. Then the number of chords c intersects in S_{AB} is $b(c) - a(c)$, by the above observation. The true value for $k(c)$ can therefore be calculated by summing this value with the recursively computed value for $k(c)$. A similar computation

can be performed for each c in S_{AB}. This step requires $O(\log n)$ time and $O(n/\log n)$ processors.

4. Repeat Step 3 to determine the intersections between S_{AB} and S_{BB} and update the $k(c)$ values accordingly. Summing all the $k(c)$ values over all chords in C gives us the value of k.

Thus, in $O(\log^2 n)$ time and $O(n \log n)$ work we can determine the number of intersection points in the circle. Since the essential computation in each step involves merging recursively constructed lists of endpoints, it is a simple exercise to apply the cascading divide-and-conquer paradigm of Atallah, Cole, and Goodrich [6] to implement this algorithm in $O(\log n)$ time using $O(n)$ processors.

Note that our intersection counting method did not depend on any geometric properties of the disk; it simply depended on the property that the boundary of the enclosing curve was simple and the endpoints were sorted around the boundary. Thus, it can also be applied to pseudo-trapezoids. We summarize:

Lemma 4.2: *Given a collection of chords C in a pseudo-trapezoid, one can compute the number of intersections $k(c)$ along each chord c in C in $O(\log n)$ time using $O(n)$ processors in the CREW PRAM model.*

In the next section we show how to combine the methods of the previous two sections to design a fast arrangement-construction algorithm.

5 Fast Arrangement Construction

We show in this section how to construct the arrangement of n lines in $O(\log n)$ time using $O(n^2/\log n)$ processors. The method is to construct, in $O(\log n)$ time, an ϵ-pseudo-net partitioning for some $r \leq n/(\log \log^2 n)$ (taking

$r = n/(\log \log^2 n)$ is sufficient). This takes $O(n^2)$ work, and results in $\lceil n^2/(\log \log n)^4 \rceil$ pseudo-trapezoids, each of which intersects $O((\log \log n)^3)$ lines. That is, it determines $O(n^2/\log \log n)$ line *segments*, with at most $O((\log \log n)^3)$ segments per pseudo-trapezoid. We then use our method for counting intersections in a "disk" to determine the number of intersections in each pseudo-trapezoid. We then group the pseudo-trapezoids into $O(n^2/\log n)$ "buckets", such that each bucket contains at most $O(\log n/\log \log n)$ segments and determines at most $O(\log n)$ intersections (in the interiors of the pseudo-trapezoids in this bucket). This can easily be done in $O(\log n)$ time using $O(n^2)$ work, say, by parallel prefix computations. Finally, we assign a single processor to each bucket, and let that processor apply the sequential segment-arrangement method of Chazelle and Edelsbrunner to construct the arrangement in each pseudo-trapezoid in this bucket. The method of Chazelle and Edelsbrunner runs in $O(n_b \log n_b + k_b)$ time, where n_b is the number of segments in bucket b and k_b is the number of intersections these segments determine. In our case, n_b is always $O(\log n/\log \log n)$ and k_b is always $O(\log n)$. Therefore, no processor will take more than $O(\log n)$ time to complete the construction of the arrangements in its assigned pseudo-trapezoids. This completes the construction and gives us the following theorem:

Theorem 5.1: *The arrangement of n lines in the plane can be constructed in $O(\log n)$ time using $O(n^2/\log n)$ processors in the CREW PRAM model, which is optimal.*

6 Extensions and Applications

We have show how to optimally construct the arrangement of n lines in the plane in $O(\log n)$ time, solving a well-known open problem in parallel computational geometry [3, 25, 4]. Using the "induction" argument of Anderson, Beame, and Brisson [4], this immediately implies that one can optimally construct the arrangement of n hyperplances in $\Re^d$, for fixed d, in $O(\log n)$ time using $O(n^d/\log n)$ processors.

In the full version of this paper we show also show how to apply our algorithms do design efficient parallel methods for hidden-line elimination, Hopcroft's problem, and the problem of finding the minimum-area triangle determined by 3 points taken from a set of n points in the plane.

7 Discussion

In the sequential setting the ideas used to design optimal line-arrangement algorithms were "stepping stones" to an optimal method for constructing the arrangement of n line segments [13]. An interesting open question, then, is the following: Can one construct the arrangement of n line segments in $O(\log n)$ time using $O(n + k/\log n)$ processors, where k is the number of intersections. Currently, the only optimal output-sensitive methods are either for the special case of axis-parallel segments [25] or are for the problem of computing the intersections between two sets of non-intersecting segments [26].

Acknowledgements

We would like to thank Richard Anderson, Richard Cole, and S. Rao Kosaraju for several stimulating discussions related to topics discussed in this paper.

References

[1] P.K. Agarwal, "A Deterministic Algorithm for Partitioning Arrangements of Lines and its Applications," *Proc. 5th ACM Symp. on Computational Geometry*, 1989, 11–22.

[2] A. Aggarwal, B. Chazelle, L. Guibas, C. Ó'Dúnlaing, and C. Yap, "Parallel Computational Geometry," *Algorithmica*, **3**(3), 1988, 293–328.

[3] A. Aggarwal and J. Wein, *Computational Geometry*, M.I.T. Report MIT/LCS/RSS 3, 1988.

[4] R. Anderson, P. Beame, and E. Brisson, "Parallel Algorithms for Arrangements," *Proc. 2nd ACM Symp. on Parallel Algorithms and Architectures*, 1990, 298–306.

[5] R.J. Anderson and G.L. Miller, "Deterministic Parallel List Ranking," *Proc. 3rd Aegean Workshop on Computing, AWOC '88*, Springer-Verlag Lecture Notes in Computer Science: 319, 1988, 81–90.

[6] M.J. Atallah, R. Cole, and M.T. Goodrich, "Cascading Divide-and-Conquer: A Technique for Designing Parallel Algorithms," *SIAM Journal on Computing*, Vol. 18, No. 3, 1989, 499–532.

[7] J.L. Bentley and T. Ottmann, "Algorithms for Reporting and Counting Geometric Intersections," *IEEE Trans. on Computers*, **C-28**, 1979, 643–647.

[8] J.L. Bentley and D. Wood, "An Optimal Worst Case Algorithm for Reporting Intersections of Rectangles," *IEEE Trans. on Computers*, **C-29**(7), 1980, 571–576.

[9] Bilardi, G., and Nicolau, A., "Adaptive Bitonic Sorting: An Optimal Parallel Algorithm for Shared Memory Machines," TR 86-769, Dept. of Comp. Sci., Cornell Univ., August 1986.

[10] A. Borodin and J.E. Hopcroft, "Routing, Merging, and Sorting on Parallel Models of Computation," *Jour. of Comp. and Sys. Sci.*, Vol. 30, No. 1, February 1985, 130–145.

[11] R.P. Brent, "The Parallel Evaluation of General Arithmetic Expressions," *J. ACM*, Vol. 21, No. 2, 1974, pp. 201–206.

[12] B. Chazelle, "Intersecting is Easier Than Sorting," *16th ACM Symp. on Theory of Comp. (STOC)*, 1984, pp. 125–134.

[13] B. Chazelle and H. Edelsbrunner, "An Optimal Algorithm for Intersecting Line Segments in the Plane," *29th FOCS*, 1988, 590–600.

[14] B. Chazelle, L.J. Guibas, and D.T. Lee, "The Power of Geometric Duality," *24th FOCS*, 1983, 217–225.

[15] A. Chow, "Parallel Algorithms for Geometric Problems," Ph.D. thesis, Comp. Sci. Dept., Univ. of Illinois, 1980.

[16] K. Clarkson, "New Applications of Random Sampling in Computational Geometry," *Discrete and Computational Geometry*, Vol. 2, 1987, 195–222.

[17] R. Cole, "Parallel Merge Sort," *SIAM J. Comput.*, **17**(4), 1988, 770–785.

[18] R. Cole and U. Vishkin, "Deterministic Coin Tossing and Accelerating Cascades: Micro and Macro Techniques for Designing Parallel Algorithms," *Proc. 18th ACM Symp. on Theory of Computing*, 1986, 206–219.

[19] R. Cole and U. Vishkin, "Approximate and Exact Parallel Scheduling with Applications to List, Tree and Graph Problems," *Proc. 27th IEEE Symp. on Foundations of Computer Science*, 1986, 478–491.

[20] P.W. Dymon and S.A. Cook, "Hardware Complexity and Parallel Comp.," *21st IEEE Symp. on Found. of Comp. Sci.*, 1980, 360–372.

[21] H. Edelsbrunner, *Algorithms in Combinatorial Geometry*, Springer-Verlag, NY, 1987.

[22] H. Edelsbrunner and L.J. Guibas, "Topologically Sweeping an Arrangement," *18th STOC*, 1986, 389–403.

[23] H. Edelsbrunner, J. O'Rourke, and R. Seidel, "Constructing Arrangements of Lines and Hyperplanes with Applications," *24th FOCS*, 1983, 83–91.

[24] M.T. Goodrich, "Efficient Parallel Techniques for Computational Geometry," Ph.D. thesis, Department of Computer Sciences, Purdue University, 1987.

[25] M.T. Goodrich, "Intersecting Line Segments in Parallel with an Output-Sensitive Number of Processors," *SIAM Journal on Computing*, to appear. (a preliminary version appeared in *Proc. 1989 ACM Symp. on Parallel Algorithms and Architectures*, 127–137).

[26] M.T. Goodrich, S. Shauck, and S. Guha, "Parallel Methods for Visibility and Shortest Path Problems in Simple Polygons," *Proc. 6th ACM Symp. on Computational Geometry*, 1990.

[27] D. Haussler and E. Welzl, "ε-Nets and Simplex Range Queries," *Discrete and Computational Geometry*, Vol. 2, 1987, 127–151.

[28] T. Hagerup, H. Jung, and E. Welzl, "Efficient Parallel Computation of Arrangement of Hyperplanes in d Dimensions," *Proc. 2nd ACM Symp. on Parallel Algorithms and Architectures*, 1990, 290–297.

[29] Karp, R.M., and Ramachandran, V., "A Survey of Parallel Algorithms for Shared-Memory Machines," Report UCB/CSD 88/408, EECS Dept., Univ. of California, Berkeley, 1988.

[30] Kruskal, C.P., Rudolph, L., and Snir, M., "The Power of Parallel Prefix," *1985 Int. Conf. on Parallel Processing*, 180–185.

[31] Ladner, R.E., and Fischer, M.J., "Parallel Prefix Computation," *J. ACM*, October

1980, 831–838.

[32] D.T. Lee and F.P. Preparata, "Computational Geometry—A Survey," *IEEE Trans. on Computers*, Vol. C-33, No. 12, December 1984, pp. 872–1101.

[33] F.P. Preparata and M.I. Shamos, *Computational Geometry: An Introduction*, Springer-Verlag, 1985.

[34] W.L. Ruzzo, "On Uniform Circuit Complexity," *J. of Comp. and Sys. Sci.*, Vol. 22, No. 3, June 1981, 365–383.

[35] Y. Shiloach and U. Vishkin, "Finding the Maximum, Merging, and Sorting in a Parallel Computation Model," *Journal of Algorithms*, Vol. 2, 1981, pp. 88–102.

[36] J.C. Wyllie, "The Complexity of Parallel Computation," Ph.D. thesis, TR 79-387, Dept. of Comp. Sci., Cornell Univ., 1979.

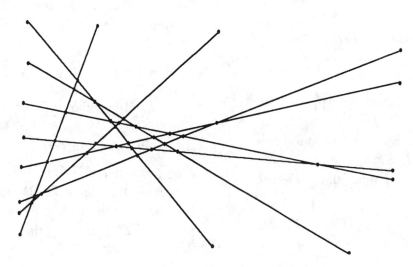

Figure 1: A line arrangement.

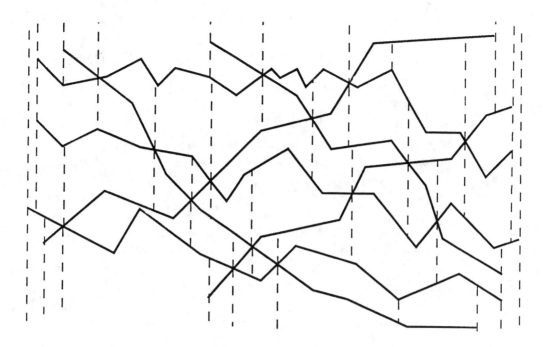

Figure 2: An ϵ-pseudo-net.

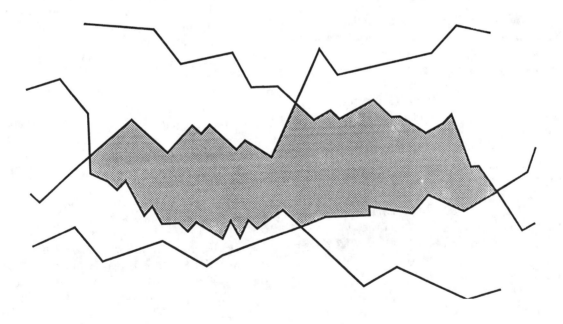

Figure 3: A cell in the pseudo grid.

Processor Efficient Parallel Solution of Linear Systems over an Abstract Field*

*Erich Kaltofen***

Department of Computer Science, University of Toronto
Toronto, Canada M5S 1A4; Inter-Net: `kaltofen@cs.toronto.edu`

Victor Pan

Department of Mathematics and Computer Science
Lehman College, City University of New York
Bronx, New York 10468; Inter-Net: `vpan@lcvax.bitnet`

Parallel randomized algorithms are presented that solve n-dimensional systems of linear equations and compute inverses of $n \times n$ non-singular matrices over a field in $O((\log n)^2)$ time, where each time unit represents an arithmetic operation in the field generated by the matrix entries. The algorithms utilize within a $O(\log n)$ factor as many processors as are needed to multiply two $n \times n$ matrices. The algorithms avoid zero divisions with controllably high probability provided the $O(n)$ random elements used are selected uniformly from a sufficiently large set. For fields of small positive characteristic, the processor count measures of our solutions are somewhat higher.

1. Introduction

A processor efficient parallel algorithm is a parallel algorithm that has a running time that is poly-logarithmic in the input size and that utilizes asymptotically as many processors as the best known sequential step count for solving the problem; a poly-logarithmic factor in the asymptotic processor count is allowed (Karp and Ramachandran 1990). This paper considers the problem of solving a linear system of n equations with n unknowns over an abstract field, as well as the closely related prob-

lems of computing the inverse, determinant, and rank of an $n \times n$ matrix. An individual step in our algorithms is an addition, subtraction, multiplication, division, or zero-test of elements in the field that the entries of the linear system generate. Gaussian elimination is a sequential method for all these computational problems over abstract fields, whose running time can be asymptotically related to the sequential complexity of $n \times n$ matrix multiplication (Bunch and Hopcroft 1974). We present processor efficient randomized parallel algorithms for solving non-singular systems and for inverting non-singular matrices.

Csanky (1976) used Leverrier's approach to devise a parallel linear system solver, but the best processor count known for this approach exceeds by a factor of almost $\sqrt{n}$ the complexity of matrix multiplication (Preparata and Sarwate 1978), (Galil and Pan 1989). Leverrier's algorithm does not work for fields whose characteristic is positive and less than n, in which case the best known parallel algorithms needed by a factor of n more processors (Berkowitz 1984), (Chistov 1985). All previous parallel solutions compute the characteristic polynomial of the coefficient matrix without divisions. For this restricted algebraic model these algorithms are processor optimal, i.e., it appears not to be known how

*This material is based on work supported in part by the National Science Foundation under Grant No. CCR-90-06077 and under Grant No. CDA-88-05910 (first author), and under Grant No. CCR-88-05782 and Grant No. CCR-90-20690 and by the PSC CUNY Awards #661340 and #669290 (second author).

**Permanent address: Department of Computer Science, Rensselaer Polytechnic Institute, Troy, New York 12180-3590; Inter-Net: `kaltofen@cs.rpi.edu`.

to compute the determinant of a matrix faster sequentially avoiding divisions.

Our processor efficient solution is not division free, but our algorithms realize shallow algebraic circuits and thus have no zero-tests. In order to avoid a division by zero, we instead randomly perturb the coefficient matrix. Our solution requires $O(n)$ random field elements, and we prove that if these elements are taken uniformly from a set containing s field elements, the probability of a zero-division on a non-singular input is no more than $3n^2/s$. In a substep our algorithm uses Leverrier's method. It thus has the same restriction on the characteristic of the field as does Csanky's solution, namely it divides by $2, 3, \ldots, n$. It should be noted that our solution uses matrix multiplication as a black-box. Therefore, the processor count and especially the constant in the big-O estimate is directly related to the particular matrix multiplication algorithm used, and for the classical method may yield a practical algorithm.

Our algorithms combine several advances in algebraic computational complexity theory. The first is the field independent randomized method for solving sparse linear systems by Wiedemann (1986). That approach provides a randomized parallel processor efficient reduction of linear system solving to the Berlekamp/Massey problem for finding a linear generator of a linear recurrence. Further reduction is possible to solving a non-singular Toeplitz system. The second advance is solving such Toeplitz systems in parallel processor-efficiently. Putting these two approaches together yields processor efficient randomized parallel algorithms for computing solutions to non-singular systems and for computing the determinant of a matrix. In order to obtain the inverse from the determinant of a non-singular matrix we employ the simple but ingenious reduction by Baur and Strassen (1983). Our contribution is to prove that this reduction can be realized without increasing the parallel time by more than a constant factor. We finally present one more application of that reduction, which relates the complexity of solving non-singular systems to the complexity of solving the transposed systems.

The methods presented here also yield randomized parallel processor efficient algorithms for the problems of computing the rank of a matrix, a single solution of a singular linear system, the basis for the nullspace of a matrix, and a least-squares solution of a linear system. We discuss these extensions briefly in the last section.

Notation: By $\omega > 2$ we denote the exponent of the matrix multiplication algorithm used, which must for dimension n yield a circuit that is simultaneously of depth $O(\log n)$ and size $O(n^\omega)$; currently the best known exponent is $\omega < 2.3755$ (Coppersmith and Winograd 1990). By $S^{\mathbb{N}}$ we denote the set of all infinite sequences $\{a_i\}_{i=0}^{\infty}$, $a_i \in S$. Finally, the function $\log x$,

$x \geq 2$, denotes $\log_2(x)$, and the function $\log\log x$, $x \geq 4$, denotes $\log_2(\log_2(x))$.

2. Wiedemann's Method

Wiedemann (1986) presents a randomized Las Vegas algorithm for computing the determinant of a sparse matrix over a finite field. As it turns out, this method is a field independent algorithm that reduces the problem of computing the determinant to the problem of solving a non-singular Toeplitz system. The reduction is processor efficient and of poly-logarithmic parallel time complexity. In the following we present Wiedemann's argument with a slight change in the probabilistic analysis, which is warranted because we work over an abstract field.

Let V be a vector space over the field K, and let $\{a_i\}_{i=0}^{\infty}$ be an infinite sequence with elements $a_i \in V$. The sequence $\{a_i\}_{i=0}^{\infty}$ is *linearly generated* over K if there exist $c_0, c_1, \ldots, c_n \in \mathsf{K}$, $n \geq 0$, $c_k \neq 0$ for some k with $0 \leq k \leq n$, such that

$$\forall j \geq 0: c_0 a_j + \cdots + c_n a_{j+n} = 0.$$

The polynomial $c_0 + c_1 \lambda + \cdots + c_n \lambda^n$ is called a *generating polynomial* for $\{a_i\}_{i=0}^{\infty}$. The set of all generating polynomials for $\{a_i\}_{i=0}^{\infty}$ together with the zero polynomial forms an ideal in $\mathsf{K}[\lambda]$. The unique polynomial generating that ideal, normalized to have leading coefficient 1, is called the *minimum polynomial* of a linearly generated sequence $\{a_i\}_{i=0}^{\infty}$. Every generating polynomial is a multiple of the minimum polynomial.

Let $A \in \mathsf{K}^{n \times n}$ be a square matrix over a field. The sequence $\{A^i\}_{i=0}^{\infty} \in (\mathsf{K}^{n \times n})^{\mathbb{N}}$ is linearly generated, and its minimum polynomial is the minimum polynomial of A, which will be denoted by f^A. For any column vector $b \in \mathsf{K}^n$, the sequence $\{A^i b\}_{i=0}^{\infty} \in (\mathsf{K}^n)^{\mathbb{N}}$ is also linearly generated by f^A. However, its minimum polynomial, denoted by $f^{A,b}$, can be a proper divisor of f^A. For any row vector $u \in \mathsf{K}^{1 \times n}$, the sequence $\{uA^i b\}_{i=0}^{\infty} \in \mathsf{K}^{\mathbb{N}}$ is linearly generated as well, and its minimum polynomial, denoted by $f_u^{A,b}$, is again a divisor of $f^{A,b}$. Wiedemann proves the following fact (loc. cit., §VI).

Theorem 1. *Let $m = \deg(f^{A,b})$, and let W be the linear space of polynomials of degree less than m in $\mathsf{K}[\lambda]$. There exists a surjective linear map $\ell \colon \mathsf{K}^{1 \times n} \longrightarrow W$*

$$\forall u \in \mathsf{K}^{1 \times n}: f_u^{A,b} = f^{A,b} \iff \mathrm{GCD}(f^{A,b}, \ell(u)) = 1.$$

Clearly, the sequence $\{uA^i\}_{i=0}^{\infty} \in (\mathsf{K}^{1 \times n})^{\mathbb{N}}$ is the symmetric counterpart of $\{A^i b\}_{i=0}^{\infty}$. We write $f^{u,A}$ for the minimum polynomial of the former. By considering the rational canonical form of A, one establishes the existence of a row vector $u_0 \in \mathsf{K}^{1 \times n}$ with $f^{u_0,A} = f^A$. Let $m' = \deg(f^A)$ and let W' be the linear subspace of $\mathsf{K}[\lambda]$

spanned by $\{1, \lambda, \ldots, \lambda^{m'-1}\}$ over K. By Theorem 1 it follows that there exist surjective linear maps

$$\ell'_{u_0} \colon K^n \longrightarrow W^{m'}$$

such that

$$\forall b \in K^n \colon f_{u_0}^{A,b} = f^{u_0,A} = f^A \iff \mathrm{GCD}(f^A, \ell'_{u_0}(b)) = 1.$$

Thus, the probability that $f_u^{A,b} = f^A$ for randomly selected vectors u and b is essentially the probability of randomly selecting two polynomials of degree less than m' that are both relatively prime to f^A. For a finite field K with q elements, Wiedemann (loc. cit., Proposition 3) proves that the probability is no less than

$$\frac{1}{12 \max\{\lceil \log_q(\deg f^A) \rceil, 1\}}.$$

We shall present a different estimate. For this, we state the following Lemma, which is a key element in our results.

Lemma 1. *Let $\{a_i\}_{i=0}^\infty \in K^{\mathbb{N}}$ be linearly generated, and let m be the degree of its minimum polynomial. For $\mu \geq 0$, consider the Toeplitz matrices*

$$T_\mu := \begin{pmatrix} a_{\mu-1} & a_{\mu-2} & \cdots & a_1 & a_0 \\ a_\mu & a_{\mu-1} & \cdots & a_2 & a_1 \\ \vdots & a_\mu & \ddots & \vdots & a_2 \\ & & & \vdots & \\ a_{2\mu-3} & & & a_{\mu-1} & \\ a_{2\mu-2} & a_{2\mu-3} & \cdots & a_\mu & a_{\mu-1} \end{pmatrix} \in K^{\mu \times \mu}.$$

Then $\mathrm{Det}(T_m) \neq 0$ and for all $M > m$, $\mathrm{Det}(T_M) = 0$.

Proof. If the polynomial $g(\lambda) = \lambda^M + c_{M-1}\lambda^{M-1} + \cdots + c_0$ generates $\{a_i\}_{i=0}^\infty$, then

$$T_M \begin{pmatrix} c_{M-1} \\ \vdots \\ c_0 \end{pmatrix} = - \begin{pmatrix} a_M \\ \vdots \\ a_{2M-1} \end{pmatrix}.$$

Clearly, for each $M > m$, the above linear system has several solutions corresponding to all the polynomials $g(\lambda)$ that are multiples of the minimum polynomial, hence $\mathrm{Det}(T_M) = 0$. For $M = m$, the only solution to the system is formed by the low order coefficients of the minimum polynomial. This is because a polynomial of degree m that linearly generates the initial segment $\{a_0, \ldots, a_{2m-1}\}$ must already generate the entire sequence, hence its monic associate must coincide with the minimum polynomial. $\boxtimes$

From this lemma we can derive, using the approach of Schwartz (1980) (see also Zippel (1979)), the following probability estimate.

Lemma 2. *Let $A \in K^{n \times n}$, and let $S \subset K$. Randomly and uniformly select a row vector $u \in S^{1 \times n}$ and a column vector $b \in S^n$. Then the probability*

$$\mathrm{Prob}(f_u^{A,b} = f^A) \geq 1 - \frac{2 \deg(f^A)}{\mathrm{card}(S)}.$$

Proof. Let $\vec{v}$ be an n-dimensional row vector with entries $v_1, \ldots, v_n$ being indeterminates, and let $\vec{\beta}$ be an n-dimensional column vector with entries being fresh indeterminates $\beta_1, \ldots, \beta_n$. Then

$$\{\alpha_i\}_{i=0}^\infty \in L^{\mathbb{N}} \text{ with } \alpha_i := \vec{v} A^i \vec{\beta},$$

$L := K(v_1, \ldots, v_n, \beta_1, \ldots, \beta_n)$, is linearly generated by f^A. For $m = \deg(f^A)$, consider the Toeplitz matrix $\mathcal{T}_m$ define in Lemma 1 with respect to $\mu = m$ and the sequence $\{\alpha_i\}_{i=0}^\infty$. Since there exist vectors $u \in K^{1 \times n}$ and $b \in K^n$ with $f_u^{A,b} = f^A$, by Lemma 1 there exist values in K for the indeterminates $v_1, \ldots, \beta_n$ such that the evaluation of $\mathcal{T}_m$ at those values yields a non-singular matrix. Hence, $\mathcal{T}_m$ is non-singular as a matrix over L, and

$$0 \neq \tau := \mathrm{Det}(\mathcal{T}_m) \in K[v_1, \ldots, v_n, \beta_1, \ldots, \beta_n].$$

If evaluating τ at the coordinates of $u \in S^{1 \times n}$ and $b \in S^n$ results in a non-zero value, the corresponding Toeplitz matrix for $\{u A^i b\}_{i=0}^\infty$ remains non-singular, which again by Lemma 1 implies that $\deg(f_u^{A,b}) \geq m$. By the Schwartz/Zippel lemma the probability that τ does not vanish is bounded from below by $1 - \deg(\tau)/\mathrm{card}(S)$. $\boxtimes$

For a matrix $A \in K^{n \times n}$, one can now in a Las Vegas randomized fashion verify that $\mathrm{Det}(A) = 0$. First, one randomly selects $u \in S^{1 \times n}$ and $b \in S^n$, with $S \subset K$ and $\mathrm{card}(S) \geq 2n/\epsilon$, where $0 < \epsilon \ll 1$. Second, one computes

$$\{a_0, a_1, \ldots, a_{2n-1}\}, \quad a_i := u A^i b.$$

Third, one finds the minimum degree linear generating polynomial for the above sequence of $2n$ elements. By the theory of linearly generated sequences, this polynomial is equal to $f_u^{A,b}$. Finally, if $\lambda \mid f_u^{A,b}(\lambda)$, then $\mathrm{Det}(A) = 0$. For a singular matrix, this condition will occur with probability no less than $1 - \epsilon$.

For a non-singular matrix $A \in K^{n \times n}$, Wiedemann presents a Las Vegas randomized algorithm for computing $\mathrm{Det}(A)$. Our parallel solution will utilize his method, but the randomization can be simplified. We owe the next theorem to B. David Saunders.

Theorem 2. *Let $A \in \mathsf{K}^{n \times n}$ be non-singular, and let $S \subset \mathsf{K}$. Consider the matrix*

$$\widehat{A} := AH, \quad H := \begin{pmatrix} h_0 & h_1 & \ldots & h_{n-2} & h_{n-1} \\ h_1 & \ldots & \cdot^{\cdot^{\cdot}} & h_{n-1} & h_n \\ \vdots & & & & \vdots \\ h_{n-1} & h_n & \ldots & & h_{2n-2} \end{pmatrix}$$

where the elements of the Hankel matrix H are randomly and uniformly selected from the set S. With $\widehat{A}_i$ denoting the leading principal $i \times i$ submatrix of $\widehat{A}$, the probability

$$\mathrm{Prob}(\mathrm{Det}(\widehat{A}_i) \neq 0 \text{ for all } 1 \leq i \leq n) \geq 1 - \frac{n(n+1)}{2\,\mathrm{card}(S)}.$$

Proof. For an $n \times n$ matrix B, denote by $B_{I,J}$ the determinant of the submatrix of B that is formed by removing from B all rows not contained in the set I and all columns not contained in the set J. First, assume that $\mathcal{H}$ is a generic Hankel matrix, whose entries are new variables $\eta_0, \ldots, \eta_{2n-2}$ replacing $h_0, \ldots, h_{2n-2}$, and let $\widehat{\mathcal{A}} = A\mathcal{H} \in \mathsf{L}^{n \times n}$, where $\mathsf{L} := \mathsf{K}(\eta_0, \ldots, \eta_{2n-2})$. For $I = \{1, \ldots, i\}$ the Cauchy-Binet formula yields

$$\widehat{\mathcal{A}}_{I,I} = \sum_{\substack{J = \{j_1, \ldots, j_i\} \\ 1 \leq j_1 < \cdots < j_i \leq n}} A_{I,J} \mathcal{H}_{J,I}.$$

We claim that $\widehat{\mathcal{A}}_{I,I}$, which is the ith leading principal minor of $\widehat{\mathcal{A}}$, is non-zero in L. The argument observes that, for $J = \{j_1, \ldots, j_i\}$, the diagonal term $\eta_{j_1-1}\eta_{j_2}\eta_{j_3+1}\cdots\eta_{j_i+i-1}$ is the lexicographically lowest order term in the minor expansion for $\mathcal{H}_{J,I}$. Therefore, all $\mathcal{H}_{J,I}$ have distinct lowest terms, hence are linearly independent over K, and thus $\widehat{\mathcal{A}}_{I,I} \neq 0$, provided there exists a J_0 with $A_{I,J_0} \neq 0$. This is true since the first i rows of A are linearly independent. If we set

$$0 \neq \sigma := \prod_{i=1}^{n} \mathcal{A}_{I,I} \in \mathsf{K}[\eta_0, \ldots, \eta_{2n-2}],$$

then it is clear that all those H whose entries are not zeros of the polynomial σ will satisfy the lemma. Again by the Schwartz/Zippel lemma, the probability that σ does not vanish on random values from S for the η's is no less than $1 - \deg(\sigma)/\mathrm{card}(S)$. $\boxtimes$

If all principal submatrices of $\widehat{A}$ are non-singular, Wiedemann shows that for the matrix

$$\widetilde{A} := \widehat{A}D, \quad D := \mathrm{Diag}(d_1, \ldots, d_n),$$

where the d_i are uniformly randomly selected from S,

the probability

$$\mathrm{Prob}(f^{\widetilde{A}}(\lambda) = \mathrm{Det}(\lambda I - \widetilde{A})) \geq 1 - \frac{n(2n-2)}{\mathrm{card}(S)}. \quad (1)$$

The algorithm picks a random Hankel matrix H, a random diagonal matrix D, a random row vector u, and a random column vector b, all with entries in S. First, it computes the sequence

$$\{\widetilde{a}_0, \ldots, \widetilde{a}_{2m-1}\}, \quad \widetilde{a}_i := u\widetilde{A}^i b, \quad \widetilde{A} := AHD.$$

Second, it determines the minimum polynomial $f_u^{\widetilde{A},b}$ of that sequence, i.e., it finds a polynomial of minimum degree that linearly generates $\{\widetilde{a}_0, \ldots, \widetilde{a}_{2m-1}\}$. If $\deg(f_u^{\widetilde{A},b}) < n$ or $f_u^{\widetilde{A},b}(0) = 0$, the algorithm reports failure. Otherwise, $\mathrm{Det}(\lambda I - \widetilde{A}) = f_u^{\widetilde{A},b}(\lambda)$, so it can return

$$\frac{f_u^{\widetilde{A},b}(0)}{\mathrm{Det}(H)\mathrm{Det}(D)}$$

as the value of the determinant of A. Note that since $f_u^{\widetilde{A},b}(0) \neq 0$, $\widetilde{A}$ is non-singular, hence both H and D must also be non-singular, and the division is possible. Putting Theorem 2, Lemma 2, and (1) together we obtain for any non-singular matrix $A \in \mathsf{K}^{n \times n}$ the probability estimate

$$\mathrm{Prob}(\deg(f_u^{\widetilde{A},b}) = n$$
$$\text{and } f_u^{\widetilde{A},b}(0) \neq 0) \geq 1 - 3n^2/\mathrm{card}(S). \quad (2)$$

For Galois fields K with $\mathrm{card}(\mathsf{K}) < 3n^2$, the algorithm is performed in an algebraic extension L over K, so that the failure probability can be bounded away from 0.

We have not specified yet how the generating polynomials for the linearly generating sequences are found. Sequentially, the best method is the Berlekamp-Massey algorithm, which can find $f_u^{A,b}$ from $\{ub, uAb, \ldots, u \times A^{2n-1}b\}$ in $O(n \deg(f_u^{A,b}))$ field operations. Our parallel solution is based on solving the Toeplitz system described in the proof of Lemma 1, and is discussed in the following section. That approach as a by-product will also produce a method for finding $\mathrm{Det}(H)$.

3. Solution of Toeplitz and General Systems

In §2 we have shown that the problem of solving general systems of linear equations can be reduced to the problem of solving the Toeplitz systems arising from the linearly generated sequences discussed. We now present an algorithm for finding the characteristic polynomial of a Toeplitz matrix. First, we observe that for any matrix $A \in \mathsf{K}^{n \times n}$ one may compute the power series expansion

$$(I - \lambda A)^{-1} = I + \lambda A + \lambda^2 A^2 + \cdots \in \mathsf{K}^{n \times n}[[\lambda]]$$

$$T^{-1} =: \begin{pmatrix} u_1 & \cdots & v_n \\ u_2 & \cdots & v_{n-1} \\ \vdots & & \vdots \\ u_{n-1} & \cdots & v_2 \\ u_n & \cdots & v_1 \end{pmatrix} = \frac{1}{u_1}\left(\begin{pmatrix} u_1 & & & & \\ u_2 & u_1 & & & \\ u_3 & u_2 & u_1 & & \\ \vdots & & \ddots & \ddots & \\ u_n & u_{n-1} & \cdots & u_2 & u_1 \end{pmatrix} \begin{pmatrix} v_1 & v_2 & v_3 & \cdots & v_n \\ & v_1 & v_2 & & v_{n-1} \\ & & \ddots & \ddots & \vdots \\ & & & v_1 & v_2 \\ & & & & v_1 \end{pmatrix} \right.$$

$$\left. - \begin{pmatrix} 0 & & & & \\ v_n & 0 & & & \\ v_{n-1} & v_n & 0 & & \\ \vdots & & \ddots & \ddots & \\ v_2 & v_3 & \cdots & v_n & 0 \end{pmatrix} \begin{pmatrix} 0 & u_n & u_{n-1} & \cdots & u_2 \\ & 0 & u_n & & u_3 \\ & & \ddots & \ddots & \vdots \\ & & & 0 & u_n \\ & & & & 0 \end{pmatrix} \right). \tag{5}$$

Figure 1: The Gohberg/Semencul formula.

by Newton iteration:

$$X_0 \leftarrow I; B \leftarrow I - \lambda A;$$
$$X_i \leftarrow X_{i-1}(2I - BX_{i-1}) \text{ for } i \leftarrow 1, 2, \ldots \tag{3}$$

Note that X_i is a matrix polynomial in λ of degree no more than $2^i - 1$. Since

$$I - BX_i = I - BX_{i-1}(2I - BX_{i-1})$$
$$= (I - BX_{i-1})(I - BX_{i-1}),$$

it follows by induction on i that $I - BX_i \equiv 0 \pmod{\lambda^{2^i}}$, i.e.,

$$X_i = I + \lambda A + \cdots + \lambda^{2^i - 1} A^{2^i - 1}.$$

We now apply (3) to Toeplitz matrices. For a non-singular $n \times n$ Toeplitz matrix over K,

$$T := \begin{pmatrix} a_{n-1} & a_{n-2} & \cdots & a_1 & a_0 \\ a_n & a_{n-1} & \cdots & a_2 & a_1 \\ \vdots & & a_n & \ddots & \vdots & a_2 \\ & & \vdots & & & \vdots \\ a_{2n-3} & & & & a_{n-1} \\ a_{2n-2} & a_{2n-3} & \cdots & a_n & a_{n-1} \end{pmatrix}, \tag{4}$$

the inverse can be represented implicitly by the Gohberg/Semencul formulas (see, e.g., Brent et al. (1980)), one of which applies in the case where

$$u_1 := (T^{-1})_{1,1} = (T^{-1})_{n,n} =: v_1 \neq 0,$$

and is stated in Figure 1. Note that T^{-1} is thus fully determined by the entries of its first and last rows.

Note that

$$\text{Trace}(T^{-1}) = \frac{1}{u_1}(nu_1v_1 + (n-2)u_2v_2 + \cdots + (-n+2)u_nv_n).$$

The algorithm (3) is now applied to the Toeplitz matrix

$B = T(\lambda) := I - \lambda T$. Then

$$X_i \equiv T(\lambda)^{-1} \pmod{\lambda^{2^i}}$$

where $T(\lambda)$ can be viewed as a Toeplitz matrix with entries in the field of extended power series $\mathsf{K}((\lambda)) = \bigcup_{k \geq 0} \lambda^{-k} \mathsf{K}[[\lambda]]$. Clearly, $T(\lambda)^{-1} \in \mathsf{K}[[\lambda]]^{n \times n}$ and $T(0)^{-1} = I$, so $(T(\lambda)^{-1})_{1,1} \bmod \lambda^i \neq 0$ for any $i \geq 1$. We compute the first and last columns of X_i from the first and last columns of X_{i-1} by formula (5). The first column, for instance, is computed as

$$X_{i-1}(2I - T(\lambda)X_{i-1}) \begin{pmatrix} 1 \\ 0 \\ \vdots \\ 0 \end{pmatrix}. \tag{6}$$

Multiplying X_{i-1} from the right by a vector reduces, by (5), to multiplying triangular Toeplitz matrices by vectors, vector subtractions, and dividing a vector by a scalar, i.e., a polynomial in λ. The Toeplitz matrix times vector products can be accomplished by polynomial multiplication. For example, for

$$\begin{pmatrix} y_1 \\ y_2 \\ y_3 \\ \vdots \\ y_n \end{pmatrix} := \begin{pmatrix} u_1 & & & & \\ u_2 & u_1 & & & \\ u_3 & u_2 & u_1 & & \\ \vdots & & \ddots & \ddots & \\ u_n & u_{n-1} & \cdots & u_2 & u_1 \end{pmatrix} \begin{pmatrix} w_1 \\ w_2 \\ w_3 \\ \vdots \\ w_n \end{pmatrix}$$

we have

$$(u_1 + \cdots + u_n z^{n-1})(w_1 + \cdots + w_n z^{n-1})$$
$$\equiv y_1 + y_2 z + \cdots + y_n z^{n-1} \pmod{z^n}.$$

Note that the entries in the first and last columns in X_{i-1}, denoted by $u_j^{(i-1)}$ and $v_j^{(i-1)}$, and the entries in the arising vectors y_i, are themselves polynomials in $\mathsf{K}[\lambda]$ of degree no more than $2^i - 1$. According to (5), the resulting polynomial vector of degree $2^i + 2^{i-1} - 2$

has to be divided by $u_1^{(i-1)}$, the first entry in the first column of X_{i-1}. This is accomplished by multiplying each entry with the power series inverse of $u_1^{(i-1)}$,

$$\frac{1}{u_1^{(i-1)}(\lambda)} \equiv 1 + w_1^{(i-1)}\lambda + \cdots + w_{2^i-1}^{(i-1)}\lambda^{2^i-1} \pmod{\lambda^{2^i}},$$

$w_j^{(i-1)} \in \mathsf{K}$. Note that expansion for the inverse of $u_1^{(i)}$ to order $\lambda^{2^{i+1}-1}$ can be obtained from the first 2^{i-1} terms of this expansion and from $u_1^{(i)}$ with 2 Newton iteration steps (Lipson 1981, §3.3). That expansion will be needed for the determination of the rows and columns of X_{i+1}.

The overall complexity of each iteration in (3) is bounded from above by the complexity of bivariate polynomial multiplication with input degrees bounded by $2n$ and 2^{i+1} in the individual variables, respectively, and can be performed on an algebraic circuit over K in

$$O(2^i n \log n \, \log\log n) \text{ size and } O(\log n) \text{ depth}$$

(Cantor and Kaltofen 1987). The overall algebraic circuit complexity for finding the first and last columns of $X_{\lceil \log_2 n \rceil}$ is thus

$$O(n^2 \log n \, \log\log n) \text{ size and } O((\log n)^2) \text{ depth.} \quad (7)$$

Again by (5), we can compute

$$\mathrm{Trace}(X_{\lceil \log_2 n \rceil}) \bmod \lambda^n = n + \mathrm{Trace}(T)\lambda + \cdots + \mathrm{Trace}(T^{n-1})\lambda^{n-1}$$

from the first and last columns of $X_{\lceil \log_2 n \rceil}$, again within the complexity (7).

Once we have for all $0 \le i \le n-1$,

$$s_i := \mathrm{Trace}(T^i) = \lambda_1^i + \lambda_2^i + \cdots + \lambda_n^i,$$

where $\lambda_1, \ldots, \lambda_n$ are all eigenvalues of T, it is possible by the Leverrier/Csanky (1976) method to obtain the coefficients of the characteristic polynomial of T. In particular, for

$$\mathrm{Det}(\lambda I - T) =: \lambda^n - c_1\lambda^{n-1} - c_2\lambda^{n-2} - \cdots - c_{n-1}\lambda - c_n,$$

we have

$$\begin{pmatrix} 1 & & & & \\ s_1 & 2 & & & \\ s_2 & s_1 & \ddots & & \\ \vdots & & & & \\ s_{n-2} & \cdots & & n-1 & \\ s_{n-1} & s_{n-2} & \cdots & s_1 & n \end{pmatrix} \begin{pmatrix} c_1 \\ c_2 \\ c_3 \\ \vdots \\ c_{n-1} \\ c_n \end{pmatrix} = \begin{pmatrix} s_1 \\ s_2 \\ s_3 \\ \vdots \\ s_{n-1} \\ s_n \end{pmatrix}$$

Clearly, in order for the system to determine all c_i uniquely, one has to divide by $n!$. However, under that condition one can solve such systems in

$$O(n \log n \, \log\log n) \text{ size and } O((\log n)^2) \text{ depth}$$

(Schönhage 1982); see also (Pan 1990a, Appendix A). We have thus proven the following theorem.

Theorem 3 (Pan 1990b). *The characteristic polynomial of an $n \times n$ Toeplitz matrix over a field of characteristic zero or greater than n can be computed on an algebraic circuit of $O(n^2 \log n \, \log\log n)$ size and $O((\log n)^2)$ depth.*

From Theorem 3 we can obtain by the approach of §3 size-efficient randomized circuits for solving general non-singular systems. Assume now that $A \in \mathsf{K}^{n \times n}$ is a general non-singular matrix. The algorithm picks a random Hankel matrix H, a random diagonal matrix D, a random row vector u, and a random column vector v, and computes

$$\{a_i\}_{i=0}^{2n-1}, \quad a_i := u\widetilde{A}^i v \in \mathsf{K}, \quad \widetilde{A} = AHD. \quad (8)$$

The algebraic circuit finds first $\widetilde{A}$, then computes all $\widetilde{A}^i v$, and finally performs the inner products with u. From the doubling argument

$$A^{2^i}(v \mid Av \mid \ldots \mid A^{2^i-1}v) = (A^{2^i}v \mid A^{2^i+1}v \mid \ldots \mid A^{2^{i+1}-1}v) \quad (9)$$

(cf. (Borodin and Munro 1975, p. 128); Keller-Gehrig (1985)) it is easily seen that the algebraic circuit for this step has complexity

$$O(n^\omega \log n) \text{ size and } O((\log n)^2) \text{ depth.} \quad (10)$$

We remark that on an algebraic PRAM, here and in the following estimates a factor $\log n$ can be saved in the asymptotic processor count.

Next, we compute the characteristic polynomial for the Toeplitz matrix T in (4), whose entries are the elements of the sequence (8). By Theorem 3, (10) dominates the complexity of this part of the construction. By (2), the generating polynomial of (8) is with high probability the characteristic polynomial $\lambda^n + \widetilde{c}_1\lambda^{n-1} + \cdots + \widetilde{c}_n$ of $\widetilde{A}$, which by Lemma 1 implies that the Toeplitz matrix T is non-singular. We deduce the solution of

$$T \begin{pmatrix} \widetilde{c}_1 \\ \vdots \\ \widetilde{c}_n \end{pmatrix} = - \begin{pmatrix} a_n \\ \vdots \\ a_{2n-1} \end{pmatrix},$$

from the characteristic polynomial of T, denoted by $\lambda^n + c_1\lambda^{n-1} + \cdots + c_n$, as

$$\begin{pmatrix} \widetilde{c}_1 \\ \vdots \\ \widetilde{c}_n \end{pmatrix} \leftarrow \frac{1}{c_n}(T^{n-1}\begin{pmatrix} a_n \\ \vdots \\ a_{2n-1} \end{pmatrix} + \cdots + c_{n-1}\begin{pmatrix} a_n \\ \vdots \\ a_{2n-1} \end{pmatrix}).$$

This is because by the Cayley/Hamilton theorem,

$$T^n + c_1 T^{n-1} + \cdots + c_n I = 0.$$

Note that $\widetilde{c}_n$ is equal to $(-1)^n \mathrm{Det}(\widetilde{A})$, which by (2) is likely to be not equal to zero. Again from (9) we deduce that the circuit complexity of this step is (10). Next, we find in the same manner and at the same complexity

$$\widetilde{x} \leftarrow -\frac{1}{\widetilde{c}_n}(\widetilde{A}^{n-1}b + \widetilde{c}_1 \widetilde{A}^{n-2}b + \cdots + \widetilde{c}_{n-1}b).$$

Now we must have $\widetilde{A}\,\widetilde{x} = b$. We finally compute $A^{-1}b =: x \leftarrow HD\widetilde{x}$. We therefore have the following theorem.

Theorem 4. *For $n \geq 1$ there exists a randomized algebraic circuit with $n^2 + n$ inputs, n outputs, $O(n)$ nodes that denote random (input) elements, and of*

$$O(n^\omega \log n) \text{ size and } O((\log n)^2) \text{ depth,}$$

with the following property. If the inputs are the entries of a non-singular matrix $A \in \mathsf{K}^{n \times n}$ and of a vector $b \in \mathsf{K}^n$, where K is a field of characteristic zero or greater than n, and if the random nodes uniformly select field elements in $S \subset \mathsf{K}$, then with probability no less than $1 - 3n^2/\mathrm{card}(S)$ the circuit outputs the entries of $A^{-1}b$. On the other hand, if the random choices are unlucky or if the input matrix is singular, the circuit divides by zero. On non-singular inputs zero-divisions occur with probability no more than $3n^2/\mathrm{card}(S)$.

4. Computing the Inverse Matrix

We now show how a circuit for the determinant of a non-singular matrix can be transformed to a circuit for the inverse of that matrix. Our solution follows the approach by Baur and Strassen (1983). Suppose that a rational function $f \in \mathsf{K}(x_1, \ldots, x_k)$ is computed from the input values $x_1, \ldots, x_k$ by a straight-line program of length l, i.e., an algebraic circuit of size l; for the following arguments it is more convenient to enumerate the nodes, hence the straight-line program model. The program can divide, but it is assumed that the division is by a rational function that is not identical to 0, i.e., there will always exist input values in the algebraic closure of K for which the program avoids a zero-division. Baur and Strassen show that then there exists a straight-line program of length no more than $5l$ that computes all first order partial derivatives

$$\partial_{x_1}(f), \partial_{x_2}(f), \ldots, \partial_{x_k}(f).$$

Furthermore, the new program will divide by exactly the same rational functions as the old, hence no new zero-division will be introduced. Their motivating example was the same as ours. Let $k = n^2$ and

$$f(x_{1,1}, \ldots, x_{n,n}) = \mathrm{Det}(A), \quad A = (x_{i,j})_{1 \leq i,j \leq n}.$$

If f is computed by a straight-line program of length

$l(n)$, then the inverse of A can also be computed by a program of asymptotic length $O(l(n))$, namely as

$$A^{-1} = \left((-1)^{i+j} \frac{\partial_{x_{j,i}}(f)}{f} \right)_{1 \leq i,j \leq n}.$$

However, the original construction of Baur and Strassen does not preserve the depth of the program within a constant factor. In order to achieve this, we have to analyze their method more closely and employ implicitly a theorem by Hoover et al. (1984).

Theorem 5 (Kaltofen and Singer 1990). *Let $f \in \mathsf{K}(x_1, \ldots, x_k)$ be computed by a straight-line program P of length l and depth d. Then f and all derivatives $\partial_{x_1}(f), \partial_{x_2}(f), \ldots, \partial_{x_k}(f)$ can be computed by a straight-line program Q of length no more than $4l$ and depth $O(d)$.*

Proof. Let $v_i \leftarrow v_{I_1(i)} \circ_i v_{I_2(i)}$, $k + 1 \leq i \leq k + l$, be the $(i - k)$-th instruction in the program P. Here the function I_1 retrieves the index of the left operand of right-hand side expression, and the function I_2 the right operand. We set $v_i := x_i$ for $1 \leq i \leq k$, hence we have a range for the operand indices of $1 \leq I_1(i), I_2(i) < i$. If the left or right operands are scalars, no such indexing will be needed. For $i > k$ the symbol v_i stands, strictly speaking, for a program variable in P, or a node in the computation DAG for f. However, we also use it to identify with it the rational function in $\mathsf{K}(x_1, \ldots, x_k)$ that is computed in this variable. Baur and Strassen's construction proceeds by viewing f as a sequence of functions

$$g_i(y_1, \ldots, y_i) \in \mathsf{K}(y_1, \ldots, y_i), \quad k + l \geq i \geq k.$$

We will have

$$g_i(v_1, \ldots, v_i) = f(x_1, \ldots, x_k) \text{ for all } k \leq i \leq k + l.$$

The interpretation of g_i is the function that gets computed in the program variable v_l if one omits the instructions for $v_{k+1}, \ldots, v_i$ in the program P and replaces $v_1 = x_1, \ldots, v_k = x_k, v_{k+1}, \ldots, v_i$ by the new variables $y_1, \ldots, y_i$ whenever they are used in the truncated program of length $l - i + k$. In particular, we will have

$$g_k(x_1, \ldots, x_k) = f(x_1, \ldots, x_k).$$

Now let

$$h_i(y_{I_1(i)}, y_{I_2(i)}) = y_{I_1(i)} \circ_i y_{I_2(i)} \in \mathsf{K}(y_1, \ldots, y_{i-1}),$$

$k + l \geq i \geq k + 1$, denote the rational function that gets formally computed by the $(i - k)$th instruction in P. The functions g_i, $i = k + l, k + l - 1, \ldots, k$, are therefore

186

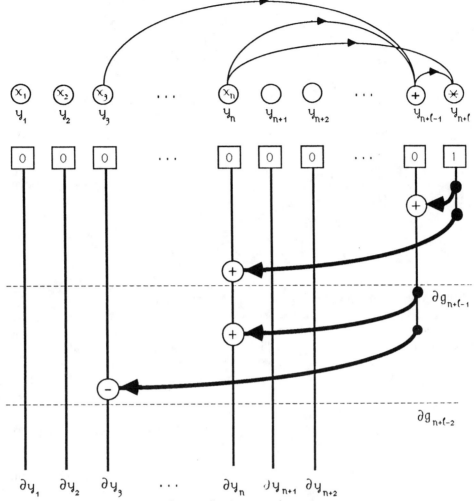

Figure 2: Coarse view of the Baur and Strassen construction.

inductively defined to be related by

$$g_{i-1}(y_1, \ldots, y_{i-1}) := g_i(y_1, \ldots, y_{i-1}, \\ h_i(y_{I_1(i)}, y_{I_2(i)})), \qquad (11)$$

where initially $g_{k+l}(y_1, \ldots, y_{k+l}) := y_{k+l}$. The goal is to compute

$$\partial_{y_1}(g_k), \partial_{y_2}(g_k), \ldots, \partial_{y_k}(g_k).$$

This is done by using the inductive definition of g_i and the chain rule for partial derivatives. This rule states for $g \in \mathsf{K}(y_1, \ldots, y_m)$ and $\hbar_1, \ldots, \hbar_m \in \mathsf{K}(x_1, \ldots, x_k)$ that

$$\partial_{x_i}(g(\hbar_1, \ldots, \hbar_m)) = \sum_{j=1}^{m}(\partial_{y_j}g)(\hbar_1, \ldots, \hbar_m)\,\partial_{x_i}(\hbar_j),$$

provided the denominator of g does not become zero in $\mathsf{K}(x_1, \ldots, x_k)$ by setting y_j to $\hbar_j(x_1, \ldots, x_k)$ for all $1 \leq j \leq m$, in which case the same is true for $\partial_{y_j}g$. Note that

this rule can be proven for any field by entirely algebraic means (see (Kaltofen and Singer 1990)). In our case, only the last function $\hbar_m$ will not be the identity.

We first have

$$\partial_{y_j}(g_{k+l}) = 0 \text{ for all } 1 \leq j \leq k+l-1,\ \partial_{y_{k+l}}(g_{k+l}) = 1.$$

Now let us assume that at level $k+l-i$ we have already computed the derivatives

$$\partial_{y_1}(g_i), \partial_{y_2}(g_i), \ldots, \partial_{y_i}(g_i).$$

From (11) we get by the chain rule for $j_1 := I_1(i)$ and $j_2 := I_2(i)$ that

$$(\partial_{y_j}g_{i-1})(y_1, \ldots, y_{i-1}) = (\partial_{y_j}g_i)(y_1, \ldots, y_{i-1}, \\ h_i(y_{j_1}, y_{j_2}))$$

for $1 \leq j \leq i-1$, $j \neq j_1$, $j \neq j_2$, and

$$(\partial_{y_j}g_{i-1})(y_1, \ldots, y_{i-1}) = \\ (\partial_{y_j}g_i)(y_1, \ldots, y_{i-1}, h_i(y_{j_1}, y_{j_2})) \\ + (\partial_y{}_ig_i)(y_1, \ldots, y_{i-1}, h_i(y_{j_1}, y_{j_2}))(\partial_{y_j}h_i)(y_{j_1}, y_{j_2})$$

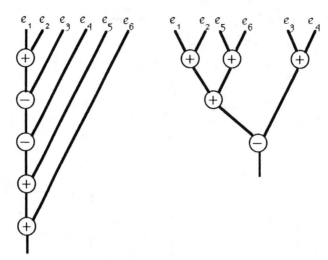

Figure 3: Balancing an accumulation tree.

for $j = j_1$ or $j = j_2$.

The dynamics of these rules are displayed in Figure 2. The substitution $h_i(y_{j_1}, y_{j_2})$ for y_i is accomplished by connecting the corresponding node to the nodes for y_{j_1} and y_{j_2} and performing the operation o_i in the node. Then the derivatives $\partial_{y_j}(g_{i-1})$ are computed from those of $\partial_{y_j}(g_i)$ plus a value derived from

$$\overline{\partial_{y_i}(g_i)} = (\partial_{y_i} g_i)(y_1, \ldots, y_{i-1}, h_i(y_{j_1}, y_{j_2}))$$

and the derivatives of $h_i(y_{j_1}, y_{j_2})$. The latter are solely dependent on the nodes corresponding to the variables y_{j_1} and y_{j_2} and require constant work. In Figure 2, this is indicated by a thick connection from the line for ∂_{y_i} to ∂_{y_j}. Let us for a moment consider the operation o_i with the most costly work, namely division. For $h_i(y_{j_1}, y_{j_2}) = y_{j_1}/y_{j_2}$ we have

$$\partial_{y_{j_1}}(h_i) = \frac{1}{y_{j_2}} \text{ and } \partial_{y_{j_2}}(h_i) = -\frac{y_{j_1}}{y_{j_2}^2}.$$

The strategy is to divide $\overline{\partial_{y_i}(g_i)}$ by y_{j_2}, add that into the $\partial_{y_{j_1}}$ line, or multiply it with y_{j_1}/y_{j_2}, the value computed in the node for y_i, and then subtract that from the ∂_{y_2} line. In other words, if $o_i = \div$ one needs 4 additional operations to go to the next level. There is one more issue that needs to be settled in the division case. Later substitutions for y_{j_2} are not allowed to cause a division by a function that is identical zero. This never occurs because the circuit computing the derivatives will only divide by quantities that the original program P divides by.

We now discuss how to accomplish the given length and depth measures. For each v_i in P, $k+1 \leq i \leq k+l$, we will introduce at most 5 instructions in our new program Q, one from the original program and at most 4 more to eliminate y_i. This leads to an upper bound of

$5l$ for the length of Q, but l of these instructions either add the initial $\partial_{y_j}(g_{k+l}) = 0$ to $\overline{\partial_{y_i}(g_i)}(\partial_{y_j}h_i)(y_{j_1}, y_{j_2})$ or multiply $\partial_{y_{k+l}}(g_{k+l}) = 1$ by $\partial_{y_j}(h_{k+l})(y_{j_1}, y_{j_2})$. Since we have each instruction v_i participate in the computation of v_{k+l}, there are at least l trivial instructions that can be eliminated from such a Q. Note that if we only have subtractions on a line for ∂_{y_j} we pass the minus sign along to the level for the derivatives of g_{j-1}. On each line for ∂_{y_j}, $1 \leq j \leq k$, we might then have to negate the final result, potentially costing us an additional k instructions. However, we also save that many instructions at the starting level of those lines, and therefore we do not need more than $4l$ instructions overall.

Lastly, we discuss how to accomplish the stated depth. First we observe that if we were to treat each line in Figure 1 on which we accumulate the ∂_{y_j} as a single node, and if we were to treat each connection from ∂_{y_i} to $\partial_{y_{j_1}}$ and to $\partial_{y_{j_2}}$ as a single edge, then the circuit that computes the derivatives would be a mirror image of the original circuit for f. Therefore, the depth of this abstraction of the part of Q that implements the chain rules and which has "superedges" and "supernodes" is d. Furthermore, on each "superedge" we only have a constant delay. Let t_j be the fan-out for v_j in P, i.e., the number of times the variable v_j is used in later instructions. Then in each supernode corresponding to the line for ∂_{y_j} we have exactly $t_j - 1$ addition and subtraction nodes. Separating the lines that get added from the ones that get subtracted, we can build with $t_j - 1$ nodes a tree that performs the same computation but which has $O(\log t)$ depth (see Figure 3). Hence the entire depth of Q can be made at least $O(d \log t)$, where $t = \max\{t_j\}$.

We finally reduce the depth of Q further to $O(d)$ without increasing the length. To accomplish this, we apply the transformation of Hoover et al. (loc. cit.) in an implicit way to the circuit constructed above. Consider the lower part of Q that is a mirror image of P (see Figure 1). Furthermore, assume that the subtrees in Q which perform additions on the ∂_{y_j} lines are again contracted to "supernodes". We suppose that subtractions are already separated out, and subtraction nodes on those lines remain untouched. Thus, the depth of this abstraction of the circuit is still $O(d)$, the extra factor of $\log t$ coming from the delay in the supernodes. Now we apply the construction by Hoover et al. to this high level description of the lower part of Q, reversing the flow of information. That construction will insert behind each node of high fan-out a binary tree of duplication nodes whose root is that node and whose leaves are the targets of the arcs leaving that node. Hoover et al. then show that if one optimizes the structure of that tree with respect to the distance of the target nodes to the output node in such a way that target nodes from which there are long paths to output nodes are close to the root, one can overall retain depth $O(d)$. Once such duplication trees are in place behind the supernodes, all we have to do is to reverse the flow of information and perform additions in both supernodes and duplication nodes.   ⊠

We now apply this Theorem to the circuit constructed in Theorem 4, which as an auxiliary value computes

$$\tilde{c}_n = (-1)^n \operatorname{Det}(AHD).$$

The random matrix H is of Hankel form, whose mirror image across a horizontal line that evenly splits the rows becomes a Toeplitz matrix. By Theorem 3, we can thus determine $\operatorname{Det}(H)$ efficiently in parallel. Therefore we have found a circuit that efficiently computes in parallel

$$\operatorname{Det}(A) = (-1)^n \tilde{c}_n / (\operatorname{Det}(H) \operatorname{Det}(D)),$$

and by applying Theorem 5 to that circuit, we obtain the following result.

Theorem 6. *For $n \geq 1$ there exists a randomized algebraic circuit with n^2 inputs, n^2 outputs, $O(n)$ nodes that denote random (input) elements, and of*

$$O(n^\omega \log n) \text{ size and } O((\log n)^2) \text{ depth},$$

with the following property. If the inputs are the entries of a non-singular matrix $A \in \mathsf{K}^{n \times n}$, where K is a field of characteristic zero or greater than n, and if the random nodes uniformly select field elements in $S \subset \mathsf{K}$, then with probability no less than $1 - 3n^2/\operatorname{card}(S)$ the circuit outputs the entries of A^{-1}. On the other hand, if the random choices are unlucky or if the input matrix is singular, the circuit divides by zero. On non-singular inputs zero-divisions occur with probability no more than $3n^2/\operatorname{card}(S)$.

There is a second interesting application of Theorem 5 to linear system solving. Assume that one is given a circuit with $n^2 + n$ inputs and n outputs that computes $A^{-1}b$ in size $l(n)$ and depth $d(n)$. Then there exists a circuit of size $4l(n)$ and depth $O(d(n))$ that computes $(A^{tr})^{-1}b$, where A^{tr} denotes the transposed matrix of A. The proof is by considering

$$f(x_1, \ldots, x_n) := (x_1 \ \ldots \ x_n)(A^{tr})^{-1}b.$$

The function f can be quickly computed by performing the multiplications from the left to the right, using the given circuit for finding

$$(x_1 \ \ldots \ x_n)(A^{tr})^{-1} = \left(A^{-1} \begin{pmatrix} x_1 \\ \vdots \\ x_n \end{pmatrix} \right)^{tr}.$$

Observing that

$$(\partial_{x_1} f \ \ldots \ \partial_{x_n} f)^{tr} = (A^{tr})^{-1}b,$$

we deduce the stated claim from Theorem 5. In a special case this construction gives us a fast transposed Vandermonde system solver based on fast polynomial interpolation. Note that for a fixed matrix A^{-1}, i.e., the case of multiplying a matrix by b vs. multiplying the transpose of that matrix by b (the non-singularity assumption can then be dropped), this fact was proven by Kaminski et al. (1988) without making use of the Baur and Strassen result.

5. Extensions

The results for computing the characteristic polynomial of a Toeplitz matrix in Theorem 3 can be extended to the case where the field of entries has small positive characteristic. The approach is to appeal to Chistov's (1985) method for finding the characteristic polynomial of an arbitrary matrix in conjunction with computing for all $i \leq n$ by the algorithm of §3 the entry $((I_i - \lambda T_i)^{-1})_{i,i} \bmod \lambda^{n+1}$ for the $i \times i$ identity matrix I_i and the $i \times i$ leading principal submatrix T_i of an $n \times n$ Toeplitz matrix $T = T_n$. The resulting circuit then can compute the characteristic polynomials of all T_i over a field of any characteristic in

$$O(n^3 \log n \, \log\log n) \text{ size and } O((\log n)^2) \text{ depth.} \quad (12)$$

The efficient parallel algorithms for computing the characteristic polynomial of a Toeplitz matrix are extendible to structured Toeplitz-like matrices such as Sylvester matrices. In particular, it is then possible to compute the greatest common divisor of two polynomials of degree n over a field of characteristic zero or greater n, and also the coefficients of the polynomials in the Euclidean scheme, on circuits of

$$O(n^2 \log n \, \log\log n) \text{ size and } O((\log n)^3) \text{ depth.}$$

Again using a factor of n more processors, the algorithms extend to fields of any characteristic. We refer to (Pan 1990b) and (Bini and Pan 1991) for the details of these results.

The complexity measures (12) in the case of small positive characteristic also apply to the problem of solving general linear systems of equations. For example, there exist randomized circuits of complexity (12) that compute the inverse of an $n \times n$ non-singular matrix over any field. Furthermore, the methods presented here can be also used to compute the rank r of a matrix and to solve a singular system. The former can be accomplished, for instance, by a randomization such that precisely the first r principal minors in the randomized matrix are not zero, and then by performing a binary search for the largest non-singular principal submatrix (cf. (Borodin et al. 1982)). Similarly, one can compute a vector in the solution manifold of a singular linear system, and a basis for the null space of a matrix. For the latter claim, one needs Theorem 6 as follows: consider $A \in K^{n \times n}$, and assume that for random non-singular matrices $U, V \in K^{n \times n}$, the product matrix $\widehat{A} := UAV$ has the property that the $r \times r$ leading principal submatrix $\widehat{A}_r$ of $\widehat{A}$ is non-singular, where r is the rank of A. Then

$$\widehat{A} E = \begin{pmatrix} \widehat{A}_r & 0^{r \times (n-r)} \\ C & 0^{(n-r) \times (n-r)} \end{pmatrix}$$

for

$$\widehat{A} =: \begin{pmatrix} \widehat{A}_r & B \\ C & D \end{pmatrix} \text{ and } E := \begin{pmatrix} I_r & -\widehat{A}_r^{-1} B \\ 0^{(n-r) \times r} & I_{n-r} \end{pmatrix},$$

hence the null space is spanned by the columns of

$$V E \begin{pmatrix} 0^{r \times (n-r)} \\ I_{n-r} \end{pmatrix}.$$

Finally, the techniques of Pan (1990a) combined with the processor efficient algorithms for linear system solving presented here immediately yield processor efficient least-squares solutions to general linear systems over any field of characteristic zero.

Literature Cited

Baur, W. and Strassen, V., "The complexity of partial derivatives," *Theoretical Comp. Sci.* **22**, pp. 317–330 (1983).

Berkowitz, S. J., "On computing the determinant in small parallel time using a small number of processors," *Inform. Process. Letters* **18**, pp. 147–150 (1984).

Bini, D. and Pan, V., *Numerical and Algebraic Computations with Matrices and Polynomials*; Lecture Notes in Theor. Comput. Sci., edited by R. V. Book; Birkhäuser Boston, Inc., 1991. To appear.

Borodin, A., von zur Gathen, J., and Hopcroft, J. E., "Fast parallel matrix and GCD computations," *Inf. Control* **52**, pp. 241–256 (1982).

Borodin, A. and Munro, I., *Computational Complexity of Algebraic and Numeric Problems*; American Elsevier, New York, N.Y., 1975.

Brent, R. P., Gustavson, F. G., and Yun, D. Y. Y., "Fast solution of Toeplitz systems of equations and computation of Padé approximants," *J. Algorithms* **1**, pp. 259–295 (1980).

Bunch, J. R. and Hopcroft, J. E., "Triangular factorization and inversion by fast matrix multiplication," *Math. Comp.* **28**, pp. 231–236 (1974).

Cantor, D. G. and Kaltofen, E., "Fast multiplication of polynomials over arbitrary rings," *Tech. Report* **87-35**, Dept. Comput. Sci., Rensselaer Polytechnic Institute, December 1987. Revised version to appear in *Acta Informatica*.

Chistov, A. L., "Fast parallel calculation of the rank of matrices over a field of arbitrary characteristic," *Proc. FCT '85, Springer Lec. Notes Comp. Sci.* **199**, pp. 63–69 (1985).

Coppersmith, D. and Winograd, S., "Matrix multiplication via arithmetic progressions," *J. Symbolic Comput.* **9/3**, pp. 251–280 (1990).

Csanky, L., "Fast parallel matrix inversion algorithms," *SIAM J. Comput.* **5/4**, pp. 618–623 (1976).

Galil, Z. and Pan, V., "Parallel evaluation of the determinant and of the inverse of a matrix," *Inform. Process. Letters* **30**, pp. 41–45 (1989).

Hoover, H. J., Klawe, M. M., and Pippenger, N. J., "Bounding fan-out in logical networks," *J. ACM* **31/1**, pp. 13–18 (1984).

Kaltofen, E. and Singer, M. F., "Size efficient parallel algebraic circuits for partial derivatives," *Tech. Report* **90-32**, Dept. Comput. Sci., Rensselaer Polytechnic Inst., Troy, N.Y., October 1990.

Kaminski, M., Kirkpatrick, D. G., and Bshouty, N. H., "Addition requirements for matrix and transposed matrix products," *J. Algorithms* **9**, pp. 354–364 (1988).

Karp, R. M. and Ramachandran, V., "Parallel algorithms for shared-memory machines," in *Handbook for Theoretical Computer Science*; North-Holland, pp. 869–941, 1990.

Keller-Gehrig, W., "Fast algorithms for the characteristic polynomial," *Theor. Comput. Sci.* **36**, pp. 309–317

(1985).

Lipson, J., *Elements of Algebra and Algebraic Computing*; Addison-Wesley Publ., Reading, Mass., 1981.

Pan, V., "Parallel least-square solution of general and Toeplitz-like linear systems," *Proc. 2nd Ann. Symp. Parallel Algorithms Architecture*, pp. 244-253 (1990a).

Pan, V., "Parameterization of Newton's iteration for computations with structured matrices and applications," *Tech. Report* **CUCS-032-90**, Comput. Sci. Dept., Columbia University, New York, N. Y., 1990b.

Preparata, F. P. and Sarwate, D. V., "An improved parallel processor bound in fast matrix inversion," *Inform. Process. Letters* **7**/3, pp. 148–150 (1978).

Schwartz, J. T., "Fast probabilistic algorithms for verification of polynomial identities," *J. ACM* **27**, pp. 701–717 (1980).

Schönhage, A., "The fundamental theorem of algebra in terms of computational complexity," *Tech. Report*, Univ. Tübingen, 1982.

Wiedemann, D., "Solving sparse linear equations over finite fields," *IEEE Trans. Inf. Theory* **IT-32**, pp. 54–62 (1986).

Zippel, R. E., "Probabilistic algorithms for sparse polynomials," *Proc. EUROSAM '79, Springer Lec. Notes Comp. Sci.* **72**, pp. 216–226 (1979).

In-Place Techniques for Parallel Convex Hull Algorithms

(Preliminary Version)

Mujtaba R. Ghouse*   and   Michael T. Goodrich†

Dept. of Computer Science
Johns Hopkins University, Baltimore, MD 21218-2686

Abstract

We present a number of efficient parallel algorithms for constructing 2- and 3-dimensional convex hulls on a randomized CRCW PRAM. Specifically, we show how to build the convex hull of n pre-sorted points in the plane almost surely in $O(1)$ time using $O(n \log n)$ processors, or, alternately, almost surely in $O(\log^* n)$ time using an optimal number of processors. We also show how to find the convex hull of n unsorted points in $\Re^2$ (resp., $\Re^3$) in $O(\log n)$ time using $O(n \log h)$ work (resp., $O(\log^2 n)$ time using $O(\min\{n \log^2 h, n \log n\})$ work), with very high probability, where h is the number of edges in the convex hull (h is $O(n)$, but can be as small as $O(1)$). Our algorithms for unsorted input depend on the use of new *in-place* procedures, that is, procedures that are defined on a subset of elements in the input and that work without re-ordering the input. For the pre-sorted case we also exploit a technique that allows one to modify an algorithm that assumes it is given points so that it can be used on hulls; we call such algorithms *point-hull invariant*.

---

*This research supported in part by NSF and DARPA under Grant CCR-8908092. Email: ghouse@cs.jhu.edu.

†This research supported in part by the National Science Foundation under Grant CCR-9003299, and by NSF and DARPA under Grant CCR-8908092. Email: goodrich@cs.jhu.edu.

1 Introduction

The problem of constructing the convex hull of a set of n points is perhaps the most studied problem in computational geometry (see [3, 4, 7, 10, 18, 19, 26, 31]). The problem is generally defined as that of constructing the boundary of the smallest convex set containing all n points. The 2-dimensional convex hull can be constructed sequentially in $O(n)$ time [27], assuming the input points are pre-sorted (say, by increasing x-coordinates), which of course can be done in $O(n \log n)$ time [27]. The 3-dimensional convex hull can also be constructed in $O(n \log n)$ time [27]. These sequential algorithms are in fact optimal, since the 2-dimensional convex hull problem has an $\Omega(n \log n)$ lower bound [34]. Nevertheless, Kirkpatrick and Seidel [21] show that one can beat this lower bound in some cases, in that they give a 2-dimensional convex hull algorithm that runs in $O(n \log h)$ time, where h is the size of the output. Strictly speaking, their method does not contradict the lower bound arguments, as these arguments assume that the output size is linear. Similarly, for the 3-dimensional case, Edelsbrunner and Shi [16] show that one can beat the lower bound in some cases, by giving an algorithm that runs in time $O(n \log^2 h)$. In both the 2- and 3-dimensional case, h is $O(n)$, but can be as small as $O(1)$. Algorithms such as those of Kirkpatrick and Seidel [21], and Edelsbrunner and Shi [16], are said to be *output-size sensitive*.

Convex hull construction has also been well-studied in parallel. For the 2-dimensional convex hull problem, Chow [12] achieved $O(\log^2 n)$ time with n processors, and optimality was achieved by the deterministic, $O(\log n)$ time, n processor algorithm of Atallah and Goodrich [5], Aggarwal *et al* [1] and the simpler (deterministic) technique of Atallah and Goodrich [6]. All these results were on the CREW PRAM, but Miller and Stout [25] achieved the same result on the EREW

PRAM. For the 3-dimensional problem, both Chow [12] and Aggarwal *et al* [1] achieved $O(\log^3 n)$ time, with n processors, and Dadoun and Kirkpatrick [15] achieved $O(\log^2 n \log^* n)$ time with n processors. Reif and Sen [30] give a randomized algorithm that achieves $O(\log n)$ expected time with very high probability [1], using n processors. For the case in which the input is presorted, Berkman *et al* [8] achieved $O(\log \log n)$ time with optimal work. Stout [33] gives a randomized algorithm that achieves constant expected time with n processors for convex hull assuming a uniform input distribution. However, as Stout observes, given such a uniform distribution, the expected number of points on the convex hull is $O(\log n)$, which allows "brute-force" constant-time techniques to be used that would not be constant-time otherwise.

None of these previous algorithms achieve the sequential output-sensitive work bounds described above, however. Nevertheless, using standard parallel techniques, one can implement the algorithm of Kirkpatrick and Seidel [21] in $O(\log^2 n)$ time, using $O(n \log h)$ work. An analogous implementation of the method of Edelsbrunner and Shi would run in $O(\log^3 n)$ time, using $O(n \log^2 h)$ work. It is not clear how one can improve these times without the introduction of new techniques, however.

In this paper we present efficient parallel algorithms for convex hull construction in 2- and 3-dimensions. We address both the pre-sorted and unsorted cases. For the pre-sorted case we give an algorithm that runs almost surely [2] in $O(1)$ time using $O(n \log n)$ processors. We then show how to modify our algorithm so that, even though it assumes the input is a set of points, it can be implemented to run on a set of upper hulls [3]. We call such algorithms *point-hull invariant*, and show how such an algorithm can be used to derive a solution to the convex hull problem running almost surely in $O(\log^* n)$ time with an optimal number of processors. Our analysis does not depend on any assumptions about the input distribution.

For the unsorted case, we give efficient output-sensitive parallel methods for both the 2- and 3-dimensional convex hull problems. Our algorithms attain work bounds that are lower than previous bounds,

and match those attained sequentially by Kirkpatrick and Seidel [21] for the 2-dimensional problem, and by Edelsbrunner and Shi [16] for the 3-dimensional problem. Specificallly, we show how to solve the 2-dimensional convex hull problem in $O(\log n)$ time using $O(n \log h)$ work with very high probability, and how to solve the 3-dimensional convex hull problem in $O(\log^2 n)$ time using $O(\min\{n \log^2 h, n \log n\})$ work, again, with very high probability.

All of our methods depend upon the use of new *in-place* techniques, whereby we mean methods that are defined on a subset S' of elements in the input and work without re-ordering the input. Intuitively, we have a virtual processor "standing by" each element in S', and this virtual processor does all the work necessary because of the inclusion of this element in S'. The significance of these techniques is that they allow one to perform each level in a parallel divide-and-conquer scheme very fast (in our case, $O(1)$ time with very high probability) without ever needing to explicitly perform the "divide" step. Instead, one simply divides the subproblems logically, and by keeping a virtual processor with each element e, we can associate e with the correct subproblem. This contrasts with most previous parallel techniques, which require that the elements in a subproblem belong to a contiguous portion of some array.

Our methods are also based on various adaptations of a method of Alon and Megiddo [2] for performing linear programming in fixed dimensions almost surely in $O(1)$ time using $O(n)$ processors in a randomized CRCW PRAM model. The general approach of our methods is based on the approaches of [21] and [16]: namely, to use linear programming to "probe" the convex hull, finding a facet about which we may then split the problem and recurse. By adapting Alon and Megiddo's method to be both point-hull invariant and in-place we allow for such probes to be repeated recursively.

In addition, as we use algorithms on subproblems that have confidence bounds dependent on subproblem size, in order to achieve confidence bounds dependent on the total problem size we employ a technique we call *failure sweeping*. Intuitively, we "sweep" those subproblems that have not been solved within the desired time into a limited space m, then solve them all with a number of processors that is super-linear with respect to m.

In Section 2 we present our method for the presorted case, which in turn motivates our approach for the unsorted case, which we describe in Section 4. Before we describe our methods for the unsorted case, however, we first present a number of general in-place techniques

---

[1] *Very high probability* - the probability that this will not occur $\leq n^{-c}$, where $c \geq 1$ is a constant.

[2] *Almost surely* - the probability that this will not occur $\leq c^{-n^d}$, where $c > 1$, $d > 0$.

[3] An *upper hull* is a convex chain monotone in the x-direction that "curves to the right" as one traverses it by increasing x-coordinates.

in Section 3. We follow our algorithm description with a discussion of processor allocation issues in Section 5, and conclude in Section 6.

2 Convex Hull Algorithms for Presorted Input

Given n presorted points in the plane (assume, wlog, that they are sorted in increasing order of x-coordinates) in an array, we find their upper hull such that every point in the array has a pointer to the hull edge that it is beneath (or on). Thus, one edge may occur in this list many times, as it will be stored by every point below it.

2.1 Preliminaries

First, we review some elegant results due, respectively, to Ragde, to Alon and Megiddo, and to Chernoff, that we use in our algorithm:

Lemma 2.1 (The Approximate Compaction Lemma (Ragde [28])): *Given an array of size n containing at most k non-zero elements, one can determine whether $k < n^{\frac{1}{4}}$ and if so, one can compress these k elements into an area of size k^4, all in constant time on a CRCW PRAM (deterministically) with n processors.*

The next lemma deals with the linear programming problem: given m constraints (half-spaces) in $\Re^d$, and some particular linear (objective) function, finding the point in $\Re^d$ that maximizes the objective function, subject to the constraints.

Lemma 2.2 (Alon and Megiddo [2]): *Given n constraints in $\Re^d$, linear programming can be performed in constant time with n processors on a CRCW PRAM, with the probability of taking more than some constant amount of time given by $2^{-cn^{\frac{1}{3}}}$, where $c > 1$ is a constant.*

Lemma 2.3 (Tail Estimation (Chernoff [11], and, in this form, Raghavan [29])): *Let $X_1, X_2, \ldots, X_n \in \{0,1\}$ be n bernoulli trials: independent trials with probability p_i that $X_i = 1$, where $p_i \in (0,1)$. Define $X = \Sigma_{i=1}^n X_i$, $\mu = \Sigma_{i=1}^n p_i$. Then, for all $\delta > 0$,*

$$Prob(X > (1+\delta)\mu) < \left[\frac{e^\delta}{(1+\delta)^{1+\delta}}\right]^\mu,$$

and, for all δ such that $0 < \delta \leq 1$,

$$Prob(X < (1-\delta)\mu) < \left[\frac{e^{-\delta}}{(1-\delta)^{1-\delta}}\right]^\mu.$$

We also make use of the following observations:

Observation 2.1 (Eppstein and Galil [17]) *The first non-zero element of an array of size n can be found in constant time on a CRCW PRAM, with n processors.*

Observation 2.2 (Brute Force Linear Programming) *It is possible to solve linear programming in d dimensions in constant time, with n^{d+1} processors.*

Proof sketch: We find the intersection of all d-tuples of constraints, then for each such tuple, check whether its intersection, which is a candidate solution, is violated by any other constraint in the subproblem. ∎

Observation 2.3 (Brute Force Convex Hull) *It is possible to find the upper hull of n points in the plane in constant time with n^3 processors.*

Definition *The bridge is the upper hull edge that intersects the vertical line through one specified point.*

Kirkpatrick and Seidel [21] observed the following:

Observation 2.4 (Linear Programming for Bridge Finding) *The problem of finding a bridge can be reduced to, and hence solved by, linear programming.*

The final result we review is that of constant-time convex hull determination using an inefficient number of processors.

Lemma 2.4 *For any integer $k \geq 1$, one can find the upper hull of n points in the plane in time $O(k)$, using $n^{1+\frac{1}{k}}$ processors, deterministically, on a CRCW PRAM.*

Proof: This result is part of the "folklore" of parallel computational geometry. For completeness, however, we include the details in the final version. ∎

2.2 A More Efficient Algorithm

Having reviewed the above results, we now present an $n \log n$ processor, constant time, algorithm. Suppose we are given n input points in the plane, such that they are sorted in increasing order of x-coordinate. We consider a complete binary tree T, built "on top" of these points, and note that finding the bridge for each median point in the subtree of every node v in T would result in finding all the hull edges.

Given $n \log n$ processors in a randomized CRCW PRAM, we can, for each v in T, simultaneously solve the associated linear programming problem (see Observation 2.4), using Alon and Megiddo's algorithm (see Lemma 2.2).

Having done this, we then assigned $\log n$ processors to each node v, and check whether any of v's ancestors store a bridge that covers (i.e. is the bridge for) the solution to v, in constant time (this amounts to an OR). Finally, assigning $\log n$ processors to each point (leaf)

194

p, we find the lowest ancestor of p that is not covered by another edge: this will be the edge above p. (See Observation 2.1.)

Thus, it might seem that, as Alon and Megiddo's algorithm takes constant time and has confidence bounds that are exponential in the size of the input, we have achieved our result. This is not the case, however, as Alon and Megiddo's algorithm is, in general, not used on the entire input but on subproblems, some of which are very small. Since the confidence bounds are only exponential in m, the size of these subproblems, they are not exponential in n. (For example, if $m = O(\log n)$, then the confidence bounds are only polynomial in n, and for smaller subproblems they are not even polynomial in n.)

We overcome this lack of confidence by using Lemma 2.4 for any problems containing fewer than $\log^3 n$ points, and by using a technique that we call *failure sweeping* for problems of size m such that $\log^3 n \leq m \leq n^{\frac{1}{4}}$.

Before we describe our failure sweeping technique, however, let us analyze the processor bounds needed so far. For small problems, that is to say, problems of size $m < \log^3 n$ we use an $m^{\frac{4}{3}}$ processor, constant time, algorithm (see lemma 2.4, with $k = 3$). So the number of processors required for each level of height $h < 3 \log \log n$ in the tree, ($m = 2^h$) is $m^{\frac{4}{3}} n/m = nm^{\frac{1}{3}}$. As the highest level that uses brute force has $m < \log^3 n$, the total number of processors required is $< n \log n (1 + \frac{1}{2^{\frac{1}{3}}} + \frac{1}{4^{\frac{1}{3}}} + \ldots)$ which is $O(n \log n)$. Note that all these small problems are solved deterministically in constant time. All other problems are solved using Alon and Megiddo's algorithm, with a linear number of processors in constant time, with probability of failure $\leq 2^{-cm^{\frac{1}{3}}}$, where $c > 1$ (see Lemma 2.2). Thus, all these other problems require n processors per level, and hence $O(n \log n)$ processors in total.

2.3 Improving Confidence by Failure Sweeping

In this subsection, we describe *failure sweeping*: a technique for improving the confidence bounds of an iterative or recursive randomized algorithm.

Consider a randomized algorithm with expected running time $t(n)$ when run on input of size n, and which has a failure probability $p(n)$ so the probability of taking longer than $ct(n)$ for some constant c, is $p(n)$. Also, assume that there is a "brute-force" technique for solving this problem with a super-linear, but polynomial, number of processors. (For the sake of concreteness, let

us say we have an n^3 processor "brute-force" method.) If this algorithm is run on $\frac{n}{m}$ subproblems, each of size $m = \Omega(p^{-1}(n))$ (such that $p(p^{-1}(n)) = n$), then failure sweeping can improve the failure probability from $p(m)$ to $p(n)$, and thus improve the confidence from $1 - p(m)$ to $1 - p(n)$.

This is achieved as follows: the algorithm is run for $ct(m)$ steps on the subproblems, so the expected number of *failures* is $\frac{n}{m} p(m) \leq 1$, where a *failure* is a subproblem that has not yet been solved. The failures are then compacted into an area of size $n^{\frac{1}{r}}$, where $r \geq 4$, using Ragde's algorithm (see lemma 2.1). Then, we assign $n^{1-\frac{1}{r}}$ processors to each failure, and use a "brute-force" method to solve them.

In our problem, we use Alon and Megiddo's algorithm on all problems of size $\geq \log^3 n$, and perform failure sweeping on each level of the binary tree that is of height h such that $3 \log \log n \leq h \leq \frac{1}{4} \log n$. From Lemma 2.2, we have $p(n) = 2^{-cn^{\frac{1}{3}}}$, and from Observation 2.2, we have an appropriate brute force technique, so we can perform failure sweeping.

Now, we use Ragde's compaction algorithm, from Lemma 2.1, which will attempt to compact the failures into a space of size $n^{\frac{1}{4}}$. Then, we use the brute force algorithm of Observation 2.2, with $n^{\frac{3}{4}}$ processors assigned to each failure. (This is a sufficient number of processors for all problems of size $m \leq n^{\frac{1}{4}}$ as the brute force technique requires m^3 processors.)

Analysis

After spending some constant α amount of time on Alon and Megiddo's technique, at each level the expected number of failures is $\mu = \frac{n}{m} 2^{-cm^{\frac{1}{3}}}$, but as $m \geq \log^3 n$, we have $\mu \leq \frac{1}{n^{c-1}}$, so $\mu \leq 1$.

Therefore, by the Chernoff bounds (Lemma 2.3), the number of failures is greater than $n^{\frac{1}{16}}$ with probability

$$f \leq \left(\frac{e^{n^{\frac{1}{16}} - 1}}{(n^{\frac{1}{16}})^{n^{\frac{1}{16}}}} \right), \text{ which implies}$$

$$f \leq \frac{1}{e} \left(\frac{n^{\frac{1}{16}}}{e} \right)^{-n^{\frac{1}{16}}},$$

$$f \leq \frac{1}{e} 2^{-n^{\frac{1}{16}}(\frac{1}{16} \log n - \log e)}.$$

So the number of failures is less than $n^{\frac{1}{16}}$ with probability

$$1 - f \geq 1 - \frac{1}{e} 2^{-n^{\frac{1}{16}}}$$

for all n greater than a constant, g, which is exponentially small in n.

We then use Ragde's approximate compaction method, which will succeed if there are not more than $n^{\frac{1}{16}}$ failures, which is true with probability $1 - f$.

This gives us the following lemma:

Lemma 2.5 *The 2d convex hull problem can be solved in constant time with $O(n \log n)$ processors, with probability $\geq 1 - 2^{-n^{\frac{1}{16}}}$, for all n larger than a constant, g.*

Over the next three subsections, we show how to use this result to derive an $O(\log^* n)$ time, optimal algorithm.

2.4 Making Alon and Megiddo's Method Point-Hull Invariant

Here, we define the property of *point-hull invariance* and we show that our application of Alon and Megiddo's linear programming algorithm [2] is point-hull invariant.

The algorithm of Alon and Megiddo [2] for linear programming in any fixed dimension comprises two parts: repeatedly choosing a subset of the constraints, and finding the solution to this subset of constraints, as a linear programming problem. The initial subset is chosen at random from all the constraints, and later choices are made at random from those that violate the currently known solution. These can be found by considering the current solution (a point s), for every constraint (a line c). The constraint c violates s iff s is not *above* c.

To find the solution to the subproblem, one uses brute force (see observation 2.2). The subset is chosen to be so small that this can be done in constant time with n processors.

The only primitive operations required are the following:

- choosing a sample at random;

- intersecting two lines; and

- determining whether a point is above or below a line.

Since we wish to apply their method to objects that are themselves upper hulls, we note that these operations on points and lines have corresponding operations on upper hulls. In particular,

- finding the x (or y) coordinate of a point, or determining on which side of a line a point lies, corresponds to finding the intersection of a line with a upper hull;

- finding the line defined by two points corresponds to finding the common tangent of two upper hulls; and

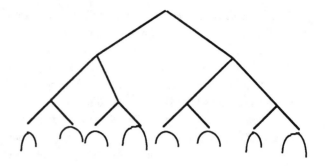

Figure 1: The Use of Point-Hull Invariance.

- finding the intersection of two lines corresponds to finding the intersection of two hulls (assuming, of course, that one knows there can be only one intersection).

Any algorithm on n points that would require only these operations to function with n upper hulls as input instead, is defined as *point-hull invariant*. See Figure 1. Atallah and Goodrich [6] show that each of these upper hull problems can be solved in constant time with $O(n^{\frac{1}{b}})$ processors, where b is a constant and n is the total number of edges in the upper hull.

This gives us the following observation:

Observation 2.5 Both the brute force algorithm and Alon and Megiddo's technique (of Observation 2.2 and Lemma 2.2, respectively) are point-hull invariant. In addition, the constant time upper hull algorithm (of Lemma 2.5) is also point-hull invariant.

As a result, given m upper hulls, each containing q points, we can run the constant time convex hull algorithm of lemma 2.5, using a modification of Alon and Megiddo's algorithm such that in place of constant time calls to the trivial operations on points, we call the constant time operations on upper hulls due to Atallah and Goodrich [6]. This gives us the following lemma:

Lemma 2.6 The algorithm obtained from the method of lemma 2.5, by replacing all calls to the point-primitives by calls to the primitive hull operations of Atallah and Goodrich, will run in $O(1)$ time with the same probability as given in section 2.1, namely $1 - f$ where $f = \left(2^{-\Omega(n^*)}\right)$, but now requires $mq^{\frac{1}{b}}$ processors, where b, e are constants.

2.5 An Almost-Optimal Algorithm

Here, we show how to find the convex hull of a set of pre-sorted points in the plane in $O(\log^* n)$ time with

196

n processors on a CRCW PRAM. (In the next subsection, we show how to reduce the number of processors to $\frac{n}{\log^* n}$, making the algorithm optimal.)

Our method uses the constant-time point-hull invariant algorithm of Lemma 2.6 as a subroutine.

Our algorithm is as follows:

1. We split the input of n points into $\frac{n}{\lceil \log^b n \rceil}$ contiguous groups of size $\lceil \log^b n \rceil$ points each, where b is a constant that will be set in the analysis. Given that t is the expected amount of time required to solve these subproblems recursively, we spend time ct, where c is a constant, to solve the problem recursively for each of the subproblems in parallel. Any subproblem that has not been solved by this time, we label a *failure*.

2. We then perform failure sweeping on the subproblems. As with the constant time algorithm, we use Ragde's approximate compaction algorithm to sweep the *failures* into a space of size $n^{\frac{1}{4}}$, then solve them using the brute force technique of Observation 2.3.

3. We assign $O(\lceil \log n \rceil)$ processors to each group of size $\lceil \log^b n \rceil$, and use the constant-time algorithm on hulls of Lemma 2.6, to find the upper hull with these upper hulls as input (acting like points).

It should be clear that the above algorithm uses only $O(n)$ processors. We also have the following:

Lemma 2.7 (Confidence Bounds) *The above algorithm runs in time $O(\log^* n)$, and the probability of failure is $p(m) \leq 2^{-m^{\frac{1}{b}}}$, for a problem of size m.*

Proof: Omitted in this preliminary version. ∎

2.6 An Optimal Algorithm

Here, we show how to reduce the number of processors required in the "almost-optimal" algorithm above, by the use of two-level arrays, and halting the recursion early. This allows our algorithm to run optimally in $O(\log^* n)$ time with $\frac{n}{\log^* n}$ processors. We give the details in the full version of the paper.

This gives us the following theorem:

Theorem 2 *One can find the convex hull of n presorted points in the plane in time $O(\log^* n)$ time with probability $\geq 1 - 2^{-n^{\frac{1}{b}}}$ (where $b > 16$ is a constant), using $\frac{n}{\log^* n}$ processors, on a randomized CRCW PRAM.*

In the next section we present the techniques that we will eventually use in our convex hull algorithms for unsorted inputs.

3 In-Place Techniques

Four basic techniques used in our algorithms for the general (unsorted input) case are the *random vote*, the *random sample*, *in-place approximate compaction* and *in-place bridge-finding*. These are all in-place techniques: they do not require any reordering of the data, and none of them require that the points be at contiguous array locations. They achieve this in-place property through the use of $o(n)$ work space.

3.1 Random Samples and Random Votes

Given m points, each with an associated processor, the random sample procedure is to choose a sample of size $\Theta(k)$, where k is $o(m)$. This sample is to be uniformly random (that is to say, every point must have an equal probability of being included in the sample) and is to be stored in a work space of size $16k$. The random vote procedure is to pick one of the points at random, such that every point has an equal probability of being chosen.

The random sample procedure is as follows:

1. Each processor decides whether it will attempt a write, with probability $2k/m$.

2. Each processor that has decided to write chooses a random location in the work space, and attempts to write its id to that location if it is unoccupied.

3. Every processor that performed a successful write then checks whether any other processors attempted to write to this location. This can be done by having the unsuccessful processors re-attempt their write.

4. Each processor that wrote to a location that did not suffer a collision, writes the coordinates of its point into that location. Each processor that did suffer a collision repeats steps 2-4 for a total of up to d attempts, where d is a constant.

Note that all the above steps can be performed in constant time with m processors, on the CRCW PRAM.

By the Chernoff bound [11] (lemma 2.3), fewer than $4k$ processors will attempt a write, with probability

$$\geq 1 - \left(\frac{4}{e}\right)^{2k},$$

and more than k processors, with probability

$$\geq 1 - \left(\frac{e}{2}\right)^{-k}.$$

Thus, given that m' processors attempt to write, with $k \leq m' \leq 4k$, the probability of such a processor suffering a collision is $\leq \frac{1}{4}$. So the number of processors that do suffer a collision is $\leq \frac{k}{2}$ with probability $\leq \left(\frac{e}{2}\right)^{-k}$ (from the Chernoff bound).

Thus, m'', the number of processors that write and do not suffer a collision, is $\geq \frac{k}{2}$, with probability $\geq 1 - \left(\frac{e}{2}\right)^{-k}$. This gives us the following lemma:

Lemma 3.1 *An in-place random sample of size $\Theta(k)$, from an array of size n, can be found in constant time, with n processors on a randomized CRCW PRAM, using work space of size $\Theta(k)$. It is uniformly random with probability $\geq 1 - 2\left(\frac{e}{2}\right)^{-k}$.*

In order to perform a random vote, we take a random sample, and then pick any one element in it, using any method that does not favor some points over others. For example, as the location written to is uniformly random, the first location in the work space that has been written to could have been written to by any point with equal probability, and can be found in constant time (see observation 2.1). This gives us the following:

Corollary 3.1 *An in-place random vote, choosing one out of n elements in an array, can be performed in constant time, with n processors on a randomized CRCW PRAM. It uses $\Theta(k)$ work space where it is uniformly random with probability $\geq 1 - 2\left(\frac{e}{2}\right)^{-k}$.*

3.2 In-Place Approximate Compaction

Lemma 2.1 describes the result of an elegant approximate compaction technique due to Ragde [28]. Unfortunately, this technique is not in itself in-place, so here we present an in-place approximate compaction technique that uses Ragde's method as a subroutine. We achieve the following result:

Lemma 3.2 *Given an array of size m, containing at most k non-zero elements, one can determine whether $k < m^\epsilon$, and if so, one can perform an in-place approximate compaction of these elements into an area of size k^4, all deterministically, using $\max\{k, m^{4\epsilon+\delta}\}$ processors on a CRCW PRAM, with workspace of size $m^{4\epsilon+\delta}$, where $\delta < 1$ and $\epsilon < \frac{1-\delta}{4}$ are constants.*

Proof We split the array into $m^{4\epsilon+\delta}$ groups of size $m^{1-(4\epsilon+\delta)}$, and for every non-zero element in group i, we write a 1 into the ith location of an array of bits, of size $m^{4\epsilon+\delta}$. Note that there can be at most $\min\{m^{4\epsilon+\delta}, k\}$

non-zero bits in this array. We then perform approximate compaction (see Lemma 2.1) on this second array, to compress the bits into an area of size $m^{4\epsilon}$. If $k > m^\epsilon$, then this will be detected (see Lemma 2.1). We then split each original group into m^δ groups of size $m^{1-4\epsilon-2\delta}$, and repeat the procedure, ignoring all of the original groups that were found to contain no non-zero elements.

We can iterate this process at most $\frac{1}{\delta}$ times, after which we will have compressed the non-zero elements into an area of size $m^{4\epsilon}$, or determined that $k \geq m^\epsilon$. ∎

3.3 In-Place Bridge Finding

Recall the bridge-finding problem: Given m unsorted points in d dimensions, find the *bridge*, the convex hull facet that intersects a vertical line passing through one specified point (which we call the *splitter*). We address a slightly more general version of the problem, namely, that of finding the bridge for each of q point sets (each with its own splitter), in an array of n points, such that the points corresponding to any one point-set cannot be assumed to be contiguous.

Alon and Megiddo's algorithm [2] solves this problem, but it is not an in-place method. In our algorithm for the unsorted input problem we must deal with many unrelated problems scattered through the input such that the processors of any one problem cannot be assumed to be contiguous, while Alon and Megiddo's algorithm assumes contiguous input for one problem. In this section we show how to achieve almost surely constant time m-constraint linear programming using m processors in-place. Our technique takes a similar approach to that of Alon and Megiddo's algorithm, but has the advantage of being simpler to implement, although it achieves the same time, work and confidence bounds.

We solve the bridge-finding problem by considering the associated linear programming problem (see Observation 2.4). This is solved by repeatedly picking and (deterministically) solving a *base problem*, until the solution has been found. The base problem consists of $\Theta(k)$ constraints, where k is sufficiently small that there are enough processors available to solve the base problem by brute force (see observation 2.2). The work space used for the base problem is $16k$.

In more detail, the 2d problem is solved as below, with $p \geq m$ processors and $k = p^{1/3}$ (the 3d case differs only in that the size of the base problem, k, is $p^{1/4}$, not $p^{1/3}$):

1. Apply the random sample procedure to find a base

problem of size $\Theta(k)$.

2. Solve the base problem deterministically in constant time.

3. After solving the base problem, check for every point whether it violates the solution just found. All constraints that violate the solution in this manner are candidates to be in the next base problem, and are said to be *survivors*.

    At iteration j, having solved $j-1$ base problems, each survivor decides whether to attempt to write into the base problem with probability $p_j = \min\{1, 2kp_{j-1}\}$ in the 2d case, and $p_j = \min\{1, 2kp_{j-1}\}$ in the 3d case. Then the base problem is chosen as above. (From above, $p_1 = \frac{2k}{p}$, and $p_j = 1$ for $j > 4$.)

4. Repeat steps 1-3 for a constant β number of iterations (where β will be set in the analysis). Then perform in-place approximate compaction (see Lemma 3.2) on the survivors, compressing them all into the base problem. (If there are too many to be so compressed, then repeat steps 1-3 once more.) The solution to this problem will be the final solution. Note that if at any earlier point there are no survivors, then *the solution to the last base problem is the convex hull facet sought*.

This completes our procedure. Let us, therefore, analyze this procedure.

3.4 Analysis of the In-Place Bridge-Finding Algorithm

Lemma 4.1 *With probability* $\geq 1 - e^{-\Omega(k^r)}$, *where* $1 > r > 0$ *is a constant, the number of survivors will be reduced to* $\leq k^{\frac{1}{5}}$ *within a constant number of iterations.*
Proof The proof follows the same lines as the analysis in Alon and Megiddo [2], and will be given in the full version of the paper.
Lemma 4.2 *With probability* $\geq 1 - e^{-\Omega(k^r)}$, *where* $1 > r > 0$ *is a constant, the convex hull facet (edge) through the splitting point can be found in a constant number of iterations, of solving base problems.*
Proof From Lemma 4.1, after a constant, β, number of iterations, the number of survivors will be less than $k^{1/5}$, almost surely (with probability $\geq 1 - e^{-\Omega(k^r)}$). Once this is the case, we perform in-place approximate compaction, which then compresses the survivors into an area of size k (see Lemma 3.2), which is the space

for the base problem. We then solve the base problem, and as it contained all the survivors, the solution to the base problem will be the solution to the entire problem. This can only fail if the number of survivors $> k^{\frac{1}{4}}$, which from Lemma 4.1, is true with probability $e^{-\Omega(k^r)}$. ■

4 Convex Hull Algorithms for Unsorted Input

4.1 The 2d Algorithm

Suppose we are given an array of n points in the plane, in no particular order. We wish to find the upper convex hull of these points such that each point has a pointer to the edge above it. (Thus, there may be many points referring to any one edge.) We output the hull edges in a binary tree, built "on top" of the unsorted input points.

The algorithm is similar in structure to randomized quicksort, picking a point at random, uniformly, from the input, then splitting the input about that point and recursing. However, there is no compaction performed, and the convex hull facet above the splitting point is found before recursion. In this sense, the algorithm uses the "marriage-before-conquest" paradigm of Kirkpatrick and Seidel [21].

Initially, every point has a processor assigned to it, and every processor is *active*, i.e., it is assigned operations. If a point is found to be below a convex hull edge, then its associated processor ceases to be active: it ceases to perform any operations associated with the point, and is regarded as *dead*.

The algorithm consists of a number of phases, each of which consists of $\frac{\log n}{32}$ iterations. At the end of each phase, we perform compaction of the subproblems remaining, then reassign the workspace, and reset a counter for the level of recursion.

In phase q, at the ith level of recursion, there are $\leq n^{\frac{1}{32}}2^i$ subproblems, with average size $s_i = n/(n^{\frac{1}{32}}2^i)$. (See step 3 below.) The size of the base problems solved is $16k$ where $k = s_i^{1/3}$. For each problem j, $1 \leq j \leq n^{\frac{1}{32}}2^i$, we do the following:

1. Apply the random vote procedure to choose a splitting point p (see corollary 3.1). We then attempt to find the convex hull edge above p, by applying the in-place bridge-finding procedure (see lemma 4.2). See figure 2. If the bridge-finding procedure for problem j has not naturally terminated after α

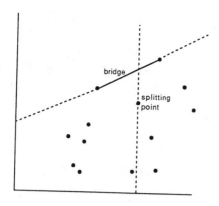

Figure 2: 2D convex hull by bridge-finding

steps (α will be set in the analysis), then we terminate the procedure and say that subproblem j has *failed*.

2. In this step, we use failure sweeping to compact those problems that failed in the previous step, so that each problem can be assigned $n^{\frac{3}{4}}$ processors. We assign $k = n^{\frac{1}{4}}$ space, and $p = n^{\frac{3}{4}}$ processors, to each problem, and use the in-place bridge-finding procedure to find the bridge.

3. If $i \geq \frac{\log n}{32}$, then the algorithm has already taken $O(\log n)$ time, so use parallel prefix sum to compact the remaining points and find the number of subproblems remaining, m. Add m to the number of hull edges found thus far to get l, which is a lower bound on h. If $l \geq n^{\frac{1}{32}}$ (on the first such check it won't be), then solve the problem using any $O(\log n)$ time, n processor algorithm, e.g. the algorithm of Atallah and Goodrich [6]. Otherwise, we reassign the work space among the remaining problems (so each problem recieves $\frac{n}{l} \geq n^{\frac{31}{32}}$), and continue, each subproblem resetting i to 1, incrementing q, and resetting its problem number j to its rank in the compacted list of subproblems.

4. Change the problem number of each point that is active such that a problem number j is changed to $2j-1$, if it is to the left, and to $2j$, if it's to the right, of the solution to problem j. If a point is under the solution edge (a hull edge), then it is given a pointer to that edge, after which it does nothing and it is regarded as a *dead* point. Once this has been done for all points, we halve the work space for each of the problems that has just been solved, and assign the halves to its two "child' problems. Then, we recurse on the subproblems.

The algorithm then continues at recursion level $i+1$, with the above actions, until all points are dead (this can be tested by a concurrent write of all active processors to one location), or until we switch to using the method of Atallah and Goodrich [6].

This completes our description. Let us, therefore, analyze our method.

4.2 Analysis of the 2d algorithm

We first observe that the total number of subproblems active at any step in our algorithm is at most $l2^i \leq n^{\frac{1}{16}}$. In addition, we have the following:

Lemma 5.1 *At the ith level of recursion, with probability $\geq 1 - 2^{-2i}$, each subproblem is of size $< (15/16)^i n$.*

Proof: The likelihood that at least 15/16 of the points are on the same side of the splitting point is 2/16. Thus, after i such splits, the probability that subproblem j is of size $\geq (15/16)^i n$ is $\leq 2^{-3i}$. So the probability p that not all subproblems are of size less than $(15/16)^i n$) is

$$p = 2^i / 8^i = 2^{-2i}.$$

∎

This implies that the parallel time for our method is $O(\log n)$, with very high probability ($\geq 1 - n^b$, where b is a constant). Let us, then, analyze our space requirements. It is easy to see that the work space available for any active subproblem is $\geq \frac{n^{\frac{31}{32}}}{2^i} \geq n^{\frac{15}{16}}$.

Therefore, the total space needed is $O(n)$.

Lemma 5.2 *At each level of recursion, with probability $\geq 1 - e^{-\Omega(n^f)}$, where $1 > f > 0$ is a constant, every bridge is found in constant time.*

Proof: Lemma 4.2 states that after a constant number of steps, which we call α, the in-place bridge-finding procedure will have found the bridge with probability $\geq 1 - e^{-\Omega(k^r)}$, and in this case, $k = \left(\frac{n}{2^i}\right)^{\frac{1}{3}}$. So, after α steps, we terminate any failures, and use Ragde's approximate compaction algorithm. The total number of problems at each recursion level is always $< n^{\frac{1}{16}}$, so Ragde's approximate compaction algorithm [28] can be used to compress the problem **ids** into an area of size $n^{\frac{1}{4}}$, giving $p = n^{\frac{3}{4}}$ processors for each problem. Given in-place bridge-building with a sample size of at most $k = n^{\frac{1}{4}}$, and $p = n^{\frac{3}{4}}$, lemma 4.2 gives the result. ∎

Lemma 5.3 *The work required to find the 2d convex hull is $O(n \log h)$.*

Proof: Given that $W(n, h)$ is the work required to find the convex hull of n points, with h edges, using the above algorithm, we can show the result in a manner similar to the analysis in Seidel [32]. We give the details in the full version of the paper.

Theorem 5 *With probability $1 - n^{-b}$, where b is a constant, the 2d convex hull can be found in $O(\log n)$ time with $O(n \log h)$ work.*

Proof: This is a consequence of the above lemmas, and Lemma 7. (Lemma 7 is the observation of Matias and Vishkin [24] on processor allocation discussed in section 5.) ■

4.3 The 3d Algorithm

Suppose we are given an array of n points in $\Re^3$, in no particular order. We wish to find the upper convex hull of these points such that each point knows the face above it. (Thus, there may be many points referring to any one face.)

Our algorithm is similar in structure to quicksort, and to the sequential 3d convex algorithm of Edelsbrunner and Shi [16]. Unlike Edelsbrunner and Shi, however, we do not split the input into subproblems about the "ham-sandwich cut", but about a point chosen at random, uniformly, from the input.

The algorithm consists of a number of phases, each of which consists of $O(\log n)$ iterations. At the end of each phase, we perform compaction of the subproblems remaining, reassign workspace, and reset a counter for the level of recursion. In the qth phase, at the ith level of recursion, there are at most $n^{\frac{1}{32}} 4^i$ subproblems, with average size $s_i = n/(n^{\frac{1}{32}} 4^i)$ (see step 4 below). The size of the base problems solved is $O(k)$ where $k = s_i^{1/4}$. For each problem j, $1 \le j \le n^{\frac{1}{32}} 4^i$:

1. We choose a splitting point by the random vote procedure, (see corollary 3.1) and find the convex hull face that it is under, using the 3d in-place bridge-finding technique (see lemma 4.2) (which, in this case, finds a triangular face of the upper hull). Note that if the in-place bridge finding technique for problem j does not naturally terminate after α steps (α will be set in the analysis) , then we terminate the procedure and say that subproblem j has *failed*.

2. In this step we use failure sweeping to compact those problems that have not yet been completed, so that each problem can be assigned $n^{\frac{3}{4}}$ processors. Using $16k = 16n^{\frac{1}{4}}$ as the space for the random sample, we use the in-place bridge-finding procedure to find the bridge.

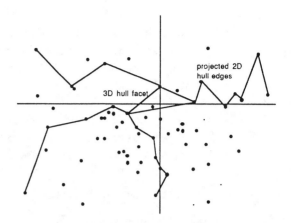

Figure 3: Division of the point set

3. We divide each problem into 4 subproblems as follows:

    We project all the points onto both the xz and yz planes through the splitting point, projecting them along directions parallel to that of the convex hull face just found. Then, we use our 2d algorithm (unsorted case) to find the 2d hulls of the projected points in these planes: the 2d hull edges will also be edges of the 3d hull [16] and due to the nature of our 2d algorithm, each point will store its position relative to these hulls. The hulls necessarily divide each problem into 4 (possibly unequal) parts, defined by the intersection of the 2 hulls. The depth of recursion taken to find the 2d convex hulls is added to the total *depth* taken, i.e., the depth of recursion in the 3d algorithm, plus the depth of recursion in previous calls to the 2d algorithm. If the 2d algorithm must resort to using the method of Atallah and Goodrich [6], then the total work required must be $O(n \log n)$, so use the algorithm of Reif and Sen [30], to find the 3d convex hull in $O(\log n)$ time using n processors with very high probability.

4. If $i \ge \frac{1}{64} \log n$ or the total depth (as defined in step 3) $\ge \log n$, then perform parallel prefix sum, to compact and take and a count of the problems left, and the number of edges found thus far, the sum of these two giving l. If $l \ge n^{\frac{1}{32}}$, then find the convex hull using the algorithm of Reif and Sen [30], in $O(\log n)$ time using n processors with very high probability. Otherwise, redivide the workspace among the remaining problems, reset i to 1, increment q, and continue. See figure 3.

5. For all points, change their problem number from j to $4j-3, 4j-2, 4j-1$ or $4j$, depending on the quadrant of the solution it finds itself in. If a point

is under the solution facet, then it is given a pointer to the solution, which is the hull facet above it. After this, the point does nothing, and is regarded as a *dead* point. Once this has been performed for all points, recurse on the subproblems. The algorithm then continues at recursion level $i + 1$, with the above actions, until all points are dead, or the method of Reif and Sen [30] must be used.

4.4 Analysis of the 3d algorithm

We first observe that the total number of subproblems active at any step in our algorithm is $\leq l2^{2i} \leq n^{\frac{1}{16}}$. In addition, we have the following:

Lemma 6.1 *At the ith level of recursion, with probability $\geq 1 - 2^{-4i}$ each subproblem is of size $< (15/16)^i n$.*

Proof: Consider the quadrants that are defined in the xy-plane, by the xz- and yz-planes through the splitter. Now if one quadrant contains $\geq \frac{15}{16}$ of the points, then both quadrants with a different z-coordinate range must contain at most $\frac{1}{16}$ of the the points, (which occurs with probability $\frac{2}{16}$) and the same must be true of the two quadrants that have a different y-coordinate range. So the probabiity of this happening for any one splitter is $\frac{4}{256} = \frac{1}{64}$.

Thus, after i such splits, the probability that subproblem j is of size $\geq (15/16)^i n$ is $\leq 2^{-6i}$. So the probability p that all subproblems are of size less than $(15/16)^i n$ is $\geq 1 - 2^{-4i}$. ∎

This implies that the depth of recursion for our method is $O(\log n)$, and thus our method takes $O(\log^2 n)$ parallel time (by Theorem 5), Let us, then, analyze our space requirements. It is easy to see that the work space available for any active subproblem is $O(n^{\frac{15}{16}})$. Therefore, the total space needed is $O(n)$.

In the full version of the paper, we prove a series of lemmas analogous to lemmas 5.2-5.3, which lead to the following theorem

Theorem 6 With probability $1 - n^{-b}$, where b is a constant, the 3d convex hull can be found in $O(\log^2 n)$ time with $O(min\{n \log^2 h, n \log n\})$ work, on a randomized CRCW PRAM.

Proof: The proof is given in the full version of the paper. ∎

5 Processor Allocation

As described above, our algorithms assume that some number of processors (n, if the input is unsorted) are available. If the number of processors p is less than this,

then the work must be divided such that each processor will be assigned tasks so as to preserve the total amount of work w, and achieve time $O(\frac{w}{p} + t)$ or as close to these bounds as possible. Here, t is the time taken by the algorithm if the number of real processors = the number of virtual processors. If $p \leq n/\log n$, then the simplistic method used for the algorithms for presorted input will suffice. Otherwise, we need to use an observation of Matias and Vishkin [24].

Lemma 7 Given an algorithm with a work bound w, and time bound t, that requires at least n processors, assuming that w is known and that p processors are available, the algorithm can be simulated with p processors in time $T = t + \frac{w}{p} + t_c \log t$ with work $W = pt + w + pt_c \log t$.

Proof: given by Matias and Vishkin [24]. ∎

6 Conclusion

We have shown how to use randomization, generalized linear programming, and a number of in-place techniques to achieve fast work bounds that are very efficient for 2 and 3d convex hulls. It would be interesting to see how these results generalize to higher dimensions.

7 Acknowledgements

We would like to thank Omer Berkman for discussions that led to the developement of the $O(\log^* n)$ time algorithm for pre-sorted input 2d convex hull computation.

References

[1] Aggarwal, A., Chazelle, B., Guibas, L., Ó'Dunlaing,C., and Yap, C., "Parallel Computational Geometry," *Proc. 26th IEEE FOCS* (1985), pp.468-477.

[2] N. Alon and N. Megiddo, "Parallel Linear Programming in Fixed Dimension Almost Surely in Constant Time", *Proc. 31st IEEE FOCS Symposium* (1990), pp. 574-582.

[3] Andrew, A.M., "Another efficient algorithm for convex hulls in two dimensions," *Info. Proc. Lett.* **9**, (1979) pp.216-219.

[4] Avis, D., "On the complexity of finding the convex hull of a set of points," Report SOCS 79.2, (1979), School of Computer Science, McGill University,

[5] Atallah, M. J., and Goodrich, M. T., "Efficient Parallel Solutions to Some Geometric Problems," *Journal of Parallel and Distributed Computing*, **3** (1986), pp. 492-507.

[6] Atallah, M. J., and Goodrich, M. T., "Parallel Algorithms for Some Functions of Two Convex Polygons", *Algorithmica* **3** (1988), pp. 535-548.

[7] Bentley, J. L., Faust, G. M., and Preparata, F. P., "Approximation algorithms for convex hulls," *Comm. ACM* **25**, (1982) pp.64-68.

[8] Berkman, O., Breslauer, D., Galil, Z., Schieber, B., and Vishkin, U., "Highly Parallelizable Problems," *Proc. 21st ACM STOC* (1989), pp.309-319.

[9] O. Berkman and U. Vishkin, "Recursive Star-Tree Parallel Data-Structure", UMIACS-TR-90-40 CS-TR-2437, University of Maryland Institute of Advanced Computer Studies (1990).

[10] Chand, D.R., and Kapur, S.S., "An algorithm for convex polytopes," *JACM* **17**(1), (1970), pp.78-86.

[11] Chernoff, H., "A measure of asymptotic efficiency for tests of a hypothesis based on the sum of the observations," *Annals of Math. Stat.*, **23** (1952), pp. 493-509.

[12] Chow, A., "Parallel Algorithms for Geometric Problems," PhD dissertation, Computer Science Department, University of Illinois at Urbana-Champagne, 1980.

[13] Cole, R., and Vishkin, U., "Approximate and exact parallel scheduling with applications to list, tree and graph problems," *Proc. 27th IEEE FOCS*, (1986) pp.478-491. pp.128-142.

[14] Cole, R., Zajicek, O., "An Optimal Parallel Algorithm for Building a Data Structure for Planar Point Location", *J. Parallel and Distributed Computing* **8** (1990) pp. 280-285.

[15] Dadoun, N., and Kirkpatrick, D.G., "Parallel Construction of Subdivision Hierarchies," Tech. Report 87-13 (1987), Department of Computer Science, University of British Columbia.

[16] H. Edelsbrunner and W. Shi, "An $O(n \log^2 h)$ Time Algorithm for the Three-dimensional Convex Hull Problem", *SIAM J. on Computing* **20** (1991), pp. 259-269.

[17] Eppstein, D., and Galil, Z., "Parallel Algorithmic Techniques for Combinatorial Computation", *Ann. Rev. Comput. Sci.*, 3, pp. 233-283.

[18] Graham, R.L., "An efficient algorithm for determining the convex hull of a planar set," *Info. Proc. Lett.* **1**, (1972) pp.132-133.

[19] Jarvis, R.A., "On the identification of the convex hull of a finite set of points in the plane," *Info. Proc. Lett.* **2**, (1973) pp. 18-21.

[20] Karloff, H. J., and Raghavan, P., "Randomized Algorithms and Pseudorandom Numbers", *Proc. 20th ACM STOC* (1988), pp. 310-321.

[21] Kirkpatrick, D., G., and Seidel, R., " The ultimate planar convex hull algorithm?", *SIAM J. Comput.* **15** (1), (1986), pp. 287-299.

[22] Ladner, R. E., Fischer, M. J., "Parallel prefix computation," *JACM* **27** (1980), pp. 831-838.

[23] Mathews, "Number Theory", Chelsea Publications, New York, (1961).

[24] Matias, Y., and Vishkin, U., "Converting High Probability into Nearly-Constant Time - with Applications to Parallel Hashing", to appear in *Proc. 23rd ACM STOC* (1991).

[25] Miller, R., and Stout, Q., F., "Parallel Algorithms for convex hulls," *Proc. Comp. Vision and Pat. Recogn.* (1988).

[26] Overmars, M.H., van Leeuwen, J., "Maintenance of configurations in the plane," *J. Comput. and Syst. Sci.* **23** (1981), pp.166-204.

[27] Preparata, F. P., and Shamos, M. I., "Computational Geometry *An Introduction*", published by Springer-Verlag (1985).

[28] Ragde, P., "The Parallel Simplicity of Compaction and Chaining," *Proc. 17th International Colloquium on Automata, Languages and Programming (ICALP)*, Springer-Verlag Lecture Notes in Computer Science: 443, 1990, 744–751.

[29] Raghavan, P., "Lecture Notes on Randomized Algorithms", unpublished manuscript.

[30] Reif, J. H., and Sen, S., "Polling: A New Randomized Sampling Technique For Computational Geometry", *Proc. 21st ACM STOC* (1989) pp. 394-404.

[31] Seidel, R., "A convex hull algorithm optimal for points in even dimensions," M. S. Thesis, Tech. Rep. 81-14, (1981) Dept. of Comput. Sci., Univ. of British Columbia, Vancouver, Canada.

[32] R. Seidel, "Output-Size Sensitive Algorithms for Constructive Problems in Computational Geometry", (PhD Thesis) TR 86-784, Department of Computer Science, Cornell University, (1986), pp 15-16.

[33] Stout, Q. F., "Constant-Time Geometry on PRAMs", *Proc. of the 17th International Conference on Parallel Processing* 1988, pp 104-107.

[34] Yao, A.C., "A lower bound to finding convex hulls," *J. ACM* **28** (1981) pp.780-787.

Multisearch Techniques for Implementing Data Structures
on a Mesh-Connected Computer

(Preliminary Version)

Mikhail J. Atallah[*]
Department of Computer Science
Purdue University
West Lafayette, IN 47907, USA.

Frank Dehne[†]
School of Computer Science
Carleton University
Ottawa, Canada K1S 5B6.

Russ Miller[‡]
Department of Computer Science
State University of New York at Buffalo
Buffalo, NY 14260, USA.

Andrew Rau-Chaplin[§]
School of Computer Science
Carleton University
Ottawa, Canada K1S 5B6.

Jyh-Jong Tsay[¶]
National Chung Cheng University
Inst. of Comp. Sci. and Inform. Eng.
Chiayi, Taiwan 62107, ROC.

Abstract

The *multisearch* problem consists of efficiently performing $O(n)$ search processes on a data structure modeled as a graph G with n constant-degree nodes. Denote by r the length of the longest search path associated with a search process, and assume that the paths are determined "on-line". In this paper, we solve the multisearch problem in $O(\sqrt{n} + r\frac{\sqrt{n}}{\log n})$ time on a $\sqrt{n} \times \sqrt{n}$ mesh-connected computer. For most data structures, the search path traversed when answering one search query has length $r = O(\log n)$. For these cases, our algorithm processes $O(n)$ such queries in asymptotically optimal time, $O(\sqrt{n})$. The classes of graphs considered contain most of the important data structures that arise in practice (ranging from simple trees to Kirkpatrick hierarchical search DAGs). Multisearch is a useful abstraction that models many specific problems and can be used to implement parallel data structures on a mesh. Applications include interval trees and the related multiple interval intersection search, as well as hierarchical representations of polyhedra and its many applications (e.g., lines-polyhedron intersection queries, multiple tangent plane determination, intersecting convex polyhedra, and three-dimensional convex hull).

[*]Research partially supported by the Office of Naval Research under Contracts N00014-84-K-0502 and N00014-86-K-0689, the Air Force Office of Scientific Research under Grant AFOSR-90-0107, the National Science Foundation under Grant DCR-8451393, and the National Library of Medicine under Grant R01-LM05118.

[†]Research partially supported by the Natural Sciences and Engineering Research Council of Canada.

[‡]Research partially supported by the National Science Foundation under Grant IRI-8800514.

[§]Research partially supported by the Natural Sciences and Engineering Research Council of Canada.

[¶]Research partially supported by the Office of Naval Research under Contract N00014-84-K-0502, the Air Force Office of the Scientific Research under Grant AFOSR-90-0107, and the National Science Foundation under Grant DCR-8451393.

1   Introducion

Given a search structure modeled as a graph G with n constant-degree nodes, and given $O(n)$ search processes on that structure, the *multisearch* problem is that of performing as fast as possible all of the search processes on that structure. The searches need not be processed in any particular order, and can simultaneously be processed in parallel by using, for example, one processor for each. However, the path that a search query will trace in G is *not* known ahead of time, and must instead be determined "on-line": only when a search query is at (say) node v of G can it determine which node of G it should visit next (it does so by comparing its own search key to the information stored at v — the nature of this information and of the comparison performed depend on the specific problem being solved). The multisearch problem is a useful abstraction that can be used to solve many problems (more on this later). It is a challenging problem both for EREW-PRAMs and for networks of processors, since many searches might want to visit a single node of G, creating a "congestion" problem (with the added complication that we cannot even tally ahead of time how much congestion will occur at a node, since we do not know ahead of time the full search paths, only the nodes of G at which they start). When the parallel model used to solve the problem is a network of processors, the graph G is initially stored in the network in the natural way, with each processor containing one node of G and that node's adjacency list. It is important to keep in mind that the computational network's topology is *not* the same as the search structure G, so that a neighbour of node v in G need not be stored in a processor adjacent to the one containing v. Each processor also contains initially (at most) one of the search queries to be processed (in which case that search does not necessarily start at the node of G stored in that processor).

In the EREW-PRAM, the difficulty comes from the "exclusive read" restriction of the model: if k processes were to simultaneously access node v's information, the k processors assigned to these k search processes are, at least apparently, unable to simultaneously access v's information. An elegant way around this problem was given by Paul, Vishkin and Wagener [PVS83] for the case where G is a 2-3 tree (although they assume a linear ordering on the search keys, something which we cannot afford to do here since we also consider applications involving multidimensional search keys for which no linear ordering can be used).

The multisearch problem is even more challenging for networks of processors. In such models, data is not stored in a shared memory, but is distributed over a network and requires considerable time to be permuted to allow different processors access to different data items. Furthermore, similarly to the EREW-PRAM, each memory location can be accessed only by one query process at a time, since a processor containing (say) node v's information would be unable to simultaneously store more than a constant number of search queries.

The main contribution of this paper is in solving the multisearch problem in $O(\sqrt{n} + r\frac{\sqrt{n}}{\log n})$ time on a $\sqrt{n} \times \sqrt{n}$ mesh-connected computer, where r is the length of the longest search path associated with a

query. Note that, for most data structures, the search path traversed when answering a query has length $r = O(\log n)$. That is, for these cases our algorithm processes $O(n)$ such queries in asymptotically optimal time, $O(\sqrt{n})$. The classes of graphs considered are listed below. They contain most of the important cases of G that arise in practice (ranging from simple trees to the powerful Kirkpatrick hierarchical search DAG that is so important in both sequential and parallel computational geometry).

As already mentioned, multisearch is a useful abstraction that models many specific problems (and hence can be used to solve them). We shall later in the paper use it to solve the problem of implementing parallel data structures on a mesh-connected computer. Applications include interval trees and the related multiple interval intersection search, as well as hierarchical representations of polyhedra and its myriads of applications including lines-polyhedron intersection queries, multiple tangent plane determination, three-dimensional convex hull[1], and intersecting convex polyhedra. Note that these problems are of considerable importance in robotics and solid modeling, computational geometry, vision, pattern recognition, etc. In addition, multisearching is such a fundamental problem that it probably has many additional applications that we have not yet explored (perhaps in parallel databases and related areas).

The multisearch problem for *hypercube multiprocessors* was studied in [DR90]. That hypercube technique was based on the idea of moving the search queries synchronously through G, and required time proportional to the diameter of the network to move all queries to the next nodes in their search paths. Such an approach is not viable on the *mesh* since, in order to obtain *optimal* mesh algorithms based on multisearch, the time per advancement of all queries by one step needs to be *less* than the diameter of the network.

The techniques we use to solve the multisearch problem for the mesh are very different from those used in [DR90], and they are also very different from [PVS83]. In very broad terms, our techniques for solving the problem are a judicious combination of the following ideas:

- Partitioning G into pieces and processing some of these in sequence, others in parallel.
- Making many copies of some pieces of G (the "bot-

---

[1]The 3-D convex hull problem has optimal mesh solutions, recently obtained independently of ours and using different, purely geometric approaches rather than the multisearch method we use [LPJC90, HI90].

tleneck" ones, i.e., those with too many searches trying to go through them), and distributing these copies to various submeshes, each of which then advances some of the "congested" searches. Of course the simple-minded copying strategy of making many copies of G itself, and using one copy for each search, does not work; not only would this take too much time ($O(n)$ time, since we have n searches) but there is not even enough space to store all these copies of G (there is only enough space to store $O(1)$ copies of G, since G has n nodes).

- Mapping some pieces of G into suitably shaped portions of the mesh (not necessarily rectangular submeshes).

Of course, the above-mentioned partitionings, duplications, and mappings cannot be pre-computed, since we do not yet know how the full search paths will develop (in fact the problem of "tracing" the search paths is nontrivial even if we did know them ahead of time). The partitionings/duplications/mappings must instead be done on-line, as the searches advance through G. The above description is necessarily an over-simplification, and only a careful look at the details can reveal the exact interplay between the above ideas, as well as the exact nature of each.

The classes of graphs G considered are hierarchical directed acyclic graphs (hierarchical DAGs for short), α-partitionable (directed) graphs, and α-β-partitionable (undirected) graphs. For the exact definitions of the latter two, we refer the reader to Section 4. The first one (hierarchical DAGs) is easy to state in one sentence: the vertex set can be partitioned into levels $L_0, \ldots, L_h$ ($h = O(\log n)$) such that every edge is from some L_i to L_{i+1}, $|L_0| = 1$, and $|L_{i+1}| = \mu |L_i|$, for some $\mu > 1$ (i.e., $|L_i| = \mu^i$). (Our algorithm can also handle the case where the last condition is replaced by $c_1 \mu^i \leq |L_i| \leq c_2 \mu^i$, for some positive constants c_1 and c_2.) See Figure 1.

The next section contains a more formal definition of the multisearch problem, and of the various terms used in the paper. Sections 3 and 4 contain the main results: our solutions to the multisearch problem for each of the above-mentioned classes of graphs. Sections 5 and 6 use multisearching to solve various problems efficiently on the mesh.

2 Definition of the Multisearch Problem

Let $G = (V, E)$ be a directed or undirected graph of size $n = |V| + |E|$, where the out-degree or degree, respectively, of any vertex is bounded by some constant. Let U be a universe of possible *search queries* on G. Define the *search path* of a query $q \in U$, denoted $path(q)$, to be a sequence of h vertices $(v_1, \ldots, v_h)$ of G defined by a successor function $f : (V \cup start) \times U \to V$ with $f(start, q) = v_1$, and $v_{i+1} = f(v_i, q)$ for $i = 1, \ldots, h-1$. The function f has the following properties: If G is directed, then for every vertex $v \in V$ and query $q \in U$, $(v, f(v, q)) \in E$. If G is undirected, then for every vertex $v \in V$ and query $q \in U$, $\{v, f(v, q)\} \in E$. Furthermore, $f(v, q)$ can be computed by one processor, that stores q and v's information, in $O(1)$ time.

We say that a query $q \in U$ *visits a node* $v \in V$ *at time* t if and only if, at time t, the mesh is in a state where there exists a processor which contains a description of both the query q and the node v. (Note that this definition implies that many queries can simultaneously visit node v, if each such query uses a different copy of v's information.) The *search process* for a search query q with search path $path(q) = (v_1, \ldots, v_h)$ is a process divided into h time steps, $t_1 < t_2 < \ldots < t_h$, such that at time t_i, $1 \leq i \leq h$, query q visits node v_i. We will refer to the change of state between t_i and t_{i+1}, $1 \leq i < h$, as *advancing query q one step in its search path*. Recall that we do not assume the search path to be given in advance. Rather, we assume that the search path for each query is constructed *online* during the search by successive applications of the function f.

Of course, for a *directed* graph, a query can be advanced along an edge only in the indicated direction, whereas for *undirected* graphs a query can advance along an edge in both directions.

Given a set $Q = \{q_1, \ldots, q_m\} \subseteq U$ of m search queries, where $m = O(n)$, then the *multisearch problem* for Q on G consists of executing (in parallel) all m search processes induced by the m search queries. It is important to note that the m search processes can overlap arbitrarily. In particular, at any time t, any node v of G may be visited by an arbitrary number of queries (of course each such query would be using a different copy of v's information).

We will refer to the process of advancing, in parallel, all (or a subset) of the m search queries by one step in their search paths as a *multistep*. A sequence of multisteps such that every search query is advanced $\Omega(\log n)$ steps in its search path, will be referred to as a *log-phase.*

3   A Mesh Solution to the Multisearch Problem for Hierarchical DAGs

Let $G = (V, E)$ be a hierarchical DAG of size n and height h, and let $L_0, \ldots, L_h$ be the levels of G. Note that G has out-degree $O(1)$, $h = O(\log n)$, and $|L_i| = \mu^i$ for some $\mu > 1$.

Consider a set $Q = \{q_1, \ldots, q_n\}$ of n search queries. Due to the structure of the hierarchical DAG, a search path for a query q has length $r \leq h + 1$ and consists of r vertices in consecutive levels $L_i, \ldots, L_{i+r-1}$ for some $i \in \{0, \ldots, h - r + 1\}$. We will henceforth assume, w.l.o.g., that each query has a search path of length $h + 1$.

In this section we show how to solve the multisearch problem for G on a mesh-connected computer of size n in time $O(\sqrt{n})$. The graph G and the set of search queries Q are initially stored in the mesh in the natural way; a precise description of the initial configuration is given in the Appendix. In addition, we assume that every processor storing a node $v \in L_i$ also stores the index i, referred to as *level index* of v in G. Note that the level indices can be easily computed in time $O(\sqrt{n})$ by successively identifying the vertices in each level L_i, starting with level L_h, and compressing after each step the remaining levels into a subsquare of processors.

For $i \geq 1$, we will use $\log^{(i)}$ to denote the function obtained by applying the log function i times, i.e. $\log^{(1)} x = \log x$ and $\log^{(i)} x = \log \log^{(i-1)} x$. For convenience, we define $\log^{(0)} x = \frac{x}{2}$. Note that there exists a constant c such that $\mu^y \geq y^2$ for any $y \geq c$. For any $x \geq \mu^c$, we define $\log_\mu^* x = \max\{i \,|\, \log_\mu^{(i)} x \geq c\}$ (hence, $\log_\mu^{(i)} x \geq (\log_\mu^{(i+1)} x)^2$ for $0 \leq i \leq \log_\mu^* x$). For the remainder of this section, all logarithms are to the base μ.

Let $B_i = (V_i, E_i)$, $0 \leq i \leq \log^* h - 1$, be the subgraph of G induced by the vertices of G between levels $h - 2\log^{(i)} h$ and $h - 1 - 2\log^{(i+1)} h$ inclusive. We will use $|B_i|$, $h_i = h - 1 - 2\log^{(i+1)} h$, and Δh_i to refer the size of B_i, the highest index of a level in B_i, and the number of levels in B_i, respectively. See Figure 4 for an illustration. Note that, $|B_i| = O(\mu^{h-2\log^{(i+1)} h}) = O(\frac{n}{(\log^{(i)} h)^2})$ and $\Delta h_i = O(\log^{(i)} h)$.

Let B^* be the subgraph induced by the vertices between levels $h - 2\log^{(\log^* h - 1)} h$ and h inclusive. Note that B^* consists of $O(1)$ levels.

The general strategy for solving the multisearch problem on G is to solve the multisearch problem for B_0 first, then for B_1, etc., eventually for $B_{\log^* h - 1}$, and finally for B^*. Here, the multisearch problem for B_i [B^*] consists of all queries visiting those vertices on their search path that lie in B_i [B^*], assuming that for each query the first of those vertices is known.

Since B^* has $O(1)$ levels, the multisearch problem for B^* can be easily solved in time $O(\sqrt{n})$. What remains to be shown is how to solve the multisearch problem for $B_0, \ldots, B_{\log^* h - 1}$ (together) in time $O(\sqrt{n})$.

Consider the partitioning of the entire mesh-connected computer into $\log^{(i)} h \times \log^{(i)} h$ submeshes of $\frac{\sqrt{n}}{\log^{(i)} h} \times \frac{\sqrt{n}}{\log^{(i)} h}$ processors. Such a partitioning will be called a B_i-*partitioning*, and each submesh will be called a B_i-*submesh*. Note that each B_i-submesh can store a copy of the subgraph B_i. Each B_{i+1}-submesh, Δ, contains several B_i-submeshes. The top-left of those B_i-submeshes will be referred to as the *top-left* B_i-*submesh of* Δ.

Let B_i^1 be the subgraph of G induced by the vertices of G between levels $h_i - \Delta h_i$ and $h_i - 1 - 2\log \Delta h_i$ included, and let B_i^2 be the subgraph induced by the vertices between levels $h_i - 2\log \Delta h_i$ and h_i included. See Figure 5 for an illustration. Note that $|B_i^1| = O(\mu^{h_i - 2\log \Delta h_i}) = O(\frac{|B_i|}{(\Delta h_i)^2})$. On each B_i-submesh in parallel, we will solve the multisearch problem for B_i for those queries stored in that submesh. We next describe our solution for one B_i-submesh. The solution consists of two phases: in Phase 1, every query visits the vertices on its search path that lie in B_i^1; in Phase 2 the queries will visit the vertices on their search path that lie in B_i^2. For Phase 1, the B_i-submesh is partitioned into $\Delta h_i \times \Delta h_i$ submeshes of size $\frac{|B_i|}{(\Delta h_i)^2}$, called B_i^1-*submeshes*. Note that each B_i^1-submesh can store a copy of B_i^1. In time $O(\sqrt{|B_i|})$, we can identify B_i^1 from B_i and duplicate B_i^1 such that each B_i^1-submesh contains a copy of B_i^1. Each B_i^1-submesh then (independently and in parallel) solves the multisearch problem for B_i^1 for those queries stored in that submesh. This can be easily done in $O(\sqrt{|B_i|})$ time since $|B_i^1| = O(\frac{|B_i|}{(\Delta h_i)^2})$ and B_i^1 consists of $O(\Delta h_i)$ levels. For Phase 2, the search process is advanced level by level. Since B_i^2 consists of $O(\log \Delta h_i)$ levels, Phase 2 can be executed in $O(\sqrt{|B_i|} \log \Delta h_i)$ time.

Lemma 1 *Consider a B_i-partitioning of the mesh-connected computer, $0 \leq i \leq \log^* h - 1$, and assume that every B_i-submesh stores a copy of B_i, then the multisearch problem for B_i can be solved in time $O(\sqrt{|B_i|} \log \Delta h_i) = O(\sqrt{|B_i|} \log^{(i+1)} h)$.*

Obviously, if every B_i-submesh stores a copy of B_i

then we need $O(log^*n)$ memory per processor. Our strategy will be to distribute the subgraphs B_i over the mesh in such a way that, when the multisearch problem for B_i needs to be solved, then all the required copies of B_i can be created in time $O(\sqrt{|B_{i+1}|})$. From this, we obtain a $O(\sqrt{n})$ time solution to the multisearch problem for G.

To simplify the presentation, we assume $\log^{(i)} h$ is divisible by $\log^{(i+1)} h$ for $0 \leq i \leq \log^* h - 1$. Our algorithm can be easily modified to handle the general case. Let $B_{\log^* h}$-submesh denote the entire mesh.

Algorithm 1: An algorithm for solving the multisearch problem for a hierarchical DAG G.

1. A register $label(p)$ is allocated at every processor p, and the following is executed for $i = \log^* h - 1, \ldots, 0$:

   (a) In each B_{i+1}-submesh, Δ, every processor p in the top-left B_i-submesh of Δ sets $label(p) := i$.

   Note: The label of a processor may be overwritten by smaller indices in later iterations. In the next step, in each B_{i+1}-submesh, the processors with $label = i$ will be used to store a copy of B_i. Since, for $j \leq i - 1$, each B_{j+1}-submesh contains one B_j-submesh in its top-left corner whose processors' labels are set to j, the labels of at most $\frac{n}{(\log^{(i)} h)^2}(\frac{\log^{(j+1)} h}{\log^{(j)} h})^2$ processors are changed from i to j. Hence, the number of processors in each B_i-submesh with $label = i$ is at least $\frac{n}{(\log^{(i)} h)^2}(1 - \sum_{j=0}^{i-1}(\frac{\log^{(j+1)} h}{\log^{(j)} h})^2) = \Theta(\frac{n}{(\log^{(i)} h)^2})$.

2. For $i = \log^* h - 1, \ldots, 0$, on each B_{i+1}-submesh the following is executed independently and in parallel:

   (a) The subgraph B_i is identified and its data is distributed evenly among the processors with $label = i$. For details, see proof of Theorem 2 in the Appendix.

   (b) $(\frac{\log^{(i)} h}{\log^{(i+1)} h})^2$ copies of the union of $B_0, \ldots, B_{i-1}$ are created and one copy is moved to each B_i-submesh.

   Note that, after this step, each $B_{(i+1)}$-submesh stores a copy of B_i using the processors with $label = i$.

3. For $i = 0, \ldots, \log^* h - 1$, on each B_{i+1}-submesh the following is executed independently and in parallel:

   (a) B_i is duplicated such that each B_i-submesh stores a copy of B_i.

   (b) For each B_i-submesh, the multisearch problem for B_i with respect to those queries stored in that submesh is solved as indicated by Lemma 1.

4. Finally, the multisearch problem for B^* is solved.

Theorem 2 *Let G be a hierarchical DAG of size n and let $Q = \{q_1, \ldots, q_m\}$ be a set of $m = O(n)$ search queries, then the multisearch problem for Q on G can be solved on a mesh of size n (with $O(1)$ memory per processor) in time $O(\sqrt{n})$.* (For proof see Appendix.)

4 A Mesh Solution to the Multisearch Problem For Partitionable Graphs

In this section, we present mesh solutions to the multisearch problems for α-partitionable graphs and α-β-partitionable graphs. After defining these classes of graphs, we will first introduce a tool referred to as *constrained multisearch* which will be utilized in Sections 4.5 and 4.6.

4.1 Definition of δ-Splitters

Let $G = (V, E)$ be a (directed or undirected) graph with vertex set V, edge set E, and size $n = |V| + |E|$. Let $S \subset E$. Then $(V, E - S)$ is a graph with vertex set V and edge set $E - S$ that consists of a set of connected components, denoted $\{G_1, \ldots, G_k\}$, for some $k \leq n$.

We define S to be an δ-*splitter* of G, $0 < \delta < 1$, if and only if $|G_i| = |V_i| + |E_i| = O(n^\delta)$, for all $1 \leq i \leq k$. Given a δ-splitter S, we will refer to $G(S) = \{G_1, \ldots, G_k\}$ as a δ-*splitting* of G.

A vertex $v \in V$ is defined to be *at the border* of a δ-splitter S if and only if v is a vertex of an edge $e \in S$. A δ-splitting $G(S) = \{G_1, \ldots, G_k\}$ is called *normalized*, if $k = O(n^{1-\delta})$.

4.2 Definition of α-Partitionable (Directed) Graphs

Let $G = (V, E)$ be a directed graph, where the out-degree of any vertex is bounded by some constant. Let $dist_G(v_1, v_2)$ denote the length of the shortest directed path in G connecting two vertices v_1 and v_2. We define G to be α-*partitionable* if and only if G has an α-splitter S, $0 < \alpha < 1$, such that $G(S)$ can be partitioned into two sets of graphs, $\{H_1, \ldots, H_{k_1}\}$ and $\{T_1, \ldots, T_{k_2}\}$, such that for every edge $(v_1, v_2) \in S$ (directed from v_1 to v_2), $v_1 \in H_i$ and $v_2 \in T_j$, for some i, j.

Note that, for example, every balanced k-ary search tree with all edges either direct towards the leaves or direct towards the root (i.e., all search queries can only move in one direction, either from the root towards the leaves, or from the leaves towards the root) is α-partitionable; see Figure 2.

4.3 Definition of α-β-Partitionable (Undirected) Graphs

Let $G = (V, E)$ be an undirected graph of size $n = |V| + |E|$, where the degree of any vertex is bounded by some constant. For two vertices $v_1, v_2 \in V$, let $dist_G(v_1, v_2)$ denote the length of the shortest (undirected) path in G connecting v_1 and v_2.

Let S_1 and S_2 be an α-splitter and a β-splitter, respectively, of G $(0 < \alpha, \beta < 1)$. We define that, S_1 and S_2 have distance k if and only if $k = \min\{dist_G(v_1, v_2) : v_1 \text{ is at the border of } S_1 \text{ and } v_2 \text{ is at the border of } S_2\}$.

G is called α-β-partitionable if and only if G has an α-splitter S_1 and a β-splitter S_2, $0 < \alpha, \beta < 1$, such that S_1 and S_2 have distance $\Omega(\log n)$.

Note that, e.g., every undirected balanced k-ary search tree (i.e., search queries can move within the tree in arbitrary direction, e.g. inorder traversal) is α-β-partitionable; see Figure 3.

4.4 Constrained Multisearch

Let $G = (V, E)$ be a directed or undirected graph. Consider a set $\Psi = \{G_1, ..., G_k\}$ of k edge and vertex disjoint subgraphs of G such that $|G_i| = O(n^\delta)$ and $k = O(n^{1-\delta})$ for some $0 < \delta < 1$. Note that we do not assume that the union of the subgraphs in Ψ contains all vertices of G.

Consider any stage of the multisearch for Q on G, and let $v(q) \in path(q)$ denote the node currently visited by query $q \in Q$.

The *constrained multisearch problem* with respect to Ψ consists of advancing, for every $G_i \in \Psi$, every search query q with $v(q) \in G_i$ by x steps in its search path, such that either $x = \log_2 n$ or the next node to be visited by q is not in G_i. Note that different queries may be advanced by a different number of steps.

In the remainder of this section, we present a procedure *Constrained-Multisearch(Ψ, δ)* which solves the constrained multisearch problem, on a mesh of size n with $O(1)$ memory per processor, in time $O(\sqrt{n})$

For every $G_i = (V_i, E_i) \in \Psi$ define $\Gamma_\Psi^\delta(G_i) = \left\lceil \frac{|\{q \in Q : v(q) \in V_i\}|}{n^\delta} \right\rceil$.

Procedure Constrained-Multisearch(Ψ, δ): Implementation of constrained multisearch with respect to Ψ.

Initial configuration: A stage of the multisearch for Q on G, where every $q \in Q$ currently visits some node $v(q) \in path(q)$. Furthermore, every processor storing a vertex $v \in V$, also stores an index indicating to which $G_i \in \Psi$ the vertex v belongs, if any.

1. All queries $q \in Q$ such that $v(q)$ is in some subgraph $G_i \in \Psi$ are *marked*; all others queries are *unmarked*. (Queries whose search paths have already terminated are also unmarked.)

2. For every $G_i \in \Psi$, the value of $\Gamma_\Psi^\delta(G_i)$ is computed.

3. If $\sum_{G_i \in \Psi} \Gamma_\Psi^\delta(G_i) = 0$ then **EXIT**.

4. For each $G_i \in \Psi$, $\Gamma_\Psi^\delta(G_i)$ copies of G_i are created. Each copy is placed in a $\sqrt{n^\delta} \times \sqrt{n^\delta}$ subsquare of the mesh-connected computer (δ-submesh).

5. Every marked query $q \in Q$ with $v(q) \in G_i$ is moved to one of the δ-submeshes storing a copy of G_i, such that each δ-submesh contains at most $O(n^\delta)$ queries.

6. Within each δ-submesh storing a subgraph $G_i \in \Psi$, the following is executed $\log_2 n$ times:

   (a) For every marked query $q \in Q$, the next node in its search path is determined (by applying the successor function f).

   (b) Every marked query for which the next node in its search path is not in G_i, is unmarked. (A query whose search path terminates is also unmarked.)

   (c) Every marked query visits the next node in its search path.

7. Discard the copies of the subgraphs $G_i \in \Psi$ created in Step 4.

Lemma 3 *The constrained multisearch problem with respect to Ψ can be solved, on a mesh of size n with $O(1)$ memory per processor, in time $O(\sqrt{n})$ (For proof see Appendix.)*

4.5 A Mesh Solution to the Multisearch Problem for α-Partitionable Directed Graphs

Let $G = (V, E)$ be a directed and α-partionable graph. Consider a set $Q = \{q_1, ..., q_m\}$ of $m = O(n)$ search queries, and let r denote the length of the longest search path associated with a query $q \in Q$. In this section, we present an algorithm to solve the multiserach problem for Q on G in time $O(\sqrt{n} + r\frac{\sqrt{n}}{\log n})$. Our strategy is

209

to give an algorithm which executes one log-phase of the multisearch in time $(\sqrt{n})$. The entire multisearch algorithm consists of iterating the log-phase algorithm $O(\lceil \frac{r}{\log n} \rceil)$ times.

Let $G(S) = \{H_1, \ldots, H_{k_1}, T_1, \ldots, T_{k_2}\}$ be an α-splitting of G such that for every edge $(v_1, v_2) \in S$ (directed from v_1 to v_2), $v_1 \in H_i$ and $v_2 \in T_j$, for some i, j. Recall that this implies $0 < \alpha < 1$, $|H_i| = O(n^\alpha)$, and $|T_i| = O(n^\alpha)$.

We assume that the α-splitter S is known a priori. That is, every processor stores in addition to a vertex $v \in V$ also an index indicating to which graph in $G(S)$ the vertex v belongs. Note that, for most data structures (e.g., balanced k-ary trees; see Figure 2), the determination of the indices is trivial. We can also assume, without loss of generality, that $G(S)$ is normalized. That is, we can assume that $k = k_1 + k_2 = O(n^{1-\alpha})$; see Section 4.1. Otherwise, we group the subgraphs H_i and T_i, respectively, such that each resulting subgraph has size $\Theta(n^\alpha)$. This operation is easily performed, on a mesh of size n, in time $O(\sqrt{n})$. Furthermore, the algorithm described in this section does not require that every subgraph in $G(S)$ consists of only one connected component of the graph $(V, E - S)$.

Algorithm 2: Implementation of one log-phase of multisearch on an α-partionable graph.

1. If this is the first log-phase, then every query $q \in Q$ visits the first node in its search path; otherwise, every $q \in Q$ visits the next node in its search path.
2. Constrained-Multisearch $(\{H_1, \ldots, H_{k_1}, T_1, \ldots, T_{k_2}\}, \alpha)$.
3. Every $q \in Q$ visits the next node in its search path.
4. Constrained-Multisearch $(\{H_1, \ldots, H_{k_1}, T_1, \ldots, T_{k_2}\}, \alpha)$.

Lemma 4 *One log-phase of multisearch on an α-partionable (directed) graph of size n can be performed , on a mesh of size n with $O(1)$ memory per processor, in time $O(\sqrt{n})$. (For proof see Appendix.)*

Therefore, by iterating Algorithm 2 $O(\lceil \frac{r}{\log n} \rceil)$ times, the multisearch problem can be solved for α-partitionable graphs.

Theorem 5 *Let G be an α-partionable (directed) graph of size n and let $Q = \{q_1, \ldots, q_m\}$ be a set of $m = O(n)$ search queries. The multisearch problem for Q on G can be solved on a mesh of size n (with $O(1)$ memory per processor) in time $O(\sqrt{n} + r\frac{\sqrt{n}}{\log n})$, where r is the length of the longest search path associated with a query.*

4.6 A Mesh Solution to the Multisearch Problem for α-β-Partitionable Undirected Graphs

Let $G = (V, E)$ be a directed and α-partionable graph. Consider a set $Q = \{q_1, \ldots, q_m\}$ of $m = O(n)$ search queries, and let r denote the length of the longest search path associated with a query $q \in Q$. In this section, we present an algorithm to solve the multisearch problem in $O(\sqrt{n} + r\frac{\sqrt{n}}{\log n})$ time. As in Section 4.5, we will again give an algorithm to execute one log-phase of the multisearch problem in time $(\sqrt{n})$. The multisearch algorithm consists of iterating the log-phase algorithm $O(\lceil \frac{r}{\log n} \rceil)$ times.

Let S_1 and S_2 be an α-splitter and a β-splitter, respectively, of G such that S_1 and S_2 have distance $\Omega(\log n)$. We assume that S_1 and S_2 are known a priori. That is, every processor stores in addition to a vertex $v \in V$ also two indices indicating to which graphs in $G(S_1)$ and $G(S_2)$ the vertex v belongs. Note that, for most data structures (e.g., balanced k-ary trees; see Figure 3), the determination of the indices is trivial.

With the same argument as in Section 4.5, we also assume that $G(S_1)$ and $G(S_2)$ are normalized. Let $G(S_1) = \{W_1^1, \ldots, W_{k_1}^1\}$ and $G(S_2) = \{W_1^2, \ldots, W_{k_2}^2\}$. Recall that $0 < \alpha < 1$, $0 < \beta < 1$, $|W_i^1| = O(n^\alpha)$, $|W_i^2| = O(n^\beta)$, $k_1 = O(n^{1-\alpha})$, and $k_2 = O(n^{1-\beta})$.

Algorithm 3: Implementation of one log-phase of multisearch on an α-β-partionable graph.

1. If this is the first log-phase, then every query $q \in Q$ visits the first node in its search path; otherwise, every $q \in Q$ visits the next node in its search path.
2. Constrained-Multisearch $(\{W_1^1, \ldots, W_{k_1}^1\}, \alpha)$.
3. Every $q \in Q$ visits the next node in its search path.
4. Constrained-Multisearch $(\{W_1^2, \ldots, W_{k_2}^2\}, \beta)$.

Lemma 6 *One log-phase of multisearch on an α-β-partionable (undirected) graph of size n can be performed , on a mesh of size n with $O(1)$ memory per processor, in time $O(\sqrt{n})$. (For proof see Appendix.)*

Therefore, by iterating Algorithm 3 $O(\lceil \frac{r}{\log n} \rceil)$ times, the multisearch problem can be solved for α-β-partitionable graphs.

Theorem 7 *Let G be an α-β-partitionable (undirected) graph of size n and let $Q = \{q_1, \ldots, q_m\}$ be a set of $m = O(n)$ search queries. The multisearch problem for Q on G can be solved on a mesh of size n (with $O(1)$ memory per processor) in time $O(\sqrt{n} + r\frac{\sqrt{n}}{\log n})$, where r is the length of the longest search path associated with a query. (For proof see Appendix.)*

210

5 Applying Multisearch for Hierarchical DAGs: Subdivision Hierarchies, Hierarchical Representations of Polyhedra, and Applications

In [DK87], $O(\log n \log^* n)$ time deterministic and $O(\log n)$ time randomized PRAM algorithms are presented for constructing well known data structures: the subdivision hierarchy for a planar graph (with n nodes) [Kir83] and the hierarchical representation for a convex polyhedron (with n vertices). Both are hierarchical DAGs of size $O(n)$ with triangles and triangular faces, respectively, associated with their vertices. As stated in [DK87], once these hierarchies are given, Problems 1-3 listed in Theorem 8 can be solved on the PRAM in time $O(\log n)$.

For the mesh-connected computer, it has been shown in [DSS88] that the subdivision hierarchy for a planar graph (with n nodes) as well as the hierarchical representation for a convex polyhedron (with n vertices) can be constructed in time $O(\sqrt{n})$ using $O(n)$ processors with $O(1)$ memory each. Using Theorem 2, we obtain

Theorem 8 *The following problems can be solved in time $O(\sqrt{n})$ on a mesh of size n with $O(1)$ memory per processor:*

1. *Multiple line-polyhedron queries (Given a 3-d convex polyhedron P of size n, and n lines in 3-space, determine for each line l whether it intersects P and, if not, determine the two planes through l tangent to P).*
2. *3-d convex polyhedron separation (Given two convex 3-d polyhedra P and Q of size n each, determine whether there exists a plane which separates P and Q).*
3. *Merging 3-d convex hulls.*
4. *Determining the convex hull of n points in 3-space[1].*

6 Applying Multisearch for Partitionable Graphs: Interval Trees and Multiple Interval Intersection Search

Obviously, multisearch for α-partitionable directed graphs can be utilized to obtain optimal parallel mesh implementations for all those data structures based on balanced k-ary search tree (possibly with augmentation), where all queries are moving in the same direction (either from the root to the leaves, or from the leaves to the root).

Multisearch for α-β-partitionable undirected graphs can be applied, e.g., to obtain parallel mesh implementations for data structures based on balanced k-nary search trees (possibly with augmentation) where queries are moving along tree edges in arbitrary directions. Such queries can, e.g., traverse parts of the subtree in inorder.

In the full paper, we explore the following application of our mesh solution to multisearch for α-β-partitionable undirected graphs. Consider a set S of n intervals. The *interval intersection problem* consists of reporting the k intervals in S that intersect a query interval q. The *multiple interval intersection problem* consists of answering, in parallel, m interval intersection queries on S.

References

[AH86]   M. J. Atallah and S. Hambrusch. Solving tree problems on a mesh-connected processor array. *Information and Control*, 69:168–186, 1986.

[DK87]   N. Dadoun and D. G. Kirkpatrick. Parallel construction of subdivision hierarchies. In *Proceedings of the Third Annual Symposium on Computational Geometry*, pages 205–214, 1987.

[DSS88]   F. Dehne, J.-R. Sack, and I. Stojmenovic. A note on determining the 3-dimensional convex hull of a set of points on a mesh of processors. In *Scandinavian Workshop on Algorithm Theory*, pages 154–162, 1988.

[DR90]   F. Dehne and A. Rau-Chaplin. Implementing data structures on a hypercube multiprocessor and applications in parallel computational geometry. *Journal of Parallel and Distributed Computing*, 8(4):367-375, 1990.

[Ede83a]   H. Edelsbrunner. A new approach to rectangle Intersections - Part I. *International Journal of Computer Mathematics*, 13:209–219, 1983.

[HI90]   J. A. Holey and O. H. Ibarra. Triangulation in a Plane and 3-D convex hull on Mesh-Connected Arrays and Hypercubes. Tech. Rep., Univ. of Minnesota, Dept. of Computer Science, 1990.

[Kir83]   D. G. Kirkpatrick. Optimal search in planar subdivisions. *SIAM Journal of Computing*, 12(1):28–35, 1983.

[LPJC90]   D. T. Lee, F. P. Preparata, C.S. Jeong and A. L. Chow. SIMD Parallel Convex Hull Algorithms, manuscript.

[PVS83]   W. Paul, U. Vishkin and H. Wagener. Parallel dictionaries on 2-3 trees. in Proceedings 10th International Colloquium on Automata, Languages, and Programming (ICALP), *LNCS 154*, Springer-Vergerlag, Berlin, 1983, pp. 597-609.

7 Appendix

Details of the Initial Configuration of the Mesh (Before Multisearch):

Let $G = (V, E)$ be a directed or undirected graph of size $n = |V| + |E|$, where the out-degree or degree, respectively, of any vertex is bounded by some constant. Furthermore, let $Q = \{q_1, ..., q_m\}$ be a set of $m = O(n)$ search queries. G and Q will be represented on the mesh as follows: Every processor stores

- one arbitrary vertex $v \in V$,
- the addresses of all processors storing a vertex $w \in V$ such that $(v, w) \in E$, and
- one arbitrary query $q \in Q$.

Note that, the assignments of vertices and queries to processors is not fixed and may change during the course of the algorithms. Every processor p is assumed to have an additional register $visit(p)$. At any stage of the multisearch algorithms to be presented, a query $q \in Q$ will be said to *visit* a node $v \in V$ if the processor p storing the query q also stores, in its register $visit(p)$, a copy of v.

Proof of Theorem 2:

We first study the correctness of Algorithm 1, and then give some implementation details and prove the claimed time complexity and space requirement. In Steps 1 and 2, each B_i, for $0 \leq i \leq \log^* h - 1$, is duplicated such that each B_{i+1}-submesh contains a copy of B_i. In Step 3, the multisearch problem for B_i, $i = 0, 1, \ldots, \log^* h - 1$, is solved (in that order). In every loop iteration, within each B_{i+1}-submesh the graph B_i is copied into every B_i-submesh, such that Lemma 1 can be applied to solve the multisearch problem for B_i. Finally, in Step 4, the multisearch problem for B^* is solved. Thus, the multisearch problem for G is solved.

Next, we analyze the time and space complexity of Algorithm 1 and show that it requires only $O(1)$ space per processor. This is obvious for Steps 1, 3 and 4; a potential problem lies in the duplication scheme in Step 2. For Step 2(b) we observe that $\sum_{j=0}^{i-1} |B_j| = O(|B_i|)$ and, hence, it requires only $O(1)$ storage per processor. For Step 2(a), we need to show that in each B_i-submesh there are at least $\Theta(|B_i|)$ processors with $label = i$. Note that for $j \leq i - 1$, each B_{j+1}-submesh contains one B_j-submesh in its top-left corner whose processors' labels are set to j (see Step 1). That is, in Step 1, the labels of at most $\frac{n}{(\log^{(i)} h)^2}(\frac{\log^{(j+1)} h}{\log^{(j)} h})^2$ processors are changed from i to j. Hence, the number of processors in each B_i-submesh with $label = i$ is at least $\frac{n}{(\log^{(i)} h)^2}(1 - \sum_{j=0}^{i-1}(\frac{\log^{(j+1)} h}{\log^{(j)} h})^2) = \Theta(\frac{n}{(\log^{(i)} h)^2})$. Since

$|B_i| = O(\frac{n}{(\log^{(i)} h)^2})$, these processors can store B_i with $O(1)$ storage per processor provided that the B_i's data can be evenly distributed among them. The following is a detailed $O(\sqrt{|B_{i+1}|})$ time implementation of Step 2(a).

1. Every B_i is compressed into top-left B_i-submesh of each B_{i+1}-submesh.
2. Each B_i-submesh is partitioned into four subsquares of equal size.
3. For each subsquare, the number of processors with $label = i$ is determined.
4. The data for B_i is distributed among these subsquares according to the ratio of number of processors with $label = i$.
5. in Steps 2-4 are repeated recursively, in parallel, on each of the four subsquares, until the subsquares are of size $O(1)$.

Summarizing, we obtain that Algorithm 1 requires $O(1)$ storage per processor.

Next, we prove the claimed $O(\sqrt{n})$ time complexity of Algorithm 1. Since $\sum_{i=0}^{\log^* h - 1} \sqrt{|B_i|} = O(\sqrt{n})$ and $O(\sum_{i=0}^{\log^* h - 1} \sqrt{|B_{i+1}|}) = O(\sqrt{n})$, the time complexity of Steps 1 and 2 is $O(\sqrt{n})$. Since B^* contains $O(1)$ levels, the $O(\sqrt{n})$ time complexity of Step 4 is obvious. Since each B_{i+1}-submesh contains a copy of B_i, the total time complexity for Step 3a (over all iterations) is $O(\sum_{i=0}^{\log^* h - 1} \sqrt{|B_{i+1}|}) = O(\sqrt{n})$. From Lemma 1 it follows that, for each $i = 0, \ldots, \log^* h - 1$ the time time complexity of Step 3b is $O(\sqrt{|B_i|} \log \Delta h_i)$. Thus, the total time for all iterations of Step 3b is $O(\sum_{i=0}^{\log^* h - 1} \sqrt{|B_i|} \log \Delta h_i) = O(\sum_{i=0}^{\log^* h - 1} \sqrt{n} \frac{\log^{(i+1)} h}{\log^{(i)} h}) = O(\sqrt{n})$. Hence, the time complexity of Algorithm 1 is $O(\sqrt{n})$. $\square$

Proof of Lemma 3:

We first study the correctness of Constrained-Multisearch(Ψ, δ), and then give some implementation details and prove the claimed time complexity. Obviously, every query q either visits the next at most $log_2 n$ nodes in its search path until the next node in its search path is not in the same subgraph $G_i \in \Psi$ that contains $v(q)$, or it will not advance any step in its search path (in case $v(q)$ is not in any $G_i \in \Psi$). The crucial step for proving the correctness of the procedure is to show that (1) the total size of the copies of subgraphs G_i created in Step 4 is $O(n)$, and (2) in Step 5, the sizes and total number of subgraphs to be moved match the sises and total number of δ-submeshes available. Item (1) follows from the fact that $\sum_{G_i \in \Psi} \Gamma_\Psi^\delta(G_i) = O(n^{1-\delta})$, and Item (2) follows from the definition of $\Gamma_\Psi^\delta(G_i)$ and the fact that each δ-submesh is of size $O(n^\delta)$. We will now prove the claimed time complexity. Steps 1, 2, 3, and 5 can be easily implemented in time $O(\sqrt{n})$ by applying a constant number of standard mesh operations.

For Step 4, the mesh is subdivided into a grid of $\sqrt{n^{1-\delta}} \times \sqrt{n^{1-\delta}}$ submeshes of size n^δ. The total number of copies created of subgraphs G_i is $\sum_{G_i \in \Psi} \Gamma_\Psi^\delta(G_i) = O(n^{1-\delta})$. Hence, each such submesh needs to simulate only a constant number of "virtual" δ-submeshes, with each of the "virtual" δ-submeshes storing one copy of a subgraph G_i. Creating the required copies of subgraphs and moving them to the "virtual" δ-submeshes can be implemented by a constant number of standard mesh operations. We finally discuss the time complexity of Steps 5. Note that, each execution of the loop body is executed independently and in parallel on each $O(n^\delta)$ size δ-submesh created in Step 4. Hence, each loop iteration can be implemented in time $O(\sqrt{n^\delta})$, using a standard random access read/write operation on each δ-submesh. Since $0 < \delta < 1$, the total time complexity of Step 5 is $O(\log n \sqrt{n^\delta}) = O(\sqrt{n})$. $\square$

Proof of Lemma 4:

We first study the correctness of Algorithm 2. The basic idea behind the algorithm is that if, in Step 2, a query reaches a vertex at the border of the α-splitter S, the next and all further vertices to be visited are in the same subgraph T_i. These vertices will then be visited in Steps 3 and 4. That is, for every query $q \in Q$, one of three possible cases applies:

1. All nodes visited by q within the log-phase are in one subgraph H_i.

2. All nodes visited by q within the log-phase are in one subgraph T_i.

3. Within the log-phase, query q visits first only nodes within one subgraph H_i, and once it "leaves" H_i it will only visit nodes in one subgraph T_j.

For those queries to which either Case 1 or Case 2 applies, all nodes to be visited within the log-phase are visited during Steps 1 and 2; see Lemma 3. Let q be a query to which Case 3 applies, and let $(v_1, \ldots, v_x, v_{x+1}, \ldots, v_y)$ be the sequence of nodes to be visited within the log-phase, where $v_1, \ldots, v_x$ are in some subgraph H_i and $v_{x+1}, \ldots, v_y)$ are in some subgraph T_j. It follows from Lemma 3 that $v_1, \ldots, v_x$ are visited during Steps 1 and 2, and that $v_{x+1}, \ldots, v_y$ are visited during Steps 3 and 4.

From Lemma 3 it also follows that Algorithm 2 has time complexity $O(\sqrt{n})$ and requires a mesh of size n

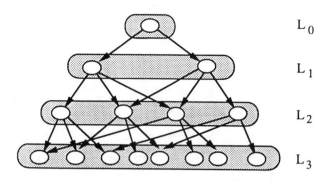

Figure 1. A Hierarchical DAG with $\mu = 2$.

with $O(1)$ memory per processor. $\square$

Proof of Lemma 6:

We first study the correctness of Algorithm 3. The basic idea behind the algorithm is that if, in Step 2, a query reaches a vertex at the border of the α-splitter S_1, we will then, in Steps 3 and 4, switch to using the subgraphs defined by the β-splitter S_2. From the definition of α-β-partitionable graphs it follows that such a query can then advance $\Omega(\log n)$ more steps in its search path without visiting a node at the border of S_2; by this time, the log-phase is completed. That is, for every query $q \in Q$, one of the following cases applies:

1. All nodes visited by q within the log-phase are in one subgraph W_i^1.

2. All nodes visited by q within the log-phase are in one subgraph W_i^2.

3. Within the log-phase, query q first visits some nodes in one subgraph W_i^1 of $G(S_1)$. Once it "leaves" W_i^1, it is sufficient (for the completion of a log-phase) to consider only the subgraph W_j^2 of $G(S_2)$ visited at that point in time, and let the query continue on its search path until it reaches a vertex at the border of S_2.

From this, the correctness of Algorithm 3, as well as the claimed time complexity, follow immediately from Lemma 3. $\square$

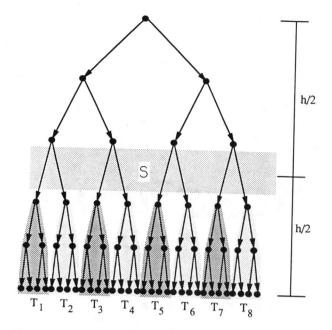

Figure 2. A Directed Balanced Binary Tree And Its α-Splitter ($\alpha = \frac{1}{2}$).

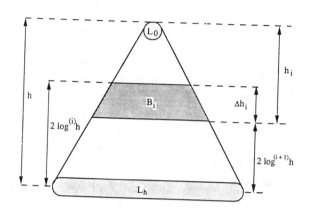

Figure 4. Illustration of the Definition of Subgraphs B_i.

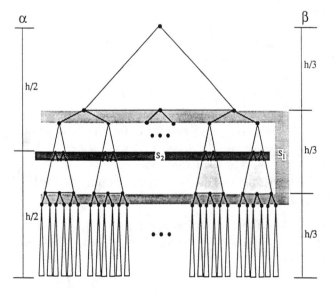

Figure 3. An Undirected Balanced Binary Tree With Its α-Splitter S_1 ($\alpha = \frac{1}{2}$) And β-Splitter S_1 ($\beta = \frac{1}{3}$), Such That S_1 And S_2 Have Distance $\frac{h}{6} = \Omega(\log n)$.

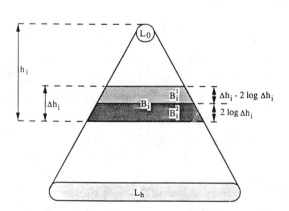

Figure 5. Illustration of the Definition of Subgraphs B_i^1 And B_i^2.

214

SESSION 6

Generalised Multiprocessor Scheduling Using Optimal Control

G.N.Srinivasa Prasanna and Bruce R. Musicus
Laboratory for Computer Science and
Research Laboratory for Electronics,
Massachusetts Institute of Technology
Cambridge, MA 02139
prasanna@vindaloo.lcs.mit.edu

Abstract

This paper presents a novel approach to multiprocessor scheduling using the theory of optimal control. We start by assuming that every task can be executed in parallel on an arbitrary number of processors, and that a continuously variable number of processors can be assigned to the task at any time (by time-sharing). The optimal scheduling problem can then be shown to be equivalent to a time optimal control problem; each task is characterized by a state variable, and the amount of processing power applied is the control variable. Under general assumptions about task dynamic behaviour, a number of powerful and elegant theorems can be derived. In certain special cases, the scheduling problem is shown to be equivalent to shortest path problems and network flow problems. These results greatly simplify the scheduling, as very simple techniques can be shown to be provably optimal. These techniques have been applied to scheduling matrix arithmetic, and the theory validated.

1 Introduction

In this paper we present several new results in the theory of homogeneous multiprocessor scheduling. We start with a set of tasks and associated precedence constraints, a finite pool of processor resources, and specified speedup functions for each task as a function of applied processing power. Our goal is to specify work for each processor over time such that the entire set of tasks is computed in the shortest time, satisfying all precedence constraints, and using only the available processor resources. This is the classical multiprocessor scheduling problem, and has been explored in depth by numerous researchers [4]. Our contribution is a generalisation of multiprocessor scheduling to include parallelism in tasks. We assume that any number of processors can be applied to each task at any time, and that the higher the parallel processing power applied to the task, the faster it can execute (higher its speedup). Our problem is to specify both an optimal number of processors applied to a task, as well as an optimal sequencing of tasks. Classical scheduling theory addresses only task sequencing. In this paper we show that the optimal generalised scheduling problem can be solved by optimal control theory, and that for certain special speedup functions the optimal schedules can often be derived by inspection.

We start with a (acyclic) graph of tasks, with arcs representing precedence constraints. We assume that each task can be treated as a dynamical system, whose state can be changed by applying processing power. Each task starts with state at 0, and must end with its state advanced to completion. We assume that all tasks are dynamically parallelizable, so that any number of processors can be applied to any runnable task at any time, and that the task state advances more rapidly as more processing power is applied. Pre-emptive schedules are thus allowed. A critical assumption we make is that non-integer amounts of processing power can be applied to tasks. This makes the number of processors a *continuous* variable, and permits us to apply powerful techniques of continuous optimization - calculus of variations incarnated in the form of optimal control theory - to solve what would otherwise be a discrete problem.

In this framework, we will show that solving for a time-optimal schedule is equivalent to solving a time-optimal control problem. The state variables reflect the status of the tasks, the control variables are the amounts of processing power applied to each task, the task states obey dynamical state equations, there are constraints imposed by finite processor resources and by precedence constraints, and the objective function is to minimize time.

We use the methods of time-optimal control to derive elegant theorems valid under very general assumptions about task dynamic behaviour (theorem 4.1). An important special case is when the task speedup function behaves like p^α, where p is the amount of processing power applied to the task, and $0 < \alpha < 1$. In this special case, interesting equivalences between scheduling, shortest path problems (with obstacles), and network flow problems emerge. We show that non-preemptive schedules, in which the number of processors allocated to a task is constant over time, are optimal over the entire class of schedules in which the number of processors changes arbitrarily over time (theorem 5.1). Notice that a *functional optimization* is being performed, with the processors allocated to tasks allowed to be arbitrary, real valued, generally discontinuous, functions of time. Most interestingly, processing power behaves much like electrical charge, passing from task to task along the arcs of the precedence graph. Processing power is released from each task only as it completes, and flows only to those successors of the task that become enabled to run at this moment. All tasks with no successors finish simultaneously at the end of the schedule. If the task precedence graph is tree structured, then an optimal schedule can be computed quickly using divide and conquer techniques (Section 7). We show that this optimal solution can also be interpreted as the shortest path in the task state space from the initial to the final state, with distance measured using an $\ell_{1/\alpha}$ norm, and subject to obstacle constraints imposed by the precedence constraints. Our results take on added significance when it is noted that classical scheduling theory, in which at most one processor can be applied to a task at any time, is a limiting case of p^α dynamics, as $\alpha \to 0$, and with the restriction that p must be an integer.

Our results have considerable practical significance. The assumptions we require are close to being realistic for applications like matrix arithmetic computation, where tasks can be systematically decomposed into large numbers of parallel operations. Non integer processor allocations assumed can be obtained by time sharing. Indeed a matrix arithmetic compiler, incorporating some of the techniques in this work, has been written for the massively parallel MIT Alewife machine [8], providing preliminary experimental validation of these ideas (Section 8).

Previous work [5, 6, 2, 4] primarily deals with the complexity of scheduling task systems. However, their approaches, relying on approximately solving NP-Hard problems, are quite different from the one pursued here. They do not use the continuous approximation we have used here.

The paper first presents the scheduling model in Section 2. Section 3 formulates the optimal scheduling problem in the framework of optimal control theory. Standard methods of optimal control theory are then applied to yield the solution in Section 4. When the particular speedup function p^α is assumed, we are able to derive a powerful pair of theorems in Section 5. The shortest path interpretation is developed in Section 6. Two simple but powerful scheduling techniques are presented in Section 7, based on recursively clustering the tasks into series and parallel sets. Section 8 presents an application of these scheduling techniques to scheduling matrix arithmetic. Remaining issues are discussed in Section 9.

2   Model of the Parallel Task System

We start with a formal model of a parallel task system. Let $\Omega = \{1, \ldots, N\}$ be a set of N tasks to be executed on a system with $P(t)$ processors available at each time t. Notice that we have allowed the total processing power to be changing dynamically with time. Suppose task i has length L_i. Also suppose there are precedence constraints among the tasks so that task i cannot start until after all preceding tasks in the set Ω_i (predecessor set) have finished. Let Ω^i (successor set) be the set of tasks which in turn depend on task i finishing before they can start. We will assume that the tasks are partially ordered with no feedback loops.

It is convenient to define the *state* $x_i(t)$ of task i at time t to be the amount of work done so far on the task, $0 \le x_i(t) \le L_i$. Let t_i be the earliest time at which all predecessors of i (if any) have finished, so that i can begin running. Thus $x_i(t) = 0$ for $t < t_i$, and $x_j(t_i) = L_j$ for all of i's predecessor tasks, $j \in \Omega_i$. If task i has no predecessors, $t_i = 0$.

Let $p_i(t)$ be the processing power (number of processors) applied to task i at time t, and let $P(t)$ be the total processing power available at time t. The $p_i(t)$ are all non-negative, and must sum to less than $P(t)$. Furthermore, we reiterate the $p_i(t)$ are not constrained to be integers, but are assumed continuous.

Finally, assume that once a task's predecessors have finished, the rate at which a task proceeds, $dx_i(t)/dt$, depends in some nonlinear fashion on the amount of processor power applied, $p_i(t)$, but not on the state $x_i(t)$ of the task, nor explicitly on the time t. We call this the assumption of *space-time invariant dynamics*. Thus we can write:

$$\frac{dx_i(t)}{dt} = \begin{cases} 0 & \text{for } t < t_i \\ f_i(p_i(t)) & \text{for } t \ge t_i \end{cases} \qquad (1)$$

where $f_i(p_i(t))$ will be called the *speedup function*. With no processing power applied, the task state should not change, $f_i(0) = 0$. With processing power applied, the task should proceed at some non-zero rate, $f_i(p) > 0$ for $p > 0$. We further assume that $f_i(p)$ is non-decreasing, so that adding more processors can only make the task run faster. Also, to ensure mathematical tractability, we will assume that $f_i(p)$ is differentiable, with non-negative derivative for $p \ge 0$. In most of our theory, $f_i(p)$ is taken to be *convex* in p. This convexity reflects the increasing amount of communication, synchronization, and scheduling overhead as the number of processors working on one task increases.

Our assumptions about task speedup are clearly the simplest theoretical abstraction possible. In effect, this form of the speedup function implies that tasks can be dynamically configured into arbitrary numbers of parallel modules for execution on separate processors. Processors can be added or removed at any time, and in such a manner that the processors assigned to the task can all do useful work. The speedup depends only on the total number of processors allocated to the task at a given time, and is independent of the state or the time variable. There are many matrix arithmetic

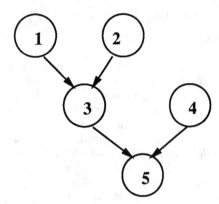

Figure 1: Example of a parallel task system

problems in signal processing, linear algebra, and numerical computation, which are sufficiently parallelizable to fit this model. We will see later that for certain special speedup functions, the number of processors assigned to a task in the optimal solution is actually constant.

Our goal is to finish all tasks in the minimum amount of time t^F, by properly allocating processor resources $p_i(t)$.

An example should clarify our notation. Consider the task system in Figure 1. Let task i have processing rate function $f_i(p_i)$, and total length L_i. Then the predecessor task sets are:

$$\Omega_1 = \Omega_2 = \Omega_4 = \phi, \qquad \Omega_3 = (1,2), \qquad \Omega_5 = (3,4)$$

The successor task sets are:

$$\Omega^1 = \Omega^2 = (3), \qquad \Omega^3 = \Omega^4 = (5), \qquad \Omega^5 = \phi$$

The system equations are:

$$
\begin{aligned}
\dot{x}_1 &= f_1(p_1(t)) \\
\dot{x}_2 &= f_2(p_2(t)) \\
\dot{x}_3 &= \begin{cases} f_3(p_3(t)) & \text{for } t \geq t_3 \\ 0 & \text{for } t < t_3 \end{cases} \\
\dot{x}_4 &= f_4(p_4(t)) \\
\dot{x}_5 &= \begin{cases} f_5(p_5(t)) & \text{for } t \geq t_5 \\ 0 & \text{for } t < t_5 \end{cases}
\end{aligned}
$$

3 Optimal Control Formulation

We can state the scheduling problem in Section 2 in a form appropriate for applying standard control theoretic approaches [3]. We must specify the state variables and their constraints, the control variables and their constraints, the system dynamics, and the objective function.

State Variables and Terminal Constraints

The state variables are the $x_i(t)$'s. Clearly they satisfy the terminal constraints

$$x_i(0) = 0, \qquad x_i(t^F) = L_i, \qquad \text{for } i = 1, \ldots, N \quad (2)$$

In vector notation

$$\vec{x}(0) = 0, \qquad \vec{x}(t^F) = \vec{L}$$

Control Variables and Constraints

The control variables are the processor powers allocated to each task over time, $p_i(t)$ (in vector notation $\vec{p}(t)$.) Each $p_i(t)$ is clearly non-negative. Also, the total processing power at any time t is at most $P(t)$. These two constraints can be written as

$$C(\vec{p}, t) \leq 0, \qquad \text{where } C(\vec{p}, t) = \sum_i p_i(t) - P(t) \quad (3)$$

$$D_i(\vec{p}, t) \leq \vec{0}, \text{ where } D_i(\vec{p}, t) = -p_i(t), \text{ for } i = 1, \ldots, N \quad (4)$$

System Dynamics

An approximation is required in order to write the state dynamics in a form suitable for control theory. First, write (1) in the form:

$$\frac{dx_i(t)}{dt} = f_i(\vec{x}(t), \vec{p}(t), t) \quad (5)$$

where we define:

$$f_i(\vec{x}(t), \vec{p}(t), t) = \begin{cases} 0 & \text{for } t < t_i \\ f_i(p_i(t)) & \text{for } t \geq t_i \end{cases}$$

We now replace this definition with an approximation which is differentiable everywhere:

$$f_i(\vec{x}(t), \vec{p}(t), t) = g_i(\vec{x}) f_i(p_i(t))$$

where

$$g_i(\vec{x}) = \prod_{k \in \Omega_i} \tilde{U}(x_k(t) - L_k)$$

where $\tilde{U}(x)$ is a differentiable approximation to a step function, $\tilde{U}(t) = 0$ for $t \leq -\epsilon$, $= 1$ for $t \geq 0$, and rises monotonically from 0 to 1 over the range $-\epsilon \leq t \leq 0$. Let $\tilde{\delta}(t)$ be the derivative of $\tilde{U}(t)$; note that $\tilde{\delta}(t)$ is a finite approximation to an impulse function with width ϵ, and which is non-zero (positive) only for $-\epsilon < t < 0$. Thus $g_i(\vec{x})$ is a function which is zero until the predecessors of task i are all within ϵ of finishing, at which point it smoothly increases up to a final value of 1 when all predecessors completely finish. For ϵ much smaller than the task lengths, this form of the state dynamics will be nearly the same as our original model (1).

For our previous example in Figure 1, we would approximate the dynamics of tasks 3 and 5 as follows:

$$\dot{x}_3(t) = f_3(p_3(t)) \tilde{U}(x_1(t) - L_1) \tilde{U}(x_2(t) - L_2)$$

$$\dot{x}_5(t) = f_5(p_5(t)) \tilde{U}(x_3(t) - L_3) \tilde{U}(x_4(t) - L_4)$$

Because of this "soft" start for each task, we need to carefully redefine the starting and finishing times of the tasks. Let t_i be the earliest time that all predecessors of task i reach to within ϵ of completion, so that:

$$\prod_{k \in \Omega_i} \tilde{U}(x_k(t) - L_k) > 0$$

for all $t > t_i$. We call t_i the start time for task i. Similarly, let t_i^ϵ be the time at which task i first reaches to within ϵ of the end, $x_i(t_i^\epsilon) = L_i - \epsilon$, and let t_i^F be the finish time, when task i first reaches the end, $x(t_i^F) = L_i$.

Objective Function

Our goal is to minimize the final task completion time $t^F = \max_i t_i^F$, when all tasks have reached their end, $x_i(t^F) = L_i$ for all $i \in \Omega$, subject to constraints (2), (3), (4), and (5). Typical optimal control problems minimize an objective function formed of a penalty on the final state, $\phi(\vec{x}(t^F), t^F)$ plus an integrated penalty on the state trajectory and control values $L(\vec{x}(t), \vec{p}(t), t)$. We can state our objective in this form as follows:

$$\min_{\vec{p}(t)} \left[\phi(\vec{x}(t^F), t^F) + \int_0^{t^F} L(\vec{x}, \vec{p}, t) dt \right] \qquad (6)$$

if we define:

$$\phi(\vec{x}(t^F), t^F) \equiv 0, \qquad L(\vec{x}, \vec{p}, t) \equiv 1$$

4 Solution Method

The problem we have defined can be solved by standard methods of optimal control. To apply these, introduce Lagrange multipliers ("influence functions") $\lambda_i(t)$, $\mu(t)$ and $\psi_i(t)$ associated with constraints (5), (3) and (4) respectively. Then form the *Lagrangian*:

$$
\begin{aligned}
J &= \phi(\vec{x}(t^F), t^F) + \int_0^{t^F} L(\vec{x}, \vec{p}, t) dt \\
&+ \int_0^{t^F} \left(\sum_i \lambda_i(t) [f_i(\vec{x}, \vec{p}, t) - \dot{x}_i] \right) dt \qquad (7) \\
&+ \int_0^{t^F} \left[\mu(t) C(\vec{p}, t) + \sum_i \psi_i(t) D_i(\vec{p}, t) \right] dt
\end{aligned}
$$

It is also convenient to define the *Hamiltonian*

$$
\begin{aligned}
H(\vec{x}, \vec{p}, t) &= L(\vec{x}, \vec{p}, t) + \sum_i \lambda_i(t) f_i(\vec{x}, \vec{p}, t) \\
&+ \mu(t) C(\vec{p}, t) + \sum_i \psi_i(t) D_i(\vec{p}, t) \quad (8)
\end{aligned}
$$

Necessary conditions for an optimal scheduling solution for $\vec{p}(t)$ and $\vec{x}(t)$ can now be derived (c.f. [3, Chap 2,3]). For our problem, this optimal solution must not only satisfy all the constraints (2), (3), (4), and (5), but also the states $x_i(t)$, controls $p_i(t)$, and Lagrange multipliers $\lambda_i(t)$, $\mu(t)$, and $\psi_i(t)$ must satisfy the following constraints:

$$\frac{d\lambda_i(t)}{dt} = -\frac{\partial H(\vec{x}(t), \vec{p}(t), t)}{\partial x_i} \qquad (9)$$

$$0 = \frac{\partial H(\vec{x}(t), \vec{p}(t), t)}{\partial p_i} \qquad (10)$$

where

$$\begin{cases} \mu(t) > 0 & \text{if } \sum_i p_i(t) = P(t) \\ \mu(t) = 0 & \text{if } \sum_i p_i(t) < P(t) \end{cases} \qquad (11)$$

$$\begin{cases} \psi_i(t) > 0 & \text{if } p_i(t) = 0 \\ \psi_i(t) = 0 & \text{if } p_i(t) > 0 \end{cases} \qquad (12)$$

and also there is a terminal constraint:

$$H(\vec{x}(t), \vec{p}(t), t)|_{t^F} = 0 \qquad (13)$$

Using this basic result, we can prove the following general theorem [9]. A key quantity, we will see, is the *marginal speedup*, which we define as the partial derivative of the speedup function with respect to the processing power, $\partial f_i(p_i)/\partial p_i$.

Theorem 4.1 (Strictly Increasing Speedups)
Suppose that all $f_i(p_i)$ are strictly increasing, $\frac{\partial f_i(p_i)}{\partial p_i} \geq \delta > 0$, for all $p_i \geq 0$, where δ is an arbitrary small positive constant. Then the optimal solution always uses all processors, i.e.,

$$\sum_i p_i(t) = P(t)$$

Furthermore, if two tasks i and j are scheduled to run in parallel at time t, with non-zero processor power $p_i(t) > 0$, $p_j(t) > 0$, if neither is within ϵ of completion, and if all predecessors of both i and j have finished, so that $g_i(\vec{x}) = g_j(\vec{x}) = 1$, then the ratio of marginal speedups is fixed:

$$\lambda_i \frac{\partial f_i(p_i)}{\partial p_i} = \lambda_j \frac{\partial f_j(p_j)}{\partial p_j} = -\mu(t)$$

where $\lambda_i = \lambda_i(0)$ and $\lambda_j = \lambda_j(0)$ are the initial values of the Lagrange multipliers.

In other words, if more processing power becomes available during execution, it is applied to the runnable tasks in such a way that the marginal speedups of the running tasks maintain their fixed ratios.

5 Speedup Function p^α

The optimal control solution takes a particularly elegant form when the speedup function is:

$$\dot{x}_i(t) = g_i(\vec{x}) p_i^\alpha(t) \qquad \text{where } 0 < \alpha < 1 \qquad (14)$$

Note that all tasks have to have the *same* α. It is true that this function is not physically realizable for $0 < p_i(t) < 1$, since $p_i^\alpha(t)$ is supralinear in this range. Furthermore, $\partial f_i(\vec{x}, \vec{p}, t)/\partial p_i \to \infty$ as $p_i(t) \to 0$, so the marginal speedup with $p_i(t) \approx 0$ is asymptotically infinite. Nevertheless, this is an interesting function to study, as it is not unreasonable for $p_i(t) \geq 1$, and the solution is comparatively simple yet interesting. In [9], we show that

Theorem 5.1 (Optimal Scheduling & p^α Dynamics)
With $f_i(\vec{x}, \vec{p}, t)$ given by (14), the optimal scheduling solution satisfies:

1. *Once a process is runnable, it is assigned non-zero processor power until it finishes, $p_i(t) > 0$ for all $t_i < t < t_i^F$. Otherwise, $p_i(t) = 0$ for $t < t_i$ and $t > t_i^F$.*

2. *When task i finishes, either $t_i^F = t^F$ and the entire graph is finished, or else all the (fractional) processing power originally allocated to i is reallocated to the successors of i which begin at the same time that i ends.*

3. *The optimal schedule is non-preemptive, in the sense that once all the predecessors of a task finish and the task is running, the fraction of processing power allocated to the task does not change until the task completes.*

We reiterate that a *functional optimization* is being performed, with the $p_i(t)$'s allowed to be arbitrary, real valued, generally discontinuous, functions of time.

It follows from this theorem that under p^α dynamics, we can treat processing power as if it were electric charge and precedence constraints as if they were wires. When a task completes, its charge flows to those of its successors which are enabled to run at that time. Not all successors of the task get this processor charge - only the ones which become enabled to run at this time because all of their predecessors are finishing. The flow continues until finally the tasks with no successors are all running and they all complete at the same moment, t^F.

This flow property clearly results in a major reduction in the combinatorial complexity of scheduling. Section 7.2 makes extensive use of this flow property to develop a pair of powerful scheduling techniques - viz. series reduction and parallel reduction.

Another important property of systems with p^α dynamics is one which relates to the homogeneity of the speedup function. It is easily shown [9] by direct substitution into the system dynamic equations that,

Theorem 5.2 (Homogeneity and p^α dynamics)
Assume the speedup functions are p_i^α. Suppose that $P(t)$ total processing power is available, and that the optimal scheduling solution to a graph is $p_i(t)$, with resulting states $x_i(t)$. Now suppose that $\check{P}(t)$ total processing power were available instead. Then the optimal scheduling solution $\tilde{p}_i(t)$ for the new situation is given by:

$$\tilde{p}_i(\tilde{t}) = \frac{p_i(t)}{P(t)} \tilde{P}(\tilde{t})$$

for all i, with resulting states:

$$\tilde{x}_i(\tilde{t}) = x_i(t)$$

where $\tilde{t}$ is a new time variable which is a monotonically increasing function of t, $\tilde{t} = T(t)$, defined by:

$$dt = \frac{\tilde{P}^\alpha(\tilde{t})}{P^\alpha(t)} d\tilde{t}, \qquad \tilde{t}\big|_{t=0} = 0$$

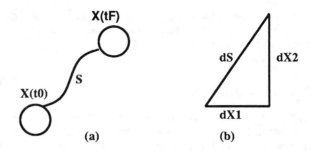

Figure 2: Scheduling and Shortest Path Problems

In other words, the available processing power $P(t)$ does not affect the structure of the optimal scheduling solution. Tasks start and complete in exactly the same order, the same fraction of processing power is allocated to the tasks, and the states evolve along the same trajectory, regardless of the power $P(t)$. The only effect of changing $P(t)$ is to effectively warp the time axis, speeding up or slowing down the optimal schedule. Note that this theorem allows us to find the optimal solution for any time varying total processing power $P(t)$, by first solving for a constant processing power $P(t) = P$, and then applying a time warp.

6 p^α Dynamics and Shortest Path Problems

The optimal control formulation of the scheduling problem derives the control functions (the processing powers $p_i(t)$) which drive the state trajectory along a path which goes from the initial to the terminal states as quickly as possible, subject to the precedence constraints. We will show that under p^α dynamics, the time-optimal state trajectory is the path with the shortest length, as measured by an $\ell_{1/\alpha}$ norm.

Theorem 6.1 (Scheduling & Shortest Path Problems)
Suppose $f_i(p_i) = p_i^\alpha$ for $0 < \alpha < 1$. Then the scheduling problem is equivalent to a shortest path (with obstacles) problem with $\ell_{1/\alpha}$ norms.

Proof: We demonstrate this result by explicitly computing the time taken by a schedule specified by a trajectory in task space.

With reference to Figure 2 (a), the time taken for a schedule specified by the state trajectory S is

$$\int_S dt = \int_S \frac{dt}{dS} dS$$

where dS is the path element. The time taken for moving along dS can be computed as follows. Let

$$dS = [dx_1, dx_2, \cdots, dx_N]$$

(Figure 2 (b)). Then a motion along dS is equivalent to processing dx_1 of the first task, dx_2 of the second, and so

220

on, *simultaneously*. Thus the elapsed time dt is the same for all of them. If the number of processors allocated to the ith task is $p_i(t)$, then we have

$$dt = \frac{dx_1}{p_1^\alpha(t)} = \frac{dx_2}{p_2^\alpha(t)} = \cdots = \frac{dx_N}{p_N^\alpha(t)}$$

Since

$$\sum_{i=1}^N p_i(t) = P(t)$$

we can simplify this to

$$dt = \frac{\left(\sum_{i=1}^N dx_i^{1/\alpha}\right)^\alpha}{P^\alpha(t)} = \frac{\ell_{1/\alpha}(dx_1, dx_2, \cdots, dx_N)}{P^\alpha(t)}$$

which is the (scaled) $\ell_{1/\alpha}$ norm of the path increment in task space. Thus the elapsed time t is a *metric* in task space. Thus the time-optimal path must also be the shortest path in task space, as measured by the $\ell_{1/\alpha}$ norm. If $\alpha = 1/2$, the time optimal schedule minimises the Euclidean Distance. The precedence constraints behave like *obstacles* to the trajectory, forcing the path to reach certain hyperplanes (i.e. having a task finish, $x_i = L_i$) before it can veer off in certain directions (by having one or more successor tasks begin). It should be noted that our scheduling techniques yield closed form solutions for such obstacle constrained shortest path problems, when the obstacles are tree structured.

Under p^α dynamics, we can easily show a couple of other interesting theorems.

Theorem 6.2 (Limiting Cases of p^α) *For any system of tasks with $f_i(p) = p^\alpha$ dynamics, the time for an optimal schedule with $P(t)$ processors total satisfies the following relations.*

$$\lim_{\alpha \to 0} t^F = CP$$

where CP is the critical path length of the precedence graph of the task system.

$$\lim_{\alpha \to 1} \int_0^{t^F} P(t)dt = \sum_{i=1}^N L_i$$

7 Scheduling Algorithms for p^α dynamics

Theorem 5.1 (3) implies that the optimal schedule for the processing assignments assigns a constant fraction ϕ_i of the available processing power to task i while it runs, (ignoring startup and shutdown transients). This in itself yields a major simplification in the scheduling, since the processor assignments $p_i(t)$ are no longer functions of time, but constants ϕ_i. Further simplifications can be obtained by exploiting the series-parallel nature of the task precedence graph.

7.1 Series and Parallel Decompositions

Here we present rules for simplifying the scheduling when the task system has series-parallel structure, and p^α dynamics. These techniques yield a very simple closed form solution for the optimal schedule for tree structured task graphs.

We define tasks $1, \ldots, K$ to be in series if the only successor of k is $k+1$ for $k = 1, \ldots, K-1$, and the only predecessor of k is $k-1$ for $k = 2, \ldots, K$. We define tasks $1, \ldots, K$ to be in parallel if they all have the same predecessors and the same successors, $\Omega_k = \Omega_1$ and $\Omega^k = \Omega^1$ for $k = 1, \ldots, K$.

Suppose tasks $1, \ldots, K$ are a series task set. We will replace this task set with a single composite task, which we refer to as $1:K$. This task will have the same predecessors as 1, $\Omega_{1:K} \equiv \Omega_1$, and the same successors as K, $\Omega^{1:K} \equiv \Omega^K$. It will start at the same time as 1, $t_{1:K} \equiv t_1$, and end at the same time as K, $t_{1:K}^F \equiv t_K^F$.

We define the state of the composite task as the sum of the individual states:

$$x_{1:K}(t) \equiv \sum_{k=1}^K x_k(t)$$

with initial and terminal values

$$x_{1:K}(t_{1:K}) = 0, \qquad x_{1:K}(t_{1:K}^F) = L_{1:K}$$

where the length of the composite task, $L_{1:K}$, is defined as the sum of the lengths of the individual tasks:

$$L_{1:K} \equiv \sum_{k=1}^K L_k$$

With these definitions, it is easy to show that the composite state obeys exactly the same p^α dynamics as all the other tasks:

$$\dot{x}_{1:K}(t) = \begin{cases} p_{1:K}^\alpha(t) & \text{for } t_{1:K} < t < t_{1:K}^F \\ 0 & \text{else} \end{cases}$$

where $p_{1:k}(t)$ is the processor allocation to the series task system at time t (this is the processor power $p_j(t)$ applied to the one and only running task j in the series system at time t).

An optimal schedule for the original graph maps exactly into an optimal schedule for a new graph with the series set replaced by this single composite task. This immediately yields a very useful graph reduction technique for scheduling (*series reduction*).

Parallel task sets can be dealt with in a similar manner. Suppose tasks 1 through K are in parallel. We will replace these tasks with a single composite task $1:K$. This composite task has the same predecessors and successors as all the original tasks,

$$\Omega_{1:K} \equiv \Omega_1 = \cdots = \Omega_K, \qquad \Omega^{1:K} \equiv \Omega^1 = \cdots = \Omega^K$$

Theorem 5.1 (2) implies that all tasks 1 through K in the parallel system start and stop together. The composite task starts and stops at the same time as the original tasks:

$$t_{1:K} \equiv t_1 = \cdots = t_K, \qquad t_{1:K}^F \equiv t_1^F = \cdots = t_K^F$$

221

Define the processing power applied to the composite parallel task as the sum of the processing powers allocated to all the original tasks:

$$p_{1:K}(t) \equiv \sum_{k=1}^{K} p_k(t)$$

We also define define the state of the composite parallel task $L_{1:K}$ as the $\ell_{1/\alpha}$ norm of the states of the subtasks:

$$x_{1:K} \equiv \ell_{1/\alpha}(x_1, \ldots, x_K)$$

and the length $L_{1:K}$ as the $\ell_{1/\alpha}$ norm of the lengths of the subtasks:

$$L_{1:K} \equiv \ell_{1/\alpha}(L_1, \ldots, L_K)$$

Then, using the constancy of processing power allocations (Theorem 5.1 (3)), we can show that the state of the composite parallel task also has p^α dynamics:

$$\dot{x}_{1:K}(t) = \begin{cases} p_{1:K}^\alpha(t) & \text{for } t_{1:K} < t < t_{1:K}^F \\ 0 & \text{else} \end{cases}$$

An optimal scheduling solution for the original graph also corresponds to an optimal scheduling solution for the graph with tasks (processor allocations) 1 through K replaced by the single composite task (processor allocation) $1 : K$ (*parallel reduction*). This implies that the optimal solution for the original graph can be found indirectly as follows. Compute the optimal solution for the reduced graph with tasks 1 through K replaced by $1 : K$. Then the optimal solution for the original graph can be found by splitting the fraction of processing power allocated to $1 : K$ among the subtasks in proportion to the $\ell_{1/\alpha}$ norms of their lengths.

Because the composite series or parallel task has the same p^α dynamics as the original tasks, we can apply series and parallel reductions technique recursively.

If the graph can be expressed entirely in terms of parallel and series configurations of tasks (tree/forest like graphs), then we recursively reduce the entire graph to a single task with p^α dynamics. Now the finishing time of the schedule is easily computed. Undoing the recursion, we allocate the processing power to each of the series and parallel components according to their lengths, and determine their start and stop times. Continuing recursively, we eventually derive the optimal processing schedule for every task in the original graph. For general DAGS, our reductions enable the graph to be reduced to a minimal form, for which the optimal control problem has to be explicitly solved.

Typical graph structures that can be recursively decomposed into parallel and series components include trees, inverted trees, and forests of trees or inverted trees. Most matrix expression computations, for example, have the form of an tree, and thus if we are willing to approximate the speedup of the individual matrix operations as p^α, then the expression can be optimally scheduled by this simple parallel/series trick.

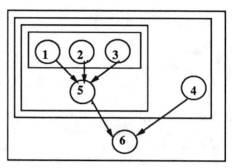

(a) Tree Recursive Decomposition

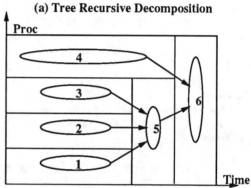

(b) Optimal Nonpreemptive Schedule

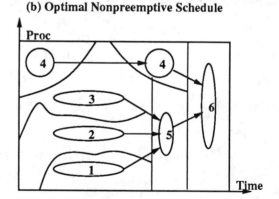

(c) General Suboptimal Preemptive Schedule

Figure 3: Optimal Tree Scheduling using series-parallel reductions

7.2 Examples of Optimal Schedule for a Tree

Figure 3 (a) shows a tree-structured task system, together with the unique recursive series-parallel decomposition. Combining tasks recursively gives composite task lengths:

$$L_{1:3} = \left(L_1^{1/\alpha} + L_2^{1/\alpha} + L_3^{1/\alpha} \right)^\alpha$$
$$L_{1:3,5} = L_{1:3} + L_5$$
$$L_{1:3,4,5} = \left(L_{1:3,5}^{1/\alpha} + L_4^{1/\alpha} \right)^\alpha$$
$$L_{1:6} = L_{1:3,4,5} + L_6$$

The optimal time t^F is such that

$$\int_0^{t^F} P^\alpha(t)dt = L_{1:6}$$

The optimal schedule (for constant $P(t) = P$), is shown in Figure 3 (b), and mimics the decomposition. The fraction of processing power applied to each task as it runs can be computed recursively as follows (it is important to note that this is optimal even for time varying total processing power $P(t)$ - this follows from homogeneity).

$$p_6(t) = P(t)$$

$$p_5(t) = \frac{L_{1:3,5}^{1/\alpha}}{L_{1:3,5}^{1/\alpha} + L_4^{1/\alpha}} P(t)$$

$$p_4(t) = \frac{L_4^{1/\alpha}}{L_{1:3,5}^{1/\alpha} + L_4^{1/\alpha}} P(t)$$

$$p_1(t) = \frac{L_1^{1/\alpha}}{L_1^{1/\alpha} + L_2^{1/\alpha} + L_3^{1/\alpha}} \frac{L_{1:3,5}^{1/\alpha}}{L_{1:3,5}^{1/\alpha} + L_4^{1/\alpha}} P(t)$$

$$p_2(t) = \frac{L_2^{1/\alpha}}{L_1^{1/\alpha} + L_2^{1/\alpha} + L_3^{1/\alpha}} \frac{L_{1:3,5}^{1/\alpha}}{L_{1:3,5}^{1/\alpha} + L_4^{1/\alpha}} P(t)$$

$$p_3(t) = \frac{L_3^{1/\alpha}}{L_1^{1/\alpha} + L_2^{1/\alpha} + L_3^{1/\alpha}} \frac{L_{1:3,5}^{1/\alpha}}{L_{1:3,5}^{1/\alpha} + L_4^{1/\alpha}} P(t)$$

For comparision, a general time-varying preemptive suboptimal schedule is shown in Figure 3 (c). In this case all tasks (except the final task) have dynamically varying processor allocations, with task 4 being completely shut off for a while, and then restarted. Theorem 5.1 states that the schedule in (b) is faster than any other schedule, eg. (c). Its power should be clear from this example.

7.3 General Directed Acyclic Graphs (DAG's)

DAG's cannot in general be reduced to single nodes using the series-parallel reductions. The optimal control problem has to be explicitly solved to yield the optimal solution. In such cases, however, Theorem 5.1 prunes the search space by yielding stringent constraints on the optimal solutions.

Firstly, tasks with no successors must all finish at the same time, and tasks with successors must finish only when at least one successor becomes enabled to execute. Next, when one task finishes, its fraction of the available processing power must only be allocated among the successors which are first enabled to run at this moment. Finally, the fraction of processing power allocated to a task cannot change while it is running. Typically, very few schedules can be devised which meet all these constraints, and thus we need only check the finish times of this small set to choose the optimum.

As an example, consider the task precedence graph in Figure 4. Only three schedules could conceivably be optimal; Figure 5 displays the processor flows corresponding to each. In schedule A, task 1 finishes before task 2 and pours all its processing power into task 3, while task 2 pours all its processing power into 4 and 5. In schedule B, tasks 1 and 2 complete simultaneously, and the released processing power is applied to tasks 3, 4 and 5. In schedule C, task 2 finishes before task 1, and pours all its processing power into task 5, while task 1 pours its processing power into 3 and 4. In this example, all three possible schedules have a parallel/series structure, and thus our previous formulas can be applied to compute processor allocations and start/stop times for each task. For example, the equivalent lengths of the graph (ie. the length of the single task to which it is reduced) would be:

$$\tilde{L}_A = \ell_{1/\alpha} \left[(L_1 + L_3), \left(\ell_{1/\alpha}(L_4, L_5) + L_2 \right) \right]$$
$$\tilde{L}_B = \left[\ell_{1/\alpha}(L_1, L_2) + \ell_{1/\alpha}(L_3, L_4, L_5) \right]$$
$$\tilde{L}_C = \ell_{1/\alpha} \left[(L_2 + L_5), \left(\ell_{1/\alpha}(L_3, L_4) + L_1 \right) \right]$$

Once processor allocations are determined for each schedule, we need to verify that the task start and complete times satisfy the assumptions made in deriving the schedule. For example, for schedule A we need to check whether task 1 does indeed complete before task 2. If the assumptions are not satisfied, then the schedule cannot be valid and cannot be optimal. If several of the schedules are valid, then the optimal is the one with the fastest execution time. In general, which schedule is optimal will depend on the relative lengths of the tasks.

8 Application to Scheduling Matrix Arithmetic

This section applies the generalised scheduling techniques of Section 7 to multiprocessor compilation of matrix arithmetic computations [8]. Our results were taken on the MIT Alewife machine [1], a large scale cache coherent, shared memory multiprocessor being built at MIT. The processors were assumed to be connected in a 3-D mesh, and the chained directory cache coherence scheme was used [8, chapter 4]. A compiler was written which took a matrix computation (in the form of a matrix expression), and automatically generated parallelised Mul-T [7] code for Alewife.

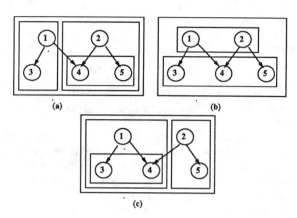

Figure 4: General DAG with three possible decompositions

Operation	Length
Scalar Operation	1
$N_1 \times N_2$ Addition	$N_1 N_2$
N point Dot Product	N
$N_1 \times N_2$ Outer Product	$N_1 N_2$
$N_1 \times N_2$ Matrix Scale	$N_1 N_2$
$N_1 \times N_2$ Matrix Transpose	$N_1 N_2$
$N_1 \times N_2 \times N_3$ Matrix Product	$N_1 N_2 N_3$

Table 1: Lengths of various operators

Matrix arithmetic problems can be conveniently expressed as compositions of a small number of well understood matrix operators - viz. as matrix expressions. The basic operators - matrix sums, products, inverses, etc., are characterised by extensive data parallelism. These operators can be (dynamically) configured into arbitrary numbers of parallel modules for execution on a multiprocessor, yielding a library of parallel operator routines.

For each different parallelism, the operator dataflow graphs can be optimally partitioned using bin packing techniques, to maximise load balancing and minimise communication overhead [8, chapter 2]. This yields a set of optimal parallel routines for each matrix operator. Each member of the set is optimal for a specific parallelism. Inspite of this optimization, as the parallelism increases, the marginal speedup obtained generally keeps decreasing, and the speedups are generally convex.

Thus these operators roughly fit the task model in Section 2. Schedules which minimise the parallelism at which a task (matrix operator) is computed, and execute many tasks simultaneously, are superior. It is hence of interest to explore how well the generalised scheduling techniques (Section 7) perform in this domain. It is important to note that the behaviour of the parallel operator routines depends on complex processor, network, cache, and task spawning characteristics, and does not exactly fit the assumptions made in developing the optimal scheduling techniques. But the results show that they are still of value in scheduling such task systems.

The scheduling techniques outlined in Section 7 are methods to determine the parallelism of each task in the task system. Under p^α dynamics, these techniques are optimal and yield simple closed form solutions for tree structured task systems. If the dynamics are not p^α, these techniques can be employed as heuristics. These techniques, together with two other similar heuristic techniques, were experimented with. The heuristics are enumerated below:

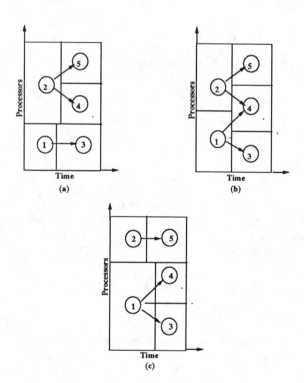

Figure 5: Processor flows for three possible DAG schedules

- The *Naive* heuristic computes each task using all the available processors, in some sequence satisfying the precedence constraints. Since each task is run at the finest granularity (maximum parallelism) possible, this method is clearly slow. But it is included because of its simplicity.

- The *Greedy* heuristic operates in cycles. In each cycle, all the tasks which can be executed (upto a maximum equal to the number of processors), are fired. The processing resource is distributed in a manner so as to equalise the finishing times of all fired tasks. In the next cycle, the next set of ready tasks is fired, and so on.

To equalize the finishing times of all tasks fired in a cycle, the processors are distributed among them in proportion to their lengths. The lengths are estimated crudely, by a simple operation count (workload). The lengths for each particular operation are specified in Table 1.

- The *Tree* heuristic, used for tree-structured matrix expressions, is derived from the optimal tree scheduling heuristic for p^α dynamics (Section 7). The processor resource is partitioned among sibling subtrees in proportion to their lengths. If all the tasks of each subtree have the same α, the length of each subtree is the $\ell_{1/\alpha}$ norm of the length of its children, plus the length of the root (Section 7). But for this technique to be useful, α must be known. Also, in general fractional processor allocations result. Currently, in this version of the compiler, α is assumed to be unity. The total length of each subtree is simply the sum of lengths of all its constituent tasks. The processor allocations have also been quantised to avoid fractional processor allocations.

The finishing time estimates for the overall task system are clearly extremely erroneous if we assume that $\alpha = 1$, as each task is assumed to have linear speedup. Also, all the three heuristics are equally fast if $\alpha = 1$. However, in practice this assumption does not cause much error in the processor allocations.

Figure 6 illustrates the operation of the three heuristics on a tree structured task system. The Naive heuristic (Figure 6 (a)) runs each task on all the available processors. Tasks 1, 2, 3, 4, and 5 are run in sequence. The Greedy heuristic (Figure 6 (b)) runs tasks 1, 2, and 4 in parallel, distributing the processor resources among them. Subsequently tasks 3 and 5 are computed, each using all available processors. The Tree heuristic (Figure 6 (c)) does a slightly better job of partitioning the processor resource by recognizing the fact that tasks 1, 2, and 3 form a subtree, which can be run in parallel with task 4, by splitting the available processors. Finally task 5 is run on all the available processors. The Tree heuristic outperforms Greedy, since it reduces the parallelism of task 3. The two subtrees, one comprising tasks 1, 2, and 3, and the other comprising the lone task 4 are computed in a "balanced" manner by the Tree heuristic.

8.1 Matrix Expression Examples

The matrix expression compiler produces Mul-T code for each expression, for various number of processors. Code performance statistics were gathered on the Alewife machine simulator. The processors were arranged in a 3 dimensional mesh, of sizes either $1 \times 1 \times 1$ (uniprocessor), $2 \times 2 \times 2$, or $4 \times 4 \times 4$. Depending on the total number of processors P used to compute the matrix expression, some of the mesh

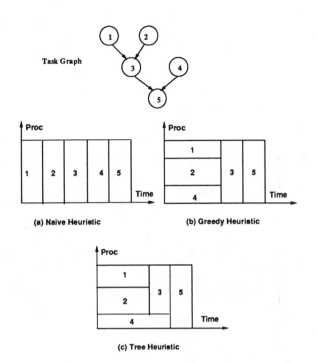

Figure 6: Generalised Scheduling Heuristics

was unused. Processors P_i, for $0 \le i < P$ were used, and the rest were idle.

The compiler first uses the generalised scheduling heuristics and specifies the parallelism for each particular task (matrix operator). Then code is generated as a sequence of calls to the parallel operator routines for each task, optimised for the specified parallelism. Synchronization is embedded using the future-touch mechanism of Mul-T. For more details see [8].

We present results for a basic matrix operator - the matrix product first, and then discuss compilation of expressions. All matrices are of size 20×20, unless otherwise specified.

8.1.1 Matrix Product

Figure 7 shows the speedup curve for a basic matrix operator, viz. the matrix product. The speedups fall dramatically after about 8 processors. Excessive task startup and communication overhead are the causes of this behaviour. There is an anomalous concave region, with the speedup first decreasing from 4 for 8 processors, to 2.9 for 16 processors, then slightly increasing to 3.2 for 35 processors. The speedup falls dramatically to 2.3 for 64 processors.

225

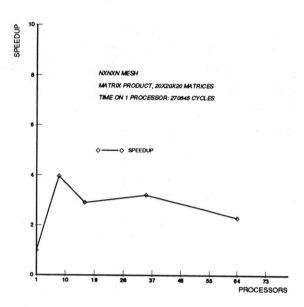

Figure 7: Speedup Curve for 20×20 matrix product

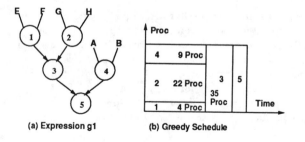

(a) Expression g1   (b) Greedy Schedule

Figure 8: Greedy Schedule for g_1

While the speedup function is clearly not p^α, we will nevertheless approximate it as one such, so that we can apply the generalised scheduling theory of Section 7. In particular, the insight that tasks have to be run in parallel if possible is critical. This will be demonstrated in the succeeding examples.

8.1.2 Expression g_1

Consider the matrix expression (Figure 8 (a))

$$g_1 = AB + (EF)(GH)$$

This is prototypical of systems typically encountered in signal processing and linear algebra. It could represent the iteration of an inner loop, or a filter bank.

Suppose A and B are 20×20 matrices, E is a 20×9 matrix, F is a 9×20 matrix, G is a 20×43 matrix, while H is a 43×20 matrix. These strange data sizes have been deliberately chosen to illustrate size-matching (bin-packing) problems encountered in parallelising compilers. Each scheduling heuristic produces different parallelisms for each of the operators. Writing code by hand for each problem size, and each number of processors, is a very tedious job, which should be automated. This is indeed done by the matrix expression compiler.

For example, Figure 8 (b) shows a Gantt chart for a schedule for 35 processors using the Greedy Heuristic. The matrix products $A \times B$, $E \times F$, and $G \times H$ are computed together. Then, after at least $E \times F$ and $G \times H$ are completed, their outputs are multiplied. Finally, the addition is performed. The matrix multiply $A \times B$ is assigned 9 processors, the matrix multiply $E \times F$ is assigned 4 processors, the matrix multiply $G \times H$ is assigned 22 processors. Code for g_1 with the above specified parallelism for each operator is produced automatically by the compiler.

The speedup curves (Figure 9) show the relative performance of the scheduling heuristics. The exploitation of parallelism by the Greedy and Tree scheduling heuristics clearly greatly increases speed.

The speedup curves (Figure 9) show two distinct regimes, one upto 8 processors, and one beyond. All three heuristics perform roughly equally well till about 8 processors. Beyond this, the Greedy and the Tree heuristic outperform the naive heuristic (by a factor of 1.5 for the Tree heuristic on 35 processors). This agrees with the considerable drop of speedup evidenced in the basic matrix product beyond 8 processors. The Tree heuristic is slightly better than the Greedy heuristic, providing at least preliminary vindication of the theory. The drop off of the curves at 64 processors probably reflects excessive task startup and communication overhead due to improper placement of tasks on processors.

The next example shows that even better performance is

226

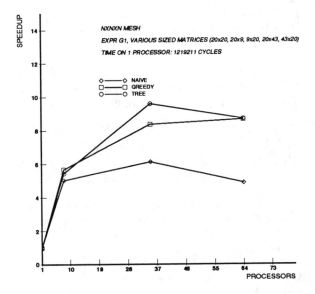

Figure 9: Speedup Curves - g_1

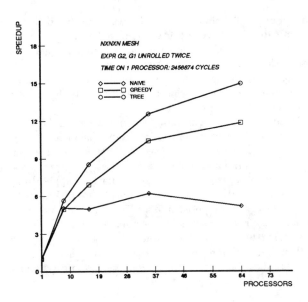

Figure 10: Speedup Curves - g_2

obtained if the task system exhibits more parallelism.

8.1.3 Expression g_2

Consider the matrix expression g_2

$$g_2 = (A_1B_1 + (E_1F_1)(G_1H_1)) + ((A_2B_2) + (E_2F_2)(G_2H_2))$$

g_2 is essentially two copies of g_1 performed together in parallel, with their results summed.

The increased parallelism in g_2 enables tasks to be run at coarser granularity. The speedup curves (Figure 10), again show two regimes, with a break around 8 processors. A substantial increase in absolute speedups is evident, with the speedup at 64 processors being close to 15 (25 %) for the Tree heuristic. The Greedy and Tree heuristics outperform the naive heuristic by factors of 2 to 3. The gain is substantially more than in the case of g_1. The Tree heuristic is also substantially better than the Greedy heuristic in this case. This example well illustrate the gains in performance by exploiting parallelism in the task precedence graph, and utility of the generalised scheduling heuristics of Section 7.

9 Discussion and Summary

In this paper we have discussed multiprocessor scheduling theory from the viewpoint of optimal control theory. Each task was treated as a dynamic system, whose state advances when processing power is applied. We assumed that the rate at which the task was processed depended only on the amount of processing power applied, and not on the state or the time. Also, we assumed that the number of processors was a continuous variable. This eliminates the discrete nature of scheduling, and enables us to apply continuous optimization techniques - viz. the calculus of variations incarnated in the form of control theory.

The scheduling problem was formulated as a time-optimal control problem, which in turn led to a general description of the optimal solution. In the special case of p^α dynamics, we were able to solve for this optimal solution directly, deriving very strong theorems. Processing power behaves like charge in an electrical network, with tasks holding onto a fixed fraction of the "charge" while they execute, then releasing it as they finish to flow along arcs in the precedence graph into only those successor tasks which become enabled to run at this moment. For graphs built recursively as parallel and series combinations of tasks, closed form analytic formulas describe total task length and detailed processor allocations over time. Furthermore, we were able to show that the optimal solution corresponds to the shortest path, as measured by an $\ell_{1/\alpha}$ norm, through a task space with precedence constraint obstacles.

From a practical standpoint, an important issue is that whether the optimal scheduling algorithm is still close to optimal even if the assumptions about the task speedup functions are only approximately true. Our hope and intuition is that many realistic tasks exhibit speedup functions which at least qualitatively behave similarly to p^α for large p, and therefore our scheduling algorithm ought to do well even for realistic tasks.

The practical applicability of our ideas was tested on the highly parallel MIT Alewife machine, using a matrix arithmetic compiler incorporating our scheduling algorithms. Given the quantity of computation required for each matrix operator, and assuming that all speedups are p^α, this compiler computes an "optimal" integer amount of processing power to allocate to the operator, then writes custom code modules which decompose the operator into the appropriate number of parallel chunks. Though actual speedup behavior is dominated by processor, cache, and network limitations, and by task spawning overhead, our scheduling algorithm nevertheless achieves better measured speedups than several alternative approaches. It would be enlightening to repeat this exercise for other machines to measure this algorithm's effectiveness in other contexts.

Despite its limitations, however, our approach to optimal scheduling provides new insights into scheduling theory. It has revealed interesting connections between scheduling, optimal control, network flow, and shortest path problems. The methodology is particularly appropriate for applications such as matrix arithmetic computation where tasks can be systematically decomposed into arbitrary numbers of parallel modules. For these applications, our theorems are quite powerful and the optimal algorithms are practical and easily applied. Furthermore, we believe that these scheduling approaches should be near optimal for systems whose dynamics are similar to, but not exactly p^α.

10 Acknowledgements

We are indebted to the MIT Alewife research group for the experimental results reported in this paper. Prof Ananth Agarwal was a perennial source of ideas and ever ready to help. Jose M. Vidal implemented the first version of the compiler. Our friends Dave Chaiken, Beng-Hong Lim, Kirk Johnson, Dann Nussbaum, John Kubiatowicz, Dave Kranz, and many others were critical to the implementation of the compiler on the Alewife machine.

This research has been funded in part by the Advanced Research Project Agency monitored by ONR under # N00014-89-J-1489, in part by Draper Laboratory, in part by DARPA contract # N00014-87-K-0825, and in part by NSF grant #MIP-9012773.

References

[1] A. Agarwal, B.H. Lim, D. Kranz, and J. Kubiatowicz. APRIL: A Processor Architecture for Multiprocessing. In *Proceedings 17th Annual International Symposium on Computer Architecture*, June 1990.

[2] M. Blazewicz, J. Drabowski and J. Welgarz. Scheduling multiprocessor tasks to minimise schedule length. *IEEE Transactions on Computers*, C-35(5):389–393, 1986.

[3] Bryson and Ho. *Applied Optimal Control*. Halstead Press, 1975.

[4] Coffman E.F., Jr., editor. *Computer and Job Shop Scheduling Theory*. John Wiley and Sons, N.Y., 1976.

[5] J. Du and J.Y.T Leung. Complexity of Scheduling Parallel Task Systems. *SIAM J. Discrete Math.*, 2(4):473–487, Nov 1989.

[6] C.C Han and K.J. Lin. Scheduling Parallelizable Jobs on Multiprocessors. In *IEEE Conf. on Real-Time Systems*, pages 59–67, 1989.

[7] D. Kranz, R. Halstead, and E. Mohr. Mul-T: A High-Performance Parallel Lisp. In *Proceedings of SIGPLAN '89, Symposium on Programming Languages Design and Implementation*, June 1989.

[8] G.N.Srinivasa Prasanna. *Structure Driven Multiprocessor Compilation of Numeric Problems*. Technical Report MIT/LCS/TR-502, Laboratory for Computer Science, MIT., April 1991.

[9] G.N.Srinivasa Prasanna and Bruce R. Musicus. The Optimal Control Approach to Generalised Multiprocessor Scheduling. *To be Published*, 1991.

Lock-Free Garbage Collection for Multiprocessors

Maurice P. Herlihy
Digital Equipment Corporation
Cambridge Research Laboratory
One Kendall Square
Cambridge, MA 02139
herlihy@crl.dec.com

J. Eliot B. Moss[*]
Dept. of Comp. and Info. Sci.
University of Massachusetts
Amherst, MA 01003
moss@cs.umass.edu

Abstract

Garbage collection algorithms for shared-memory multiprocessors typically rely on some form of global synchronization to preserve consistency. Such global synchronization may lead to problems on asynchronous
architectures: if one process is halted or delayed, other,
non-faulty processes will be unable to progress. By
contrast, a storage management algorithm is *lock-free* if
(in the absence of resource exhaustion) a process that is
allocating or collecting memory can be delayed at any
point without forcing other processes to block. This
paper presents the first algorithm for lock-free garbage
collection in a realistic model. The algorithm assumes
that processes synchronize by applying *read*, *write*, and
compare&swap operations to shared memory. This algorithm uses no locks, busy-waiting, or barrier synchronization, it does not assume that processes can observe
or modify one another's local variables or registers, and
it does not use inter-process interrupts.

1 Introduction

Garbage collection algorithms for shared-memory multiprocessors typically rely on some form of global synchronization to preserve consistency. Shared memory
architectures, however, are inherently *asynchronous*:
processors' relative speeds are unpredictable, at least

in the short term, because of timing uncertainties introduced by variations in instruction complexity, page
faults, cache misses, and operating system activities
such as preemption or swapping. Garbage collection
algorithms that rely on global synchronization may lead
to undesirable blocking on asynchronous architectures
because if one process is halted or delayed, other, non-
faulty processes may also be unable to progress. By
contrast, a storage management algorithm is *lock-free*
if any process can be delayed at any point without forcing any other process to block.[1] This is a very strong
view of blocking, since even very short term locks could
lead to blocking in our sense. The benefit of this view
is that we can make a strong guarantee of progress if
a system is lock-free. This paper presents a lock-free
incremental copying garbage collection algorithm.

We note from the outset, however, that our garbage
collection algorithm, like any resource management algorithm, blocks when resources are exhausted. In our
algorithm, for example, a delayed process may force
other processes to postpone storage reclamation, although it will not prevent them from allocating new
storage if any free storage is available. If that process has actually failed, then the non-faulty processes
will eventually be forced to block when their remaining free storage is exhausted. If halting failures are a
concern, then our algorithm should be combined with
higher-level (and much slower) mechanisms to detect
and restart failed processes, an interesting extension we
do not address here. Nevertheless, our algorithm tolerates substantial delays and variations in process speeds,
and may therefore be of value for real-time or "soft"
real-time continuously running systems.

Previous algorithms typically include two distinct
forms of synchronization. One is synchronization of
access, update, etc., to individual objects, which we
call *local synchronization*. For example, Halstead [Hal-

---
[*]Eliot Moss is supported by National Science Foundation Grant
CCR-8658074, by Digital Equipment Corporation, Apple Com-
puter, and GTE Laboratories.

---
[1]Note that we do not use *blocking* to mean that ordinary execution, e.g., *mutator* processes, stops during collection. In fact, we do
not make a mutator/collector distinction, as will be seen.

stead, 1985] uses short term locks on objects. The other is some form of barrier for phases of the garbage collection computation and/or locks on such data structures as a free list. This we call *global synchronization*. Our algorithm is lock-free in both local and global synchronization, and distinct techniques are used for each.

2 Model

There are three aspects to our model of memory: the underlying shared memory hardware and its primitive operations, the application level heap memory semantics that we will support, and the structuring of the contents of shared memory in order to support the application level semantics.

2.1 Underlying Architecture

We focus on a multiple instruction, multiple data (MIMD) architecture in which n processes, executing asynchronously, share a common memory. Each process also has some private memory (e.g., registers and stack) inaccessible to the other processes. The processes are numbered from 1 to n, and each process knows its own number, denoted by *me*. The primitive memory operations are *read*, which copies a value from shared memory to private memory, *write*, which copies a value in the other direction, and *compare&swap*, shown in Figure 1. We do *not* assume that processes can interrupt one another.

We chose the *compare&swap* primitive for two reasons. First, it has been successfully implemented, having first appeared in the IBM System/370 architecture [IBM]. Second, it can be shown that some form of read-modify-write primitive is required for non-blocking solutions to many basic synchronization problems, and that *compare&swap* is as powerful in this respect as any other read-modify-write operation [Herlihy, 1991; Herlihy, 1988]. Most multiprocessors, even ones based on load/store architectures, have primitives of adequate power. For example, the forthcoming MIPS II architecture [Kilian, 1991] includes two relevant instructions, Load Linked and Store Conditionally. The first does an ordinary load but sets a special status bit in the processor called the LL bit. This bit is automatically cleared if an underlying cache consistency protocol detects updates that might affect the location previously loaded. The Store Conditionally instruction, which is required to store into the location previously loaded, performs the store only if the LL bit is still set, and returns the LL bit value. It is easy to implement any conditional or unconditional, single memory location, read-modify-write operation with these two instructions, including *compare&swap*.

Note that we assume that *compare&swap* forces appropriate cache consistency, not only for the location updated, but also for most previous writes (certainly writes to the same object, and possibly other writes to shared memory as well). It is easy to examine our code sequences and determine the exact cache consistency requirements, so we omit the details.

```
compare&swap(w: word, old, new: value)
   returns(boolean)
   if w = old
     then w := new
            return true
     else  return false
   end if
end compare&swap
```

Figure 1: The Compare&Swap operation

2.2 The Application's View

An application program has a set of private *local variables*, denoted by x, y, z, etc., and it shares a set of *objects*, denoted by A, B, C, etc., with other processes. To an application, an object appears simply as a fixed-size array of *values*, where a value is either immediate data, such as a boolean or integer, or a pointer to another object. The storage management system permits applications to create new objects, to fetch component values from objects, and to replace component values in objects. The *create* operation creates a new object of size s,[2] initializes each component value to the distinguished value *nil*, and stores a pointer to the object in a local variable.

$$x := create (s)$$

The *fetch* operation takes a pointer to an object and an index within the object, and returns the value of that component.

$$v := fetch (x, i)$$

The *store* operation takes a pointer to an object, an index, and a new value, and replaces that component with the new value.

$$store (x, i, v)$$

We assume that applications use these operations in a type-safe manner, and that index values always lie within range.

---

[2]We assume that objects do not vary in size over time, though our techniques could be extended to support such a model.

In the presence of concurrent access to the same object, the *fetch* and *store* operations are required to be *linearizable* [Herlihy and Wing, 1990]: although executions of concurrent operations may overlap, each operation appears to take effect instantaneously at some point between its invocation and its response. Applications are free to introduce higher-level synchronization constructs, such as semaphores or spin locks, but these are independent of our storage management algorithm.

2.3 Basic Organization

Memory is partitioned into *n* contiguous *regions*, one for each process. A process may access any memory location, but it allocates and garbage collects exclusively within its own region. Locations in process *p*'s region are *local* to *p*, otherwise they are *remote*. Each process can determine the process in whose region an address *x* lies, denoted by *owner* (*x*). This division of labor enhances concurrency: each process can make independent decisions on when to start collecting its own region and can use its own techniques for allocation. The region structure is also well-suited for *non-uniform memory access* (NUMA) architectures (e.g., [BBN, 1985; Li, 1986; Pfister *et al.*, 1985]), in which any process can reference any memory location, but the cost of accessing a particular location varies with the distance between the processor and the memory module.

An object is represented as a linked list of *versions*, where each version is a contiguous block of words contained entirely within one process's region. Versions are denoted by lower case letters *a*, *b*, *c*, etc. A version includes a snapshot of the vector of values of its object, and a *header* containing size information and a pointer to the next version. Version *a*'s pointer to the next version is denoted *a.next*. A version that has a next version is called *obsolete*; a version that does not have a next version is called *current*.

An object can be referred to by pointing to any of its versions. The *find-current* procedure (Figure 2 locates an object's current version by chaining down the list of *next* pointers until it reaches a version whose *next* pointer is *nil*. The *fetch* and *store* procedures appear in Figures 3 and 4. *Fetch* simply reads the desired field from the current version. *Store* modifies the object by creating and linking in a new current version[3]. Later we will discuss how *store* can avoid creating new versions. The *store* procedure is *lock-free*: an individual process may starve if it is overtaken infinitely often, but the system as a whole cannot starve because one *compare&swap* can fail only if another succeeds.

---

[3]This method can implement arbitrary atomic updates to a single object, including read-modify-write operations, modifications of multiple fields, and growing or shrinking the object size.

Any allocation technique can be used to implement *create*; the details are not interesting because each process allocates and garbage-collects its own region, so no inter-process synchronization is required.

Multiple versions serve two purposes: first, they allow us to perform concurrent updates without mutual exclusion [Herlihy, 1990], and second, they allow our copying collector to "move" an object without locking it. In Section 5 we discuss approaches to performing updates in place.

```
find-current(x: object) returns(object)
    while x.next ≠ nil do
        x := x.next
    end while
    return x
end find-current
```

Figure 2: Find-current: locate current version of *x*

```
fetch(x: object, i: integer) returns(value)
    x := find-current (x)
    return x[i]
end fetch
```

Figure 3: Fetch: obtains current contents of a slot

```
store(x: object, i: integer, v: value)
    temp := local space for new version
    loop /* retry from here, if necessary */
        x := find-current (x)
        for j in 1 to x.size do
            temp[j] := x[j]
        end for
        temp[i] := v
        if compare&swap (x.next, nil, temp) then
            return
        end if
    end loop
end store
```

Figure 4: Store: updates contents of a slot

3 The Algorithm

Our algorithm is an incremental copying garbage collector in the style of Baker [Baker, 1978] as extended to multiprocessing by Halstead [Halstead, 1985]. Each region is divided into multiple contiguous spaces: a single *to* space, zero or more *from* spaces, and zero or more *free* spaces. Initially, a process's objects reside in *from* spaces, and new objects are allocated in the *to* space. As computation proceeds, the processes cooperate to move objects from *from* spaces to *to* spaces, and to redirect reachable pointers to the *to* spaces. Once it can be guaranteed that there is no path from any local variable to any version in a particular *from* space, that *from* space becomes *free*. When the storage allocated in a *to* space exceeds a threshold, it becomes a *from* space, and a *free* space is allocated to serve as the new *to* space. This structure is standard for copying collectors; our contribution is a lock-free implementation of such a collector.

First, some terminology. A process *flips* when it turns a *to* space into a *from* space. A version residing in *from* space is *old*, otherwise it is *new*. Note that an old version may be either current or obsolete, and similarly for new versions. Further, it is possible for a new version to have an old version as its next version. Our procedures use the function *old* to test whether a version is old. This function could be implemented by associating an *old* bit with the space as a whole, or with individual objects, or by maintaining a table mapping memory pages to spaces.

Each process alternates between executing its application and executing a *scanning* task that checks local variables and *to* space for pointers to old versions. When such a pointer is found, the scanner locates the object's current version. If that version is old, the object is *evacuated*: a new current version is created in the scanner's own *to* space.

A scan is *clean* with respect to process *p* if it completes without finding any pointers to versions in any of *p*'s *from* spaces; otherwise it is *dirty*. A scan is done as follows:

1. Examine the contents of the local variables. This stage can be interleaved with assignments as long as the variables' original values are scanned before being overwritten.

2. Examine each memory location in the allocated portion of *to* space. This stage can be interleaved with allocations, as long as each newly allocated version is eventually scanned.

Scanning does not require interprocess synchronization.

How can we determine when a *from* space can be reclaimed? Define a *round* to be an interval during which each process starts and completes a scan. A *clean* round is one in which every scan is clean and no process flips. Our algorithm is based on the following claim: once a process flips, the *from* space can be reclaimed after a clean round starts and finishes.

How does one process detect, without locks or barrier synchronization, that another has started and completed a scan? Call the detecting process the *owner*,

and the scanning process the *scanner*. The two processes communicate through two atomic bits, called *handshake bits*, each written by one process and read by the other. Initially, both bits agree. To start a flip, the owner creates a new *to* space, marks all versions in the old *to* space as being old, and complements its own handshake bit. On each scan, the scanner reads the owner's handshake bit, performs the scan, and sets its own handshake bit to the previously read value for the owner's bit. This protocol guarantees that the handshake bits will agree again once the scanner has started and completed a scan in the interval since the owner's bit was complemented. (Similar techniques appear in a number of asynchronous shared-memory algorithms [Afek *et al.*, 1990; Peterson, 1983; Lamport, 1986].)

How does the owner detect that *all* processes have started and completed a scan? The processes share an *n*-element boolean array *owner*, where process *q* uses owner[*q*] as its "owner" handshake bit. The processes also share an *n*-by-*n*-element boolean array *scanner*, where process *q* uses scanner[*p*][*q*] as its "scanner" handshake bit when communicating with owner process *p*. Initially, all bits agree. An owner *q* starts a round by complementing owner[*q*]. A scanner *p* starts a scan by copying the *owner* array into a local array. When the scan is finished, *p* sets each scanner[*p*][*q*] to the previously saved value of owner[*q*]. The owner process *q* detects that the round is complete as soon as owner[*q*] agrees with scanner[*p*][*q*] for all *p*. An owner may not start a new round until the current round is complete.

How does a process detect whether a completed round was clean? The processes share an *n*-element boolean array, *dirty*. When a process flips, it sets dirty[*p*] to *true* for all *p* other than itself, and when a process finds a pointer into *p*'s *from* space, it sets dirty[*p*] to *true*. If a process's *dirty* bit is *false* at the end of a round, then the round was clean, and it reclaims its *from* spaces. The process sets its own *dirty* bit to *false* before starting each round.

We are now ready to discuss the algorithm in more detail. To flip (Figure 5), a process allocates a new *to* space, marks the versions in the old *to* space as old, sets everyone else's *dirty* bit, and complements its *owner* bit. (A process may not flip in the middle of a scan.) To start a scan (Figure 6), the process simply copies the current value of the *owner* array into a local array. The scanner checks each memory location for pointers to old versions (Figure 7). When such a pointer is found, it sets the owner's *dirty* bit, and redirects the pointer to a new current version, evacuating the object to its own *to* space if the current version is old. When the scan completes (Figure 8), the scanner informs the other processes by updating its *scanner* bits to the previously-saved values of the *owner* array. The scanner then checks whether a round has completed. If the round is completed and the scanner's dirty bit is *false*, the scanner reclaims its *from* spaces. If the round is completed but the dirty bit is *true*, then the scanner simply resets its *dirty* bit. Either way, it then starts a new scan.

```
flip()
    mark versions in current to space as old
    create new to space
    for i in 1 to n do
        if i ≠ me then dirty[i] := true end if
    end for
    owner[me] := not owner[me]
end flip
```

Figure 5: Starting a flip

```
scan-start()
    for i in 1 to n do
        local-owner[i][me] := owner[i]
    end for
end scan-start
```

Figure 6: Starting a scan

```
scan-value(x: object) returns(object)
    if old (x) then dirty[owner (x)] := true end if
    loop /* evacuate object if necessary */
        x := find-current (x)
        if new (x) then return x end if
        temp := local space for new version
        for j in 1 to x.size do
            temp[j] := x[j]
        end for
        if compare&swap (x.next, nil, temp)
            then return temp
            else release space for new version
        end if
    end loop
end scan-value
```

Figure 7: Scanning a pointer

4 Correctness

For our algorithm there are two correctness properties of interest: *safety*, ensuring that the algorithm implements the application-level model described in Section 2.2, and *liveness*, ensuring that as long as processes continue to take steps, then garbage is eventually collected. We outline the arguments here; more details may be found in [Herlihy and Moss, 1992].

```
scan-end()
    /* Notify other from spaces */
    for i in 1 to n do
        scanner[i][me] := local-owner[i]
    end for
    /* Did a round complete? */
    if (∀i) scanner[i][me] = owner[me] then
        if not dirty[me] then
            reclaim from spaces
        end if
        dirty[me] := false
    end if
    /* start new scan */
    scan-start()
end scan-end
```

Figure 8: Completing a scan

There are two safety properties to be demonstrated: that the implementations of the model's basic operations are linearizable, and that non-garbage objects are never collected. One way to show an operation implementation is linearizable is to identify a single primitive step where the operation "takes effect" [Lamport, 1983]; in this case the last access to the *next* field of an object is such a primitive step.

The argument that only garbage is collected proceeds by demonstrating these three claims:

Claim 1 *Every process starts and completes at least one scan during the interval between the start and end of* p's *clean round.*

Claim 2 *Every process starts and completes at least one scan clean with respect to* p *during the interval between the start and end of* p's *clean round.*

Claim 3 *When a process reclaims a* from *space, no path exists into that space from any other process's local variables.*

Liveness is shown by proving this claim:

Claim 4 *If each process always eventually scans, then some process always eventually reclaims its* from *spaces.*

5 Update in place

A significant obstacle to general practical use of our algorithm is the requirement to create a new version for each update. However, inspired by [Massalin and Pu, 1991], we devised a very simple technique for update in place using the *cas-two* operator, defined in

Figure 9. Later versions of the M68000 architecture define a CAS2 instruction that implements this operator [Motorola, Inc., 1989], so our algorithm is practical, at least on that architecture. The *cas-two* operator may be difficult to incorporate smoothly into RISC architectures; for example, the previously mentioned MIPS II instructions are inadequate for implementing *cas-two* directly.

```
compare&swap-two
    (w1, w2: word, o1, o2, n1, n2: value)
  returns(boolean)
  if w1 = o1 and w2 = o2
    then w1 := n1
         w2 := n2
         return true
    else return false
  end if
end compare&swap-two
```

Figure 9: The Compare&Swap-Two operation

In using *cas-two* for update in place the idea is to verify that the *next* pointer is still nil *and* to do the update in the *same* atomic step. Figure 10 shows the revised *store* routine. Note that versions are still needed for garbage collection, and are permitted, but no longer required, for *store* operations. Making new versions might be sensible, e.g., to increase locality on a NUMA multiprocessor.

```
store-cas-two(x: object, i: integer, v: value)
  loop /* retry from here, if necessary */
    x := find-current (x)
    if cas-two (x.next, x[i], nil, x[i], nil, v) then
      return
    end if
  end loop
end store-cas-two
```

Figure 10: Update in place using *cas-two*

Unfortunately, few architectures now include *cas-two*. It is possible to allow a single writer, namely the owner, to update in place by adding extra fields to each object and requiring creators of new versions to examine the additional fields for a pending update. Another approach is to abandon lock-free implementation of local (per-object) synchronization, and to use short term locks. Details are available in an expanded version of the paper [Herlihy and Moss, 1992], which discusses some additional extensions as well.

6 Related Work

Our algorithm is an intellectual descendant of Baker's single-processor algorithm [Baker, 1978], and can be viewed as a lock-free refinement of Halstead's multi-processor algorithm [Halstead, 1985]. Our algorithm differs from Halstead's because it does not require processes to synchronize when flipping *from* and *to* spaces, and we do not require locks on individual objects.

A number of researchers [Ben-Ari, 1984; Dijkstra *et al.*, 1978; Kung and Song, 1977] have proposed two-process mark-sweep schemes, in which one process, the *mutator*, executes an arbitrary computation, while a second process, the *collector*, concurrently detects and reclaims inaccessible storage. The models underlying these algorithms differ from ours in an important respect: they require that the collector process observe the mutator's local variables, which are treated as roots. Many current multiprocessor architectures, however, cannot meet this requirement, since the only way to copy a pointer is to load it into a private register, and then store it back to memory, leaving a "window" during which the collector cannot tell which objects are referenced by the mutator. The problem is that one processor generally cannot examine another processor's registers, and the registers are a crucial part of the state of the mutator. These algorithms synchronize largely through read and write operations, although some kind of mutual exclusion appears to be necessary for the free list and other auxiliary data structures. Pixley [Pixley, 1988] gives a generalization of Ben-Ari's algorithm in which a single collector process cleans up after multiple concurrent mutators. This algorithm, as Pixley notes, behaves incorrectly in the presence of certain race conditions, which Pixley explicitly assumes do not occur. Our algorithm introduces multiple versions to avoid precisely these kinds of problems.

The Ellis, Li, and Appel [Ellis *et al.*, 1988] describe the design and implementation of a multi-mutator, single-collector copying garbage collector. This algorithm is blocking, since processes synchronize via locks, and flipping the *from* and *to* spaces requires halting the mutators and inspecting and altering their registers.

Massalin and Pu [Massalin and Pu, 1991] describe how to implement an operating system kernel without locks. From them we realized the existence and usefulness of the *cas-two* operator; they also appear to have introduced the term *lock-free*. Beyond that there is little similarity between our work and theirs since they were considering lock-free solutions to different problems.

7 Conclusions

The garbage collection algorithm presented here is (to our knowledge) the first shared-memory multiprocessor algorithm that does not require some form of global synchronization. The algorithm's key innovations are lock-free object operations for local synchronization and the use of asynchronous "handshake bits" for global synchronization, to detect when it is safe to reclaim a space.

There are several directions in which this research could be pursued. First, as noted above, although our algorithm tolerates delays, it does not tolerate halting failures, since *from* space reclamation requires a clean sweep from each process. It would be of great interest to know whether halting failures can be tolerated in this model, and how expensive it would be. Second, our algorithm makes frequent copies of objects. Some copying, such as moving an object from *from* space to *to* space, is inherent to any copying collector. Other copying, such as moving an object from one process's *to* space to another's, is primarily intended to avoid blocking synchronization, although it might also improve memory access time in a NUMA architecture. The "pure" algorithm also copies objects within the same *to* space, although this copying can be eliminated by using a stronger operator (*cas-two*), by adding extra fields (owner-only update in place), or by locking individual objects. It would be useful to have a more systematic understanding of the trade-offs between copying, blocking synchronization, and the power of synchronization operators. Third, it appears that *cas-two* allows substantially more efficient implementation of our algorithms and it would be helpful to have a precise formal characterization and proof of this conjecture. Fourth, since our algorithms assume enough resources are available to prevent blocking resulting from resource exhaustion, it would be helpful to have a quantitative analysis of the resources required to prevent exhaustion, and a qualitative development of reasonable assumptions leading to practical guarantees that resources will not be exhausted. Finally, it would be instructive to gain some practical experience with this (or similar) lock-free algorithms. The version of the algorithm that uses *cas-two* appears to be practical; other versions may be practical in more limited circumstances, e.g., when objects are updated infrequently.

References

[Afek *et al.*, 1990] Y. Afek, H. Attiya, D. Dolev, E. Gafni, M. Merritt, and N. Shavit. Atomic snapshots. In *Ninth ACM Symposium on Principles of Distributed Computing* (1990).

[Baker, 1978] Henry G. Baker. List processing in real time on a serial computer. *Commun. ACM 21*, 4 (Apr. 1978), 280–294.

[BBN, 1985] BBN. The uniform system approach to programming the Butterfly parallel processor. Tech. Rep. 6149, Bolt, Beranek, and Newman Adv. Computers, Inc., Cambridge, MA, Oct. 1985.

[Ben-Ari, 1984] M. Ben-Ari. Algorithms for on-the-fly garbage collection. *ACM Trans. Program. Lang. Syst. 6*, 3 (July 1984), 333–344.

[Dijkstra *et al.*, 1978] E. W. Dijkstra, L. Lamport, A. J. Martin, C. S. Scholten, and E. F. M. Steffins. On-the-fly garbage collection: An excercise in cooperation. *Commun. ACM 21*, 11 (Nov. 1978), 966–975.

[Ellis *et al.*, 1988] John R. Ellis, Kai Li, and Andrew W. Appel. Real-time concurrent collection on stock multiprocessors. Tech. Rep. 25, Digital Systems Research Center, 130 Lytton Avenue, Palo Alto, CA 94301, Feb. 1988.

[Halstead, 1985] R. H. Halstead, Jr. Multilisp: A language for concurrent symbolic computation. *ACM Trans. Program. Lang. Syst. 7*, 4 (Oct. 1985), 501–538.

[Herlihy, 1988] Maurice P. Herlihy. Impossibility and universality results for wait-free synchronization. In *Seventh ACM SIGACT-SIGOPS Symposium on Principles of Distributed Computing* (Aug. 1988), pp. 276–290.

[Herlihy, 1990] Maurice P. Herlihy. A methodology for implementing highly concurrent data structures. In *Second ACM SIGPLAN Symposium on Principles and Practice of Parallel Programming* (Mar. 1990), pp. 197–206.

[Herlihy, 1991] Maurice P. Herlihy. Wait-free synchronization. *ACM Trans. Program. Lang. Syst. 13*, 1 (Jan. 1991), 124–149.

[Herlihy and Moss, 1992] Maurice P. Herlihy and J. Eliot B. Moss. Lock-free garbage collection for multiprocessors. *IEEE Transactions on Parallel and Distributed Systems* (1992). To appear.

[Herlihy and Wing, 1990] Maurice P. Herlihy and Jeannette M. Wing. Linearizabilty: a correctness condition for concurrent objects. *ACM Trans. Program. Lang. Syst. 12*, 3 (July 1990), 463–492.

[IBM] IBM. System/370 Principles of Operation. Order Number GA22-7000.

[Kilian, 1991] Earl Kilian, Apr. 1991. Personal communication.

[Kung and Song, 1977] H. T. Kung and S. W. Song. An efficient parallel garbage collection system and its correctness proof. In *18th Symposium on Foundations of Computer Science* (Oct. 1977), pp. 120–131.

[Lamport, 1983] Leslie Lamport. Specifying concurrent program modules. *ACM Trans. Program. Lang. Syst. 5*, 2 (Apr. 1983), 190–222.

[Lamport, 1986] Leslie Lamport. On interprocess communication, parts I and II. *Distributed Computing 1* (1986), 77–101.

[Li, 1986] Kai Li. *Shared Virtual Memory on Loosely Coupled Multiprocessors*. PhD thesis, Yale University, New Haven CT, Sept. 1986.

[Massalin and Pu, 1991] Henry Massalin and Calton Pu. A lock-free multiprocessor OS kernel. Technical Report CUCS-005-91, Columbia University, Department of Computer Science, New York, NY, Mar. 1991.

[Motorola, Inc., 1989] Motorola, Inc. *M68000 Family Programmer's Reference Manual*. Motorola, Phoenix AZ., 1989. Document M68000PM/AD.

[Peterson, 1983] G. L. Peterson. Concurrent reading while writing. *ACM Trans. Program. Lang. Syst. 5*, 1 (Jan. 1983), 46–55.

[Pfister *et al.*, 1985] Greg H. Pfister *et al.* The IBM Research Parallel Processor Prototype (RP3): Introduction and architecture. In *International Conference on Parallel Processing* (1985).

[Pixley, 1988] C. Pixley. An incremental garbage collection algorithm for multi-mutator systems. *Distributed Computing 3*, 1 (Dec. 1988), 41–49.

A Simple Load Balancing Scheme for
Task Allocation in Parallel Machines

Larry Rudolph

Department of Computer Science

Hebrew University, Jerusalem, Israel

and currently visiting

IBM TJ Watson Research Center

Yorktown Heights, NY

Miriam Slivkin-Allalouf

John Bryce Ltd.

Science Based Industries

PO BOX 23838

Jerusalem, Israel

Eli Upfal

Department of Applied Mathematics

Weizman Institute, Rehovot, Israel

and

IBM Almaden Research Center

San Jose, Ca

Abstract

A collection of local workpiles (task queues) and a simple load balancing scheme is well suited for scheduling tasks in shared memory parallel machines. Task scheduling on such machines has usually been done through a single, globally accessible, workpile. The scheme introduced in this paper achieves a balancing comparable to that of a global workpile, while minimizing the overheads. In many parallel computer architectures, each processor has some memory that it can access more efficiently, and so it is desirable that tasks do not mirgrate frequently.

The load balancing is simple and distributed: Whenever a processor accesses its local workpile, it performs a balancing operation with probability inversely proportional to the size of its workpile. The balancing operation consists of examining the workpile of a random processor and exchanging tasks so as to equalize the size of the two workpiles. The probabilistic analysis of the performance of the load balancing scheme proves that each tasks in the system receives its fair share of computation time. Specifically, the expected size of each local task queue is within a small constant factor of the average, i.e. total number of tasks in the system divided by the number of processors.

1 Introduction

The scheduling of the activities of a parallel program on a parallel machine can significantly influence its performance. A poor scheduling policy may leave many processors idle while a clever one may consume an unduly large portion of the total CPU cycles. The main goal is to provide a distributed, low cost, scheme that balances the load across all the processors.

Scheduling schemes are only important when the system is allowed to schedule and map tasks to processors. Many users of today's parallel machines demand maximum performance and are therefore willing to invest an Herculerian effort in doing the mapping and scheduling themselves. On the otherhand, shared memory machines as well as a few message passing ones wish to relieve the user of this job and allow development of more portable code. We focus on shared memory, asynchronous parallel machines, but believe that our results are more widely applicable.

Many load balancing schemes for parallel processing have been studied, although most make different assumptions or require a detailed knowledge of either the architecture or the application. For example, when adaptive meshes are used in applications such as Particle-in-cell methods, finite difference and finite element calculations, load balancing schemes are concerned with how to move boundries to equalize the number of particles allocated to each processor ([DG89]). Here information is exchanged at natural synchronization points.

Independent of the application, some schemes try to find the global average load and the least and most loaded node in the system using a minimum of communication steps. The strategy is to query only a small number of neighbors at periodic intervals in the hope of keeping its own information up-to-date (e.g. [CK79],[BKW89],[JW89]). Sometimes a central server is considered ([BK90]). There have also been attempts to use simulated annealing ([FFKS89]).

Schemes are often directly related to the machine architectures. There have been many schemes proposed for hypercubes ([DG90],[DG89]) and either balance only between local neighbors or recursively balance between adjacent subcubes.

Similar to our scheme, Hong et al. [HTC89] try to achieve global balance by equalizing the loads between pairs of processors. The balancing, however, occurs at fixed, predetermined intervals and they are interested in the effects of changing the interval times. Another approach that also uses random polling [KR89] has the processors poll only when they are idle.

In contrast, our work is concerned with tightly coupled shared memory parallel machines where the tasks may all be part of the same parallel program. We assume that communication between PEs is uniform and inexpensive although it appears that our results can also apply to restricted communication architectures, such as hypercubes. Moreover, we are able to prove a bound of the performance of the balancing scheme.

Parallel shared-memory machines designed in the past often provided a flat global memory and so there was a minimal cost in moving a task from one processor to another. The single global workpile is sufficient for these architectures (e.g. see [R87]). Each processor (PE) chooses the next task in the global workpile and executes it for a given time-quantum. If the task does not terminate within the time-quantum, it is returned to the end of the global workpile and the PE chooses the next task. Thus, unless the number of tasks matched the number of PEs, it was unlikely that task would be resumed on the same PE. The global workpile with time-slicing gives the appearance that there are many more PEs executing in parallel than may physically exist in the system. The work-load of the tasks is also evenly balanced among all the PEs and no PE will be idle while there is a task ready to be executed.

The global workpile scheme is not well suited for more advance architectures in which there is a more complex memory hierarchy and where the amount of local state is significant. Here, it is preferable for a task to resume its execution by the same processor that executed it previously. A local workpile associated with each PE will provide this continuity, but it suffers from a potential unequal distribution of the work (tasks) among the processors. One PE may have a very long workpile while another may have a very short or empty one. Unless the system employs some load balancing technique, tasks will then execute at different rates, inversely proportional to the average length of their workpiles.

We first state our assumptions and requirements for a parallel task system. Our load balancing scheme is then presented. Its behavior and performance is then analyzed and the results of simulations are presented. Finally, we show that there are cases in which a task allocation scheme based on local workpiles with load balancing performs better than one based on global workpiles.

2 Foundations

Each processing element consists of a CPU, registers, local memory for local computation and I/O ports which will enable it to work independently on a task. We consider the task as an indivisible entity, the smallest viable computational unit.

We assume a parallel processor that is executing a parallel program. A *task* is a piece of code that is to be executed, possibly in parallel with other tasks. We assume that tasks are generated dynamically by the processors and can be executed by any of the processors. All existing, ready-to-run tasks in the system are either being executed by some processor or are are maintained in a data structure that we call a *workpile*. We use this term instead of the traditional term of *task queue* since a strict FIFO order is not required. Tasks are inserted to and deleted from the workpile.

The workpile can be organized two different ways: as a single, global workpile accessible to all processors or as set of local workpiles, one associated with each processor. Of course hybred schemes are also possible although not considered in this paper. All tasks are assumed to have the same priority; multiple priority levels can be implemented with the schemes presented here used within each distinct priority level.

Since tasks may closely interact and since there may be more tasks than the number of processors, a preemptive scheduling strategy is required. That is, a processor executes a task for a period of time, usually called a *time-quantum*, or until the task voluntarily gives up control.

2.1 The Workpile as a Global Queue

When the task allocation scheme is based on a single global queue, all insertions and deletions of tasks are directed to the same data-structure. Each idle processor removes a task from the workpile and begins to process that task. The process executes the task until the task either terminates, suspends, or a quantum of time has elapsed. In the latter case, the task is returned to the global workpile for continued processing at a later time. The processor is then considered idle and thus chooses another task from the global workpile and the process continues. If the workpile is empty, the processor retries after a short idle period. Access to the global workpile is sequential in that only one processor may be adding or removing a task from the global workpile at any time. If multiple PEs simultaneously attempt access, they are serialized in an arbitrary fashion.

```
x
x                                   x
x       x           x               x
x       x           x       x       x
x       x           x       x       x       x
x       x       x   x       x   x   x       x

PE₁    PE₂    PE₃    PE₄    PE₅    PE₆    PE₇    PE₈
```

Figure 1: Each PE has a workpile associated with it. It inserts and deletes only to this workpile. A load balancing mechanism may move tasks from one workpile to another. PE_i executes a load balancing operation with probability $1/l_i$ where l_i is the length of the i workpile.

```
Balancing Task for PE i
    lock workpileᵢ;
    r = random number in the range [1, p] but not i
    lock workpileᵣ
    if | size of workpileᵢ − size workpileᵣ | > τ
    then move task from the end of the longer
              to the end of the smaller so as to
              equalize their workpile sizes.
    unlock workpileᵢ and workpileᵣ
```

Figure 2: The load balancing task

This scheme appears to provide the best load balancing since it is never the case that a processor remains idle while there is a task ready to be executed. But this is true only in a very limited setting. First, since many processors may concurrently access the global workpile, some of these access may have to be delayed. Second, if the number of tasks is only slightly larger than the number of processors, there will be too many needless context switches. Finally, it is highly unlikely that a task will be rescheduled on the same processor that previously executed it and if the processors have the ability to keep a significant amount of task state in their local memory then this migration will be expensive.

2.2 The Workpile As A Set Of Local Queues

An alternative to the global workpile is for each processor to maintain its own local workpile of tasks. Each processor chooses the next task only from its own local workpile (Figure 1). The local workpile is organized as a FIFO queue so that the tasks are processed in a round-robin fashion. If the local workpile is empty, the associated processor remains idle.

Newly created tasks are also placed into the local workpile of the processor executing the creation operation. This allows an optimization in certain situations. Many parallel languages, and or operating systems, allow a task to be spawned or created with an associated *multiplicity* count, m. In a single call, m distinct tasks are created, each one assigned a different index in the range 0 to $m - 1$. The optimization consists of placing only a single templete into the workpile and as each task begins execution, the full task control block is created. If the tasks require only a small amount of CPU time, this optimization will be significant.

There are several advantages and disadvantages to the local workpile organization. The advantages are that tasks may be inserted and removed in parallel and tasks remain on the same processor that first executed them. On the otherhand, there may be many idle processors. Indeed, without any explicit *load balancing*, all the tasks might be on a single local workpile. Two types of load balancing are possible, initial allocation where newly created tasks are inserted onto any of the local workpiles and continuous balancing where tasks may be moved from one local workpile to another whenever they are not executing. Any combination of these two are possible; we focus on the latter case.

3 The Balancing Scheme for Local Workpiles

The most striking feature of our load balancing scheme is that it is adaptive, distributed, and very simple. Each processor makes its own local, independent decision as to when to balance and with whom. It is suprising that although no processor has global knowledge of the system load, the expected load on each node is about the average load thoughout the system.

The main problem related to the function of controlling and balancing the workpiles is the conflict between the desire to control and the unwillingness to have one single master processor. Also it is not desirable that each processor check the situation of the whole system during each time period. Rather the load-balancing is done dynamically with minimal interference.

Load balancing has traditionally been exectued in one of two different ways. In the *periodic solution* a time period is fixed throughout the system during which load balancing is performed. In the *when necessary* or *polling* solution, whenever a PE is idle it polls the other PEs to share in their work.

We propose using a different approach to scheduling the load balancing work. There is no set time during which a processor executes the load balancing task. Instead, the load or size of the local workpile dictates the frequency of its execution. Let $l_{i,t}$ be the number of tasks on the workpile associated with processor i at time t. Let t be the time at which processor i is accessing its scheduling code. At time t, before scheduling the next task from its local workpile, processor i flips a coin and executes the load balancing task with probability $1/l_{i,t}$. If $l_{i,t} = 0$, then the processor delays a certain amount before executing the balancing task once again. In our implementation, we use an exponential backoff scheme in this case.

A processor with many tasks in its local workpile will thus execute the load-balancing task infrequently while one with a short workpile will frequently try to load-balance. The fraction of time that a processor will invest in load balancing is inversely proportional to its own workload.

The load-balancing task simply chooses some other PE at random and tries to equalize the load between the two workpiles (see Figure 2). If the difference in load between the two workpiles is greater than some lower limit, tasks are then migrated from the heavier loaded workpile to the lighter one. If the other workpile is currently being accessed, then either the PE may give up or else wait until the workpile becomes free. Our implementations suggest that there is little difference between these strategies.

There are several implementation details that require further explanation:

- The simplist way of choosing another local workpile with which to balance is by choosing one at random. Each processor begins with a unique seed for its random number generator.

- Concurrent access to a local workpile is not allowed.

- Local workpiles are accessed in FIFO order.

- The load of a workpile is measured as the number of tasks on the workpile.

- A system-wide threshold value, τ, is fixed such that only task workpiles whose length differs by more than τ will perform a balancing operation.

- A balancing operation consists of moving tasks from one workpile to another in order to equalize their lengths. Tasks from the end of the longer workpile are moved to the end of the shorter workpile.

- No starvation occurs. Since workpiles are accessed in FIFO order a task the does not migrate will eventually be executed. If it is migrated, it is moved to a position closer to the head of the queue.

In summary, in a heavily loaded system, there is little load balancing and in a lightly loaded system, load balancing is frequently attempted. This also holds true for each individual processor. Furthermore, since the sizes of the workpiles are roughly equal, there is very little task migration. It is also very rare that some processor will attempt to access a workpile will some other processor is currently accessing it.

4 Results

Since there is no single, generally accepted performance criteria for task scheduling, we present several different analyses of the behavior of our scheme. Of prime importance is how well does our scheme perform in a real system with real workloads. Many factors, such as memory access time, network traffic, type of application, and low level implementation details influence the performance. We have therefor measured and compared the performance of our scheme and the global workpile one using a simulation system of a parallel computer with sample application programs. The results are reported in the first subsection. Simulations are not sufficent, however, to prove the general applicability of our result. The second subsection, therefore, presents analytical results proving that each tasks in the system receives computation time that is proportional to its size in the entire system, that is, p/T, where p is the number of processors and T is the total number of active tasks in the system. The final subsection explains the effect of the scheduling and load balancing and presents an example where the decentralized scheme outperforms the centralized one.

4.1 Simulation Results

For two different application programs, we present the results of a simulation system of an ideal parallel computer. The simulation system makes many simplifications:

1. there is no difference in the costs of memory accesses.

2. no overhead in moving a thread from one processor to another.

3. no overhead in updating cache or page table entries.

4. no contention on the global workpile and insertion/deletion takes no time.

5. load balancing takes zero time.

All these assuptions, save the latter, favor the global workpile scheme since such overheads are higher in the global workpile scheme than in any other scheme.

240

We wish to argue that even without these benefits, the decentralized workpile scheme with adaptive load-balancing is competitive with the global workpile scheme. There are, of course, many situations that favor the centralized scheme. Thus, the ultimate choice depends on how costly are these measures on a particular machine.

We present the results of two different applications and four different schemes. The applications are a parallel version of quicksort and a master/slave skeleton program. In the first, a random splitting element is choosen, the array is subdivided into those elements larger and those smaller than the splitting element. The sort is recursively and in parallel applied to these two sets. The second application has a master process executing and then spawns off a number of slave tasks, 16 of them in our case, to work in parallel with the master. The slaves run for a short time. Somewhat later, the master once again spawns off a set of slave tasks. The process continues a number of times, 16 in our case. In both cases, the problem size is fixed and we vary the number of processors and measure the time to completetion.

Figures 5, and 5 summarize the results of the simulation that focuses only on the load-balancing features. There are two points to note. First, the scheduling schemes affect the performace even when one ignores the overheads of migration and concurrent access to the global workpile. This is important since it gives credence to the simulations and the same applications. Second, when one considers just the balance, the local workpile scheme gives a balance which is as good as the global workpile.

We also examined what happends when the first two simplifications are dropped. That is, we assumed that memory references can be either local, shared, or remote. We present results when these values are 1, 2, and 3, respectively. In the global workpile situation, all memory references are charged as shared. In the local workpile situation, memory references are either local or remote. Without loab balancing, tass are initially allocated to random processors and never moved. Their memory accesses always are charged as local. When there is migration, a task is first charged at the remote rate and after a while, it reverts to a local rate. We hope to capture the fact that initially, there is a high cost but after some time, the state can be transfered to the local memory. Figure 5 presents these results. We can see that the global workpile case is always twice as expensive as the others. This implies that there is not too much migration. It is also interesting to note that without load balancing, performace is as bad as the global case. The unbalanced work load wastes about half the processing power.

4.2 Analysis

We prove that the load balancing scheme indeed provides a good balance. The expected length of local workpiles is within a small constant factor times the average length. The key observation is that if the system starts in balanced, then it will stay that way. Of course this result depends on some reasonable assumptions concerning the creation and termination of tasks.

Denote by $L_{p,t}$ the load (= number of tasks) processor p has at the start of step t, and by $\Delta_{p,t}$ its change to its own load at time t ignoring load balancing changes, i.e. the number of new tasks processor p generates at step t minus the number of tasks terminated at processor p at this step. $\Delta_{p,t}$ might have an arbitrary distribution, but we require that $|\Delta_{p,t}|$ is bounded by some constant δ.

Denote by $L_t = \sum_{p \in V} L_{p,t}$ the total load of the system at time t, and by $A_t = \frac{L_t}{n}$ the average load at time t; there are n processors. Let $P_{p,t}$ denote the probability that processor p initiates a load balancing procedure at time t. We prove that if the system starts balanced, and if $P_{p,t} \geq \frac{\theta}{L_{p,t}}$, for some constant $\theta > 1$, then the system achieves optimal load balancing up to a constant factor. In other words, the expected waiting time of processes in workpiles of different processors differ only by a constant factor.

Theorem 1: *There are constants α, and C, independent of the number of processors n, and the distribution of $\Delta_{p,t}$ (the schedule of tasks to the processors), such that when the system starts balanced, and the load balancing algorithm is executed, for each processor p, and at each step t,*

$$E[L_{p,t}] \leq \alpha A_t + C.$$

proof: To simplify the analysis we consider a weaker load balancing scheme in which $P_{p,t}$ (the probability that processor p initiates a load balancing procedure at time t) is always bounded by $\min[\frac{\mu}{A_t}, \frac{1}{2}]$ for some $\mu > 0$. Thus, we restrict the activity of the very lightly loaded processors. We also assume a very weak conflict arbitration scheme: If processor p is initiating a load balancing procedure at a given step, it ignores messages from other processors initiating load balancing at this step. Furthermore, if processor p did not initiate a load balancing procedure but was chosen by more than one processor, then p does not balance its load with any processor. The performance of the original algorithm clearly dominates the performance of this algorithm.

We prove by induction on t that $E[L_{p,t}] \leq \alpha A_t + C$. The theorem assumes that the system started balanced, thus the induction hypothesis holds for $t = 0$. Assuming that the claim holds for t we bound $E[L_{p,t+1}]$.

$E[L_{p,t+1}] = E[L_{t,p}] + E[\Delta_{p,t}] + E[C_1] - E[C_2]$, where C_1 gives the contribution to $L_{p,t+1}$ from load balancing with a processor chosen by p, and C_2 gives the load lost by a load balancing with a processor choosing p.

Clearly, p never receives more than half the load of the processor it chooses, the probability that p initiates a load-balancing procedure at step $t + 1$ is bounded by $\frac{\mu}{A_t}$. If it initiates load balancing, the probability that it chooses processor x is $1/(n-1)$, and in that case it receives no more than $L_{x,t}/2$ tasks. Thus,

$$E[C_1] \leq E[\frac{\mu}{A_t} \frac{1}{n-1} \sum_{x \neq p} \frac{L_{x,t}}{2}] \leq \frac{\mu}{2}.$$

Bounding $E[C_2]$ is more complicated since we need a lower bound. Let M_t denote the set of processors with $L_{x,t} \leq 2A_t$. Clearly $|M_t| \geq n/2$. The probability that a processor $x \in M$ initiates load balancing is at least $\min[\frac{\theta}{2A_t}, \frac{\mu}{A_t}, \frac{1}{2}]$. The probability that processor x chooses p, p is not chosen by any other processor, and p is not initiating load balancing at this step is at least

$$(1 - \frac{\mu}{A_t}) \frac{1}{n-1} \prod_{y \neq p,x} (1 - \frac{P_{y,t}}{n-1}) \geq \frac{1}{4(n-1)}.$$

Let $\gamma = \min[\theta/2, \mu]$, then

$$
\begin{aligned}
E[C_2] \quad &\geq \min \quad \left[E[\frac{1}{4(n-1)} \frac{\gamma}{A_t} \sum_{x \in M} \frac{L_{p,t} - L_{x,t}}{2}], \right. \\
&\qquad\qquad \left. E[\frac{1}{4(n-1)} \frac{1}{2} \sum_{x \in M} \frac{L_{p,t} - L_{x,t}}{2}] \right] \\
&\geq \min \quad \left[E[\frac{\gamma}{8A_t}(L_{p,t} - 2A_t)], E[\frac{(L_{p,t} - A_t)}{16}] \right].
\end{aligned}
$$

Set $\alpha = 6 + 8\delta$, $\mu = \theta/2 = \alpha + 1$, $C = 8\mu + 16(\alpha + 1)\delta$, and recall that $A_{t+1} \geq A_t - \delta$.
If $\frac{\gamma}{A_t} \leq \frac{1}{2}$ then

$$E[L_{p,t+1}] = E[L_{t,p}] + E[\Delta_{p,t}] + E[C_1] - E[C_2]$$
$$\leq \alpha A_t + C + \delta + \mu/2 - \gamma(\alpha - 2)/8 \leq \alpha A_{t+1} + C.$$

If $\frac{\gamma}{A_t} > \frac{1}{2}$ then

$$E[L_{p,t+1}] = E[L_{t,p}] + E[\Delta_{p,t}] + E[C_1] - E[C_2]$$
$$\leq \alpha A_t + C + \delta + \mu/2 - C/16 \leq \alpha A_{t+1} + C.$$

$\square$

We measured how much the length of the task queues differed from the global average and plotted the resutls in Figure 5. We ran 10 master-slave applications together and measured how the local workpile lengths differed from the global average. At each time step,

we computed the global average, A_t, and summed the square of the differences of the queue lengths from A_t. We averaged this value and then took the average over alltime steps. That is,

$$\frac{1}{T} \sum_{t \in T} \frac{1}{n} \sum_{i \in n} (L_{i,t} - A_t)^2$$

We see that the load balancing keeps the size of the workpiles very near the average. This value ranged between 2 and 3.

4.3 FIFO Not Always Best

We present another example when the decentralized scheme provides better schedualing than the centralized one. It is interesting since at first blush, the global queue seems to provide the best possible balance. We use the term queue in place of workpile in order to emphasize its FIFO nature. Let us assume p PEs and $p+1$ tasks. One of the tasks is much longer than the other and it takes h time quantum units to execute it. The other tasks are equal sized - each requiring s time quantum units, where $s << h$. First, consider the global task queue scheme: The time until all the short tasks complete requires $((p+1)/p) * s$ time quantum units. The remainder part of the long task has $h - s$ units of time. Thus, the whole execution takes

$$h - s + ((p+1)/p) * s = h + s/p$$

units.

Next, consider the local task queue scheme with load balancing and a threshold $\tau = 1$. There are two diffent possiblities: The long task can be inserted into a queue with another short task (this happens with a probability of $1/p$) or the long task is alone and some other task queue has two short tasks. If the long task is alone in the queue the execution time is h. Otherwise it takes $h+s/2$. Thus, the whole execution is expected to require

$$1/p(h + s/2) + ((p-1)/p)h = h + s/(2p).$$

Since $s/(2p) < s/p$ the global task queue scheme does not provide the best scheduling.

5 Conclusions

We believe that the local workpile with load balancing is ideally suited for shared memory parallel processors. It gives the programmer the ability to program at a higher level of abstraction since he does not need to know the exact number of processors available. Moreover, the load balancing scheme adapts to the current load on the system.

It is interesting to consider how our scheme performs when faced with the popular paridigm of "loosly synchronous" programs and a multiprogrammed environment. Here, each program consists of a set of tasks that execute in a loosely synchronous fashion. That is, each task executed for a period of time and then participates in a communication or information exchange step with all the other tasks in the program. It is expected that the execution periods of the tasks are about equal. Now suppose there are several of these programs running concurrently. If there are enough processors for all the tasks, then our scheme will quickly approach that mapping. If the total number of tasks is much larger than the number of processors, then our scheme will cluster together tasks belonging to the same program since there tasks were initially placed on the same task queue.

Our experimental results showed that there is hardly any difference between the two schemes in terms of the distribution of work among the processors. Thus, architectures that encourage local state, would be better served with the local workpile scheme.

The key insight in the analysis is to demand that the system begin in a balanced state. It can be shown that the random selection is necessary to get our result. It each processor had chosen to balance only with a small set of neighbors, the it is possible to form little mountains or heaps with the peak located at a processor that continues to generate new tasks and the size of the workpiles decreasing as one gets further from the peak processor.

One of the weaknesses of the scheme is that the load-balancing tasks are executed with the same frequency whether the system is balanced or not. A possible improvement is in the dynamically setting the threshold value.

The scheme should be investigated for non-fully connected topologies such as the hypercube. It is our belief that it is nevertheless worthwhile to treat the hypercube as a completely interconnected network and to simply pay the extra cost when sampling or moving tasks between non-adjacent processors.

Another extention to this work involves treating newly created tasks differently from already executing ones. If is cheaper to move a task before it has executed. One should move such tasks first and only when that does not provided a good enough balance should other tasks be moved. Of course both types of migration can be based on the same load balancing scheme, only using different probabilities.

References

[BKW89] Baumartner, K., R. Kling, and B. Wah, "Implementation of GAMMON: an efficient load balancing strategy for a local computer system," *Proceedings of the International Conference on Parallel Processing*, **Vol 2**, pp. 77-80, Aug. 1989.

[BK90] Bonomi, F. and A. Kumar, "*Adaptive optimal load balancing in a nonhomogeneous multiserver system with a central job scheduler,*" *IEEE Transactions on Computers*, **Vol. 39**, pp. 1232-50, Oct. 1990.

[CK79] Y.C. Chow and W. Kohler, "*Models for Dynamic Load Balancing in a Heterogeneous Multiple Processor System,*" *IEEE Transactions on Computers*, **Vol. C-28**, pp. 334-361, May 1979.

[DG90] Dehne, F. and M. Gastaldo, "*A note on the load balancing problem for coarse grained hypercube dictionary machines,*" *Parallel Computing*, **Vol 16**, pp. 75-79, Nov 1990.

[DG89] Dragon, K, and J. Gustafson, "*A low cost hypercube load balancing algorithm,*" *Proceedings of the Fourth Conference on Hypercubes, Concurrent Computers and Applications*, **Vol 1**, pp. 583-589, March 1989

[FFKS89] Fox, G., W. Furmanski, J. Koller, and P. Simic, "*Physical optimization and load balancing algorithms,*" *Proceedings of the Fourth Conference on Hypercubes, Concurrent Computers and Applications*, **Vol 1**, pp. 591-594, March 1989

[HTC89] Hong, J., X. Tan, and M. Chen, "*Dynamic cyclic load balancing on hypercubes,*" *Proceedings of the Fourth Conference on Hypercubes, Concurrent Computers and Applications*, **Vol 1**, pp. 595-598, March 1989

[JW89] Juang, J. and B. Wah, "*Load balancing and ordered selection in a computer system with multiple contention buses,*" *Journal of Parallel and Distributed Computing*, **Vol 7**, pp 391-415, Dec. 1989.

[KR89] Kumar, V, and V. Rao, "*Load balancing on the hypercube architecture,*" *Proceedings of the Fourth Conference on Hypercubes, Concurrent Computers and Applications*, **Vol 1**, pp. 603-608, March 1989

[K89] Koller, J., "*The MOOS II Operating System and Dynamic Load Balancing*" *Proceedings of the Fourth Conference on Hypercubes, Concurrent Computers and Applications*, **Vol 1**, pp 599-602, March 1989

[R87] Raetz, G. "*Sequent general purpose parallel processing system,*" *Northcon/87*, pp. 7/2/1-5, Sept. 1987.

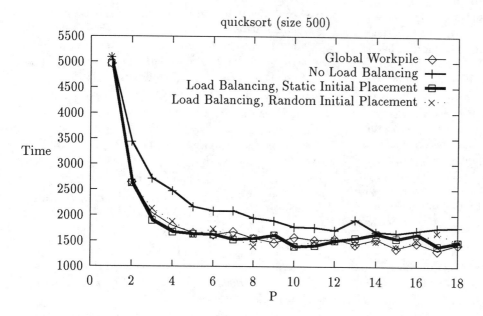

Figure 3: Quicksort application of size of 500. The scheduling strategy clearly affects the performance and there are times when the global workpile does not yield the best performance. Even without the local memory access advantages, we see that the load balancing scheme yields good performance.

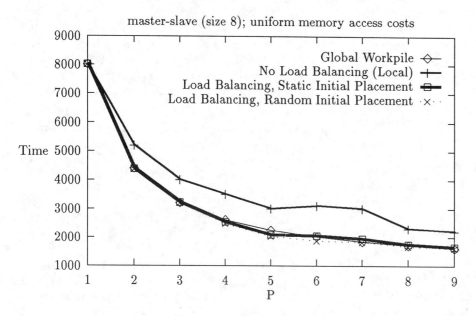

Figure 4: This data shows that when memory access costs are the same and the number of tasks is a little more than the number of processors, then our load balancing gives better results than then global workpile.

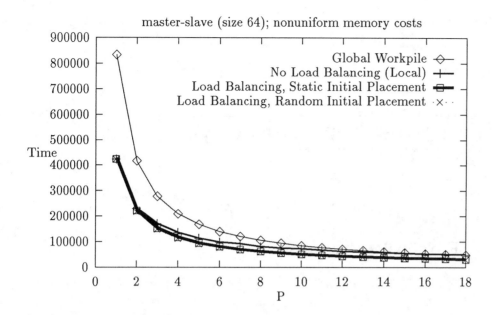

Figure 5: A memory access to local memory is charged 1 unit and to remote meory is charged 3 units. Shared memory access are charged 2 units. After a task migrates, its 10 access are charged at the highest rate of 3 units. Each task executes a total of 64 accesses. In this application, the master task spawns 64 slave tasks. After all these slaves finish, another batch is started. The results shows that the global workpile is about twice as bad due to the fact that each memory access time is twice as expensive. Thus we see that very few of the accesses are remote. Without load balancing performance degrades due to the poor scheduling even though all the accesses are charged 1 unit.

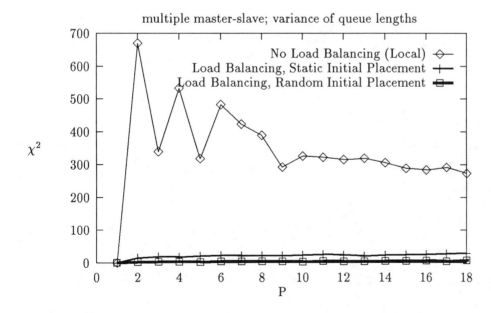

Figure 6: We ran 10 master-slave applications together and measured how the local workpile lengths differed from the global average. We plotted the following $\frac{1}{T} \sum_{t \in T} \frac{1}{n} \sum_{i \in n} (L_{i,t} - A_t)^2$, where T ranges over all time values, n is the number of processors, $L_{i,t}$ is the length of workpile at processor i at time t, and A_t is the average number of tasks in the system at time t. We see that the load balancing keeps the size of the workpiles very near the average.

Invited Speaker: Theory

Franco P. Preparata

Wang Professor of Computer Science
Brown University

"The Many Faces of Concurrency"

SESSION 7

The Efficiency of Greedy Routing
in Hypercubes and Butterflies *

George D. Stamoulis   John N. Tsitsiklis

Laboratory for Information and Decisions Systems
Massachusetts Institute of Technology
Cambridge, Mass. 02139, USA

Abstract

We analyze the following problem: Each node of the d-dimensional hypercube independently generates packets according to a Poisson process with rate λ. Each of the packets is to be sent to a randomly chosen destination; each of the nodes at Hamming distance k from a packet's origin is assigned an a priori probability $p^k(1-p)^{d-k}$. (For $p = \frac{1}{2}$, the destination distribution is uniform.) Packets are routed under a simple greedy scheme: each of them has to follow the canonical path leading to its destination. Assuming unit packet length and no other communications taking place, we show that this scheme is stable (in steady-state) if $\rho < 1$, where $\rho \stackrel{\text{def}}{=} \lambda p$ is the load factor of the network; this is seen to be the broadest possible range for stability. Furthermore, we prove that the average delay T per packet satisfies $T \leq \frac{dp}{1-\rho}$, thus showing that an average delay of $\Theta(d)$ is attainable for any fixed $\rho < 1$. We also establish similar results in the context of the butterfly network. Our analysis is based on a stochastic comparison with a product-form queueing network.

1 INTRODUCTION

1.1 Problem Definition

During the execution of distributed algorithms in a parallel computer, it is necessary that processors communicate with each other in order to exchange information. In message-passing systems, this is accomplished

by routing messages through the underlying interconnection network. In the present paper, we consider a well-known problem: the nodes (i.e., processors) of the binary hypercube (see §1.4) generate packets at random time instants; each packet has a single destination, which is selected at random. We discuss a simple greedy scheme for routing these packets and we analyze its steady-state stability and delay properties. The results to be derived extend to the butterfly network.

The underlying assumptions for communications are as follows: Each piece of information is transmitted as a packet with unit transmission time. Only one packet can traverse an arc at a time; all transmissions are error-free. Each node may transmit packets through all of its output ports and at the same time receive packets through all of its input ports. Each node has infinite buffer capacity. Finally, for analytical convenience, the time axis is taken to be continuous. The results also extend to the case of slotted time; see §2.4.

Routing a packet from a node x to another node z may be accomplished optimally by transmitting the packet along one of the shortest paths from x to z; this takes time equal to the Hamming distance $H(x, z)$ between the two nodes (see §1.4), provided that the packet does not encounter any *contention* en route. This is the simplest conceivable communication task. Under more general tasks, several packets are to be transmitted at the same time, with the set of origin-destination pairs having a special structure. (e.g., the permutation task, where each node transmits one packet, with different packets having different destinations; see also §1.3.) By exploiting this special structure, one may devise an algorithm to perform such a task efficiently. Such routing problems are called *static*, because they involve tasks to be performed only *once*, in the *absence* of other transmissions. In the *dynamic* version of the routing problem, it is assumed that multiple tasks are generated over an *infinite* time-horizon; moreover, different tasks may *interfere* with each other. As discussed below, most of

*Research supported by the NSF under Grant ECS-8552419 and by the ARO under Grant DAAL03-86-K-0171.

the routing literature deals with static problems. In the present paper, we consider a dynamic problem with a simple structure:

Each node of the d-cube generates packets according to a Poisson process with rate λ; different nodes generate their packets independently of each other. Each packet has a *single* destination, which is selected *randomly*; in particular, we assume that

$$\Pr[\text{a packet generated by } x \text{ is destined for } z]$$
$$= p^{H(x,z)}(1-p)^{d-H(x,z)}, \qquad (1)$$

where $p \in (0, 1]$; different packets make their selections independently of each other. (A simple interpretation of this rule is presented at the end of §2.1.)

It is seen from Eq. (1) that for $p = \frac{1}{2}$ the destination distribution is uniform; that is, each node (including its origin) is equally likely to be chosen as a packet's destination. This is the case usually considered in the literature (see §1.3); in most of the related works, a packet's origin is not a permissible destination; however, our results (when rescaled appropriately) also apply to this case. For $p < \frac{1}{2}$, the destination distribution favors nodes at shorter distance from a packet's origin; in this case, packet transmissions tend to be more localized.

1.2 Summary of the Results

First, we derive the necessary condition for stability of any routing scheme applicable to our problem. The average total number of packets generated in the network per time unit equals $\lambda 2^d$. Moreover, it is easily seen from Eq. (1) that each packet's destination is at an average Hamming distance of dp from the packet's origin; therefore, under any routing scheme, each packet will have to traverse at least dp hypercube arcs on the average. Thus, during each time unit, an average total demand for at least $\lambda 2^d dp$ packet transmissions is generated in the system. Since at most $d2^d$ packet transmissions may take place per time unit, it follows that the system can be stable only if $\lambda 2^d dp < d2^d$. Thus, we obtain the following *necessary* condition for *stability* under *any* routing scheme:

$$\rho \stackrel{\text{def}}{=} \lambda p < 1 , \qquad (2)$$

where ρ is the *load factor* of the system. This terminology is appropriate, because when $\rho \approx 1$ all hypercube arcs are almost always busy, even if no redundant packet transmissions take place. Notice that inequality (2) is a necessary condition for stability under more general arrival processes.

In light of Eq. (2), it is of particular interest to devise a routing scheme that is guaranteed to be stable for all $\rho < 1$. Moreover, it is desirable that such a scheme

does not introduce excessive *delay*; in particular, it is required that for each $\rho < 1$ there exists some C_ρ (which does not depend on d) such that the average delay T per packet does not exceed $C_\rho d$. Here, T is defined as the steady-state average time elapsing until a packet reaches its destination. The aforementioned requirement on the delay is motivated by the fact that, in the absence of other transmissions, it would take dp time units (on the average) to route a packet to its (random) destination, by using shortest-path routing; thus, it is desirable that the additional delay due to contention does not increase this quantity by more than a multiplicative factor depending on the load of the network.

The simplest approach to our routing problem is for each packet to choose a shortest path leading to its destination and attempt to traverse this path as fast as possible. Although it is intuitively clear that such *greedy* schemes may possibly be efficient, their performance has not been analyzed rigorously in the literature. In this paper, we prove that a particular greedy scheme is very efficient. The routing scheme to be analyzed is as follows: Consider a packet originating at node x and destined for node z; this packet will be routed through the unique shortest path (from x to z) in which the hypercube *dimensions* (see §1.4) are crossed in *increasing* index-order; these paths are referred to as *canonical* paths. For example, a packet traveling from node $(0, 0, 0, 0)$ to node $(1, 0, 1, 1)$ in the 4-cube would follow the path

$$(0, 0, 0, 0) \rightarrow (0, 0, 0, 1) \rightarrow (0, 0, 1, 1) \rightarrow (1, 0, 1, 1) . \quad (3)$$

It will be proved that this simple routing scheme is stable for all $\rho < 1$, which is the broadest possible stability region. By the term "stable" it is meant that the time spent by the nth packet in the system converges (as $n \rightarrow \infty$) to a limiting random variable, which is finite with probability 1. Moreover, it will be established that, for $\rho < 1$, the delay T induced by the scheme satisfies

$$dp + p\frac{\rho}{2(1-\rho)} \leq T \leq \frac{dp}{1-\rho} .$$

Of particular interest is the upper bound on the delay, which guarantees that, for any fixed ρ, each packet reaches its destination in an average time $\Theta(d)$. Notice also that under heavy traffic (i.e., for $\rho \rightarrow 1$) the delay T increases as $\frac{1}{1-\rho}$. It will be established that such a behavior under heavy traffic is *optimal* for any fixed d; indeed, it will be proved that $\lim_{\rho \rightarrow 1}[(1-\rho)T] > 0$ under *any* legitimate routing scheme.

In the course of the analysis, we establish a rather general interim result (namely, Theorem 3). Using this, we can analyze the performance of greedy routing also in the context of crossbar switch networks with arcs arranged in *levels*; such networks are the butterfly, the Omega and the Banyan networks etc. In fact, the analysis is still applicable even if different arcs have different (yet fixed) transmission times. In §3, we consider the case of the d-dimensional butterfly, which is an "unfolded" version of the d-cube; see [4]. In this context, it is assumed that packets are generated at one of the fronts of the butterfly and destined for a randomly chosen node at the opposite front; the destination distribution is identical to that presented in Eq. (1), except for the fact that x and z belong to opposite fronts of the butterfly. Notice that crossing the dimensions in increasing index-order is the only legitimate choice of paths for the butterfly. Thus, the scheme simply reduces to greedy routing; this will be seen to be stable for all $\rho < 1$, where ρ is now defined as $\rho \stackrel{\text{def}}{=} \lambda \max\{p, (1-p)\}$; moreover, for $\rho < 1$, the average delay T per packet satisfies

$$
d + p\frac{\lambda p}{2(1 - \lambda p)} + (1-p)\frac{\lambda(1-p)}{2[1 - \lambda(1-p)]}
$$
$$
\leq T \leq \frac{dp}{1 - \lambda p} + \frac{d(1-p)}{1 - \lambda(1-p)} .
$$

Again, the delay T is $\Theta(d)$ for any fixed $\rho < 1$, which is the optimal order of magnitude; also, the asymptotic behavior of T in heavy traffic will be seen to be optimal, for any fixed d.

To the best of our knowledge, these results are new. Moreover, our analysis provides the first proof that some routing scheme (on either the d-cube or the butterfly) is stable for all $\rho < 1$ while satisfying the requirement for $\Theta(d)$ average delay; proving that greedy routing has these properties was an important open question in the routing literature. Also, this is the first routing scheme for which the bounds on the delay are expressed in simple formulae involving the system's parameters ρ and d. Finally, the approach for deriving the aforementioned results is new as well: it is established that the hypercube (resp., the butterfly) behaves as a queueing network with deterministic servers (each corresponding to an arc) and with Markovian routing among the various servers; then, by using sample-path arguments, it is shown that the delay induced by this queueing network is dominated by that corresponding to a product-form network. This kind of approach relies on the assumption of Poisson arrivals; nevertheless, we hope that our analysis will be suggestive of the efficient performance of greedy routing under more general packet-generating processes; in fact, the conditions for stability derived in our analysis are much more general.

1.3 Survey of Previous Work

As already mentioned, there exists considerable literature on algorithms for communication tasks in various interconnection networks. However, several of the related articles analyze static problems, where each task has to be performed only *once*, and no other packet transmissions are taking place at the same time. In particular, for the hypercube network, Bertsekas et al. [3] have devised optimal algorithms for a variety of communication tasks. Previously, Saad and Schultz [15], as well as Johnsson and Ho [10], had constructed optimal or nearly optimal algorithms for hypercubes, under somewhat different assumptions on packet transmissions. The interested reader may find more references in these three papers and in [4].

The communication tasks considered in the aforementioned papers as well as the respective algorithms do not employ any randomization. In his famous paper [19], Valiant has demonstrated how to use randomization in order to perform a deterministic task. In particular, in the context of the d-cube, he considered the permutation task and showed that it may be accomplished in time $\Theta(d)$ with high probability, by using a randomized two-phase algorithm. In the first phase, each packet chooses a random intermediate destination (with all nodes being equiprobable) and is sent there; in the second phase, each packet travels from its intermediate destination to its actual destination. In a later paper, Valiant and Brebner [21] modified this algorithm, thus simplifying considerably the analysis. In particular, they assumed that, in each of the two phases, packets follow canonical paths (as is the case with the scheme analyzed in the present paper). It was established (for both permutation algorithms) that there exists some constant R such that the completion time is at most Rd with high probability. Notice, however, that these algorithms make inefficient use of the communication resources of the network; indeed, the average traffic per arc is $O(\frac{1}{d})$ packets per time unit. This performance was improved later by Chang and Simon [6] as well as by Valiant [20]. Each of these articles presents an algorithm for routing d permutations on the d-cube in $O(d)$ time (with high probability); these algorithms result in an average traffic of $O(1)$ packets per arc and time unit. [6] also contains a scheme for routing continuously batches of permutations, by pipelining. Related works are also those by Aleliunas [2], Upfal [18], and Ranade [14], dealing with permutation algorithms in the butterfly. In particular, the algorithm of [14] runs in time $\Theta(d)$ (with high probability), uses constant buffer capacity per node, and is deadlock-free.

We can obtain simple routing schemes for our dynamic problem, by pipelining successive instances of the first phase of the aforementioned permutation algorithms (we assume for simplicity that $p = \frac{1}{2}$). For example, using the algorithm of [21], each node x routes one of its packets every Rd time units (approximately); thus, stability may prevail only if $\lambda Rd \leq 1$, or equivalently $\rho \leq \frac{1}{2Rd}$; hence, for any fixed ρ, this simple scheme becomes unstable for large d. Improved performance is attained if we pipeline successive instances of an efficient static algorithm for d permutations, such as those in [6] and [20]. Such an approach would lead to a routing scheme which would be stable for $\rho < \rho^*$ with ρ^* being some small constant; e.g., using the algorithm of [6] would lead to $\rho^* \approx 0.005$, which is very small compared to the upper bound given in Eq. (2). All of the schemes described above are non-greedy, i.e. they involve *idling*: it often occurs that packets wait at their respective origins, while some of the arcs to be traversed are idle. As will be seen in §2, avoidance of this idling phenomenon improves performance dramatically.

The dynamic routing problem of this paper has been dealt with in several articles, which we discuss below; all of them consider the case of uniform destination distribution. Abraham and Padmanabhan [1] have constructed an approximate model for this problem, under various assumptions on the buffer capacity of the nodes. In particular, they assume that packets advance in the respective paths independently of each other; the model involves some parameters, which are determined by solving a system of non-linear equations. Greenberg and Hajek [8] have analyzed this problem under the assumption that *deflection* routing is used instead of shortest path routing; that is, packets may be temporarily misrouted, rather than stored or dropped. The analysis in [8] is approximate too. Varvarigos [22] has formulated a Markov chain model for evaluating the performance of deflection routing, and has investigated its steady-state statistics numerically. Note that all three [1], [8] and [22] are dealing with the hypercube network. The same problem has been analyzed in the context of the Manhattan network (square mesh) by Greenberg and Goodman [7], with their analysis being again approximate. Leighton [12] proved that greedy routing in the square mesh has very satisfactory average performance. Also, Bouras et al. [5] considered the problem in the context of Banyan networks; however, we are unable to follow some of the steps in the analysis in [5].

Problems similar to ours were also analyzed by Mitra and Cieslak [13], as well as by Hajek and Cruz [9], in the context of the extended Omega network (which is a crossbar switch); it was assumed (in both papers) that, for each individual packet, transmission times over the various arcs are independent and exponentially distributed random variables. This assumption (called "Kleinrock's independence assumption") simplifies the

analysis considerably; in fact, our problem would have been trivial under this assumption, because the underlying networks would have been of the Jackson type. Such an independence assumption is often a good approximation for problems in data networks; on the other hand, this does not apply to routing problems in interconnection networks.

Finally, another dynamic routing problem, was analyzed by Stamoulis and Tsitsiklis in [16], where it is assumed that packets generated at random instants by random nodes of the hypercube are *broadcast* to all other nodes.

1.4 The Hypercube

In this subsection, we briefly discuss the main properties of the d-dimensional *binary hypercube* (or d-cube); e.g., see [4]. This network consists of 2^d nodes, numbered from 0 to $2^d - 1$. Associated with each node z is a binary identity $(z_d, \ldots, z_1)$, which coincides with the binary representation of the number z. For $j \in \{1, \ldots, d\}$, we denote by e_j the node numbered 2^{j-1}; that is, all entries of the binary identity of e_j equal 0 except for the jth one (from the right), which equals 1. For two nodes z and y, we denote by $z \oplus y$ the vector $(z_d \oplus y_d, \ldots, z_1 \oplus y_1)$, where $\oplus$ is the symbol for the XOR operation. The d-cube has $d2^d$ arcs; each arc is directed and connects two nodes whose binary identities differ in a single bit. That is, arc (z, y) exists if and only if, for some $m \in \{1, \ldots, d\}$, $z_i = y_i$ for $i \neq m$ and $z_m \neq y_m$; this is equivalent to $y = z \oplus e_m$ for some $m \in \{1, \ldots, d\}$. Such an arc is said to be of the mth *type*; the set of arcs of the mth type is called the mth *dimension*. Note that (z, y) stands for a *unidirectional* arc pointing from z to y; of course, if arc (z, y) exists, so does arc (y, z). The *Hamming distance* between two nodes z and y is defined as the number of bits in which their binary identities differ; it is denoted by $H(z, y)$. Any path from z to y contains at least as many arcs as the Hamming distance between z and y. Moreover, there always exist paths that contain exactly that many arcs; these paths are called *shortest*. It is easily seen that the *diameter* of the d-cube equals d.

2 GREEDY ROUTING IN THE HYPERCUBE

In this section, we analyze the efficient greedy routing scheme for the hypercube network. As already mentioned in §1.1, the scheme is as follows: Each packet proceeds towards its destination through the corresponding canonical path; see the example in Eq. (3). Packets advance at their respective paths as fast as possible; that is, no idling occurs (hence the characterization "greedy"). Also, whenever several packets present at a node y wish to traverse the same arc, then priority is given to the one that arrived at y the first.

The routing scheme presented above is the *non-idling* version of one of the schemes described in §1.3 (namely, of that based on the algorithm of [21]). It will be seen in §2.1 that, under this scheme, the hypercube is equivalent to a queueing network with certain useful properties. The analysis in §2.2 deals with the performance of this equivalent queueing network.

2.1 The Equivalent Queueing Network

It is straightforward that, under our routing scheme, the d-cube may be viewed as a queueing network, with $d2^d$ deterministic FIFO "servers"; each "server" has unit service duration and corresponds to a hypercube *arc*. This equivalent queueing network (to be referred to as $\mathcal{Q}$) has the following properties:

Property A: After crossing arc $(y, y \oplus e_i)$, a packet will *never* traverse again an arc $(z, z \oplus e_j)$ with $j \in \{1, \ldots, i\}$; this is due to fact that only the *canonical* paths of the hypercube are used. Therefore, the equivalent network $\mathcal{Q}$ is a *layered* network; that is, its "servers" are organized in d levels, with the ith level comprising all arcs $(y, y \oplus e_i)$ for $y \in \{0, \ldots, 2^d - 1\}$, i.e. all arcs of the ith dimension. Upon "service completion" at a certain level, a packet either joins a queue at a higher level or it departs from the network.

Property B: The *external* arrival stream at each arc $(x, x \oplus e_i)$ is Poisson with rate $\lambda p(1-p)^{i-1}$; streams corresponding to different arcs are mutually independent.

Property C: Routing is *Markovian*; that is, the next arc to be crossed by a packet *only* depends on the arc just traversed (as opposed to depending on the entire path up to that point). In particular, upon crossing arc $(y, y \oplus e_i)$, a packet takes one of the following actions: either it joins the queue at arc $(y \oplus e_i, y \oplus e_i \oplus e_j)$ with probability $p(1-p)^{j-i-1}$ for $j = i+1, \ldots, d$; or it departs from the network with probability $(1-p)^{d-i}$. After crossing arc $(y, y \oplus e_d)$, a packet departs from the network with probability 1. Different packets make their routing decisions independently of each other.

Properties B and C can be established by making use of the definition of the destination distribution in Eq. (1); see [17]. According to these two properties, propagation of a packet $\mathcal{P}$ on the hypercube may also be visualized as follows: Upon generation, $\mathcal{P}$ decides whether or not to cross dimension 1; the probability that it decides positively equals p. If it does so, then it takes its step on this dimension and *then* it decides whether or not to cross dimension 2; if it does not decide to cross dimension 1, then it considers crossing dimension 2 etc.

2.2 The Analysis

In the previous subsection, we established that, under the routing scheme analyzed, the hypercube is equivalent to a queueing network $\mathcal{Q}$ with Markovian routing. Henceforth, we analyze the performance of this equivalent network. First, we prove the following result:

Theorem 1 *The total arrival rate at any arc of the d-cube equals $\lambda p = \rho$.* ∎

Proof: By symmetry among the hypercube nodes, all arcs belonging to the same dimension j have the same total arrival rate θ_j. Furthermore, each of the packets generated within the d-cube crosses the jth dimension for an expected number of p times; this fact is an immediate consequence of Eq. (1). Thus, the total arrival rate for the jth dimension equals $2^d \lambda p$. It follows from the above discussion that $2^d \theta_j = 2^d \lambda p$, which gives $\theta_j = \lambda p = \rho$ for all $j \in \{1, \ldots, d\}$. **Q.E.D.**

The properties of the equivalent network $\mathcal{Q}$, allow us to apply a result on the stability of *acyclic* networks; see [23], p. 246. It thus follows that network $\mathcal{Q}$ is *stable* if the total arrival rate for each "server" is less than unity. By stability it is meant that the time spent by the nth packet in the network converges (as $n \to \infty$) to a limiting random variable, which is finite with probability 1 and is independent of the initial state. Using the result of [23] and Theorem 1, we reach the following conclusion:

Theorem 2 *The greedy routing scheme under analysis is stable for all $\rho < 1$.* ∎

In light of the necessary condition for stability $\rho < 1$ (see §1.2), it is seen that the routing scheme under analysis has *optimal* stability properties. In fact, Theorem 2 applies to more general arrival processes.

Next, we establish the upper bound for the average delay T induced by the routing scheme under analysis. In particular, we will show that $T \leq \frac{dp}{1-\rho}$ for all $\rho < 1$. The basic idea for proving this result is as follows: If the service discipline at the "servers" of the equivalent network $\mathcal{Q}$ is *changed* from FIFO to *Processor Sharing* (PS), then the average delay per packet *increases*; under the PS discipline, $\mathcal{Q}$ becomes a *product-form* network, and its delay is easily computed.

Recall that under the PS discipline all customers present at a server receive an *equal* proportion of service simultaneously; see [23], p. 354. For example, consider a deterministic PS server, with unit service rate; assume that it has two customers to serve; the first customer arrives at time 0 and the second at time $\frac{1}{4}$. Upon arrival of the second customer, the first one has $\frac{3}{4}$ units of service remaining; however, due to the presence of the second customer, she will be served at rate $\frac{1}{2}$; thus, she will depart at time $\frac{1}{4} + 2\frac{3}{4} = \frac{7}{4}$; similarly, it can be seen that the second customer will depart at time 2. Notice that we are using the term "service rate" for a PS server (rather than the term "service duration"), because the time duration for which a customer receives service depends on previous and future arrivals.

The proof of the upper bound on the delay T is based on Theorem 3 (see below); this is established in the Appendix, following the derivation of some technical lemmas that prove sample-path results.

Theorem 3 *Let $N(t)$ [resp. $\tilde{N}(t)$] denote the (random) total number of packets present in network $\mathcal{Q}$ (resp. $\tilde{\mathcal{Q}}$) at time t. There holds*

$$N(t) \leq_{\text{st}} \tilde{N}(t), \qquad \forall t \geq 0.$$ ∎

Note that "$\leq_{\text{st}}$" is the symbol for *stochastic domination*; for two random variables X and Y, there holds $X \leq_{\text{st}} Y$ if $\Pr[X > \alpha] \leq \Pr[Y > \alpha]$ for all α.

Next, we present the main result of this subsection.

Theorem 4 *The delay T of the greedy routing scheme under analysis satisfies*

$$T \leq \frac{dp}{1 - \rho}, \qquad \forall \rho < 1.$$ ∎

Proof: As established in [23], pp. 93–94, network $\tilde{\mathcal{Q}}$ is of the *product form*, provided that it is stable. In particular, the steady-state probability that a certain "server" of $\tilde{\mathcal{Q}}$ hosts n packets equals $(1 - \rho)\rho^n$. Therefore, the steady-state average total number $\tilde{N}$ of packets present in $\tilde{\mathcal{Q}}$ equals $\tilde{N} = d2^d \frac{\rho}{1-\rho}$. This together with Theorem 3 implies that the average total number N of packets present in network $\mathcal{Q}$ (in steady-state) satisfies

$$N \leq d2^d \frac{\rho}{1 - \rho}. \qquad (4)$$

Recall now the equivalence of network $\mathcal{Q}$ with the d-cube under the greedy routing scheme analyzed. By Little's law (see [11]), the average delay T induced by this scheme satisfies

$$T = \frac{N}{\lambda 2^d} = \frac{Np}{\rho 2^d}.$$

This together with Eq. (4) proves the result. **Q.E.D.**

Theorem 4 implies that $T = \Theta(d)$ for each fixed ρ. This is the optimal order of magnitude for the delay, because the average *propagation* time per packet is at least dp under *any* routing scheme.

Next, we comment on the number of packets stored per hypercube *node*. The steady-state average number of packets per node equals $\frac{N}{2^d}$; according to Eq. (4),

this satisfies $\frac{N}{2^d} \leq d\frac{\rho}{1-\rho}$. Thus, it is seen that, for any fixed ρ, the average size of the queue built at each node is $O(d)$. In fact, one can show that the total number of packets within the d-cube is $O(d2^d)$ with high probability. Indeed, by Theorem 3 and the product-form property of $\tilde{\mathcal{Q}}$, the limiting random variable $\lim_{t\to\infty} N(t)$ is stochastically dominated by the sum of $d2^d$ independent geometrically distributed random variables with expected value $\frac{\rho}{1-\rho}$. Using the Chernoff bound, it follows that, for $t \to \infty$, $N(t) \leq d2^d \frac{\rho}{1-\rho}(1 + \epsilon)$ with high probability, for any $\epsilon > 0$. However, this does not necessarily imply that the queue-size at each individual node is $O(d)$ with high probability.

Finally, we present a lower bound on the delay T; its proof (which can be found in [17]) is based on the following idea: Packets to cross an arc of the 1st dimension suffer an average delay of $1 + \frac{\rho}{2(1-\rho)}$, because each such arc operates as a deterministic server with *Poisson* arrivals; for each of the other hypercube dimensions, only the corresponding transmission time is taken into account.

Theorem 5 *The delay T of the greedy routing scheme under analysis satisfies*

$$T \geq dp + p\frac{\rho}{2(1 - \rho)}, \qquad \forall \rho < 1.$$ ∎

2.3 The Delay Under Heavy Traffic

First, we establish a *universal* lower bound on the steady-state average delay T per packet; that is, a bound that applies to *any* routing scheme.

Theorem 6 *The average delay T per packet induced by any routing scheme satisfies*

$$T = \Omega\left(dp + p\frac{\rho}{2^d(1 - \rho)}\right), \qquad \forall \rho < 1.$$ ∎

The proof of this result can be found in [17]. The underlying idea is as follows: We focus on a *cut* of the network (namely, all arcs of the 1st dimension), and we estimate the minimum possible delay induced by this cut. Taking also the propagation times for the remaining arcs into account, the lower bound for T follows. Reasoning similarly, we can also prove a sharper lower bound, applying to all *oblivious* schemes; that is, to schemes where each packet selects its own path independently of other packets, and insists on traversing that path regardless of the contention encountered (see also [21]). For any such scheme, there holds $T = \Omega(dp + p\frac{\rho}{1-\rho})$; see [17]. Note that our greedy routing scheme is oblivious.

Next, we discuss the asymptotic properties of the delay under heavy traffic (namely, for $\rho \to 1$ and fixed d). Theorem 6 implies that $\lim_{\rho\to 1}[(1 - \rho)T] > 0$; that is, in heavy traffic, the delay per packet grows to infinity at least as fast as $\frac{1}{1-\rho}$. On the other hand, Theorem 4 shows that $\lim_{\rho \to 1}[(1 - \rho)T] \leq dp$ for our greedy routing scheme; hence, the corresponding average delay per packet has optimal asymptotic properties under heavy traffic (because $\lim_{\rho \to 1}[(1 - \rho)T]$ is finite). Below, we investigate these properties even further, and present an open question.

Notice that $T - dp$ equals the average *queueing* delay per packet under our greedy routing scheme, the average propagation delay dp excluded. By Theorems 4 and 5, we have

$$\frac{p}{2} \leq \lim_{\rho \to 1}[(1 - \rho)(T - dp)] \leq dp . \qquad (5)$$

The lower and the upper bounds in Eq. (5) differ by a factor of $\frac{d}{2}$. It would be preferable for the two bounds to be within a constant factor (independent of both d and ρ). In fact, the lower bound of Theorem 5 can be sharpened as follows:

$$T - dp \geq \alpha d\rho + p\frac{\rho}{2(1 - \rho)} , \qquad (6)$$

where $\alpha > 0$ only depends on p, for all $p \in (0, 1)$. The underlying idea is that, for $p \in (0, 1)$, each packet $\mathcal{P}$ faces *additional* contention for each of dimensions $2, \ldots, d$ it crosses; that is, $\mathcal{P}$ contends with packets that had not entered the path of $\mathcal{P}$ up to this point. Nevertheless, the lower bound of Eq. (6) is not within a constant factor from the upper bound of Eq. (5). It is conjectured that for all $p \in (0, 1)$, the latter bound in Eq. (5) is tight; namely, it is conjectured that $T - dp \geq \beta\frac{d\rho}{1-\rho}$, where β only depends on p. On the other hand, it is easily seen that the lower bound in Eq. (5) is tight for $p = 1$. Indeed, in this case, each packet generated at node x is destined for node $\bar{x}$, where each entry of the binary identity of $\bar{x}$ is the complement of the corresponding entry of x; thus, packets generated at different nodes follow *disjoint* paths (recall that only canonical paths are used); this easily gives that $T = d + \frac{\rho}{2(1 - \rho)}$.

2.4 The Case of Slotted Time

In the analysis so far, it was assumed that the time axis is *continuous*. Next, we briefly comment on the case of *slotted* time. In particular, we assume that the time axis is divided in slots of duration τ; all nodes are synchronized to the same clock. Since packets are taken to have unit transmission times, we may assume, without loss of generality, that $\tau \leq 1$ and, in particular, that $\frac{1}{\tau}$ is integer; otherwise, there will be some waste due to the fact that packets do not "fit" exactly to time slots. (Of course, the simplest case is $\tau = 1$.) Furthermore, it

is assumed that each node of the hypercube generates a new *batch* of packets at the beginning of each slot, namely at each time $k\tau$ with $k \in \{0, 1, \ldots\}$. The batch size has Poisson distribution with expected value $\lambda\tau$; thus, the input traffic intensity is the same as in the case of continuous time. In this context, it can be seen that the new value $\overline{T}$ of the average delay per packet satisfies

$$T \leq \overline{T} \leq T + \tau \leq \frac{dp}{1 - \rho} + \tau , \qquad \forall \rho < 1 .$$

Hence, the asymptotic properties of the delay in slotted time are the same as those in continuous time.

3 GREEDY ROUTING IN THE BUTTERFLY

In this section, we extend the results derived for the hypercube to the butterfly network.

The d-dimensional butterfly is an "unfolded" version of the d-cube. It consists of $(d + 1)2^d$ nodes, organized in $d + 1$ levels, with each level having 2^d nodes. In particular, for $j \in \{1, \ldots, d + 1\}$, the nodes of the jth level are denoted by $[x; j]$ where $x \in \{0, \ldots, 2^d - 1\}$. For $j \neq d + 1$, each node $[x; j]$ is connected to two nodes, namely $[x; j + 1]$ and $[x \oplus e_j; j + 1]$. Therefore, there exist two types of arcs:

- Arcs of the form $[x; j] \to [x; j + 1]$, which are referred to as *straight* arcs of the jth level; for notational convenience, arc $[x; j] \to [x; j + 1]$ will be denoted by $(x; j; s)$.

- Arcs of the form $[x; j] \to [x \oplus e_j; j + 1]$, which are referred to as *vertical* arcs of the jth level; for notational convenience, arc $[x; j] \to [x \oplus e_j; j + 1]$ will be denoted by $(x; j; v)$.

For our routing problem, it is assumed that packets are generated at the 1st level and destined for the $(d + 1)$st level; each node $[x; 1]$ generates packets according to a Poisson process with rate λ. The probability that a packet generated at node $[x; 1]$ is destined for node $[z; d + 1]$ equals $p^{H(x,z)}(1 - p)^{d - H(x,z)}$, where $H(x, z)$ is the Hamming distance between the binary identities of x and z. For each origin-destination pair $[x; 1]$ and $[z; d + 1]$ there corresponds a *unique* path, which consists of d arcs, one from each level. Notice that if $x_j = z_j$, then the jth-level arc is straight; otherwise it is vertical. As in the canonical paths of the hypercube, the bits are corrected in increasing index-order.

Using the definition of the destination distribution, it is seen that packets to traverse arc $(x; 1; v)$ form a Poisson stream with rate λp; similarly, packets to traverse arc $(x; 1; s)$ form a Poisson stream with rate $\lambda(1 - p)$. Recalling that all packets have unit transmission time, it follows that the inequalities $\lambda p < 1$ and $\lambda(1 - p) < 1$ are both *necessary* conditions for stability of any routing scheme. Combining these conditions, we obtain the following result: Stability may prevail only if

$$\rho \overset{\text{def}}{=} \lambda \max\{p, 1 - p\} < 1 . \qquad (7)$$

Notice that, for given λ, the minimum value of ρ occurs for $p = \frac{1}{2}$, where the destination distribution is uniform. For $p > \frac{1}{2}$, the vertical arcs become the bottleneck of the system; for $p < \frac{1}{2}$, the straight arcs become the bottleneck of the system; see also Theorem 7.

The routing scheme to be analyzed below is the simplest possible: Packets are routed in a *greedy* fashion; that is, each packet advances at its respective path as fast as possible. When several packets contend for the same arc, then priority is allotted on a FIFO basis.

In fact, given that there is only one path per origin-destination pair, greedy routing is the most natural scheme arising in the context of the butterfly. It will be shown below that this simple scheme is very efficient.

Similar to the hypercube (see §2.1), under greedy routing, the butterfly may be viewed as a queueing network $\mathcal{R}$ with $d2^{d+1}$ deterministic FIFO "servers"; each of them has unit service duration and corresponds to an arc. The main properties of $\mathcal{R}$ are as follows:

Property A: $\mathcal{R}$ is a *layered* network; it consists of d levels, with the jth level comprising all arcs $(x; j; s)$ and $(x; j; v)$. Each packet receives one time unit of "service" at each level, contrary to the network described in §2.1, where a packet might skip some of the levels.

Property B: Routing is *Markovian*. In particular, after traversing arc $(y; j; s)$ [resp. $(y; j; v)$], where $j \neq d$, a packet takes one of the following two actions: either it joins the queue for arc $(y; j+1; s)$ [resp. $(y \oplus e_j; j+1; s)$] with probability $1 - p$; or it joins the queue for arc $(y; j+1; v)$ [resp. $(y \oplus e_j; j+1; v)$] with probability p. After crossing arc $(y; d; s)$ [resp. $(y; d; v)$], a packet departs from the network with probability 1. Different packets make their routing decisions independently of each other.

Next, we investigate the stability properties of our greedy routing scheme; for this purpose, we need the following result:

Theorem 7 *The total arrival rate at each arc $(x; j; s)$ equals $\theta_s = \lambda(1 - p)$. Also, the total arrival rate at each arc $(x; j; v)$ equals $\theta_v = \lambda p$.* ∎

Proof: We fix some $j \in \{1, \ldots, d\}$. By symmetry, all straight (resp. vertical) arcs of the jth level have the same total arrival rate $\theta_s^{(j)}$ [resp. $\theta_v^{(j)}$]. As already mentioned, each packet crosses some straight (resp. vertical) arc of the jth level with probability $1 - p$ (resp. p);

also the total arrival rate over all arcs of the jth level equals $\lambda 2^d$, because each packet crosses exactly one arc of this level. Therefore, we have $\lambda 2^d(1 - p) = 2^d \theta_s^{(j)}$ and $\lambda 2^d p = 2^d \theta_v^{(j)}$, which proves the result. **Q.E.D.**

As in §2.2, the sufficient condition for stability of the equivalent network $\mathcal{R}$ (and of the greedy routing scheme) is obtained by applying the result of [23] regarding acyclic networks; the condition is as follows:

Theorem 8 *Greedy routing on the butterfly is stable if*

$$\lambda p < 1 \qquad and \qquad \lambda(1 - p) < 1 ,$$

or equivalently $\rho \overset{\text{def}}{=} \lambda \max\{p, 1 - p\} < 1$. ∎

In light of the necessary condition for stability in Eq. (7), it is seen that greedy routing in the butterfly has *optimal* stability properties.

Finally, we establish the upper bound for the average delay T per packet induced by greedy routing.

Theorem 9 *There holds*

$$T \leq \frac{dp}{1 - \lambda p} + \frac{d(1 - p)}{1 - \lambda(1 - p)} , \qquad \forall \rho < 1 .$$ ∎

Proof: By Little's law, we have

$$T = \frac{N}{\lambda 2^d} , \qquad (8)$$

where N is the average total number of packets present in the equivalent network $\mathcal{R}$ in steady-state. We now consider the network $\bar{\mathcal{R}}$, which is identical to $\mathcal{R}$ except for the fact that all of its "servers" operate under a Processor Sharing (PS) discipline (see §2.2); let $\bar{N}$ be the corresponding average total number of packets. Since $\mathcal{R}$ is a layered network with Markovian routing, we can apply Theorem 3; see also the comment on the generality of that result, following its proof in the Appendix. Therefore, we have

$$N \leq \bar{N} . \qquad (9)$$

In the stable case (i.e., for $\rho < 1$), network $\bar{\mathcal{R}}$ is of the product form [23], pp. 93-94. Recalling also Theorem 7, it follows that the steady-state probability that a particular "server" $(x; j; v)$ [resp. $(x; j; s)$] of $\bar{\mathcal{R}}$ hosts n packets equals $(1 - \lambda p)(\lambda p)^n$ (resp. $[1 - \lambda(1 - p)][\lambda(1 - p)]^n$). Since there exist $d2^d$ "servers" of each of the two types, it follows that

$$\bar{N} = d2^d \frac{\lambda p}{1 - \lambda p} + d2^d \frac{\lambda(1 - p)}{1 - \lambda(1 - p)} .$$

This together with Eqs. (8) and (9) proves the result. **Q.E.D.**

Next, we comment on the number of packets stored per node of the butterfly; first, notice that only the nodes of levels $1, \ldots, d$ have to store packets. An overall estimate of the expected number of packets per node is provided by the quantity $\frac{N}{d2^d}$, which satisfies

$$\frac{N}{d2^d} \leq \frac{\lambda p}{1 - \lambda p} + \frac{\lambda(1-p)}{1 - \lambda(1-p)} \overset{\text{def}}{=} q_\rho .$$

This estimate is quite favorable because it suggests that the overall average queue-size per node is $O(1)$ for any fixed ρ. However, it is not guaranteed that this bound holds for the average number of packets stored by the nodes of each individual level. It is conjectured that this is actually the case; the following result provides strong evidence for this claim: for any $j \in \{1, \ldots, d\}$, the total number of packets stored by the nodes of levels $1, \ldots, j$ does not exceed $j2^d q_\rho(1 + \epsilon)$ with high probability, for any $\epsilon > 0$. This result may be proved by applying stochastic domination between the first j levels of networks $\mathcal{R}$ and $\tilde{\mathcal{R}}$, and using the product-form property of $\tilde{\mathcal{R}}$.

Reasoning as in Theorem 6, it can be proved that $T = \Omega(d + \frac{\rho}{1-\rho})$ for any routing scheme in the butterfly; see [17]. On the other hand, greedy routing satisfies both $T = \Theta(d)$ for fixed ρ, and $T = \Theta(\frac{1}{1-\rho})$ for fixed d and $\rho \to 1$; these properties follow from Theorem 9. Thus, greedy routing in the butterfly has optimal asymptotic properties.

An interesting open problem is to analyze the performance of greedy routing under the assumption that nodes in levels $2, \ldots, d$ have *constant* buffer capacity.

4   CONCLUDING REMARKS

In this paper, we analyzed a problem where the nodes of the hypercube network generate packets at random time instants, according to independent Poisson processes. Each packet has unit transmission time and is destined for a randomly selected node; in a special case, the destination distribution is uniform. We considered a simple greedy routing scheme, where each packet crosses the hypercube dimensions required in increasing index-order. We proved that this scheme has optimal stability properties and, when stable, it induces an average delay $T = \Theta(d)$ per packet; the bounds on the average delay were given in simple closed-form expressions. Our analysis was based on a new approach, which relates the behavior of the hypercube (under the routing scheme considered) to that of a queueing network with Markovian routing. Using the same idea, we extended the results to the butterfly network, thus proving the efficiency of greedy routing in this context.

An interesting open problem is to analyze our greedy routing scheme in the butterfly under the assumption of constant buffer capacity in each node of the intermediate levels. Regarding the hypercube, it would be of interest to investigate the performance of other greedy schemes, such as the one where each packet selects a random shortest path leading to its destination.

Acknowledgement: The authors are grateful to Dr. Teunis Ott for mentioning the possibility of comparing the FIFO and PS disciplines.

References

[1] S. Abraham and K. Padmanabhan, "Performance of the Direct Binary n-Cube Network for Multiprocessors", *Proceedings of the 1986 International Conference on Parallel Processing*.

[2] R. Aleliunas, "Randomized Parallel Communication", *Proceedings of the 1st ACM SIGACT-SIGOPS Symposium on Principles of Distributed Computing*, pp. 60-72, 1982.

[3] D.P. Bertsekas, C. Ozveren, G.D. Stamoulis, P. Tseng, and J.N. Tsitsiklis, "Optimal Communication Algorithms for Hypercubes", *J. Parallel Distrib. Comput.*, vol. 11, pp. 263-275, 1991.

[4] D.P. Bertsekas and J.N. Tsitsiklis, *Parallel and Distributed Computation: Numerical Methods*, Prentice-Hall, 1989.

[5] C. Bouras, J. Garofalkis, P. Spirakis, and V. Triantafillou, "Queueing Delays in Buffered Multistage Interconnection Networks", Dept. of Computer Science, Technical Report 289, New York University, 1987.

[6] Y. Chang and J. Simon, "Continuous Routing and Batch Routing on the Hypercube", *Proceedings of the 5th ACM Symposium on Principles of Distributed Computing*, pp. 272-281, 1986.

[7] A.G. Greenberg and J. Goodman, "Sharp Approximate Models of Adaptive Routing in Mesh Networks", preprint, 1986.

[8] A.G. Greenberg and B. Hajek, "Deflection Routing in Hypercube Networks", preprint, 1989.

[9] B. Hajek and R.L. Cruz, "Delay and Routing in Interconnection Networks", In A.R. Odoni, L. Bianco, and G. Szago (Eds.), *Flow Control of Congested Networks*, Springer-Verlag, 1987.

[10] S.L. Johnsson and C.-T. Ho, Optimum Broadcasting and Personalized Communication in Hypercubes", *IEEE Trans. Comput.*, vol. 38, pp. 1249-1267, 1989.

[11] L. Kleinrock, *Queueing Systems, Vol. I: Theory*, John Wiley, 1975.

[12] F.T. Leighton, "Average Case of Greedy Routing Algorithms on Arrays", preprint, 1990.

[13] D. Mitra and R.A. Cieslak, "Randomized Parallel Communications on an Extension of the Omega Network", *J. ACM*, vol. 34, pp. 802-824, 1987.

[14] A. Ranade, "How to Emulate Shared Memory", *Proceedings of the 28th Annual IEEE Symposium on Foundations of Computer Science*, pp. 185-194, 1988.

[15] Y. Saad and M.H. Schultz, "Data Communication in Hypercubes", Dept. of Computer Sciences, Research Report YALEU/DCS/RR-428, Yale University, 1985.

[16] G.D. Stamoulis and J.N. Tsitsiklis, "Efficient Routing Schemes for Multiple Broadcasts in Hypercubes", *Proceedings of the 29th IEEE Conference on Decision and Control*, pp. 1349-1354, 1990.

[17] G.D. Stamoulis and J.N. Tsitsiklis, "The Efficiency of Greedy Routing in Hypercubes and Butterflies", Report LIDS-P-1999, Laboratory for Information and Decision Systems, M.I.T., 1990.

[18] E. Upfal, "Efficient Schemes for Parallel Communication", *J. ACM*, vol. 31, pp. 507-517, 1984.

[19] L.G. Valiant, "A Scheme for Fast Parallel Communication", *SIAM J. Comput.*, vol. 11, pp. 350-361, 1982.

[20] L.G. Valiant, "General Purpose Parallel Architectures", in J. van Leeuwen (Ed.), *Handbook of Theoretical Computer Science*, North Holland, 1990.

[21] L.G. Valiant and G.J. Brebner, "Universal Schemes for Parallel Communication", *Proceedings of the 13th Annual ACM Symposium on Theory of Computing*, pp. 263-277, 1981.

[22] E.A. Varvarigos, "Optimal Communication Algorithms for Multiprocessor Computers", Report CICS-TH-192, Center for Intelligent Control Systems, M.I.T., 1990.

[23] J. Walrand, *An Introduction to Queueing Networks*, Prentice-Hall, 1988.

APPENDIX: THE PROOF OF THEOREM 3

In this appendix, we establish Theorem 3, which led to the upper bound on the delay T induced under the greedy routing scheme. The proof makes use of several technical lemmas, which establish sample-path results; these we present first.

Lemma 10 *Let there be a deterministic FIFO server with unit service duration. For a fixed sequence $t_1, t_2, \ldots$ of arrival times, let $D_1, D_2, \ldots$ denote the corresponding sequence of departure times. Similarly, let $\bar{D}_1, \bar{D}_2, \ldots$ be the departure times for a deterministic PS server, with unit service rate, fed by the same input stream. There holds*

$$D_i \leq \bar{D}_i , \quad for \ i = 1, \ldots \quad \blacksquare$$

Proof: Clearly, we have $D_1 = t_1 + 1$. In the context of the PS server, the 1st customer will depart at time $t_1 + 1$ only if no other customers arrive until that time; otherwise, the server will be slowed down, and the 1st customer will depart later than $t_1 + 1$. It follows that

$$\bar{D}_1 \geq t_1 + 1 = D_1 . \quad (10)$$

It is well-known that the PS discipline is *work-conserving*; see [23], pp. 353-354. That is, the unfinished work $W(t)$ at time t is the *same* for both the FIFO and the PS servers considered. By definition of $W(t)$, we have

$$D_i = t_i + W(t_i-) + 1 , \quad for \ i = 1, \ldots \quad (11)$$

We now consider the ith arrival at the PS server, where $i \geq 2$. If $W(t_i-) = 0$, then reasoning as in proving Eq. (10), it follows that $\bar{D}_i \geq t_i + 1 = D_i$. Assume now that $W(t_i-) \neq 0$; it is straightforward that customers depart from a deterministic PS server in the order they arrive; hence, the ith customer may depart only after an amount $W(t_i-) + 1$ of work has been finished by the server. Therefore, we have

$$\bar{D}_i \geq t_i + W(t_i-) + 1 = D_i ,$$

where we have also used Eq. (11). The proof of the lemma is now complete. **Q.E.D.**

Let there be two streams of events, one occuring at times $\tau_1, \tau_2, \ldots$ and the other at times $\tau_1', \tau_2', \ldots$ If $\tau_i \leq \tau_i'$ for $i = 1, \ldots$, then the latter stream of events will be said to be a *delayed version* of the former. For example, as implied by Lemma 10, for any fixed arrival stream, the departing stream of a deterministic PS server is a delayed version of the one of the corresponding FIFO server.

257

Lemma 11 *Let there be a deterministic FIFO server with unit service duration. Let $D_1, D_2, \ldots$ (resp. $D'_1, D'_2, \ldots$) be the sequence of departure times corresponding to a fixed sequence $t_1, t_2, \ldots$ (resp. $t'_1, t'_2, \ldots$) of arrival times. If $t_i \leq t'_i$ for $i = 1, \ldots$, then*

$$D_i \leq D'_i, \quad \text{for } i = 1, \ldots \quad \blacksquare$$

Proof: There holds $D_1 = t_1 + 1$ and

$$D_i = \max\{D_{i-1}, t_i\} + 1 \quad \text{for } i = 2, \ldots;$$

similarly, $D'_1 = t'_1 + 1$ and

$$D'_i = \max\{D'_{i-1}, t'_i\} + 1 \quad \text{for } i = 2, \ldots$$

Using these facts and the assumption $t_i \leq t'_i$ for $i = 1, \ldots$, the result follows by a straightforward inductive argument. **Q.E.D.**

The result to be established next is based on Lemmas 10 and 11. We consider the queueing network $\mathcal{G}$ depicted in Figure 1. This consists of three deterministic FIFO servers with unit service duration, denoted by S_1, S_2 and S_3. Customers completing service at S_1 or S_2 either depart from the network or they join the queue at S_3; routing decisions are Markovian. Obviously, $\mathcal{G}$ is a *layered* network (see §2.1). We define a *sample path* ω of $\mathcal{G}$ as the following collection of information:

- The *external* arrival times at servers S_1, S_2 and S_3.

- The routing decision taken by the ith customer upon service completion at S_1 (resp. S_2) for $i = 1, \ldots$

Clearly, given a sample path ω, network $\mathcal{G}$ evolves in a *deterministic* fashion; in the context of $\mathcal{G}$, the following holds:

Lemma 12 *Let $\tilde{\mathcal{G}}$ be a network identical to $\mathcal{G}$ except for the fact that PS service discipline applies to the servers of $\tilde{\mathcal{G}}$ (instead of FIFO); see Figure 2. For a particular sample path ω, let $B(t)$ [resp. $\tilde{B}(t)$] denote the number of customers departing from $\mathcal{G}$ (resp. $\tilde{\mathcal{G}}$) during the interval $[0, t]$; there holds*

$$B(t) \geq \tilde{B}(t), \quad \forall t \geq 0. \quad \blacksquare$$

Proof: First, we consider a network $\mathcal{G}'$ obtained from $\mathcal{G}$ by changing the service discipline *only* at S_1 and S_2 (from FIFO to PS); see Figure 3.

We define as the *output stream* of a server the stream of customers completing service therein, including those that do not depart from the network. Notice that server S_1 is not affected at all by the presence of the other two servers; the same statement applies to server S_2. Therefore, using Lemma 10, it is seen that the output stream of server S_1 in $\mathcal{G}'$ is a delayed version of that

corresponding to S_1 of $\mathcal{G}$. Recalling also that the routing decisions of customers completing service are the same for networks $\mathcal{G}$ and $\mathcal{G}'$, it follows that the substream of customers departing from $\mathcal{G}'$ at S_1 is a delayed version of the corresponding substream in $\mathcal{G}$. Similar statements apply to the streams stemming from S_2.

Next, we consider the stream feeding S_3 in $\mathcal{G}'$; this stream is a delayed version of that feeding S_3 in $\mathcal{G}$, because each arrival at S_3 of $\mathcal{G}'$ corresponds to an arrival at S_3 of $\mathcal{G}$ that occurs *no later*. [Recall the aforementioned "comparison" of the output streams of S_1 (resp. S_2) in the two networks and the coupling of the routing decisions.] Therefore, using Lemma 11, the output stream from S_3 of $\mathcal{G}'$ is a delayed version of that corresponding to S_3 of $\mathcal{G}$. The former output stream is delayed *further* when the service discipline at S_3 of $\mathcal{G}'$ is changed from FIFO to PS. This modification (which yields network $\tilde{\mathcal{G}}$) does not affect the streams of customers departing from the 1st level. Therefore, for each of the servers of $\tilde{\mathcal{G}}$, its departing stream is a delayed version of that of the corresponding server of $\mathcal{G}$; this proves the lemma.

Its should be noted that customers joining S_3 may get out of order when changing the service discipline; thus, a *particular* customer may depart earlier from $\tilde{\mathcal{G}}$ than from $\mathcal{G}$. Nevertheless, this does not affect the validity of the lemma. **Q.E.D.**

Next, we generalize Lemma 12. In the context of network $\mathcal{Q}$, a sample path ω is defined as the collection of information comprising all external arrival times and all routing decisions. Notice that routing decisions at each "server" are identified by the *order* they are taken, not by the identity of the packets deciding; e.g. "the 1st packet to cross arc $(e_1 \oplus e_2, e_1)$ will advance to $(e_1, e_1 \oplus e_3)$, the 2nd such packet will depart from the network" etc. Such an identification of the routing decisions is legitimate due to the fact that routing in $\mathcal{Q}$ is *Markovian*. As in Lemma 12, we denote as $\tilde{\mathcal{Q}}$ the network obtained from $\mathcal{Q}$ after changing the service discipline of all "servers" from FIFO to PS.

Lemma 13 *For a particular sample path ω, let $B(t)$ [resp. $\tilde{B}(t)$] denote the number of packets that have departed from $\mathcal{Q}$ (resp. $\tilde{\mathcal{Q}}$) during the interval $[0, t]$; there holds*

$$B(t) \geq \tilde{B}(t), \quad \forall t \geq 0. \quad \blacksquare$$

Outline of the Proof: This proof is done by extending the argument used in proving Lemma 12. In particular, one has to replace the FIFO "servers" by PS ones, on a level-by-level basis, starting from the 1st level and proceeding one level at a time. At the jth step of this process, all streams stemming from levels $1, \ldots, j-1$ remain the same, while all streams stemming from levels $j, \ldots, d$ are delayed. The only subtle point of this proof lies on the fact that packets may get out of order at certain steps; see also the proof of Lemma 12. Nevertheless, this creates no difficulty, due to the assumed coupling of routing decisions. If one insists on tracing the path followed by a particular packet [say the first to arrive at "server" $(0, e_1)$] it may occur that this *changes* at some step of the process described above; this is of no importance, because the "comparison" of the various streams still applies, even though the streams may consist of different packets at each step. **Q.E.D.**

Now that we have established Lemma 13, we can easily prove Theorem 3, which is restated below.

Theorem 3 *Let $N(t)$ [resp. $\tilde{N}(t)$] denote the (random) total number of packets present in network $\mathcal{Q}$ (resp. $\tilde{\mathcal{Q}}$) at time t. There holds*

$$N(t) \leq_{st} \tilde{N}(t), \qquad \forall t \geq 0 .$$ ∎

Proof: On a sample-path basis, there holds

$$N(t) = B(t) - A(t) ,$$

where $A(t)$ [resp. $B(t)$] is the number of arrivals at (resp. departures from) network $\mathcal{Q}$ during $[0, t]$; a similar relation holds for network $\tilde{\mathcal{Q}}$. Using Lemma 13, we have $N(t) \leq \tilde{N}(t)$ on a sample-path basis. Relaxing the coupling of the arrival processes and the routing decisions in the two networks, we obtain the stochastic inequality in question. **Q.E.D.**

A careful look in the analysis reveals that both Theorem 3 and Lemma 13 apply to *all* layered networks with Markovian routing and deterministic FIFO servers (possibly with different service times). Thus, if the FIFO discipline is changed to PS, then the total number of customers in such a network increases in the stochastic sense.

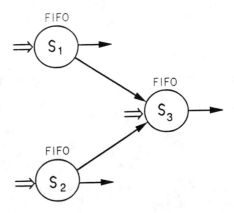

Figure 1: Network $\mathcal{G}$

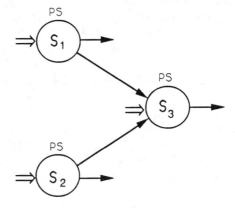

Figure 2: Network $\tilde{\mathcal{G}}$

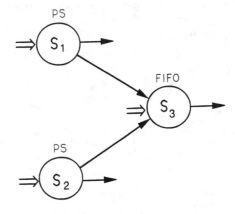

Figure 3: Network $\mathcal{G}'$

Balanced Routing:
Towards the Distance Bound on Grids

Manfred Kunde *
Institut f. Informatik, TU Munich,
Arcisstr. 21, D-8000 Munich 2, Germany

Abstract

The problem of packet routing on an r-dimensional mesh-connected array or grid of processors with side-length n is studied. Each processor is able to store $rf(n)$ packets, $f(n) < n^{1-1/r}$. The new class of balanced routing problems is introduced which includes such fundamental problems as partial $h - h$ routing. On 3-dimensional $n \times n \times n$ grids (without wrap-arounds) partial permutation problems and so-called $(1, f(n))$-balanced problems can be solved by a deterministic routing algorithm needing only $3.333n + O(n/f(n)^{1/2})$ steps which is asymptotically only 11.11 percent larger than the distance bound of $3n - 3$ steps. The result is better than those of so far known randomized algorithms, routing data only with high probability. The new algorithm also beats previous deterministic routing algorithms. For arbitrary r, $r \geq 3$, permutation routing on r-dimensional cubes can be performed in asymptotically $(2r-3+1/r)n$ steps which again is faster than the running times of so far known algorithms, both randomized and deterministic ones. A further improvement leads to an algorithm with approximately $(r+(r-2)(1/r)^{1/(r-2)})n + O(n/f(n)^{1/(r-1)})$ transport steps. For a constant buffer size of $O((r^2/\epsilon)^{r-1})$ packets, $\epsilon > 0$, a number of $(r+(r-2)(1/r)^{1/(r-2)}+\epsilon)n$ steps can be achieved. The number of steps is reduced to the half if the algorithms are adapted to tori of processors, i.e. grids with wrap-around connections. Furthermore, algorithms for the general $h - h$ routing problem are presented which also needs a smaller number of steps than previous algorithms. It is shown that these problems can be solved in $O((h + r)n)$ instead of $O(hrn)$ needed before.

*This research was supported in part by the Deutsche Forschungsgemeinschaft, Grant No. Ku658/1

1 Introduction

Data movement plays an important role in the performance of parallel computation. We present algorithms for permutation routing and balanced routing problems on grids where the number of parallel data transfers is asymptotically near to the minimum.

An $n_1 \times \ldots \times n_r$ mesh-connected array or grid is a set $mesh(n_1, \ldots, n_r)$ of $N = n_1 n_2 \ldots n_r$ identical processors where each processor $P = (p_1, \ldots, p_r)$, $0 \leq p_i \leq n_i - 1$, is directly connected to its nearest neighbours only. A processor $Q = (q_1, \ldots, q_r)$ is called nearest neighbour of P if and only if the distance between them is exactly 1. For a grid without wrap-around connections the distance is given by $d(P, Q) = |p_1 - q_1| + \cdots + |p_r - q_r|$. For grids with wrap-around connections (tori) we define $d_{wrap}(P, Q) = \min(|p_1 - q_1|, n_1 - |p_1 - q_1|) + \cdots + \min(|p_r - q_r|, n_r - |p_r - q_r|)$. The control structure of the grid of processors is thought to be of the MIMD type. A main restriction is that each processor can send data only to its nearest neighbours during one clock period, and that each processor has only a limited number of registers for data.

For the *packet routing problem* a certain amount of packets are loaded into the N processors. Each packet has a destination address specifying the processor to which it has to be sent. The routing problem is to transport each packet to its address. A fundamental subproblem in this context is the (partial) $h - h$ routing problem where each processor contains at most h packets and finally receives at most h packets. If $h = 1$ then we speak of a partial permutation problem. If each processor contains exactly one packet then it is called a full permutation routing problem which can be described by the pair $(mesh, address)$ where address is a one-to-one mapping from mesh onto itself. Very often the full permutation routing problem is directly solved by sorting.

For deriving exact lower and upper bounds for routing on meshes the possible steps for computations must be described carefully. The following conventional model is used: Interchanges of data between two directly neighbouring processors and data shifts on cycles of processors are allowed. The main restriction is that during one step interval at most one packet (as an atomic unit) can be transported on each directed channel between neighbouring processors. However, packets may be stored in a processor until a limited buffer is filled. If at most one packet may be buffered at each processor then we speak of model 1. For many of the sorting algorithms this first model is used. In all other cases we speak of the second model (with specified buffer size $f(n) \geq 2$).

For 2-dimensional $n \times n$ meshes several sorting algorithms have been proposed using the first model. They present solutions for the full permutation routing problem. On meshes without wrap-arounds the fastest ones need about $3n + o(n)$ steps [15,14,11] which has been shown to be asymptotically optimal for sorting with respect to snake-like types of indexings [14,4]. For wrap-around meshes a general lower bound for sorting of $3n/2$ was shown [6]. The fastest algorithms need $2n + o(n)$ steps [11]. The best algorithm for an $n \times \cdots \times n$ cube, $r \geq 3$, needs only $(2r-1)n + o(n)$ steps for sorting [3,5] which is asymptotically optimal for this type of sorting [4]. For meshes with wrap-around-connections the lower bound is $(r - 1/2)n$ and the so far best algorithm asymptotically needs $rn + o(n)$ steps [5].

If the buffer is limited to one packet the best sorting algorithms are more or less the best routing algorithms. However, in the case of a larger buffer size of $f(n)$ packets better algorithms can be obtained. Then routing on an $n \times n$ grid can be done within $2n + O(n/f(n))$ steps [5] which asymptotically matches the distance bound of $2n - 2$ steps. (On an $n \times n$ torus the performance can be improved to $n + O(n/f(n))$ steps which is again asymptotically optimal.) Leighton, Makedon and Tollis [10] proposed a mesh algorithm basing on the algorithm just mentioned which exactly matches the distance bound of $2n - 2$ steps with constant buffer size. The relatively large constant was recently reduced to 58 by Rajasekaran and Overholt [13]. However, an optimal solution with constant buffer size for the torus is not yet known.

For an $n \times ... \times n$ r-dimensional cube of processors with $r \geq 3$ it is still an open question whether the distance bound of $rn - r$ steps can be matched for permutation routing algorithms. The so far fastest routing algorithm, presented in [7], only needs $(2r - 2)n + O(r^2 n/f(n)^{1/(r-1)})$ steps and $(r-1)n + O(r^2 n/f(n)^{1/(r-1)})$ steps if wrap-arounds are given. It was the first deterministic algorithm which is faster than the routing algorithms based on sorting [3,5] and the randomized algorithms of Valiant and Brebner [16].

In this paper we show how one can obtain better algorithms not only for permutations but also for so-called $(1, f(n))$-balanced problems. A principal design idea lies in the combination of the rearrange-

ment technique from [7] with the technique of overlapping developed for multi-packet algorithms [8]. The proposed algorithm, built in such a manner, needs only $3.333n + O(r^2 n/f(n)^{1/2})$ transport steps on an $n \times n \times n$ cube. That means, the number of steps is only 11.11 percent larger than the distance bound. A straightforward generalization of the algorithm to an $n \times ... \times n$ r-dimensional cube leads to $(2r - 3 + 1/r)n + O(r^2 n/f(n)^{1/(r-1)})$ transport steps. A further improvement is presented showing that $(r + (r-2)(1/r)^{1/(r-2)})n + O(r^2 n/f(n)^{1/(r-1)})$ transport steps can be achieved. That is, e. g. on 4-dimensional cubes $5n + o(n)$ steps are only needed. For $r = 8$ only $(8 + 3\sqrt{2})n = 12.23n$ steps are sufficient compared to the $14n$ steps of the hitherto existing best algorithm in [7]. If wrap-around connections are given then about half the number of steps is sufficient.

Furthermore, algorithms for the general $h - h$ routing problem, $h \geq 1$ are presented which also needs a smaller number of steps than previous algorithms. For an approach working in a pipeline mode a number of $(\lfloor 5(h - 1)/4 \rfloor + 2r - 2 - min(2, \lfloor (h - 1)/4 \rfloor))n + O((h+r)hrn/f(n)^{1/r})$ transport steps can be achieved while a buffer size of $O(hf(n))$ provided. (For $r = 2$ only $(h + 1)n + O(hn/f(n)^{1/2})$ are sufficient.) Hence these problems can be solved in $O((h + r)n)$ transport steps instead of $O(hrn)$ steps needed before.

The results of this paper are remarkable in two respects. First, all so far known randomized and deterministic routing algorithms are beaten. Second, as yet, even for so-called off-line algorithms no better step number is known [1].

2 Preliminaries

In this section some basic definitions are first presented and then some results on 1-dimensional and 2-dimensional arrays are briefly repeated. We will concentrate on those grids where all sidelengths are equal, that is $n_i = n$ for all $i = 1, ..., r$.

2.1 Indexings and intervals

Substantial parts of the routing algorithms presented in the following are sorting procedures. For the sorting problem we assume that at most N elements from a linearly ordered set are initially loaded into the N processors, each receiving at most one element. If a processor contains none of the elements, then it is thought to contain a dummy element which is smallest in the linear order of elements. For denoting the place into which an element has to be sorted the processors are thought to be indexed by a certain one-to-one mapping g from $mesh(n_1, ..., n_r)$ onto $\{0, ..., N - 1\}$. With respect to this function the sorting problem is to move the i-th smallest element to the processor indexed by $i - 1$ for all $i = 1, \ldots, N$. The best results for sorting have been obtained for various kinds of snake-like indexings [3,11,15,14]. In this paper slightly different index schemes, namely lexicographical, and their rotated versions are mainly used. From a pessimistic point of view sorting with respect to these indexings takes twice as many steps as with snake-like indexings ([5]), a factor, however, vanishing within the O-Notation.

Definition 1 (indexings)

1. The *lexicographical indexing lex* is defined by
   $lex_r(p_1, p_2, \ldots, p_r) := \sum_{i=1}^{r} p_i n^{r-i}$.
   The *reversed lexicographical indexing rev* is given by $rev_r(p_1, p_2, \ldots, p_r) := lex_r(p_r, \ldots, p_2, p_1)$.

2. The *i-th rotation of a tuple* $(p_1, \ldots, p_r)$ is denoted by $rot_i(p_1, \ldots, p_r) := (p_{i+1}, \ldots, p_r, p_1, \ldots, p_i)$.
   The *i-th rotation of an indexing* g is given by $g\_rot_i(p_1, \ldots, p_r) := g(p_{i+1}, \ldots, p_r, p_1, \ldots, p_i)$.

The subscript r is omitted if it is clear, which dimension r is meant. For most parts of the paper we assume that the packets are linearly ordered with respect to the lexicographical order of their addresses, that is $address(packet_1) \leq address(packet_2)$ iff $lex(address(packet_1)) \leq lex(address(packet_2))$. Sometimes we will also use the rotated versions of indexing lex, which then will be clearly marked in the text. For submeshes the indexings are used in the corresponding manner.

As various types of intervals of processors are often dealt with a formal notation for them and some useful abreviations are introduced:

Definition 2 (indexed intervals)

1. Let g be any index function. Then an *interval of processors (or addresses) with respect to indexing g* is the set of processors $[P, Q]_g := \{X \mid g(P) \leq g(X) \leq g(Q), \quad X \text{ a processor}\}$.

2. Let for all $i = 1, \ldots, r$ let an interval of integers be denoted by $[a_i, b_i]$, $0 \leq a_i \leq b_i < n$. Then
   $([a_1, b_1], \ldots, [a_i, b_i], \ldots, [a_r, b_r])$
   $= \{(p_1, \ldots, p_i, \ldots, p_r) \mid a_i \leq p_i \leq b_i, i = 1, \ldots, r\}$.
   If $a_i = b_i = p_i$ then $p_i = [a_i, b_i]$ is used. The interval $[0, n-1]$ is abbreviated by $*$.

That is, an *interval of processors along the i-th axis* is described by $(p_1, \ldots, p_{i-1}, *, p_{i+1}, \ldots, p_r)$, which is called an *$i$-tower*. For $r - i$ fixed coordinates $p_{i+1}, \ldots, p_r$ an i-dimensional subgrid is denoted by $(*, \ldots, *, p_{i+1}, \ldots, p_r)$.

2.2 Load factors and balanced problems

During the computation each processor is able to store a limited amount of packets. For sidelength n we assume that the size of the *additional buffer* is given by $f(n)$ or $rf(n)$, $2 \leq f(n) \leq n^{1-1/r}$. Typical buffer sizes are

for example $\log n$, $n^{1/r}$ or a constant c. It turnes out that even for algorithms routing partial permutations it is helpful to solve subproblems which are not of this type. An appropriate formalization is suggested in the following definition.

Definition 3 An r-dimensional routing problem is (λ, δ)-*balanced* with respect to indexing g if and only if for all intervals of processors $[P, Q]_g$ there are at most $\lambda(g(Q) - g(P) + 1) + \delta$ packets with destination in the interval of processors $[P, Q]_g$. The problem is (λ, δ)-*balanced* with respect to the r-th axis if and only if there are at most $\lambda(b_r - a_r + 1) + \delta$ packets with addresses in all intervals of processors $(p_1, \ldots, p_{r-1}, [a_r, b_r])$, $0 \leq p_j < n$, $1 \leq j \leq r-1$, and $0 \leq a_r \leq b_r < n$. λ is called the *load factor* and δ the *load deviation*.

If it is clear which indexing or which axis is meant we only speak of a (λ, δ)-balanced problem.

Definition 4 At an arbitrary time step t an r-dimensional routing problem is said to be (λ_t, δ_t)-*loaded* or has a (λ_t, δ_t)-*loading* with respect to indexing g if and only if all intervals of processors $[P, Q]_g$ contain at most $\lambda_t(g(Q) - g(P) + 1) + \delta_t$ packets. As before λ_t is called the load factor and δ_t the load deviation (at time t).

The notation (λ, δ)-loaded problem with respect to the r-th axis will be used in the same manner as for (λ, δ)-balanced problems. Note that the term balanced desribes a property of a problem (or subproblem) independently from the actual processor loading, e.g. initially or during the routing process. The term (λ_t, δ_t)-loading is used for temporary description at time t. So it may happen that $(\lambda_t, \delta_t) \neq (\lambda_u, \delta_u)$ for different time steps $t \neq u$. From a sucessfully solved (λ, δ)-balanced routing problem we can say that it has (λ, δ)-loading finally. Note that for $\lambda_1 \leq \lambda_2$ and $\delta_1 \leq \delta_2$ a (λ_1, δ_1)-balanced problem is also (λ_2, δ_2)-balanced. (If it is clear which time step is meant, the time index t will be omitted.)

The reader might be familiar with the fundamental classes of $h - h$ routing and permutation routing. These problems are naturally included in the class of balanced problems. For an integer h, $h \geq 1$, a $(h, 0)$-balanced problem with initial $(h, 0)$-loading is called a *(partial) $h - h$ routing problem*. In case of $h = 1$ it is called a *permutation problem*. It is worthwhile mentioning that $h - h$ routing problems are $(h, 0)$-balanced and $(h, 0)$-loaded with respect to all indexings.

2.3 One- and two-dimensional arrays

Several results on routing on one-dimensional arrays are known. Some of them are presented in the following lemma. Proofs can be found in [2,7,8].

Lemma 5 Let λ be a load factor with $\lambda \geq 1$. On a one-dimensional array of n processors with buffer size

$f(n)$ routing problems which are either $(\lambda, f(n))$-balanced and $(f(n), 1)$-loaded or $(\lambda, 0)$-loaded and $(f(n), 1)$-balanced can be solved

1. in at most $\lambda n + O(f(n))$ transport steps on a linear array (without wrap-arounds).

2. in at most $\lambda n/2 + O(f(n))$ transport steps on a ring (with wrap-arounds).

For 2-dimensional arrays some results have been presented for routing problems which are balanced with respect to one of the coordinates. The algorihm called *Sort-and-Route* was originally constructed for partial permutation routing problems [5] and then extended to balanced problems. Basing on the Sort-and-Route algorithm Leighton, Makedon and Tollis [10] developed a non-oblivious algorithm for partial permutations needing only $2n - 2$ steps for $n \times n$ meshes with constant buffersize. The buffersize of at least a 600 was recently reduced to 58 by Rajasekaran and Overholt [13]. However, those optimal algorithms are not uniaxial whereas the *Sort-and-Route* algorithm and many other routing and sorting algorithms in the literature (e.g. [2,3,5,11,12,14,15]) have this property.

Definition 6 (uniaxial algorithm) In a *uniaxial algorithm* in one time step all processors can communicate along one coordinate axis only. More formally (in the r-dimensional case) for any uniaxial algorithm we can define a function α from step index $(\in \mathbb{N})$ to $\{1, \ldots, r\}$. In clock step j processors P and Q may communicate iff $P - Q = \pm u_{\alpha(j)}$ (where u_i denotes the i-th unit vector). The axis $\alpha(j)$ is called the *active* axis at step j.

Theorem 7 ([7]) A $(1, f(n))$-balanced routing problem with initial $(1, 0)$-loading can be solved uniaxially by at most

1. $2n + O(n/f(n))$ steps on an $n \times n$ grid and

2. $n + O(n/f(n))$ steps on an $n \times n$ torus of processors.

3 Routing on r-dimensional grids

In this section we present fast routing algorithms on grids with more than two dimensions. As an introductory illustration let us first discuss some aspects of the three-dimensional case.

3.1 Routing on a 3-dimensional cube

An $n \times n \times n$ cube of n^3 processors can be viewed as collection of n planes (where $plane(h) = (*, *, h) = \{(r, c, h) \mid 0 \le r, c \le n - 1\}$ for $h = 0, \ldots, n - 1$). In each plane we may consider the *projected routing* problem $(plane(h), address_{1,2})$ with $address_{1,2}((r_1, c_1, h_1)) = (r_2, c_2)$ where $(r_2, c_2, h_2) = address(r_1, c_1, h_1)$. Usually

the projected routing problems are neither permutation nor well-behaving balanced routing problems. By a *well-behaving balanced routing problem* we mean a (λ, δ)-balanced problem with not too large λ and δ, e.g. $\lambda \le 1$ and $\delta \le f(n)$. One of the main ideas for the following algorithms is to rearrange the packets in the cube in such a way that in each plane we have a well-behaving balanced routing problems.

Algorithm 8 ([7]) 3-dimensional *Sort-and-Route*

1. {Rearrangement:} Rearrange packets such that in each plane the corresponding projected routing problem becomes a $(1, f(n))$-balanced routing problem.

2. In each plane solve the balanced routing problem by the 2-dimensional *Sort-and-Route*.

3. {Correction:} For all r, c, $0 \le r, c \le n - 1$, transport packets in $tower(r, c) = (r, c, *)$ to their destination processors.

Let us assume that the first stage of the algorithm has been performed correctly. Then in each plane the projected routing problem has become a $(1, f(n))$-balanced one and can therefore be solved by algorithm *Sort-and-Route* in the second stage (see theorem 7). After this stage an arbitrary processor $P = (r, c, h)$ only contains packets with addresses of type $(r, c, j), 0 \le j < n$. That means packets have arrived at positions correct up to the third coordinate. Moreover, since the problem is $(1, f(n))$-balanced with respect to the height axis in each tower of processors there are at most $n + f(n)$ packets. Hence all the linear routing problems in all the towers can be performed in parallel by $n + f(n)$ transport steps (as shown in lemma 5).

The above algorithm was originally presented in [7]. The Rearrange algorithm was a kind of uniformly smearing the packets along the height axis. This smearing of packets is in a certain way expensive: it takes about n transport steps. In the following we will demonstrate that it is possible to reduce this smearing phase to $n/3$ for special subproblems of the original permutation routing problem. Then we show that combining these subproblems and using the overlapping techniques proposed in [8] will lead to a $3.333n$ routing algorithm for partial permutations.

Before describing the rearrange algorithm in its general form we briefly present the block notation for arbitrary s, $2 \le s \le r$, s-dimensional subcubes with sidelength n.

Definition 9 (Blocks) Let a *block parameter* k be an integer such that $2 \le k \le 1 + k + k^{r-1} \le f(n) \le n^{1-1/r}$ holds and k^2 is a divisor of n. For this k an s-dimensional cube of processors is divided into k^s blocks. For arbitrary $k_i, 0 \le k_i \le k - 1$, $i = 1, \ldots, s$ a *block* is defined by $B(k_1, \ldots, k_s) = ([k_1 n/k, (k_1 + 1)n/k - 1], \ldots, [k_s n/k, (k_s + 1)n/k - 1])$.

For a fixed k_s, $0 \leq k_s \leq k-1$, the union of blocks $\bigcup_{i=1}^{s-1} \bigcup_{k_i=0}^{k-1} B(k_1, ..., k_i, ..., k_s)$ is called the k_s-th *plane of blocks*. For fixed $k_i, i = 1, ..., s-1$, the set $\bigcup_{k_s=0}^{k-1} B(k_1, ..., k_{s-1}, k_s)$ is called a *column of blocks*.

That is, each block has sidelength $b = n/k$ and contains $(n/k)^s$ processors. Note that there are exactly k^{s-1} columns of blocks. Assume that these columns of blocks are numbered from 1 to k^{s-1} by any fixed numbering. Then let B_{ij} denote that block which is in the j-th column of blocks and in the i-th plane of blocks.

3.2 Unity-Rearrange

We will now develop a detailed presentation of a generalization of algorithm 8 which is valid for all r, $r \geq 3$. We start with an r-dimensional *rearrange algorithm*. As mentioned before the packets are ordered according to the lexicographical order of their addresses.

A *shift parameter* σ has to be introduced. At the beginning σ is assumed to be a unity fraction, i.e. $1/\sigma$ an integer, and that $n\sigma$ and $k\sigma$ also are integers. (Later on, σ may be an arbitrary fraction.) For this unity fraction σ and for $y = 0, ..., 1/\sigma - 1$ s-dimensional submeshes are given as follows: σ-$submesh(y) = submesh(y) := (*, ..., *, [yn\sigma, (y+1)n\sigma - 1])$.

Algorithm 10 *Unity-Rearrange($\sigma, s, mesh$)*

1. In each block sort the packets with respect to indexing *rev*.

2. { Shift in each s-dimensional $submesh(y)$: } For all i, $i = 1, ..., s$, and all p_i, $0 \leq p_i < n$, move packets in all s-subtowers $(p_1, ..., p_{s-1}, *) \cap submesh(y)$ from processor $(p_1, ..., p_{s-1}, p_s)$ to processor $(p_1, ..., p_{s-1}, \lfloor p_s/\sigma n \rfloor \sigma n + (p_s + (p_1 \bmod \sigma k)n/k) \bmod n\sigma)$.

3. In each block sort packets with respect to lexicographical indexing *lex*.

Complexity: For a $(1,0)$-loaded problem the shift costs σn. The sorting of s-dimensional cubes with sidelength $b = n/k$ can be done in $O(sn/k)$ (as shown in [3,5]). Thus for the rearrange $\sigma n + O(sn/k)$ steps are sufficient.

Lemma 11 Let *mesh* be an arbitrary s-dimensional submesh with $(1,0)$-loading initially. For an arbitrary interval of addresses $[P,Q]_{lex}$ let z_y be the number of packets in $submesh(y)$ with addresses in $[P,Q]_{lex}$. Then after applying the σ-rearrange algorithm along the s-axis in every $(s-1)$-dimensional submesh $(*, ..., *, p_s) \subset submesh(y)$, $0 \leq p_s < n$, there are at most $z_y/(\sigma n) + \sigma k + k^{s-1}$ packets with addresses in $[P,Q]_{lex}$.

Proof:
Let us call packets with addresses in $[P,Q]_{lex}$ critical packets. For arbitrary j, $1 \leq j \leq k^{s-1}$ and i, $0 \leq i \leq k-1$ let z_{ij} denote the number of critical packets in a block B_{ij}. That is, $z_y = \sum_{j=1}^{k^{s-1}} \sum_{i=y\sigma k}^{(y+1)\sigma k-1} z_{ij}$.

Note that after the first step of the rearrange algorithm there are at most two 1-subtowers $(*, p_2, ..., p_s) \cap B_{ij}$ and $(*, q_2, ..., q_s) \cap B_{ij}$ which may contain both critical and non-critical packets. (See Figure 3.) This is because of the reversed lexicographical indexing *rev* where the first coordinate has the smallest weight. All the other 1-subtowers in the block contain either critical or non-critical packets. For these clean towers the shift distributes the critical packets uniformly to the σk different blocks in the j-th column of blocks. Now have a closer look at the at most two dirty towers. In one tower the critical packets are gathered at one side , and in the other they are on the other side. Hence there is at most one dirty interval of length σk in each of the dirty towers. Again by the sorting in one interval of length σk the critical packets are gathered at the left side, and in the other they are on the right side. Hence after the shift operation the critical packets from dirty σk-intervals differ at most by one in the different blocks of a column of blocks. That is each block B_{hj} now contains either $\lfloor z_{ij}/\sigma k \rfloor$ or $\lceil z_{ij}/\sigma k \rceil$ critical packets from block B_{ij} where $y\sigma k \leq h, i < (y+1)\sigma k$ and $y = \lfloor h/(\sigma k) \rfloor$. Let a_{hj} denote the number of critical packets in block B_{hj} after the σ-shifting. Then for all $y = 0, ..., 1/\sigma - 1$ and all h, $y\sigma k \leq h < (y+1)\sigma k$,

$$a_{hj} \leq \sum_{i=y\sigma k}^{(y+1)\sigma k-1} \lceil z_{ij}/\sigma k \rceil .$$

W.l.o.g. let us restrict to the first smearing region, i.e. $submesh(0)$. That is, the indices h, i lie between 0 and $\sigma k - 1$ while for the second index j we have $1 \leq j \leq k^{s-1}$. After the sorting with respect to lexicographical indexing (phase 3.) there are at most two dirty s-subtowers within each block. This can be seen by the same argumentation as above. Hence in an arbitrary $(s-1)$-dimensional submesh $(*, ..., *, p_s)$, where $(*, ..., *, p_s) \cap B_{hj} \neq \emptyset$, there are either $\lfloor a_{hj}/(n/k) \rfloor$ or $\lceil a_{hj}/(n/k) \rceil$ critical packets in that intersection. Therefore in each $(s-1)$-dimensional submesh $(*, ..., *, p_s)$ the number of critical packets is at most

$$\sum_{j=1}^{k^{s-1}} \lceil a_{hj}/(n/k) \rceil \leq \sum_{j=1}^{k^{s-1}} \lceil (1/(n/k)) \sum_{i=0}^{\sigma k-1} \lceil z_{ij}/(\sigma k) \rceil \rceil$$

$$\leq \sum_{j=1}^{k^{s-1}} \lceil (k/n) \sum_{i=0}^{\sigma k-1} (z_{ij}/(\sigma k) + 1) \rceil$$

$$\leq \sum_{j=1}^{k^{s-1}} \sum_{i=0}^{\sigma k-1} (z_{ij}/\sigma n + k/n) + k^{s-1}$$

264

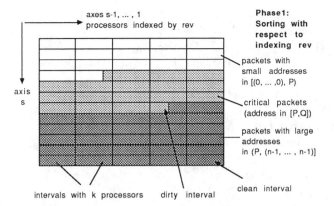

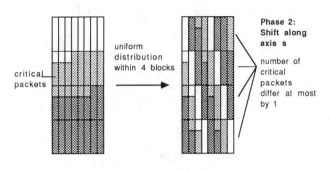

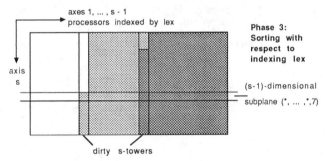

Figure 1: Rearrangement

$$= z_0/(\sigma n) + \sigma k^{s+1}/n + k^{s-1}$$

The argumentation for the other smearing regions is totally analogous. Since $k^s \leq n$ and $2 \leq s$ the lemma is proven. □

In $(s-1)$-dimensional submeshes of type $(*,...,*,p_s)$ we will consider the *projected routing* problem with $address_{1,...,s-1}((p_1,...,p_{s-1},p_s)) = (q_1,...,q_{s-1})$ where $address((p_1,...,p_{s-1},p_s)) = (q_1,...,q_{s-1},q_s)$. In the following these projected problems, where the s-th coordinate is ignored, are called s-*dropped problems*.

Lemma 12 Let *mesh* be an arbitrary s-dimensional submesh. Consider a (λ,δ)-balanced routing problem with $(1,0)$-loading initially. Then after applying the σ-rearrange algorithm along the s-axis in every $(s-1)$-dimensional submesh $(*,...,*,p_s)$, $0 \leq p_s < n$, the corresponding projected routing problems are $(1,0)$-loaded and $(\lambda/\sigma, \delta/(\sigma n) + \sigma k + k^{s-1})$-balanced.

Proof:
First of all note that by the rearrange algorithm at most one packet comes from an arbitrary processor and at most one packet is placed at each processor finally. That is, $(1,0)$-loaded problems are transposed into $(1,0)$-loaded problems.

Second, since the original problem is (λ,δ)-balanced with respect to lexicographical indexing the total number $z = \sum_{y=0}^{1/\sigma-1} z_y$ of packets with address in an arbitrary interval $[P,Q]_{lex}$ is bounded by $\lambda(lex(Q) - lex(P) + 1) + \delta$ and consequently this bound holds for each z_y. Hence by lemma 11 after the σ-rearrange along the s-axis in each submesh $(*,...,*,p_s)$ the number of packets with address in $[P,Q]_{lex}$ is bounded by

$$(\lambda(lex(Q) - lex(P) + 1) + \delta)/(\sigma n) + \sigma k + k^{s-1}$$

$$\leq (\lambda/\sigma)(lex(Q) - lex(P) + 1)/n + \delta/(\sigma n) + \sigma k + k^{s-1}.$$

Note that for the s-dropped problem the relative address of processor $Q = (q_1,...,q_{s-1},q_s)$ is $(q_1,...,q_{s-1})$. For the corresponding s- and $(s-1)$-dimensional indexings $lex_s(q_1,...,q_{s-1},q_s) = n(lex_{s-1}(q_1,...,q_{s-1})) + q_s$ holds. For an arbitrary interval $[(p_1,...,p_{s-1}),(q_1,...,q_{s-1})]_{lex_{s-1}}$ the number of packets in the mesh with address in this s-dropped interval are those that lie in the s-dimensional interval from $P_{first} = (p_1,...,p_{s-1},0)$ to $Q_{last} = (q_1,...,q_{s-1},n-1)$. For the interval $[P_{first},Q_{last}]_{lex_s}$ the following equation holds.
$$(lex(Q_{last}) - lex(P_{first}) + 1)/n$$

$$= lex_{s-1}(q_1,...,q_{s-1}) - lex_{s-1}(p_1,...,p_{s-1}) + 1.$$

Therefore in each $(s-1)$-dimensional submesh the number of packets with address in $[(p_1,...,p_{s-1}),(q_1,...,q_{s-1})]_{lex_{s-1}}$ is bounded by
$$(\lambda/\sigma)(lex_{s-1}(q_1,...,q_{s-1}) - lex_{s-1}(p_1,...,p_{s-1}) + 1)$$

$$+\delta/(\sigma n) + \sigma k + k^{s-1}.$$

Hence the s-dropped problem in each plane is $(\lambda/\sigma, \delta/(\sigma n) + \sigma k + k^{s-1})$-balanced. □

We will now give a general description of the algorithm *Sort-and-Route* for arbitrary s-dimensional subcubes of processors with arbitrary shift parameters. However, for the beginning let the smearing parameters be unit fractions and the rearrange of the following algorithm 13 be the *Unity-Rearrange* (i.e. algorithm 10). The rearranging and smearing with arbitrary fractions will be presented later. For $s \geq 3$ the general form of the algorithm call is *Sort-and-Route*$(s, mesh, (\sigma_s, \sigma_{s-1},...,\sigma_3))$. The parameter s denotes the dimension and the axis for the smearing, *mesh* stands for the actual s-dimensional submesh, and the σ_i is the shift parameter for rearranging along the i-th axis. In the two-dimensional case there is no smearing along any axis. The list of shift parameters is then empty and the algorithm denoted by $Sort\text{-}and\text{-}Route(2, mesh) =_{def} Sort\text{-}and\text{-}Route(2, mesh, empty\ list)$.

Algorithm 13 $s\text{-}dimensional\ Sort\text{-}and\text{-}Route$
$Sort\text{-}and\text{-}Route(s, mesh, (\sigma_s, \sigma_{s-1}, ..., \sigma_3))$
if $s = 2$ **then** $Sort\text{-}and\text{-}Route(2, mesh)$ **else**
begin

1. $Rearrange(\sigma_s, s, mesh)$

2. For all $p_s = 0, ..., n - 1$ do in parallel: $Sort\text{-}and\text{-}Route(s - 1, (*, ..., *, p_s), (\sigma_{s-1}, ..., \sigma_3))$

3. {$correction\ phase\ s$:} For all $j = 1, ..., s - 1$, and for all $p_j = 0, ..., n - 1$, transport packets within all s-towers $(p_1, ..., p_{s-1}, *)$ to their correct s-th coordinate.

end

We will now present a general theorem which at the moment is valid for shift parameters which are unity fractions ≤ 1. Later on it will be shown that arbitrary fractions for shift parameters are possible. For the empty set $\emptyset$ let us as usual define $\sum_\emptyset := 0$ and $\prod_\emptyset := 1$.

Theorem 14
For a $(\lambda, f(n))$-balanced routing problem, $\lambda \leq 1$, with initial $(1,0)$-loading let σ_s, $s = 3, ..., r$, be shift parameters with $\prod_{i=s}^{r} \sigma_i \geq \lambda$. Then the problem can be solved by the uniaxial r-dimensional $Sort\text{-}and\text{-}Route\ (r, mesh, (\sigma_r, \sigma_{r-1}, ..., \sigma_3))$ in at most $(r + \sum_{i=3}^{r} \sigma_i)n + O(r^2 n / f(n)^{1/(r-1)})$ transport steps and a buffersize of $f(n)$ packets.

Proof:
Let the block parameter k an integer with $1 + k + k^{r-1} \leq f(n)$ and n/k in $O(n/f(n)^{1/(r-1)})$. We will prove the theorem by induction on the dimension r. Note that for an empty parameter list, i.e. for $r = 2$, the theorem is true by theorem 7. Now assume, it is true for all s, $2 \leq s \leq r - 1$.

By the help of lemma 12 we know that after applying the rearrange algorithm in every $(r - 1)$-dimensional submesh $(*, ..., *, p_r)$ the corresponding projected routing problems are $(1,0)$-loaded and $(\lambda/\sigma_r, f(n)/(\sigma_r n) + \sigma_r k + k^{r-1})$-balanced. Since $f(n)/(\sigma_r n) + \sigma_r k + k^{r-1} \leq f(n)$ all the s-dropped subproblems in the submeshes are now $(\lambda/\sigma_r, f(n))$-balanced. As $\lambda/\sigma_r \leq 1$ and $\prod_{i=s}^{r-1} \sigma_i \geq \lambda/\sigma_r$, for all s, $s = 3, ..., r - 1$, the preconditions for the induction hypothesis are matched. Thus, all the subproblems can be solved in parallel by the corresponding calls of the $Sort\text{-}and\text{-}Route$ for $(r - 1)$-dimensional submeshes in $((r - 1) + \sum_{i=3}^{r-1} \sigma_i)n + O((r - 1)^2 n / (f(n))^{1/(r-2)})$ transport steps. Since the projected routing problems were $(\lambda/\sigma_r, f(n))$-balanced, it may happen that $\lambda/\sigma_r + f(n) \leq f(n) + 1$ packets were transported to

certain processors. That is, at the beginning of the correction phase in the r-towers we have linear problems with $(f(n), 1)$-loadings. On the other side, as the total problem is $(\lambda, f(n))$-balanced with respect to the lexicographical indexing, it is exactly the same for these linear subproblems. Thus the correction can be finished in at most $n + O(f(n))$ steps (see lemma 5). For the rearrangement $\sigma_r n + O(rn/f(n)^{1/(r-1)})$ steps are needed. Therefore, all together, at most

$$\sigma_r n + O(rn/f(n)^{1/(r-1)}) + (r - 1 + \sum_{i=3}^{r-1} \sigma_i)n$$

$$+ O((r - 1)^2 n / (f(n))^{1/(r-2)}) + n + O(f(n))$$

steps are necessary. Note that $f(n) \leq n/f(n)^{1/(r-1)}$ follows from $f(n) \leq n^{1-1/r}$ and that $f(n)^{1/(r-2)} \geq f(n)^{1/(r-1)}$. Hence

$$(r + \sum_{i=3}^{r} \sigma_i)n + O(r^2 n / (f(n))^{1/(r-1)})$$

transport steps are sufficient. Obviously, a buffer of $f(n)$ packets is never exceeded. □

For $s \geq 3$ the following corollary has already been shown for permutation routing (in [7]).

Corollary 15 ([7]) On an r-dimensional cube, $r \geq 2$, with sidelength n and buffersize of $f(n)$ packets, $f(n) \leq n^{(r-1)/r}$, a $(1, f(n))$-balanced routing problem with initial $(1,0)$-loading can be solved in at most $(2r - 2)n + O(r^2 n / f(n)^{1/(r-1)})$ transport steps.

Proof:
By theorem 14 and all $\sigma_i = 1$. □

3.3 Overlapped Routing

An helpful tool is that of colouring certain regions of the mesh. The mesh is partitioned into a fixed number of areas, where each one has a special colour.

Definition 16 (colouring) For a processor $P = (p_1, ..., p_i, ..., p_r)$ the remainder of the sum of coordinates $j = (p_1 + ... + p_i + ... + p_r)\ mod\ r$ is called the colour of P. A packet whose destination P has colour j is called a *colour-j packet*. A *colour-j problem* consists of all colour-j packets.

Since the partial permutation routing problem is $(1,0)$-loaded and $(1,0)$-balanced with respect arbitrary indexings, all colour-j problems are $(1/r, 1)$-balanced with respect to all rotated versions of the indexings *lex* and *rev*. Now take r incarnations of algorithm Sort-and-route and let *incarnation j*, $1 \leq j \leq r$, handle all packets of colour $j-1$. Let incarnation j do the rearrange phase along the j-th axis first, then (for the $(r-1)$-dimensional Sort-and-Route) operate along axis $1 + (j - 2)\ mod\ r$, then along $1 + (j - 3)\ mod\ r$, and so on. Finally do the correction along axis j. For incarnation j the corresponding indexings are *(r-j)-th rotation* of indexings *lex* and *rev*. That is, lex_rot_{r-j} and rev_rot_{r-j} are used for the j-th incarnation instead of *lex* and *rev*, respectively. In this sense the algorithm 13 given above is the r-th incarnation with corresponding rotation $rot_{r-r} = rot_0$. Furthermore, for the j-th incarnation, $j \neq r$, the linear order for the packets has to be lex_rot_{r-j} instead of *lex* used for algorithm 13, the r-th incarnation.

Hence the *j-th incarnation* can be described by $Sort\text{-}and\text{-}Route_j(j, mesh, (\sigma_r, ..., \sigma_3))$. Note that the list of shift parameters is the same for all incarnations. The *Overlapped Sort-and-Route* can then be given as follows:

Algorithm 17
Overlapped Sort-and-Route(mesh, $(\sigma_r, ..., \sigma_3)$)
begin
For all $j = 1, ..., r$ do in parallel
apply $Sort\text{-}and\text{-}Route_j(j, mesh, (\sigma_r, ..., \sigma_3))$
to the colour-j subproblem.
end

Note that for the above discussion on overlapping it was not important that the shift parameters σ are unity fractions. Thus we can summarize the above discussion in the following, slightly generalized lemma:

Lemma 18 (Overlapping lemma) For $i = 1, ..., r$ let $Prob_i$ be packet routing problems which are initially (λ_0, δ_0)-loaded, $\delta_0 \leq f(n)$, and $(\lambda, f(n))$-balanced, both with respect to the i-th rotation $lex_r\_rot_i$ of the lexicographical indexing lex_r.
If each problem $Prob_i$ can be solved by the i-th incarnation $Sort\text{-}and\text{-}Route_i(i, mesh, (\sigma_r, ..., \sigma_3))$ in $t(n)$ steps with a buffer of $f(n)$ packets, then all the problems can simultaneously be solved by the overlapped *Sort-and-Route* in the same number of $t(n)$ steps and a buffer of $rf(n)$ packets.

As a first result we state:

Theorem 19
On an r-dimensional cube with sidelength n and buffersize of $rf(n)$ packets, $f(n) \leq n^{(r-1)/r}$, the partial permutation routing problem can non-uniaxially be solved within $(2r - 3 + 1/r)n + O(r^2 n / f(n)^{1/(r-1)})$ transport steps.

Proof:
Choose $\sigma_r = 1/r$, $\sigma_{r-1} = ... = \sigma_3 = 1$. Since each j-coloured subproblem is $(1/r, 1)$-balanced theorem 14 shows that it can be solved in at most $(2r-3+1/r)n + O(r^2 n / f(n)^{1/(r-1)})$ transport steps and a buffer of $f(n)$ packets. The rest follows by lemma 18. □

Corollary 20 The partial permutation routing problem on an $n \times n \times n$ cube can be solved in at most $10/3n + O(n/f(n)^{1/2})$ transport steps and a buffersize of $3f(n)$ packets.

Although theorem 19 shows that all previous r-dimensional routing algorithms, $r \geq 3$, are beaten further improvements are possible for $r \geq 4$.

Theorem 21 Let r be a dimension which is a product of two factors a and b with $1 < a, b < r$. Then the r-dimensional partial permutation problem on a cube with sidelength n and buffersize $rf(n)$, $f(n) \leq n^{(r-1)/r}$, can non-uniaxially be solved in at most
$$(2r - 4 + 1/a + 1/b)n + O(r^2 n / f(n)^{1/(r-1)}) \text{ transport}$$
steps.

Proof:
Let $\sigma_r = 1/a$, $\sigma_{r-1} = a/r = 1/b$, and $\sigma_{r-2} = ... = \sigma_3 = 1$. By theorem 14 each of the $(1/r, 1)$-balanced j-coloured subproblems can be solved in at most $(2r-4+1/a+1/b)n + O(r^2 n / f(n)^{1/(r-1)})$ transport steps and a buffer of $f(n)$ packets. Then by lemma 18 the theorem is proven. □

The above theorem shows that on a 4-dimensional cube partial permutation routing can be done in $5n + o(n)$ transport steps instead of the $5.25n + o(n)$ steps given by theorem 19.

3.4 Arbitrary shift

As demonstrated in theorem 21 the combination of smearing and overlapping technique can be applied more sucessfully if nontrivial shift parameters different from 1 and $1/r$ are handled. In the following we will try to use nontrivial, small shift parameters for two or more axes. One disadvantage of the approach in theorem 21 is that it helps only for dimensions r which have suitable factors. The reason for this lies in the *Unity-rearrange*, which is not flexible enough with its unity fractions. We therefore develop a rearrange technique which will allow more or less arbitrary fractions $\sigma \leq 1$ as shift parameters.

As before the following rearrange algorithm can be viewed as part of the r-th incarnation of the algorithm. The smearing technique can be performed in two stages, a *coarse shift* and a *fine shift*. The latter is the same as used in the *Unity-rearrange*. The coarse shift will mainly happen on neighbouring one-dimensional submeshes, viewed as one-dimensional quasi-rings.

Definition 22 [Slices]
Let a, x be divisors of n with $0 < a < x \leq n$. For all $p_i, i = 2, ..., s-1, 0 \leq p_i < n$, and all p_1 with $p_1 \equiv 0 \bmod a$ consider a-unions of sequel s-towers given by $([p_1, p_1 + a - 1], p_2, ..., p_{s-1}, *)$. For all $y = 0, ..., x-1$, and all $i = 0, ..., a-1$ subintervals of length n/x, called *subtowers*, are defined as follows: $subtower(p_1 + i, s, y) = (p_1 + i, p_2, ..., p_{s-1}, [yn/x, (y+1)n/x - 1])$.
Then define $slice(p_1 + i, y) = subtower(p_1 + 2i, s, y)$, $0 \leq 2i \leq a - 1$, and $slice(p_1 + i, 2x - y - 1) =$

$subtower(p_1 + 2i + 1, s, y)$, $0 \leq 2i + 1 \leq a - 1$. For a slice $slice(p, z)$ let us call z the *slice number*.

That is, most of the slices lie in pairs of neighbouring s-towers which are viewed as quasi-rings of processors given by $ring(p_1, i) = ([p_1+2i, p_1+2i+1], p_2, ..., p_{s-1}, *)$, $0 \leq i \leq \lfloor a/2 \rfloor - 1$. Note that slices with slice number y and slice number $2x - y - 1$ are from the same submesh(y) provided $0 \leq y \leq x - 1$. Let $\sigma = a/x$, with a, x integers, an let k be a block parameter such that a, x are divisors of n/k, and x is a divisor of k.

Algorithm 23 $Rearrange(a/x, s, mesh)$
if $a \geq 2$ **then begin**
1. In each block sort the packets with respect to indexing rev.
2. **if** a is odd **then begin**
For $i = 0, ..., \lfloor a/2 \rfloor - 1$ shift packets from $slice(p_1 + i, y)$, $y = 0, ..., 2x - 1$, to $slice(p_1 + i, (y + 2i + 2) \bmod 2x)$.
Do not move any slice in $(p_1 + a - 1, p_2, ..., p_{s-1}, *)$.
end
else begin
For $i = 0, ..., a/2 - 1$ shift packets from $slice(p_1 + i, y)$, $y = 0, ..., 2x - 1$, to $slice(p_1 + i, (y + 2i + 1) \bmod 2x)$.
end
end
3. $Unity\text{-}Rearrange(1/x, s, mesh)$

Complexity: Note that in the odd and in the even case during the coarse shift the slice numbers of the origin and the destination slice differ at most by $a - 1$. For a $(1, 0)$-loaded problem the coarse shift therefore costs $(a-1)n/x$ transport steps. The sorting of s-dimensional cubes with sidelength n/k can be done in $O(sn/k)$. For the unity-rearrange $n/x + O(sn/k)$ steps are needed. Hence in total $an/x + O(sn/k) = \sigma n + O(sn/k)$ steps are sufficient.

The next lemma shows that for the arbitrary rearrange a result comparable to lemmas 11 and 12 can be derived.

Lemma 24 Let an arbitrary (λ, δ)-balanced routing problem with initial $(1, 0)$-loading be loaded in an arbitrary s-dimensional submesh. Let σ be an arbitrary fraction in $(0, 1]$. After applying the σ-rearrange algorithm along the s-axis in every $(s - 1)$-dimensional submesh $(*, ..., *, p_s)$, $0 \leq p_s < n$, the corresponding projected s-dropped routing problems are $(\lambda/\sigma, \delta/(\sigma n) + \sigma k + k^{s-1})$-balanced and $(1, 0)$-loaded.

Proof Sketch:
At the beginning one has to show that for the coarse smearing in each a-union the slices are distributed uniformly. That is, in each a-union the slices in submesh(y) with slice numbers y or $2x - 1 - y$ are shifted to a different submeshes. The technical proof details are left to the reader. Now let us concentrate on an arbitrary submesh(y), $0 \leq y \leq x - 1$. For this submesh with mesh

number y let $y_1, ..., y_a$, $0 \leq y_i \leq x - 1$, denote the different numbers of those submeshes where the slices have come from by the coarse shift. Note that in different a-unions the corresponding slices have been shifted in exactly the same manner.

Following the proof of lemma 11 let us call packets with addresses in an arbitrary, but fixed interval $[P, Q]_{lex}$ critical packets. Let z_{ij} denote the number of critical packets in a block B_{ij}. The number of critical packets in submesh(y) consequently is the sum of the numbers z_{ij} of those blocks B_{ij} contained in submesh(y), i.e. $\sum_{j=1}^{k^{s-1}} \sum_{i=yk/x}^{(y+1)k/x-1} z_{ij}$.

With an argumentation, similar to that in the proof of lemma 11, one can show that after the coarse shift each block B_{hj} in submesh(y) contains either $\lfloor z_{ij}/a \rfloor$ or $\lceil z_{ij}/a \rceil$ critical packets from all blocks $B_{ij} \subset \bigcup_{l=1}^{a} submesh(y_l)$. That is, the index i is from $I(y, h) = \{l \mid l \in I(y), l \equiv h \bmod k/x\}$. Note that $\mid I(y) \mid = ak/x$. Let b_{hj} denote the number of critical packets in block B_{hj} after the coarse shift. Then for all h, $yk/x \leq h < (y+1)k/x$: $b_{hj} \leq \sum_{i \in I(y,h)} \lceil z_{ij}/a \rceil$. Therefore, the number z_y of critical packets in submesh(y) is now bounded by

$$\sum_{j=1}^{k^{s-1}} \sum_{h=yk/x}^{(y+1)k/x-1} b_{hj} \leq \sum_{j=1}^{k^{s-1}} \sum_{h=yk/x}^{(y+1)k/x-1} \sum_{i \in I(y,h)} \lceil z_{ij}/a \rceil$$

$$\leq \sum_{j=1}^{k^{s-1}} \sum_{i=0}^{k-1} z_{ij}/a + (a/x)k^s \leq z/a + (a/x)k^s$$

After the final unity-rearrange with shift parameter $1/x$ we know by lemma 11 that each $(s - 1)$-dimensional submesh $(*, ..., *, p_s) \subset submesh(y)$ contains at most $z_y/(n/x) + k/x + k^{s-1}$ critical packets. Combining this fact and the above inequality shows that at most $(z/a + (a/x)k^s)/(n/x) + k/x + k^{s-1}$
$= z/(na/x) + ak^s/n + k/x + k^{s-1} \leq z/(\sigma n) + \sigma k + k^{s-1}$ critical packets are gathered in each $(s-1)$-dimensional submesh. (The last inequality followed by the observation that $k^s/n \leq 1$,and $a, k/x \geq 2$.) Note that the bound is independent of the submesh number y.

Following completely the argumentation of lemma 12 we see that in every $(s - 1)$-dimensional submesh $(*, ..., *, p_s)$, $0 \leq p_s < n$, the corresponding projected s-dropped routing problems are $(1, 0)$-loaded and $(\lambda/\sigma, \delta/(\sigma n) + \sigma k + k^{s-1})$-balanced. $\square$

With the generalized rearrange algorithm 23 the algorithm *Sort-and-Route* can be used more efficiently. Since algorithm 23 is obviously uniaxial, overlapping can be used in the same way as before (see algorithm 17).

Remark Note that in the proof of theorem 14 for the shift parameters the property of being unity fractions played no role. The only reason for demanding unity fractions was that at that point no rearrange algorithm with arbitrary shift parameters was available. Therefore, theorem 14 is valid for arbitrary shift parameters.

For the following theorem we postulate shift parameters which are not rationals. This has to be understood in that manner that rational approximations very close to the given values should be taken. The tiny deviations caused by these approximations are not especially examined here.

Theorem 25 On an r-dimensional cube with sidelength n and buffersize of $rf(n)$ packets, $f(n) \leq n^{(r-1)/r}$, a packet routing problem, which has an initial $(1,0)$-loading and which is $(1, f(n))$-balanced with respect to all rotated lexicographical indexings, can nonuniaxially be solved in nearly
$$(r + (r-2)(1/r)^{1/(r-2)})n + O(r^2 n / f(n)^{1/(r-1)})$$ transport steps.

Proof:
Note that all of the j-coloured subproblems are $(1/r, f(n))$-balanced. Choose all $\sigma_i = (1/r)^{1/(r-2)}$. It is immediately seen that the precondition of theorem 14 is fulfilled: for all s, $s = 3, ..., r$, we have $\prod_{i=s}^{r} \sigma_i = (1/r)^{(r+1-s)/(r-2)} \geq 1/r = \lambda$. Thus each of these subproblems can be solved in at most $(r - 4 + (r-2)(1/r)^{1/(r-2)})n + O(r^2 n / f(n)^{1/(r-1)})$ transport steps and a buffer of $f(n)$ packets. Hence by lemma 18 the theorem is proven. $\square$

Let us mention that the overlapped version of the algorithm *Sort-and-Route* beats randomized routing algorithms [16] as well as deterministic algorithms for full permutations based on sorting [3,5]. Both approaches need at least $(2r - 1)n$ steps. Moreover, the previously presented routing algorithm in [7] has also been improved.

3.5 Tori of processors

In the case of wrap-around connections the number of transport steps can be reduced to nearly the half. The reason for this lies in the fact that both the rearrangement and the correction can be done on rings in half the step number. For the correction this is obvious by lemma 5. For the rearrangement we need a new shift operation which makes use of the ring structure. A detailed discussion including the formal definitions, the explicit presentations of the algorithms, and the complexity calculations can be found in the full paper. It results in the following theorem.

Theorem 26 On an r-dimensional torus with sidelength n and buffersize of $rf(n)$ packets, $f(n) \leq n^{(r-1)/r}$, a packet routing problem, which has an initial $(1,0)$-loading and which is $(1, f(n))$-balanced with respect to all rotated lexicographical indexings, can be solved within

$$(r + (r-2)(1/r)^{1/(r-2)})n/2 + O(r^2 n / f(n)^{1/(r-1)})$$ transport steps.

3.6 Constant buffer size

If we assume the buffer size to be a constant independent of the side length n, then the terms of low order become more important. The following theorem can be obtained.

Theorem 27 On an r-dimensional grid, with sidelength n and a buffersize of $O((r^2/\epsilon)^{r-1})$ packets, $\epsilon > 0$, the partial permutation routing problem can be solved in $(r + (r-2)(1/r)^{1/(r-2)} + \epsilon)n$ transport steps. Half the number of steps is sufficient on a torus.

3.7 Multi-packet routing

Until now we only discussed the case of initial $(1,0)$-loadings. However, more complex initial loadings with an arbitrary λ_0 as a load factor can also be handled by the above algorithms. In this case sorting and shifting have to be performed in several layers (as described in [8]). Let us restrict to the case where λ_0 is an integer h. It is not hard to see that the central lemmas 11, 12, and 24 can be extended to arbitrary load factors $\lambda_0 > 1$. A generalized version of theorem 14 is then as follows.

Theorem 28 For a $(\lambda, f(n))$-balanced routing problem, $\lambda \leq h$, with initial $(h, 0)$-loading let σ_s, $s = 3, ..., r$, be shift parameters with $\prod_{i=s}^{r} \sigma_i \geq \lambda/h$. Then the problem can be solved by the *uniaxial r*-dimensional *Sort-and-Route* $(r, mesh, (\sigma_r, \sigma_{r-1}, ..., \sigma_3))$ in at most $n(h + max(1, \lambda) + \sum_{i=3}^{r} max(1, (\lambda / \prod_{j=i}^{r} \sigma_j)))$ $+ n\lceil h/2 \rceil \sum_{i=3}^{r} \sigma_i + O(hr^2 n / (f(n))^{1/(r-1)})$ transport steps and a buffersize of $hf(n)$ packets.

Proof Sketch:
Considerable improvements could be obtained for the rearrangement where packets in two layers are shifted simultaneously. Note that for the shift on quasi-rings for one packet only one direction on the ring was used. The positive shift mapped slice$(p_1 + i, y)$ to slice$(p_1 + i, (y + 2i + 2)\ mod\ 2x)$. Obviously, a negative shift mapping slice$(p_1 + i, y)$ to slice$(p_1 + i, (y - (2i + 2))\ mod\ 2x)$ has the same effect of a uniform distribution of packets as the positive one. It is easily seen that the negative shift never uses a directed connection used by the positive shift. That means that two layers of packets can uniformly be distributed simultaneously. $\square$

With the colouring of subproblems and the above approach we are now able to handle $h-h$ routing problems for an arbitrary h. In the previous approach in [8] the best results were only obtained for those cases where r is a divisor of h.

Theorem 29 On an r-dimensional cube with side-length n and buffersize of $hrf(n)$ packets, $f(n) \leq n^{(r-1)/r}$, a $h - h$ routing problem can non-uniaxially be solved in nearly

$$n(h + max(1, h/r) + \sum_{i=3}^{r} max(1, \; hr^{(r+1-i)/(r-2)-1}))$$
$$+ n\lceil h/2 \rceil (r-2)(1/r)^{1/(r-2)} + O(hr^2 n/(f(n))^{1/(r-1)})$$

transport steps.

Proof:
Note that the j-coloured subproblems are all $(h/r, h)$-balanced, and therefore $(h/r, f(n))$-balanced, with respect to all rotated lexicographical indexings. Choose $\sigma_r = ... = \sigma_3 = (1/r)^{1/(r-2)}$. The rest of the proof then follows by the help of theorem 28 and of lemma 18. $\square$

Furthermore, by the ability of handling balanced problems where a load deviation is possible we can now treat $h - h$ routing problems in a better pipelined fashion. For doing so a prephase for preparing the different layers has to be introduced. Let the at most h packets in each processor P lie in different layers, numbered from 0 to $h - 1$. That can be viewed as if a packet in layer i lies in a virtual processor (i, P) of a virtual $(r + 1)$-dimensional grid $layer \times mesh$. For the sorting of blocks in that phase some slightly altered restrictions on the buffer parametzer $f(n)$ and the block parameter k have to be fulfilled: $2 \leq k \leq 1 + k + k^{r-1} \leq k^r \leq f(n) \leq n^{r/(r+1)}$. Let t_{pre} the number of steps needed for the prephase, i.e. the first phase, of the following algorithm 32. Obviously, t_{pre} is in $O(hrn/f(n)^{1/r})$.

Let t_r^* be the sum of the steps needed for one call of the r-dimensional $Unity\text{-}Rearrange(1, r, mesh)$ for one layer and of the number of steps necessary for the sorting of blocks in all h layers. That means, t_r^* is bounded by $n + O(hrn/f(n)^{1/r})$. It is clear that for an $s < r$ the number of steps $t_s^* \leq t_r^*$. Assume that for the following pipelined rearrangement all the calls of s-dimensional rearrange algorithms last for t_r^* steps, even in the case that $s < r$.

Algorithm 30
$Pipeline\text{-}Rearrange_r(r, mesh, (\sigma_r = 1, ..., \sigma_3 = 1))$
if $r \geq 3$ **then begin**
1. $Unity\text{-}Rearrange(\sigma_r, r, mesh)$
2. For all $p_r = 0, ..., n - 1$ in parallel:
$Pipeline\text{-}Rearrange_{r-1}(r - 1, (p_r, *, ..., *), (\sigma_{r-1}, ..., \sigma_3))$
end

As for the preceeding pipelined rearrange algorithm assume that the correction of the s-th coordinate always takes t_r^* steps in the following pipelined correction algorithm.

Algorithm 31
$Pipeline\text{-}Correction_s(s, r, (p_1, ..., p_{s-1}, *, .., *))$
if $3 \leq s \leq r$ **then begin**
1. {$correction$ $phase$ s :} For all $j = 1, ..., r$, $j \neq s$, and for all $p_j = 0, ..., n - 1$, transport packets within all s-towers $(p_1, ..., p_{s-1}, *, p_{s-1}, ..., p_r)$ to their correct s-th

coordinate.
2. For all $i = 1, ..., s$, and all $p_i = 0, ..., n - 1$ in parallel:
$Pipeline\text{-}Correction_{s+1}(s + 1, r, (p_1, ..., p_s, *, .., *))$
end

Let $phase\text{-}time(i) := it_r^* + t_{pre}$. We say that an algorithm starts at $phase\text{-}time$ i if the algorithm starts after step $phase\text{-}time(i)$.

Algorithm 32
$Pipeline\text{-}Sort\text{-}and\text{-}Route(h, mesh, (\sigma_r, \sigma_{r-1}, ..., \sigma_3))$
begin
1. In all blocks sort packets with respect to indexing lex_{r+1} on the virtual grid $layer \times mesh$. In all processors $(p_1, ..., p_r)$ with $j = (p_1 + ... + p_r) \; mod \; h$ shift packets from layer i to layer $(i + j) \; mod \; h$.
2. For all $j = 0, ..., h - 1$ start the handling of packets in layer j with $Pipeline\text{-}Rearrange_r(r, mesh, (\sigma_r = 1, ..., \sigma_3 = 1))$ at $phase\text{-}time$ $\lfloor j/4 \rfloor$.
3. For all $j = 0, ..., h - 1$ start the handling of layer j with $2\text{-}dimensinal$ $Sort\text{-}and\text{-}Route(2, (*, *, p_3, ..., p_r))$ at $phase\text{-}time$ $j + \lfloor (h-1)/4 \rfloor + r - 2 - min(2, \lfloor (h-1)/4 \rfloor)$.
4. For all $j = 0, ..., h - 1$ start the handling of layer j with $Pipeline\text{-}Correction_3(3, r, (p_1, p_2, *, .., *)$ at $phase\text{-}time$ $j + \lfloor (h-1)/4 \rfloor + r - min(2, \lfloor (h-1)/4 \rfloor)$.
end

By the help of algorithm 32 we can state the following theorem.

Theorem 33 On an r-dimensional cube with side-length n and buffersize of $hf(n)$ packets, $f(n) \leq n^{r/(r+1)}$, a $h - h$ routing problem, $h \geq r$, can non-uniaxially be solved in
$(\lfloor 5(h-1)/4 \rfloor + 2r - 2 - min(2, \lfloor (h-1)/4 \rfloor))n$
$+ O((h + r)hrn/f(n)^{1/r})$ transport steps.

The too lengthy proof is ommitted here and can be found in the full paper. Since no rearrangement is necessary in the two-dimensional case, the number of steps is then reduced to $(h + 1)n + O(hn/f(n)^{1/2})$. In this case, for any $h > 4$, our solution is better than that given in [8]. Moreover, for $r \geq 3$ all the results on $h - h$ routing on r-dimensional cubes beat randomized algorithms (in [16]) as well as deterministic algorithms recently presented in [8]. Indeed, it demonstrates that for a large h the $h - h$ routing problem can be solved in $O((h + r)n)$ transport steps in contrast to the $O(hrn)$ of previous solutions.

4 Conclusion

In this paper we presented routing algorithms for r-dimensional $n \times \cdots \times n$ meshes with additional buffer for each processor. Balanced problems, including permutations, were mainly studied. If the buffersize is $rf(n)$ and wrap-around connections are given, then the algorithm needs $(r + (r-2)(1/r)^{1/(r-2)})n/2$ parallel data movements (neglecting low order terms). For grids without wrap-arounds the method works with $(r + (r-2)(1/r)^{1/(r-2)})n$ steps. For the r-dimensional permutation routing problem, $r \geq 3$, the algorithms are faster than so far known deterministic sorting algorithms which need processors with buffersize of only one packet. Although the full permutation routing problem seems to be easier than the sorting problem, it is still an open question whether sorting can be solved as fast as routing permutations on meshes with additional buffer. One result of this paper is that in the r-dimensional case permutation routing on meshes with additional buffer can be done faster than sorting on meshes without additional buffer.

A little bit surprising is that, as yet, even for so-called off-line algorithms no better step number is known. For r-dimensional grids, r, $r \geq 3$, it is still an open question whether the distance bound can be matched by any routing algorithm, either by on-line or by off-line algorithms. At the moment the results of this paper are closest to the distance bound for worst-case analysis. Especially on the three-dimensional cube, where only $3.333n + o(n)$ steps are needed, the distance bound seems to be within reach. However, let us mention in this context that in average case analysis the situation is better (see [9]).

Furthermore, for the general $h - h$ routing problem, $h \geq 1$, an algorithm working in a pipeline mode was presented which only needs $(\lfloor 5(h-1)/4 \rfloor + 2r - 2 - min(2, \lfloor (h-1)/4 \rfloor))n$ transport steps (neglecting low order terms). This result shows that only $O((h+r)n)$ transport steps are sufficient for solving $h - h$ routing problems instead of the $O(hrn)$ steps needed before.

The paper has demonstrated that combining different design methods may be fruitful. In our case we used a combination of obtaining local information (by sorting), of distributing this information uniformly (by the rearrange-technique), and of using the overlapping technique (originally developed for multi-packet algorithms). It might be interesting to analyse, whether these techniques are helpful for other fixed size networks such as hypercubes or butterflies.

References

[1] Annexstein, F. and Baumslag, M. A unified approach to off-line permutation routing on parallel networks. Proceedings of the 1990 ACM Symposium on Parallel Algorithms and Architectures, SPAA 90. Iland of Crete, 1990, pp. 398–406.

[2] Krizanc, D., Rajasekaran, S. and Tsantilas, T. Optimal Routing Algorithms for Mesh-Connected Processor Arrays, In J.H.Reif (ed.). VLSI Algorithms and Architectures. Proceedings of the 3rd AWOC 88, Lect. Notes Comp. Sci. 319, pp. 411–422.

[3] Kunde, M. Optimal sorting on multi-dimensionally mesh-connected computers, Proc. of STACS 87. In Brandenburg, F.J., Vidal-Naquet, G. and Wirsing, M. (eds.). Lect. Notes Comp. Sci., vol. 247. Springer, Berlin-Heidelberg-New York-Tokyo, 1987, pp. 408–419.

[4] Kunde, M. Lower bounds for sorting on mesh-connected architectures. Acta Informatica, 24 (1987), pp. 121–130.

[5] Kunde, M. Routing and Sorting on Mesh-Connected Arrays. In J.H.Reif (ed.). VLSI Algorithms and Architectures. Proceedings of the 3rd AWOC 88, Lect. Notes Comp. Sci. 319, pp. 423–433.

[6] Kunde, M. Bounds for for l-Selection and Related Problems on Grids of Processors. J. of New Generation Computer Systems, 2 (1989), pp. 129–143.

[7] Kunde, M. Packet Routing on Grids of Processors, In Djidjev (ed.). Optimal Algorithms, Proceedings, Lect. Notes Comp. Sci., vol. 401. Springer, Berlin-Heidelberg-New York-Tokyo, 1989, pp. 254–265. Revised and extended version to appear in Algorithmica.

[8] Kunde, M. and Tensi, T. k-k routing on multidimensional mesh-connected arrays. J. of Parallel and Distributed Computing, 11 (1991), pp. 146–155. Preliminary version in: Proceedings of the 1989 ACM Symposium on Parallel Algorithms and Architectures, SPAA 89. Santa Fe, 1989, pp. 336–443.

[9] Leighton, T. Average Case Analysis of Greedy Routing Algorithms on Arrays. Proceedings of the 1990 ACM Symposium on Parallel Algorithms and Architectures, SPAA 90. Iland of Crete, 1990, pp. 2–10.

[10] Leighton, T., Makedon, F. and Tollis, I. A 2n-2 Step Algorithm for Routing in an n x n Array with Constant Size Queues. Proceedings of the 1989 ACM Symposium on Parallel Algorithms and Architectures, SPAA 89. Santa Fe, 1989, pp. 328–335.

[11] Ma, Y., Sen, S. and Scherson, I.D. The distance bound for sorting on mesh-connected processor arrays is tight. Proceedings FOCS 86, pp. 255–263.

[12] Nassimi, D. and Sahni, S.: Bitonic sort on a mesh-connected parallel computer. IEEE Trans. Comput. C-28 (1979), pp. 2–7.

[13] Rajasekaran, S. and Overholt, R. Constant Queue Routing on a Mesh. Proceedings of STACS 91, In Choffrut, C. and Jantzen, M. (eds.). Lect. Notes Comp. Sci., vol. 480. Springer, Berlin-Heidelberg-New York-Tokyo, 1991, pp. 444–455.

[14] Schnorr, C.P. and Shamir, A. An optimal sorting algorithm for mesh-connected computers. Proceedings STOC 1986. Berkley, 1986, pp. 255–263.

[15] Thompson, C.D. and Kung, H.T. Sorting on a mesh-connected parallel computer. CACM 20 (1977), pp. 263–270.

[16] Valiant, L.G. and Brebner, G.J. Universal schemes for parallel communication, Proceedings STOC 81, pp. 263–277.

Parallel Algorithms for Routing
in Non-blocking Networks

Geng Lin   *Nicholas Pippenger*

Department of Computer Science
The University of British Columbia
Vancouver, British Columbia V6T 1W5
CANADA

Abstract Non-blocking networks have many applications in communications. Typical examples are telephone switching networks and communication networks among processors or between processors and memory devices. We construct non-blocking networks that are efficient not only as regards their cost and delay, but also as regards the time and space required to control them. In this paper, we present the first simultaneous "weakly optimal" solutions for the explicit construction of non-blocking networks, the design of algorithms and the design of data-structures. "Weakly optimal" is in the sense that all measures of complexity (size and depth of the network, time for the algorithm, and space for the data-structure) are within one or more factors of $logn$ of their smallest possible values. In fact, we explicitly construct a scheme in which networks with n inputs and n outputs have size $O(n(logn)^2)$ and depth $O(logn)$. And we present deterministic and randomized on-line parallel algorithms to establish and abolish routes dynamically in these networks. The deterministic algorithm uses $O((logn)^5)$ steps to process any number of transactions in parallel (with one processor per transaction), maintaining a data structure that use $O(n(logn)^2)$ words and the randomized algorithm uses $O((logn)^2)$ expected steps to process any number of transactions in parallel (with one processor per transaction), maintaining a data structure that use $O(n(logn)^2)$ words.

1. Introduction

Non-blocking networks have many applications in communications. Typical examples are telephone switching networks and communication networks among processors or between processors and memory devices. Given an acyclic directed graph with a set of distinguished vertices called *inputs* and a set of other distinguished vertices called *outputs*, it is said to be a *"non-blocking"* network if, given any set of disjoint direct routes from inputs to outputs, and given any input and output not involved in these established routes, a new route that is disjoint from the established routes can be found from the requesting input to the requesting output. Interpretations of the above network in the context of telephone switching and processor communication are clear. The most frequently applied measures of complexity for non-blocking networks are the "size" (the number of single-pole single-throw switches, i.e. the number of edges) and the "depth" (the largest number of switches, i.e. edges, on any route from an input to an output). An extensive literature exists concerning the design of non-blocking networks, minimizing the size and depth (or some combination of them) as functions of the number of inputs and outputs; see Pippenger [P82] for an introductory account, and Feldman, Friedman and Pippenger [FFP88] for recent results. The most basic results are that, if a non-blocking network has n inputs and an equal number of outputs, it must have depth at least 1 (but to achieve this requires size n^2, one switch between each input and each output); it must have size at least $\Omega(nlogn)$ (but to achieve this requires depth at least $\Omega(logn)$; see Pippenger and Yao [PY]).

In this paper we combine this concern for depth and size with concern for the time taken by an algorithm that finds the routes guaranteed by the non-blocking property, and for the space taken by the data-structure used by the algorithm. Unlike the case of depth and size alone, not much progress has been made in this setting. An exception is that Arora, Leighton and Maggs [ALM] found an on-line $O(logn)$ steps parallel path selection algorithm for non-blocking networks of size $O(n\log n)$ and of depth $O(\log n)$. Their proposal, however, assumes that the number of processors is proportional to the size of the network, irrespective of the number of transactions being processed. Our approach, in contrast, uses only one processor for each transaction, even if this number is as small as one.

In this paper, we explicitly construct a scheme in which non-blocking networks with n inputs and n outputs have size $O(n(\log n)^2)$ and depth $O(\log n)$. And we present on-line parallel algorithms to control them. The algorithms use time and space within one or more factors of $\log n$ of the smallest possible values that any control algorithm (on-line or off-line, parallel or serial) may use. More precisely, we present an on-line deterministic algorithm that uses $O((\log n)^5)$ steps to process any number of transactions in parallel (with one processor per transaction), maintaining a data structure that use $O(n(\log n)^2)$ words and an on-line randomized algorithm that uses $O((\log n)^2)$ expected steps to process any number of transactions in parallel (with one processor per transaction), maintaining a data structure that use $O(n(\log n)^2)$ words. (The meanings of "step", "word" and "transaction" will be explained in next paragraph).

Consider a non-blocking network with $n = 2^\nu$ inputs and $n = 2^\nu$ outputs. We assume that inputs and outputs are represented as binary words of length ν and a "processor" is able to perform arithmetic and logical operations on such words of length ν. We reckon "time" in such operations, and "space" in such words. We mainly consider the parallel algorithms and their data-structures. In fact, we consider the algorithm and data-structure together as an "on-line transaction processing system", in which each "batch" of transactions (requests to establish a route and requests to abolish a route) must be processed before its successors are known. Furthermore, for a batch of t transactions, which are to be processed in parallel, only t processors are allowed to be used. In other words, our approach assumes each transaction "brings its own processor", a setting convenient in situations where routing is but one part of a larger process, and the number of processes simultaneously engaged in routing is not easily predictable.

It is observed that if a non-blocking network has n inputs and an equal number of outputs, any algorithm that controls the network must use $\Omega(1)$ steps to process a batch of transactions, and the data-structure for it must have $\Omega(n)$ words (or their equivalent), since this much space is needed to represent one of $n!$ bijection between inputs and outputs.

Our results provide the first simultaneous "weakly op-

timal" solutions for the explicit construction of non-blocking networks, the design of algorithms and the design of data-structures. "Weakly optimal" is in the sense that all measures of complexity (size and depth of the network, time for the algorithm, and space for the data-structure) are within one or more factors of $\log n$ of their smallest possible values. Our results are very practical in the sense that the construction of the networks is simple and the algorithms (both the randomized and the deterministic one) and their data-structures are easy to implement. We are optimistic that the results presented in this paper will find many applications in practice.

Our main result in this paper is summarized in the following theorem.

Theorem *There is an explicit construction for a non-blocking of n inputs and n outputs with size $O(n(\log n)^2)$ and depth $O(\log n)$, and a deterministic on-line parallel algorithm that maintains a data-structure using $O(n(\log n)^2)$ words and will, for any t in the range $1 \le t \le n$, process t transactions using t processors in $O((\log n)^5)$ steps.*

2. The Non-Blocking Networks

Suppose that we wish to construct a non-blocking network with n inputs and n outputs. Set $\gamma = \lfloor \log_2(8\nu) \rfloor$, so that $2^\gamma > 4\nu \ge 2^{\gamma-1}$. Construct a Beneš rearrangeable network with $m = 2^{\nu+\gamma}$ inputs and m outputs (see Beneš [B]). Reduce the number of inputs and outputs in this network to n by retaining only every 2^γ-th input and output and discard links and switching elements that can not be reached from these n inputs and n outputs. This is to be done so that routes originating at two distinct retained inputs can meet only after passing at least $\gamma + 1$ stages of switches, and similarly for retained outputs.

Let N^+ denote the resulting network. This network is non-blocking as shown in [P82]. Indeed, consider any idle input of N^+. It has access to at least $(2^\gamma - \nu)2^\nu$ of the $2^{\nu+\gamma}$ links of the $(\gamma + \nu + 1)$-st stage regardless the status of other inputs. Similar property holds for any idle outputs. Notice that $(2^\gamma - \nu)2^\nu$ is strictly more than half (to be exact, three quarters) of $2^{\gamma+\nu}$. Thus given any idle input and idle output, a route from the input to the output that is disjoint with the established routes always exists regardless the status of other inputs and outputs. This network has size $O(\nu 2^{\nu+\gamma}) = O(\nu 2^{2\nu}) = O(n(\log n)^2)$ and depth $O(\gamma + \nu) = O(\log n)$. This network is essentially equivalent to the one described by Cantor [C71].

273

3. A Randomized Algorithm

In this section, we describe a randomized parallel algorithm which processes a batch of transactions in parallel with $O((logn)^2)$ expected steps by dynamically changing a data-structure of $O(n(logn)^2)$ words. Our deterministic parallel algorithm is obtained by eliminating the randomness from this algorithm.

The data-structure for our randomized algorithm is very simple. It only keeps the up-to-date busy/idle status for each link, input and output of the network (this is necessary for any data-structure). We describe the data-structure in terms of the dual graph G of N^+. For each input, output and link of network N^+, we create a node. Two nodes are adjacent if and only if their correspondents in the network are input and output of a same crossbar. Thus we see the duality between G and N^+. With each node ζ in G, we associate a number $G(\zeta)$, which is 0 or 1 according as its corresponding link (more precisely, link or input or output) is idle or busy. A simple calculation shows this data-structure uses $O(n(logn)^2)$ words.

Notice that N^+ has $2(\gamma+\nu)+1$ stages. The subnetwork of stage $\gamma+\nu+1$ to stage $2(\gamma+\nu)+1$ is a mirror image of the subnetwork of stage 1 to stage $\gamma+\nu+1$. We refer the former to "the right hand half of N^+" called N' and the latter "the left hand half of N^+" called N. We observe that, for each input ξ of N^+, confined to N, the dual subgraph in G of links that may appear in some route starting from ξ forms a tree T_ξ. Similarly, for each output η of N^+, there is a tree T_η. It is clear that all the T_ξ's and T_η's are binary trees having depth $\gamma+\nu$ with $2^{\gamma+\nu}$ leaves. We call the common topological structure of these trees T.

We now proceed to describe our randomized algorithm. Suppose that a batch of t transactions (requests to establish or abolish a route) are to be processed by t processors (each transaction "brings its own processor"). We need not worry about interference between requests that establish routes and requests that abolish routes by the simple device of splitting each batch into two batches, one comprising only requests to establish and the other comprising only requests to abolish. As we will see, the algorithms presented in this paper to process requests to establish are easily modified to process requests to abolish, we only consider the requests to establish here.

Suppose that when a processor attempts to establish a route from input ξ to output η, it pushes two pebbles in T_ξ and T_η respectively, from their roots to a common leaf along a path P, and then determines whether or not the two subroutes (in N and N' respectively) corresponding to the subpaths in T_ξ and T_η are both idle,

and whether or not no other processor has seized a link in the two subroutes. If we choose one of the $2^{\gamma+\nu}$ possible paths at random, the probability that the the corresponding subroute in N is busy is at most $1/4$, since every idle input in N has access to at least $(2^\gamma-\nu)2^\nu$ of its $2^{\gamma+\nu}$ outputs regardless the status of other inputs, noticing $4\nu < 2^\gamma$. Similarly, the probability that the subroute in N' is busy is at most $1/4$ too. Thus the probability that both subparts of the route are idle is at least $1/2$. That is to say, with randomly chosen paths, half of the requests are expected to be satisfied. For those failing to choose an idle path, do the same procedure again, and so forth. It is observed that, less than or equal to $t2^{-i}$ requests are expected not to be satisfied after i-th round of choosing. Thus after $\lceil log_2(t/\epsilon) \rceil$ rounds of choosing, the probability that all requests are satisfied is at least $1-\epsilon$.

Let us consider how the randomized algorithm updates the data-structure to reflects the addition of new routes to the state. Suppose that a processor establishes a route from input ξ to output η, i.e. two pebbles along the subpaths in T_ξ and T_η reach a common leaf α (T_ξ and T_η are embedded in graph G). It sends two bubbles back from α to ξ and η along the subpaths. It changes the value $G(\zeta)$ (from 0) to 1 for each node ζ that the bubbles encounter. Since the path is of length $2(\gamma+\nu)+1 = O(logn)$, the updating of data-structure to reflect the addition of new routes is performed with $O(logn)$ arithmetic operations. On the other hand, determining whether or not a path is idle, and whether or not two processors seize a same link in the path is performed in $O(logn)$ arithmetic operations since G is of bounded degree (the maximum degree is 4). Thus the parallel randomized algorithm establishes (and/or abolishes) t transactions in $O((logt)(logn)) = O((logn)^2)$ expected steps.

4. The Data-structure for the Deterministic Parallel Algorithm

In this section, we extend our simple data-structure for the randomized algorithm to support efficient deterministic parallel algorithms. Roughly speaking, we maintain some redundant information about the distribution of established routes, so that we can save some computation by retrieving the redundant information.

For each pair of inputs ξ_1 and ξ_2, we say their distance, $dist(\xi_1,\xi_2) = dist(\xi_2,\xi_1)$, is d ($1 \le d \le \nu$), if and only if the routes starting from the two inputs may share a link after $(d+\gamma)$-th stage but cannot share any link before $(d+\gamma)$-th stage. Similarly, we define the distance $dist(\eta_1,\eta_2)$ of two outputs η_1 and η_2.

It is observed that, for each input ξ there are 2^{d-1} other inputs ξ' with $dist(\xi,\xi') = d$, for any d with

$1 \leq d \leq \nu$. A similar result holds for each output. Furthermore, for any inputs ξ, ξ' and ξ'', if $dist(\xi, \xi') = d$, then $dist(\xi, \xi'') = d + \delta$ $(\delta > 0)$ if and only if $dist(\xi', \xi'') = d + \delta$ for any $1 \leq \delta \leq \nu - d$. That is to say, if the distance of two inputs is d, they share the same group of inputs of which the distance is $d + \delta$ from them. It will be much clearer if we describe the distance relationship among inputs in terms of a binary tree IND. IND is a binary tree of depth ν with 2^ν leaves. Let the leaves correspond to the inputs of N^+ in the following way. Two leaves are siblings if and only if their distance is 1; two nodes τ_1 and τ_2 at depth l are siblings if and only if the distance between leaves in the subtree rooted at τ_1 and that in the subtree rooted at τ_2 is $\nu - l + 1$ (the distance is unique, as observed above). Similarly, the distance relationship among outputs is described in terms of a binary tree $OUTD$. It is observed that two inputs (outputs, resp.) have distance d if and only if their lowest common ancestor in IND ($OUTD$ resp.) is at depth $\nu - d$.

In order to obtain an efficient deterministic parallel algorithm, we need to keep some redundant information about the distribution of established routes. The information in the data structure, on the other hand, can not be too redundant, since our algorithm dynamically updates the data structure to reflect the addition of new routes (and the subtraction of old ones). For any two inputs with distance d, the fate of whether or not the routes starting from them will block each other is determined within the first $\gamma + d + 1$ stages in N^+. Thus for each input ξ, for inputs with distance d, we confine the route distribution information to the first $\gamma + d + 1$ stages; for inputs with distance d to ξ, however, we keep their route distribution information as a whole instead of as individuals. Therefore, for each input ξ, we keep ν binary trees, of depth $\gamma + d$ having $2^{\gamma+d}$ leaves for $1 \leq d \leq \nu$, with each representing the route information of 2^{d-1} other inputs (inputs with distance d to ξ). Associated with each node ζ in such a tree is a number, measuring the number of routes that start from one of the 2^{d-1} inputs , say ξ', and contain the corresponding node of ζ in $T_{\xi'}$. Thus, for each input ξ, there are ν such trees; each input is involved in ν such trees and there are $2 \cdot 2^\nu - 1$ such trees in total (due to the large quantity of overlapping). Similar properties hold for outputs.

Our data-structure for deterministic algorithms is precisely described as follows. In addition to the dual graph G of N^+, we keep some redundant information about the distribution of established routes. For each node τ at depth $\nu - l$ $(\nu - 1 \geq l \geq 0)$ in IND, we keep a binary tree TR_τ (TR stands for "traffic"), which is of depth $\gamma + l$ with $2 \cdot 2^{\gamma+l} - 1$ nodes. Recalling the common structure T of T_ξ's and T_η's, we see TR_τ is a subtree of T truncated at depth $\gamma + l$. For each node ζ

in TR_τ, there is a corresponding node in each tree T_ξ; for the sake of simplicity of our notation, we also denote this node by ζ. Now we associate with each node ζ in TR_τ a number $TR_\tau(\zeta)$, which is the sum of $T_\xi(\zeta)$ (i.e. the value $G(\zeta)$) over every input ξ which is a leaf in the subtree rooted at τ in IND. Similarly, for each node β at depth $\nu - l$ $(\nu - 1 \geq l \geq 0)$ in $OUTD$, make a binary tree TR_β, which is of depth $\gamma + l$ with $2 \cdot 2^{\gamma+l} - 1$ node. Associated with each node ζ is the value $TR_\beta(\zeta)$, which is the sum of $T_\eta(\zeta)$ over every output η which is a leaf in the subtree rooted at β in $OUTD$.

Let us consider the space requirements of the data structure. The graph G has less than $2(\nu + 1)2^{\gamma+\nu}$ nodes, and there is one number (0 or 1) associated with each node. There are $2 \cdot 2^{\nu-l}$ nodes τ and β at depth $\nu - l$ in trees IND and $OUTD$. For each τ or β, there is a tree of $2 \cdot 2^{\gamma+l} - 1$ nodes, and associated with each node is a number (in the range $[0, 2^\nu - 1]$). Thus there are less than

$$2(\nu + 1)2^{\gamma+\nu} + \sum_{l=0}^{\nu-1}(2 \cdot 2^{\nu-l})(2 \cdot 2^{\gamma+l} - 1)$$
$$< 6(\nu + 1)2^{\gamma+\nu} = O(\nu^2 2^\nu) = O(n(logn)^2)$$

numbers to be stored. Therefore, the space requirement of the data-structure is $O(n(logn)^2)$ words.

5. A Deterministic Parallel Algorithm

The elimination of randomization from the randomized parallel algorithm of Section 3 is accomplished in two stages. In the first stage we greatly reduce the number of random bits (independent coin flips) used by the algorithm, by deterministically computing a large number of bits from a smaller number. In the second stage we show how to deterministically compute this smaller number of bits.

In the randomized parallel algorithm, each processor makes a random choice uniformly distributed over $2^{\gamma+\nu}$ possibilities; we may therefore regard it as making $\gamma + \nu$ successive independent random binary choices, corresponding to the $\gamma + \nu$ successive moves involved in pushing a pebble from the root to a leaf in T (T is the common structure of trees T_ξ and T_η). We may therefore imagine all of the choices of all the processors as being made in $\gamma + \nu$ successive "phases", with each of the t processors making its first choice in the first phase, and so forth.

We next observe that the analysis of the randomized algorithm was based on the assumption that all routes were independently chosen, but actually only relied on the routes being pairwise independent. Thus the analysis will remain valid if the binary choices in each phase are not completely independent, but are pairwise independent. These t pairwise independent bits can be computed deterministically from a set of $\nu = log_2 n$ completely independent random bits, using the following well known scheme.

Let M be an $\nu \times t$ matrix over $GF(2)$ in which each column is a distinct input index of the t requests (input indices are in their binary representations). Let X be a row of ν completely independent random elements of $GF(2)$, and let Y be the product XM (a row of t elements of $GF(2)$). Then the elements of Y are uniformly distributed over $GF(2)$ and pairwise independent. We may thus deterministically compute t pairwise independent bits in Y from the $\nu = log_2 n$ completely independent random bits in X.

Let us now return to the picture of pebbles being pushed from the root to a leaf in the trees T_ξ's and T_η's. As before, established routes will be replaced by pebbles at the leaves, and each processor is responsible for pushing two pebbles, one in a tree T_ξ and the other in a tree T_η. For the sake of simplicity, we label the two corresponding pebbles ξ and η as well. Given a disposition of pebbles in these trees, associate with each pebble a quantity called the "congestion", defined in the following way.

Imagine all pebbles being pushed in T (the common structure of T_ξ's and T_η's). If the pebble ξ is at a node σ at depth κ in T, the congestion of ξ is the sum of a contribution of $min\{1, 1/2^{\gamma+d-\kappa}\}$ for every pebble ξ' in the subtree rooted at σ, where $d = dist(\xi, \xi')$, plus a contribution of $min\{1, 1/2^{\gamma+d-\iota}\}$ for every pebble ξ'' at a node ρ at depth ι on the path from the root to σ, where $d = dist(\xi, \xi'')$. This quantity is easy to compute. Consider the $2^\nu - 1$ inputs other than ξ. Based on their distances to ξ, they fall into ν groups with size 2^{d-1} and of distance d to ξ, for $1 \le d \le \nu$. Of the inputs in the group of distance d to ξ, their lowest common ancestor in IND is at depth $\nu - d + 1$ (recall that inputs correspond to leaves in IND). Let these ancestors be $\tau_1, \cdots, \tau_\nu$. The congestion of ξ equals to the sum of $min\{1, 1/2^{\gamma+d-\kappa}\} \cdot TR_{\tau_d}(\sigma)$ over every d, $1 \le d \le \nu$, plus for each involved ρ, the sum of $min\{1, 1/2^{\gamma+d-\iota}\} \cdot TR_{\tau_d}(\rho)$ over every d. We say that the congestion of a request is the sum of the congestions of its two pebbles, and that the congestion of a batch of requests is the sum of the congestions of the t requests in the batch.

The success of the randomized algorithm may now be ascribed to three simple observations. Firstly, when all the pebbles of the requests in the batch are at the root of T ($\kappa = 0$), the congestion of a pebble is less than or equal to $\sum_{d=1}^{\nu}(1/2^{\gamma+d}) \cdot 2^d = \nu/2^\gamma < 1/4$, corresponding to contributions of $1/2^{\gamma+d}$ for each of the other pebbles at leaves or at the root. Secondly, if a pebble is moved from a node σ to one of its two children (chosen at random with equal probability), the expected conges-

tion of each pebble is unaffected; indeed, each contribution to the congestion is either unaffected or undergoes a "double-or-nothing" transformation with equal probabilities. Finally, when all pebbles are pushed to leaves ($\kappa = \gamma + \nu$), the congestion of a pebble is an integer greater than or equal to 1 if it is blocked, is 0 if it is not blocked. Therefore, the number of pebbles being blocked is less than or equal to the congestion of the batch of requests. It follows from these observations that on the average, at least one-half of requests finish with both pebbles not being blocked, and are successful.

Let us now combine this picture with the notion of phases, so that each processor pushes its two pebbles down one level in their trees during each phase. If all of the binary choices involved in these pushes were completely independent, the expected congestion would be unaffected. Since the congestion is defined as a sum of pairwise contributions, its expectation is unchanged if completely independent binary choices are replaced by pairwise independent binary choices. So let t pairwise independent choices be deterministically computed from ν completely binary choices, as described above. Since the expectation over all ν choices is unaffected, it follows that there is a particular way of making the first choice for which the expectation (over the remaining $\nu - 1$ choices) does not increase. After the first choice has been made in this way, there is a particular way of making the second choice for which the expectation (over the remaining $\nu - 2$ choices) does not increase. Proceeding in this way, we arrive at particular ways of making all ν choices, from which we may deterministically compute the t pushes of pebbles.

It remains to observe that the "particular ways" whose existence was argued in the preceding paragraph can in fact themselves be deterministically computed in a simple way. For if we assign particular values to some of the ν choices, the expected congestion over the remaining choices can be computed as follows. Assigning particular values to some of the choices commits some of the t pebbles to move from the node σ at which they began the phase to one of their two children, while leaving the other pebbles equally likely to move to either of their two children (the fate of a particular pebble is sealed when all of the entries of X for which its column of M contains a 1 have been assigned particular values; otherwise, its fate is uncompromised). Thus an advantageous value for a choice can be found by tentatively assigning one value, recomputing the congestions, and rescinding the tentative assignment in favour of its alternative if the congestion increases.

By now we have finished the description of our deterministic parallel algorithm. Let us consider the performance of this algorithm. It establishes and/or abolishes any number of routes in parallel in $O((logn)^5)$ with one

276

processor per transaction, maintaining a data structure of $O(n(logn)^2)$ words. To estimate the time complexity, we observe the following facts. Firstly, each time pebbles being pushed to their leaves, there are at least one half of the requests being satisfied, which implies $\lceil log_2 t \rceil = O(logn)$ "rounds" of pushing are sufficient to satisfy all the requests. Secondly, within each "round" of pushing, $\gamma + \nu = O(logn)$ "phases" are sufficient to push a pebble from its root to a leaf. Thirdly, in each "phase", $\nu = O(logn)$ bits in X are deterministically computed. Finally, in order to determine the value of one bit, the congestion of the batch of requests is computed, this is done with $O((logn)^2)$ steps, as the congestion of a pebble is computed in $O((logn)^2)$ steps by one processor (sum of $min\{1, 1/2^{\gamma+d-\kappa}\} \cdot TR_{\tau_d}(\sigma)$ over every d, $1 \leq d \leq \nu$, plus for every ρ involved, the sum of $min\{1, 1/2^{\gamma+d-\iota}\} \cdot TR_{\tau_d}(\rho)$ over every $d)$[1], and after the congestion of each pebble is computed, the congestion of a batch of requests in computed in $O(logn)$ steps by t processors in parallel; and the update of the data structure after determination of a bit (committing some of the t pebbles to move to one of their two children) needs $O((logn)^2)$ steps, of which one $O(logn)$ factor comes from the fact that $O(\nu) = O(logn)$ numbers in TR_{τ_d}'s, $1 \leq d \leq \nu$, are to be updated (at most two numbers in each TR_{τ_d}), and the other comes from the fact that to any one of these numbers, up to $t = O(n)$ processors may want to update it simultaneously (with each one adding 1 or subtracting 1).

References

[ALM]   S. Arora, T. Leighton and B. Maggs, "On-Line Algorithms for Path Selection in a Nonblocking Network", *ACM Symp. on Theory of Computing*, 22 (1990) 149-158.

[B]   V. E. Beneš, "Optimal Rearrangeable Multistage Connecting Networks", *Bell Sys. Tech. J.*, 43 (1964) 1641-1656.

[C53]   C. Clos, "A Study of Non-blocking Networks", *Bell Sys. Tech. J.*, 32 (1953) 406-424.

[C71]   D. G. Cantor, "On Non-blocking Switching Networks", *Networks*,1 (1971) 367-377.

[FFP88]   P. Feldman, J. Friedman and N. Pippenger, "Wide-Sense Non-Blocking Networks", *SIAM J. Discr. Math.*, 1(1988) 158-173.

[LPV]   G. Lev, N. Pippenger and L. G. Valiant, "A Fast Parallel Algorithm for Routing in Permutation Networks", *IEEE Trans. on Computers*, 30 (1981) 93-100.

[L86]   M. Luby, "A Simple Parallel Algorithm for the Maximal Independent Set Problem", *SIAM J. Computing*, 15 (19886) 1036-1053.

[L88]   M. Luby, "Removing Randomness in Parallel Computation without a Processor Penalty", *IEEE Symp. on Foundations of Computer Science*, 29 (1988) 162-173.

[PY]   N. Pippenger and A. C. Yao, "Rearrangeable Networks with Limited Depth", *SIAM J. Alg. Disc. Meth., Vol. 3, No. 4*, (1982) 411-417.

[P73]   N. Pippenger, "The Complexity Theory of Switching Networks", *Ph. D. Thesis*, Electrical Engineering, MIT, August 1973.

[P82]   N. Pippenger, "Telephone Switching Networks", *AMS Proc. Symp. Appl. Math.*, 26 (1978) 101-133.

---

[1] In fact, our algorithm computes the congestion of a pebble in $O(logn)$ steps, since pebbles are pushed "phase by phase", at most one ρ, i.e. the parent node of ξ is involved. This, in turn, implies the congestion of a batch of requests is computed in $O(logn)$ steps.

Fully-Adaptive Minimal Deadlock-Free Packet Routing in Hypercubes, Meshes, and Other Networks

Gustavo D. Pifarré *†‡
e-mail: pifarre@buevm2.vnet.ibm.com

Luis Gravano *†‡
e-mail: gravano@buevm2.vnet.ibm.com

Sergio A. Felperin *†‡
e-mail: felperin@buevm2.vnet.ibm.com

Jorge L. C. Sanz ‡†
e-mail: sanz@ibm.com

Abstract

This paper deals with the problem of packet-switched routing in parallel machines. Several new routing algorithms for different interconnection networks are presented. While the new techniques apply to a wide variety of networks, routing algorithms will be shown for the hypercube, the 2-dimensional mesh, and the shuffle-exchange. The techniques presented for hypercubes and meshes are fully-adaptive and minimal. A similar technique can be devised for tori. A fully-adaptive and minimal routing is one in which *all* possible minimal paths between a source and a destination are of potential use at the time a message is injected into the network. Minimal paths followed by messages ultimately depend on the local congestion encountered in each node of the network. In the shuffle-exchange network, the routing scheme also exhibits adaptivity but paths could be up to $3 \log N$ long for an N node machine. The shuffle-exchange algorithm is the first adaptive and deadlock-free method that requires a small (and independent of N) number of buffers and queues in the routing nodes for that network.

---

* ESLAI, Escuela Superior Latino Americana de Informática, CC 3193,(1000) Buenos Aires, Argentina.

† Computer Research and Advanced Applications Group, IBM Argentina, Ing. E. Butti 275, (1300) Buenos Aires, Argentina.

‡ Computer Science Dept., IBM Almaden Research Center, San José, California.

Furthermore, all of the new techniques are completely free of deadlock situations. In dynamic message injection models, the routing methods are also ensured to be free of livelock if messages competing for resources are handled with fairness.

In contrast to other approaches in which adaptivity, deadlock and livelock freedom can be guaranteed at the expense of complex architectures, the algorithms presented in this paper require a very moderate amount of routing hardware. In particular, it will be shown that only two central queues per routing node of the network are necessary for the cases of the 2-dimensional mesh and the hypercube, and four queues for the shuffle-exchange.

This paper demonstrates that "hanging" an interconnection network from a node [Gun81, MS80, BGSS89, Kon90] is a convenient methodology for creating and visualizing routing functions and understanding deadlock-free policies for queue utilization. In some cases, interconnections can be *hung* from an arbitrary node, producing new interesting routing functions [PFGS91]. While the methods presented in this paper are for packet routing, some generalizations are possible for worm-hole routing on 2-dimensional tori [GPS91].

In addition, simulation results corresponding to hypercubes of up to $16K$ nodes are reported for both static and dynamic injection models.

1 Introduction.

Message routing in large interconnection networks has attracted a great deal of interest in recent years. Different underlying machine models have been used [DS86a], [RBJ88, Ran85], [Upf89, LM89], [Val88], [KS90], [NS], [Hil85]. Some fundamental distinctions among routing algorithms involve the length of the messages injected in the network, the static or dynamic nature of the injection model, special assumptions on the semantic of the messages, architecture of the network and router, degree of synchronization in the hardware, and others.

In terms of message length, several issues have been studied concerning the ways to handle long messages (of potentially unknown size) and very short messages (typically of 100 bits). Recently, new techniques and architectures have been proposed based on worm-hole routing [DS86a], [DS86b], and packet-switched routing [KS90]. In between packet-routing and worm-hole lie some hybrid approaches, as the virtual cut-through technique [KK79].

Two subjects of long-standing interest in routing are deadlock and livelock freedom. Techniques that perform without deadlocks or livelocks have been shown on different models. Some algorithms succeed in accomplishing deadlock-free or livelock-free routing only in a probabilistic sense [KS90], [Pip84]. In other algorithms, deadlock freedom is guaranteed in a deterministic sense [DS86a], [Kon90], [RBJ88, Ran85], [LMR88], [Gel81], [Gun81, MS80].

Several techniques have been developed that avoid deadlock by defining an ordering on the critical resources, and allowing each message to progress throughout the network by occupying resources in a strictly monotonic fashion. The central idea for avoiding deadlock in the works of [DS86a], [RBJ88, Ran85], [Kon90], [BGSS89], [Gun81, MS80], and others is to order the use of resources potentially intervening in the generation of deadlocks. This idea results in the generation of a directed acyclic graph (DAG) of the resources. All DAG-based methods can be used for both worm-hole and packet routing. This methodology has been used by the authors of this paper to create a wide variety of new adaptive routing methods for hypercubes, meshes, shuffle-exchanges, cube-connected cycles, and other networks [PFGS91]. Some of the DAG's proposed in [PFGS91] will be utilized in this paper.

Most known techniques that completely avoid livelock and deadlock situations do that at the expense of some hardware resources. These hardware resources will increase with the degree of adaptivity desired in the routing of the messages. In the work of [DS86a], moderate resources are proposed for practical deterministic deadlock freedom on some networks, but routing techniques are oblivious. On the other hand, in [Kon90], an adaptive method for routing in the hypercube is proposed. This method performs well on simulations involving up to $16K$ nodes.

Some methods may become impractical for efficient routing on large interconnection networks due to either the amount of work done during routing or the required architecture resources in a node. The recent work reported in [KS90] shows a striking reduction of hardware resources by providing an adaptive deadlock-free routing algorithm dubbed *Chaos*. The method has a nonzero probability that a message will not reach its destination after t routing steps, for an arbitrary t. However, this probability tends to zero as t approaches infinity. Furthermore, the technique in [KS90] applies only to packet routing and paths followed by the messages are not necessarily minimal.

Restricting the set of available paths in the network to a subset suitably chosen is a common way to reduce the hardware resources necessary for deadlock-free routing. When stringent restrictions are applied, oblivious algorithms or methods with partial adaptivity will be obtained. This class of routing algorithms has been studied thoroughly for meshes and tori [Lei90]. On the other hand, if few restrictions are imposed on the set of possible routes generated by a routing function, impractical algorithms may result. For example, the structured buffer pool [Gun81, MS80] guarantees deadlock freedom by adding all necessary resources so that a DAG is obtained. This will result in an excessive amount of hardware necessary in a routing node and this situation will not be improved by allowing messages to depart from the DAG routes if queue space is available [MS80].

A *fully-adaptive minimal* routing scheme is one in which all possible minimal paths between a source and a destination are of potential use at the time messages are injected into the network. Paths followed by the messages depend on the traffic congestion found in the nodes of the network. For example, the minimal routing functions presented in [BGSS89] and [Kon90] are *not* fully-adaptive because several minimal routes are not allowed to take place. Full-adaptivity is a feature from which one can hope to obtain the best possible performance if no source of randomization is used. Full-adaptivity has been used by Upfal in [Upf89] to produce a deterministic optimal algorithm for routing in the multibutterfly. Multibutterflies are extremely rich in terms of the number of minimal paths between any pair of nodes.

Optimal performance cannot be obtained in some networks if oblivious routing is used. This involves both deterministic performance [BH82] and even probabilistic performance if only minimal paths are used [Val82]. On the other hand, fully-adaptive minimality with bounded-size queues has the potential of providing practical performance. Furthermore, finding deterministic and probabilistic bounds for static models of packet injection in adaptive routing is still an open problem for all cube-type networks.

A fully-adaptive, minimal, deadlock-free worm-hole routing algorithm for the 2-dimensional mesh has been described in [Ni90, Ni91]. Routing algorithms for worm-hole routing on general k-ary n-cubes with these characteristics have been presented in [LH91]. Recent progress done by three of the authors of this paper [GPS91] includes an algorithm for fully-adaptive minimal, deadlock- and livelock-free, worm-hole routing on 2-dimensional tori that uses fewer resources than the algorithm in [LH91] for this network. This technique is believed to be practical for the involved interconnections and the routing model because of its very moderate hardware resources, fully-adaptive minimality, deterministic assurance of deadlock and livelock freedom, and promising performance for different injection models. Also, in [GPS91] both minimal and non-minimal adaptive, deadlock- and livelock-free worm-hole routing algorithms for the hypercube have been presented.

In this paper, a number of algorithms for packet routing are shown. These techniques are fully-adaptive minimal (except for the one for the shuffle-exchange, which is not fully-adaptive), deadlock- and livelock-free and require a very moderate amount of resources in the routing nodes. The new methods are presented for hypercubes, meshes, and shuffle-exchange networks.

The organization of this paper is as follows. In Section 2, some terminology and concepts concerning static and dynamic deadlock freedom will be introduced. In Sections 3, 4, and 5, the main results of this paper are presented. In these sections, algorithms for fully-adaptive routing on hypercubes, 2-dimensional meshes, and for adaptive routing on shuffle-exchange networks will be shown. In Section 6, the functional designs of the routing node for the above three interconnections are shown. These designs give emphasis to the number of buffers sharing a physical link, and the operation and number of central queues in the node. In Section 7, the results obtained from the simulations involving hypercubes of up to $16K$ nodes are presented. Simulations on higher-dimensional hypercubes and other topologies will be reported soon.

2 Adaptive Routing and Deadlock Freedom: definitions and terminology.

In packet routing, the critical resources are the queues used to store the messages during their way towards their destinations. Deadlock will arise if and only if there exists a set of full queues occupied by messages such that all of these messages need a slot of a queue that belongs to the set in order to continue their way toward their destinations.

Each node of the network will have associated with it a certain number of queues. Each node has a pair of distinct queues, namely the injection and the delivery queues. Messages will be injected in the injection queue, and they will be consumed from the delivery queue. The routing function will be expressed in terms of the queues of each node. The set of delivery queues of all the network will be referred to as $DelivQ$. Notice that each delivery queue identifies a unique node of the network. The set of injection queues will be referred to as $InjectQ$

Each message has a destination associated with it, given by the function $Dest$: Messages $\rightarrow DelivQ$.

A total routing function $\mathcal{R}$: $Queues \times DelivQ \rightarrow \mathcal{P}(Queues)$ is such that $\mathcal{R}(q, d)$ indicates which are the next possible hops of a message with destination d that is currently in q. Possibly, a delivery queue d may not be reachable from a given non-delivery, non-injection queue q. In such a case, $\mathcal{R}(q, d)$ should be equal to $\emptyset$. $\mathcal{R}$ has to verify the following constraints:

1. if $q_2 \in \mathcal{R}(q_1, d)$, then the node to which q_2 belongs is at most one hop away in the network from q_1's.

2. $\mathcal{R}$ builds a non-empty set of paths from any injection queue to any delivery queue. Furthermore, as paths are built by selecting locally each hop among the possible ones, $\mathcal{R}$ must guarantee that no message will get stuck at a dead-end. These two conditions are expressed in the following one. Let r be an injection queue and d a delivery queue. If $q_0 q_1 \ldots q_p$ is a path in D such that $q_0 = r$, and $q_{i+1} \in \mathcal{R}(q_i, d)$ $\forall 0 \leq i < p$, then, there exists a path $q_p q_{p+1} \ldots q_k$ in D such that $q_k = d$, and $q_{j+1} \in \mathcal{R}(q_j, d)$ $\forall p \leq j < k$.

The *queue dependency graph* (QDG) corresponding to a set of queues Q and a routing function $\mathcal{R}$ is a directed graph such that its set of vertices is Q and there exists an edge from q_i to q_j ($q_i, q_j \in Q$) iff there exist an injection queue s and a delivery queue d such that $\mathcal{R}$

builds a route from s to d passing through both q_i and q_j, and $q_j \in \mathcal{R}(q_i, d)$. (This definition is related to the one presented in [DS86a] regarding *virtual channels*.) Clearly, if the QDG corresponding to a set of queues and a routing function is acyclic (i.e. it is a DAG), then, the greedy routing algorithm resulting from $\mathcal{R}$ is deadlock free.

Let $D = (Q, A_s)$ be an (acyclic) queue dependency graph. Then, Q is the set of queues and A_s the set of links between the queues. Let $d^+{}_{(Q, A_s)}(q) \overset{\Delta}{=} \{q' \in Q : (q, q') \in A_s\}$ be the set of *direct successors* of q. Whenever there is no ambiguity, the subscripts will be dropped.

Every non-delivery queue has finite (independent of the size of the network) size. The delivery queues of D will have infinite size, to model the fact that messages are eventually consumed at them. $Level(q)$ is the length of the longest path between any member of $InjectQ$ and q. For every q, $Level(q)$ is finite because D is acyclic.

In previous work, routing functions are built such that the resulting QDG's are acyclic. Although this condition is sufficient to guarantee deadlock freedom, it is too strong, and can be relaxed: the queue dependency graph has to be *dynamically* acyclic, i.e. cyclic wait must not arise in a dynamic environment [MS80].

This paper uses a model for such dynamically acyclic queue dependency graphs in the generation of practical routing algorithms for hypercubes, meshes, and shuffle-exchanges.

Let $A_d \subset Q \times Q$ be a set such that $A_s \cap A_d = \emptyset$, and, if $(q_1, q_2) \in A_d$, then q_2 is at most one hop away from q_1 in the network. Furthermore, it must hold that, if $(q_1, q_2) \in A_d$, then $q_1 \notin DelivQ$, and $q_2 \notin InjectQ$. This means that in the extended graph to be defined below, injection and delivery queues continue to have only that function. Although it is not necessary, it will be required that if $(q, q') \in A_d$ then $Level(q) \geq Level(q')$. This is not a restriction because if $Level(q) < Level(q')$ then (q, q') can be included in A_s, and D will still be acyclic. Now, let $\tilde{D} = (Q, A_s \cup A_d)$ be the extension of D by A_d. Sometimes, D will be called the underlying DAG of $\tilde{D}$. Note that $\tilde{D}$ is not necessarily a DAG. In the following, A_s will be called the *static link set* and A_d will be called the *dynamic link set*. Let $\tilde{\mathcal{R}}$ be a routing function on $\tilde{D}$, observing the following conditions: $\forall q, q' \in Q, d \in DelivQ$:

1. If $q' \in \tilde{\mathcal{R}}(q, d)$, then $(q, q') \in A_s \cup A_d$.

2. $\mathcal{R}(q, d) \subseteq \tilde{\mathcal{R}}(q, d)$.

3. If $q' \in \tilde{\mathcal{R}}(q, d)$ and $q' \notin \mathcal{R}(q, d)$ then $\mathcal{R}(q', d) \neq \emptyset$.

This means that if a message can be routed along a dynamic link, it will still have the possibility of taking a static link as a next step towards its destination. Therefore, at any moment, every message has a static-link path that takes it to its destination. In other words, every message will be able to progress towards its target queue through the underlying DAG.

Let $\tilde{\mathcal{R}}$ be a routing function and $\tilde{D}$ be the QDG associated with it. Furthermore, suppose that D is the underlying DAG of $\tilde{D}$. The following greedy algorithm can be used to route messages over $\tilde{D}$ from the injection to the delivery queues.

```
Route(q)
/* q is the queue executing the algorithm */
(01)   select q' ∈ d⁺_D̃ (q) :   ( not Full (q')
       and q' ∈ R̃ (q, Dest (Head (q))))
(02)   Insert (Head (q), q')
(03)   RemoveHead (q)
```

It is supposed that once a q finds and selects some q' verifying the condition in line (01) it gains the access to a place in q', and can execute lines (02) and (03) of the algorithm above. Note that **select** may return a q' satisfying condition in line (01) according to any criterion, as long as it does so if the set of queues satisfying (01) is not empty.

The proof of the deadlock freedom of this algorithm is easy, and it can be found in [PGFS91].

3   Hypercube Algorithm.

In this Section, a fully-adaptive minimal routing algorithm for the hypercube will be presented. A routing function will be built that uses dynamic links. So, the QDG associated with this routing function will have cycles. As said above, this routing function should be regarded as an extension of an acyclic routing function (i.e. a routing function whose QDG is acyclic) so as to guarantee that the routing algorithm is acyclic. Next, this *underlying* routing function, and how to extend it to achieve the final one will be described.

The routing function that results from routing over the hypercube as hung from node $0 \ldots 0$ will be used as the underlying acyclic function. This routing algorithm has been presented in [BGSS89], for implementing virtual barriers on the hypercube. A similar idea has been used in [Kon90] for implementing a minimal adaptive routing algorithm on the hypercube. The idea on which this *hanging* algorithm is based is the following. The algorithm consists of two phases. In phase A, each message travels as moving downwards through the network, always moving towards its destination, as much as possible. So, in this phase, each message starts heading to node $1 \ldots 1$ (which happens to be the node that is opposite to node $0 \ldots 0$). So, in phase A, each message turns the incorrect 0s in the address of its source node into 1s.

In phase B, every message arrives at its destination by following an upwards path. In this phase, messages move towards node $0 \ldots 0$ again. So, in this phase, each message turns the incorrect 1s of its source address into 0s. Therefore, all the required corrections are terminated at the end of this phase. Consequently, each message arrives at its destination.

The following implementation of this algorithm is such that the corresponding QDG is acyclic. Each node n should have two queues, $q_{A,n}$ (associated with phase A), and $q_{B,n}$ (associated with phase B), as well as an injection queue i_n and a delivery queue d_n, as discussed above. During the first phase, messages move through the q_A queues of the nodes they visit. When a message switches phase, it has to start moving through the q_B queues of the nodes visited. The QDG resulting from this implementation is acyclic. Therefore, the algorithm associated with it is deadlock-free. See Figure 1 for the QDG of a 3-hypercube, in which the injection and delivery queues have not been drawn.

As messages are forced to correct first the incorrect 0s into 1s and only afterwards the incorrect 1s into 0s, congestion around node $1 \ldots 1$ is likely to take place.

Now, dynamic links will be added to the QDG in such a way that they will allow messages to change incorrect 1s into 0s while being in phase A if the message finds place in the q_A queue of the corresponding node, at a certain moment. The resulting algorithm, which is deadlock- free (see Section 2), is the following. Each message is injected, and starts moving through the q_A queues of the different nodes it visits (phase A) while it has any 0 to correct into 1. After performing the last 0 to 1 correction, the message will enter the q_B queue of the corresponding node, and will start doing the 1 to 0 corrections needed until it arrives at its destination node.

With the queue policy just outlined, the resulting routing algorithm is deadlock-free, and allows each message to wait for correcting any of the possible dimensions it has to correct. Consequently, there will be no partic-

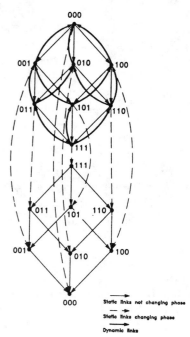

Figure 1: A 3-hypercube hung from node 000 with dynamic links.

ular congestion near node $1 \ldots 1$ as in the previous algorithm, as messages are allowed to move upwards even if they are in phase A, as a result of the newly added dynamic links. This algorithm requires only two queues per node, plus the injection and delivery queues, and is fully-adaptive.

The routing function. In the following, $\mathcal{E}^i(k)$ is the number that has the same binary representation as k but for the ith digit, k_i.

Formally, the routing function is the following:

$$
\tilde{\mathcal{R}}\,(i_s, d_m) = \begin{cases} \{q_{A,s}\} \\ \quad \text{if } \exists j : s_j \neq m_j \text{ and } s_j = 0 \\ \{q_{B,s}\} \\ \quad \text{otherwise} \end{cases}
$$

$$
\tilde{\mathcal{R}}\,(q_{A,n}, d_m) = \begin{cases} \{q_{A,\mathcal{E}^t(n)} : n_t \neq m_t\} \\ \quad \text{if } \exists j : n_j \neq m_j \text{ and } n_j = 0 \\ \{q_{B,n}\} \\ \quad \text{if } n \neq m \text{ and} \\ \quad\quad \forall j : (n_j \neq m_j \Rightarrow n_j = 1) \\ \{d_m\} \\ \quad \text{if } n = m \end{cases}
$$

$$
\tilde{\mathcal{R}}\,(q_{B,n}, d_m) = \begin{cases} \{q_{B,\mathcal{E}^t(n)} : n_t \neq m_t\} \\ \quad \text{if } n \neq m \\ \{d_m\} \\ \quad \text{if } n = m \end{cases}
$$

Then, the following theorem can be easily proved.

Theorem 1 *The routing algorithm just described for the hypercube is fully-adaptive, minimal, deadlock- and livelock-free, and can be implemented using 2 queues per node, plus an injection and a delivery queue per node.*

Simulation results of this algorithm for hypercubes of up to $16K$ nodes are reported in Section 7.

4 Mesh Algorithm.

A routing function for the mesh will be presented here in terms of the ideas of dynamic links. The scheme is minimal and deadlock free. Although the following description focuses on 2-dimensional meshes, the technique can be easily generalized for k-dimensional meshes, for any arbitrary k.

The key idea is to have two phases: in phase A the messages approach to their destination visiting nodes in such a way that if a message passes from (x, y) to (x', y') in one routing step, then $x < x'$ or $y < y'$. In phase B, messages visit nodes with lower number instead of those with higher number. In other words, the mesh is hung from node $(0, 0)$ in phase A and the messages visit nodes with higher level, where the level of (x, y) is $x + y$. In phase B, the mesh is hung from node $(n - 1, n - 1)$ and the nodes are visited in decreasing level order. A message changes from phase A to phase B if it has nothing to correct in phase A. This scheme can be implemented using two queues in each node, q_A for phase A messages and q_B for phase B messages. In this way, the scheme is deadlock free, because the queue dependency graph is acyclic.

The routing function. [1]

$$\mathcal{R}\left(i_{(x,y)}, d_{(z,w)}\right) = \begin{cases} q_{A,(x,y)} & \\ \quad \text{if } z > x \text{ or } w > y & \\ q_{B,(x,y)} & \\ \quad \text{if } z \leq x \text{ and } w \leq y \end{cases}$$

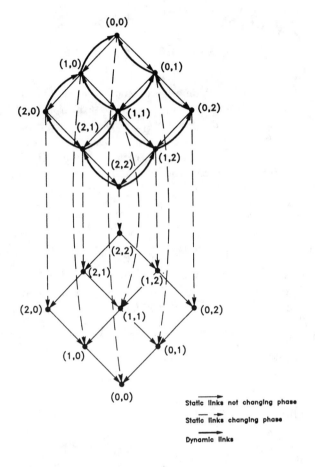

Figure 2: A 3-mesh hung from node $(0, 0)$ with dynamic links.

---

[1] In this section, $\mathcal{R}\ (a, b)$ is the set of all the right members satisfying the associated condition involving a and b. The same applies to the definition of $\tilde{\mathcal{R}}$ below.

$$\mathcal{R}\,(q_{A,(x,y)}, d_{(z,w)}) = \begin{cases} d_{(x,y)} & \\ \quad \text{if } x = z \text{ and } y = w & \\ q_{A,(x+1,y)} & \\ \quad \text{if } z > x & \\ q_{A,(x,y+1)} & \\ \quad \text{if } w > y & \\ q_{B,(x,y)} & \\ \quad \text{if } z \leq x \text{ and } w \leq y & \end{cases}$$

$$\mathcal{R}\,(q_{B,(x,y)}, d_{(z,w)}) = \begin{cases} d_{(x,y)} & \\ \quad \text{if } x = z \text{ and } y = w & \\ q_{B,(x,y-1)} & \\ \quad \text{if } w < y & \\ q_{B,(x-1,y)} & \\ \quad \text{if } z < x & \end{cases}$$

This routing function allows some degree of adaptivity. But suppose that some message starts from node (x,y) towards its destination (v,w), and let $v < x$ and $w > y$. Following the function above, this message has only one path, namely correct its second dimension, change phase and correct its first dimension. So, it has no adaptivity at all.

In the following, this scheme will be extended to a fully adaptive one, that is still deadlock free and uses the same number of queues.

This is done by allowing every message in phase A to pass to queue q_A of any neighboring node (and not only to those of higher level) *if it still has some descending path to pass through*. The phase change mechanism is the same as in the previous scheme. In phase B, the messages still have to go through ascending paths.

The routing function.

$$\tilde{\mathcal{R}}\,(i_{(x,y)}, d_{(z,w)}) = \begin{cases} q_{A,(x,y)} & \\ \quad \text{if } z > x \text{ or } w > y & \\ q_{B,(x,y)} & \\ \quad \text{if } z \leq x \text{ and } w \leq y & \end{cases}$$

$$\tilde{\mathcal{R}}\,(q_{A,(x,y)}, d_{(z,w)}) = \begin{cases} d_{(x,y)} & \\ \quad \text{if } x = z \text{ and } y = w & \\ q_{A,(x+1,y)} & \\ \quad \text{if } z > x & \\ q_{A,(x-1,y)} & \\ \quad \text{if } z < x \text{ and } w > y & \\ q_{A,(x,y+1)} & \\ \quad \text{if } w > y & \\ q_{A,(x,y-1)} & \\ \quad \text{if } z > x \text{ and } w < y & \\ q_{B,(x,y)} & \\ \quad \text{if } z \leq x \text{ and } w \leq y & \end{cases}$$

$$\tilde{\mathcal{R}}\,(q_{B,(x,y)}, d_{(z,w)}) = \begin{cases} d_{(x,y)} & \\ \quad \text{if } x = z \text{ and } y = w & \\ q_{B,(x,y-1)} & \\ \quad \text{if } w < y & \\ q_{B,(x-1,y)} & \\ \quad \text{if } z < x & \end{cases}$$

This new scheme is more adaptive than the first one described above. It can be implemented using only two queues, one for each phase, and it is still deadlock free. This can be proved using the ideas of dynamic links exposed in Section 2. Note that in the first phase the routing function $\tilde{\mathcal{R}}$ is defined as if the mesh were not hung.

Then, the following theorem can be easily proved.

Theorem 2 *The routing algorithm just described for the mesh is fully-adaptive, minimal, deadlock- and livelock-free, and can be implemented using 2 queues per node, plus an injection and a delivery queue per node.*

A fully-adaptive and minimal routing technique for packet-switching over tori can be achieved using 4 queues per node (plus an injection and delivery queue per node) following an idea similar to the one presented in [GPS91] for worm-hole routing over tori.

5 Shuffle-Exchange Algorithm.

In [PFGS91], a deadlock-free routing technique for the shuffle-exchange network using only a constant number of virtual channels per link has been presented. Next, a description of a modification of that technique for packet switching is given, followed by a possible extension using dynamic links to achieve adaptivity.

First, consider a 2^n-node shuffle-exchange network as without the exchange links. Each connected component of the graph will be called a *shuffle cycle*. Note that every node in a shuffle cycle has the same number of 1s in its binary address. Then, the *level* of a shuffle cycle can be defined as the number of ones in the address of any of its nodes. The idea of the algorithm is to break the shuffle cycles using the technique presented in [DS86a] in the context of worm-hole routing, and then, visit the cycles so as to avoid deadlock. Any node of a cycle can be chosen to break it.

The routing strategy can be defined in two phases. In the first one, messages can move from one shuffle cycle to another whenever the new cycle has higher level. In the second phase, messages visit the shuffles cycles in

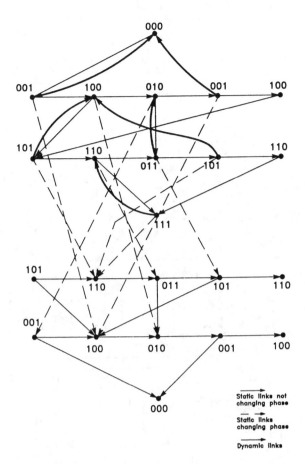

Figure 3: A 3-shuffle-exchange hung from node 000 with dynamic links.

decreasing order with respect to their level. The routing algorithm consists of visiting the dimensions of the address to correct twice, once in each phase. In each phase, dimensions are visited using the shuffle links. Consequently, every path has at most $3n$ steps: at most $2n$ shuffle steps and at most n exchange steps (see Figure 3).

After going through a shuffle link, every message has to know which dimension of the destination corresponds to the current least significant bit so as to know whether the least significant bit has to be corrected or not. So, each message must record the number of shuffle links it has already traversed. This is necessary to compare the least significant bit of the current node address with the corresponding bit of the destination address so as to decide what to do as the next step. If these bits disagree, that dimension will have to be corrected at that step or not depending on the phase the message is in. In the first phase, a dimension will be corrected if it has to be changed from 0 to 1. Note that this restriction implies that the new cycle has higher level. In the second phase, the reverse direction of the exchange links is used. Only will a change from 1 to 0 be allowed. So, the level of

the cycles that are visited decreases during the second phase.

The routing function that has just been described needs only two queues per node for breaking the shuffle cycles. It is necessary to break the shuffle cycles twice: once for each phase. Therefore, each node will have 4 queues, and an injection and a delivery queue.

The messages can either be consumed as soon as they arrive at their destinations for the first time, or when arriving at their destinations after finishing the $2n$ shuffle transitions.

Next, the modification of the routing function described above by adding dynamic links is presented. Basically, the main change introduced is that a message will be allowed to traverse an exchange link that corrects the current dimension from 1 to 0 even if the message is in its first phase. In other words, a message will be allowed to correct a 1 to 0 if it happens to find place to do it during the first phase. If not, that dimension will have to be changed during the second phase. As a result of these changes, the resulting routing algorithm is adaptive, as a given message may take alternative paths as a consequence of local congestion: e.g. it may or may not correct a 1 into a 0 during the first phase (see Figure 3). See [PGFS91] for a formal and more detailed definition of the routing function.

Then, the following theorem can be easily proved.

Theorem 3 *The routing algorithm just described for the 2^n-node shuffle-exchange network is adaptive, deadlock- and livelock-free, and can be implemented using 4 queues per node, plus an injection and a delivery queue per node. Furthermore, the route each message takes has at most $3n$ steps.*

6 The design of the node.

In this Section, a possible node model to implement the routing algorithms presented in Sections 3, 4, and 5 will be presented. The node models are a modification of the one presented in [Kon90] to implement a partially adaptive routing algorithm for the hypercube.

As described above, a message can move from a queue to another queue following two types of transitions, either through dynamic links or through static links, following the terminology used in Section 2. There exists a dynamic or static link between a pair of queues only if these queues are at distance at most one in the physical network, i.e. if either the queues are in the same node or at adjacent nodes (nodes connected by a physical link in the network). If $(q_1, q_2) \in A_s \cup A_d$, then q_2 will receive messages from q_1. So, there must exist a physical connection between q_1 and q_2. If q_1 and q_2 belong to adjacent nodes, then this physical connection is the physical link between the two nodes. On the other hand, if q_1 and q_2 belong to the same node, then, there must exist an internal connection between the two queues so as to allow internal passage of message within the nodes. Given a queue q, some fair policy must be implemented so as to guarantee fair access to q to all the resources that may want to access q.

Each node will have both an injection and a delivery queue, as explained above, as well as all the queues used by the routing algorithm. Each physical link will have associated with it input and output buffers. In general, there will be two types of buffers associated with each physical link: those associated with dynamic links and those with static links. Consider link j, incident to nodes n and n'. If traffic corresponding to dynamic links can enter node n from node n' through link j, then link j will have an input buffer in node n and an output buffer in node n' associated with the dynamic transitions. So, when a message wants to go out of node n' through link j via a dynamic transition, it will be placed in the output buffer corresponding to dynamic traffic of link j and it will arrive at the input buffer in node n that is associated with both dynamic transitions and link j. If traffic corresponding to static links can enter queue q in node n through link j, then link j will have an input buffer associated with queue q in node n and an output buffer associated with queue q in node n'. So, if some queue q' in node n' wants to send a message through link j to queue q via a static transition, then it will place the message in the output buffer corresponding to link j and queue q in node n'.

Figures 4, 5 and 6 illustrate the node model corresponding to the algorithms presented in Sections 3, 4 and 5, respectively. A more detailed description of these models can be found in [PGFS91].

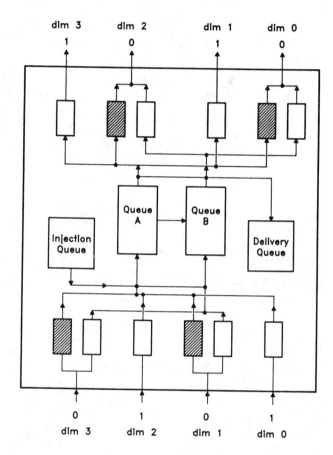

Figure 4: Node 0101 of the 4-Hypercube.

7 Simulation of the algorithm.

In this Section, simulations results of the routing algorithm proposed will be shown for the hypercube.

7.1 The activity of the node.

In the simulations presented below, each node is supposed to have an injection queue of size 1. The size of

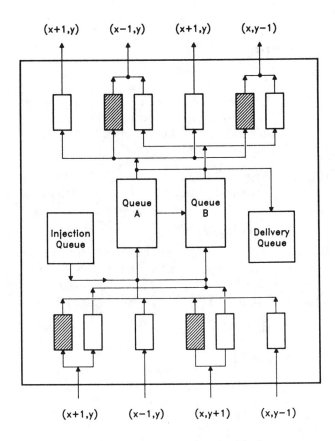

Figure 5: The node for the Mesh.

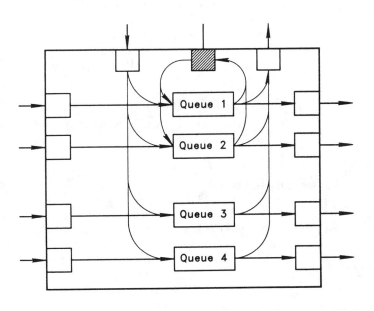

Figure 6: The node for the Shuffle-Exchange.

q_A and q_B queues has been fixed arbitrarily to 5. The idea is to have a queue size that *does not* change with the size of the network. Following the node description given in Section 6, nodes and links should work in a synchronous manner, but are independent of each other. So, each routing cycle consists of one node cycle and one link cycle. In the node cycle, each node fills its output buffers from low to high dimensions, taking messages from the queues in FIFO order. This means that if two messages want to enter the same buffer, the first one in the queue in FIFO order will get it. Then, the node reads its input buffers and its injection buffer and moves their messages to the required queues, if there is place to do so. This is carried out in a fair way. It should be noted that it takes a message at least *two* routing steps to go through a node: one to go from the input (or injection) buffer to some queue and another to go from the queue to the output buffer.

During the link cycle, each link tries to send a packet in each direction. Note that some links have associated two output buffers. As only one packet can use the link during a single cycle, packets may have to wait in the output buffers. Of course, a packet can go through a link only if the corresponding input buffer (on the other side of the link) is empty.

The simulations that have been performed show the behavior of the algorithm for many different injection models and communication patterns, described by the following parameters:

- **Injection Model:** The injection model can be either dynamic or static.

  - In the *dynamic* model, each node tries to inject a message in the network in every cycle with some probability λ. The simulations have been run for $\lambda = 1$. The dynamic injection of randomly destined packets models the situation in which the nodes communicate with each other independently. The dynamic injection of messages with the same destination is a very useful pattern of communication that models a coarse-grain parallel program with structured communication patterns. In the first case, the destinations of messages from a given source are chosen at random. In the second case, a permutation σ is chosen in advance, and every node i selects $\sigma(i)$ as destination for every message it injects into the network.

  - The injection is *static* if each node has an a priori fixed number of packets to inject in the network. The simulations have been run for both 1 and $\log N$ packets at each node.

For both models, the average latency and maximum latency messages suffer is measured. For dynamic injection, also the effective injection rate is measured. The effective injection rate is defined as the ratio between the number of times the nodes succeeded in injecting messages into the network and the number of times the nodes attempted to inject.

- **Communication Pattern:** The following communication patterns have been tried:

  - **Random Routing:** The destination of each message is chosen randomly[2]. It should be noted that this pattern of communication does not necessarily generate permutations.

  - **Complement:** The destination of each message is the node whose binary address is the complement of the address of its origin.

  - **Transpose:** If $\acute{n} = \log N$ is even, the transpose of the binary address $b_{n-1}, \ldots, b_{\frac{n}{2}}, b_{\frac{n}{2}-1}, \ldots, b_0$ is $b_{\frac{n}{2}-1}, \ldots, b_0, b_{n-1}, \ldots, b_{\frac{n}{2}}$. If n is odd, its central bit remains unchanged and the address is modified as before.

  - **Leveled Permutation:** It has been defined that the level of a node is its Hamming weight. A leveled permutation is one in which every node sends messages to a node in its same level. In [FCS90] it has been reported that congestion may arise for this sort of permutations in an oblivious routing technique where minimal paths are chosen at random.

In tables 1 to 8 the results of the simulations that have been performed for static injection are presented. Tables 9 to 12 show the results for dynamic injection. It should be emphasized that node activities are considered to take two time cycles. In the tables, N is the number of nodes of the hypercube, n is the number of dimensions of the hypercube, L_{avg} is the average latency of the messages, L_{max} is the maximum latency any packet experienced, and I_r (%) is the effective injection rate.

8 Acknowledgments.

We would like to thank S. Konstantinidou, C. T. Ho, J. Bruck and R. Cypher for their many suggestions and comments.

---

[2]Node p will choose the destination of every message it injects with uniform probability over the set $V - \{p\}$.

References

[BGSS89] Y. Birk, P.B. Gibbons, D. Soroker, and J.L.C. Sanz. A simple mechanism for efficient barrier synchronization in MIMD machines. RJ 7078 (67141) Computer Science, IBM Almaden Research Center, October 1989.

[BH82] A. Borodin and J.E. Hopcroft. Routing, Merging and Sorting on Parallel Models of Computation. In *Symposium on Theory of Computing*, pages 338–344, 1982.

[DS86a] W. Dally and C. Seitz. Deadlock-free routing in multiprocessor interconnection network. 5206:TR:86, Computer Science Department, California Institute of Technology, 1986.

[DS86b] W. J. Dally and C. L. Seitz. The Torus Routing Chip. *Distributed Computing*, (1):187–196, 1986.

[FCS90] M.L. Fulgham, R. Cypher, and J.L.C. Sanz. A comparison of SIMD hypercube routing strategies. RJ 7722 (71587), IBM Almaden Research Center, 1990.

[Gel81] D. Gelernter. A DAG-based algorithm for prevention of store-and-forward deadlock in packet networks. *IEEE Transactions on Computers*, c-30:709–715, October 1981.

[GPS91] L. Gravano, G.D. Pifarré, and J.L.C. Sanz. Adaptive Worm-hole Routing in Tori and Hypercubes. TR:91-10, IBM Argentina - CRAAG, March 1991.

[Gun81] K.D. Gunther. Prevention of deadlocks in packet-switched data transport system. *IEEE Transactions on Communications*, com-29(4), April 1981.

[Hil85] D. Hillis. *The Connection Machine*. The MIT Press, 1985.

[KK79] P. Kermani and L. Kleinrock. Virtual Cut-Through: A new computer communication switching technique. *Computer Networks*, (3):267–286, 1979.

[Kon90] S. Konstantinidou. Adaptive, minimal routing in hypercube. In *6th. MIT Conference on Advanced Research in VLSI*, pages 139–153, 1990.

[KS90]   S. Konstantinidou and L. Snyder. The Chaos router: A practical application of randomization in network routing. In *2nd. Annual ACM SPAA*, pages 21–30, 1990.

[Lei90]   T. Leighton. Average Case Analysis of Greedy Routing Algorithms on Arrays. In *SPAA*, 1990.

[LH91]   D.H. Linder and J.C. Harden. An Adaptive and Fault Tolerant Wormhole Routing Strategy for k-ary n-cubes. *IEEE Transactions on Computers*, 40(1):2–12, January 1991.

[LM89]   T. Leighton and B. Maggs. Expanders might be practical: Fast algorithms for routing around faults on multibutterflies. In IEEE, editor, 30th *Annual Symposium on Foundations of Computer Science*, pages 384–389, October 1989.

[LMR88]   T. Leighton, B. Maggs, and S. Rao. Universal packet routing algorithms. 1988.

[MS80]   P.M. Merlin and P.J. Schweitzer. Deadlock avoidance in store-and-forward networks. 1: Store-and-forward deadlock. *IEEE Transactions on Communications*, 28(3), March 1980.

[Ni90]   L.M. Ni. Communication Issues in Multicomputers. In *Proceedings of the First Workshop on Parallel Processing, Taiwan*, 1990.

[Ni91]   L.M. Ni, February 1991. Personal Communication.

[NS]   J.Y. Ngai and C.L. Seitz. A framework for adaptive routing. 5246:TR:87, Computer Science Department, California Institute of Technology.

[PFGS91]   G.D. Pifarré, S.A. Felperin, L. Gravano, and J.L.C. Sanz. New techniques for combination, adaptivity, deadlock-freedom and synchronization in massively parallel routing. In Preparation, 1991.

[PGFS91]   G.D. Pifarré, L. Gravano, S.A. Felperin, and J.L.C. Sanz. Fully-Adaptive Minimal Deadlock-Free Packet Routing in Hypercubes, Meshes, and Other Networks. Technical report, IBM Almaden Research Center, 1991.

[Pip84]   N. Pippenger. Parallel communication with limited buffers. In *Foundations of Computer Science*, pages 127 – 136, 1984.

Table 1: Random Routing, 1 packet.

n	N	L_{avg}	L_{max}
10	1024	10.96	19
11	2048	12.09	21
12	4096	13.08	25
13	8192	14.03	27
14	16384	15.04	29

Table 2: Complement, 1 packet.

n	N	L_{avg}	L_{max}
10	1024	21	21
11	2048	23	23
12	4096	25	25
13	8192	27	27
14	16384	29	29

[Ran85]   A.G. Ranade. How to emulate shared memory. In *Foundations of Computer Science*, pages 185 – 194, 1985.

[RBJ88]   A.G. Ranade, S.N. Bhat, and S.L. Johnson. The Fluent Abstract Machine. In J. Allen and F.T. Leighton, editors, *Fifth MIT conference on advanced research in VLSI*, pages 71 – 93. The MIT press, March 1988.

[Upf89]   E. Upfal. An $\mathbf{O}(\log N)$ deterministic packet routing scheme. In 21st *Annual ACM-SIGACT Symposium on Theory of Computing*, May 1989.

[Val82]   L. G. Valiant. Optimality of a two-phase strategy for routing in interconnection networks. March 1982.

[Val88]   L.G. Valiant. General purpose parallel architectures. In J. van Leeuwen, editor, *Handbook of Theoretical Computer Science*. North-Holland, 1988.

Table 3: Transpose, 1 packet.

n	N	L_{avg}	L_{max}
10	1024	11.09	21
11	2048	11.09	21
12	4096	13.13	25
13	8192	13.13	25
14	16384	15.23	29

Table 4: Leveled Permutation, 1 packet.

n	N	L_{avg}	L_{max}
10	1024	10.10	21
11	2048	10.98	21
12	4096	12.06	25
13	8192	13.07	25
14	16384	14.03	29

Table 5: Random Routing, n packets.

n	N	L_{avg}	L_{max}
10	1024	11.33	22
11	2048	12.52	25
12	4096	13.76	27
13	8192	15.02	30
14	16394	16.54	32

Table 6: Complement, n packets.

n	N	L_{avg}	L_{max}
10	1024	21	21
11	2048	24.99	30
12	4096	28.61	35
13	8192	32.74	39
14	16384	36.23	44

Table 7: Transpose, n packets.

n	N	L_{avg}	L_{max}
10	1024	12.27	26
11	2048	12.40	32
12	4096	16.01	37
13	8192	16.22	36
14	16384	20.49	43

Table 8: Leveled Permutation, n packets.

n	N	L_{avg}	L_{max}
10	1024	10.78	23
11	2048	11.77	25
12	4096	13.17	28
13	8192	14.60	32
14	16384	16.03	37

Table 9: Random Routing, $\lambda = 1$.

n	N	L_{avg}	L_{max}	I_r (%)
10	1024	12.10	30	93
11	2048	13.47	35	89
12	4096	15.01	37	85
13	8192	16.58	44	81
14	16364	18.30	49	76

Table 10: Complement, $\lambda = 1$.

n	N	L_{avg}	L_{max}	I_r (%)
10	1024	33.32	52	55
11	2048	39.29	58	49
12	4096	45.60	68	45
13	8192	52.87	79	41
14	16384	60.70	90	38

Table 11: Transpose, $\lambda = 1$.

n	N	L_{avg}	L_{max}	I_r (%)
10	1024	14.67	36	83
11	2048	14.67	36	83
12	4096	15.78	49	73
13	8192	20.31	54	71
14	16384	27.33	66	61

Table 12: Leveled Permutation, $\lambda = 1$.

n	N	L_{avg}	L_{max}	I_r (%)
9	512	11.28	37	94
10	1024	12.47	43	91
11	2048	13.50	48	89
12	4096	15.17	56	84
13	8192	16.91	53	80
14	16384	18.46	57	75

Proving Sequential Consistency of High-Performance Shared Memories

(extended abstract)

Phillip B. Gibbons*
AT&T Bell Laboratories
Murray Hill, NJ 07974

Michael Merritt
AT&T Bell Laboratories
Murray Hill, NJ 07974

Kourosh Gharachorloo[†]
Stanford University
Stanford, CA 94305

Abstract

Relaxed consistency models such as *weak consistency* or *release consistency* may be understood as a contract between programmer and hardware designer, in which the programmer is restricted to some subset of the legal programs, and the shared memory in turn need support sequential consistency for only those programs. This paper develops a framework for proving the correctness of such high-performance shared memories. Previous work states consistency conditions for such memories in terms that reference details of the implementation. A specific base automaton is proposed as an instantiation of those architectural assumptions. A relaxed consistency condition can be understood as a restriction on the actions of this automaton, resulting in a more restricted automaton. This more restricted automaton should appear sequentially consistent to the class of programs for which the relaxed consistency condition is defined. Specific shared memories implementing this condition may be proven correct by showing they implement this restricted automaton.

This framework is illustrated by studying the release consistency model for multiprocessor memory systems, which relies on a classification of memory accesses into ordinary and synchronization, such that conflicting ordinary accesses are protected by synchronization. These conditions are formalized as restrictions on the base automaton, which is shown to be sequentially consistent when driven by the class of *PL programs*. Finally, a specification of the consistency algorithm used by the Stanford DASH machine is shown to implement this release consistent memory.

*Supported in part by DARPA contract N00014-87-K-0828.

[†]Supported in part by DARPA contract N00014-87-K-0828, and by Texas Instruments.

1 Introduction

1.1 High-speed shared memories and relaxed consistency models

One of the most important research areas in parallel computation is the design of convenient programming models that can be efficiently supported by large multiprocessors. In particular, the programmer's view of the memory system should be simple and easy to use, yet permit an efficient implementation. A popular assumption is that the memory system appear to be a serial shared memory, providing the same semantics as a uniprocessor, namely that only one read or write occurs at a time. Such a memory is called a *sequentially consistent* memory [Lam79]. Of course, this view is for correctness issues only; the programmer is fully aware that high efficiency requires wide-spread concurrency in memory operations.

There has been considerable effort in devising hardware that permits efficient support for a sequentially consistent memory (e.g. [ABM89, AH90a]), with limited success. Moreover, experience has shown that the full semantics of sequential consistency is rarely, if ever, used by programmers. The granularity of atomicity, single words of memory, is simply too fine for most applications. Instead, order and mutual exclusion are obtained in programs through the use of synchronization primitives (e.g. locks). The demand for high efficiency in shared memories has motivated the exploration of more relaxed consistency models, such as *weak consistency* [DSB86, DS90], *DRF0* [AH90b] and *release consistency* [GLL+90], that exploit a distinction between such synchronization accesses and ordinary accesses. Providing the synchronization accesses are correctly identified, shared memories implementing these models may permit more efficient processing of ordinary accesses, while retaining sequential consistency as the fundamental correctness condition. (The performance benefits for sample programs are quantified in [GGH91].)

Relaxed consistency models may be understood as a contract between the programmer and the hardware designer, in which the programmer is restricted to some subset of the legal programs, and the shared memory in turn need support sequential consistency for only those programs [AH90b, GLL+90].

1.2 The framework: a generic memory architecture

This paper develops a formal framework for proving the correctness of such high-performance shared memories. In part, this is an extension to more relaxed consistency models of the work in [ABM89], which provided formal definitions of sequential consistency and proved the correctness of a particular consistency algorithm. Providing a precise specification and a language for describing consistency algorithms permits formal statement and proof of such algorithms, and exposes any implicit assumptions present in informal descriptions. This paper exposes the architectural assumptions that are implicit in the literature on relaxed consistency models. As discussed in Section 2, previous work states correctness conditions in terms that reference details of the implementation. We propose a specific automaton, M_{base}, as an instantiation of those architectural assumptions. These details can be interpreted in the context of M_{base}, and the consistency conditions (CC) can be understood as restrictions on the actions of M_{base}. The result is a more restricted automaton, M_{cc}, which should appear sequentially consistent to the class of programs for which the relaxed consistency condition is defined. Once M_{cc} is proven sequentially consistent for the specific class of programs, a particular multiprocessor shared memory algorithm may be proven correct by showing that it implements the intermediate abstraction provided by M_{cc}.

1.3 Proving sequential consistency

Although sequentially consistent memories are indistinguishable from serial memories to parallel programs, the relationship is not that of "implementation" [AL88, LT87] or "bisimulation" [Mil80]. This is because the two memories must appear indistinguishable, not to a single omniscient observer, but to a collection of independent observers. These observers are the programs at each processor, which communicate only via the shared memory. (See [ABM89] for a discussion of the relationship between the stronger condition, satisfied by serial memories, and sequential consistency.)

This means that the general-purpose verification techniques (e.g. the "refinement mappings" of [AL88, Mer90] or "possibilities mappings" of [LT87]) for proving such relationships as bisimulation or implementation cannot be used directly to prove that sequentially consistent memories are appropriately indistinguishable from serial memories. In designing the relaxed consistent automaton M_{cc}, our goal is to capture as much

nondeterminism as possible in implementing the particular relaxed consistency condition, while providing a concrete mechanism. (A trivially general automaton allows any step that retains correctness, evaluated as an atomic predicate over the entire history. Such a specification provides little insight or support for correctness arguments.) The hope is that the somewhat non-standard sequential consistency proof can be done once for M_{cc}, and specific implementations then proven correct by showing them to be implementations of M_{cc}, allowing the use of more general verification tools.

1.4 Release consistent memories and PL programs

In this paper, we illustrate this framework by studying one relaxed consistency model in detail, the *release consistency* (RC) model [GLL+90]. This model exploits a finer distinction between accesses than do the weak consistency or DRF0 consistency models referenced above. Synchronization read accesses (*acquires*) are distinguished from synchronization write accesses (*releases*) in their treatment. As in weak consistency, release consistency is designed to exploit the assumption that ordinary accesses are protected by synchronization accesses, in the sense that there are never any race conditions involving ordinary accesses. There is also a third class of accesses, called *nsyncs*, that differ from both ordinary and synchronization in their assumed use and consequently their treatment. A program that correctly classifies accesses is called a *properly-labeled (PL) program*.

The framework described above is illustrated by formalizing the particular conditions imposed by release consistency as restrictions on the actions of M_{base}, resulting in the automaton M_{rc}, a generic model for release consistent memories. Release consistency is shown to imply sequential consistency for PL programs, in that executions of M_{rc} driven by a PL program are indistinguishable (by the program) from executions of the same program on a serial memory. Finally, the remaining part of the framework is illustrated by proving that the consistency algorithm used by the Stanford DASH multiprocessor [LLG+90] implements M_{rc}.

Release consistency generalizes both weak consistency (WC) and known conditions for the DRF0 model (DRF0) in that the restrictions these conditions impose on M_{base} are strictly stronger than those imposed by release consistency. It follows immediately that the corresponding automata M_{wc} and M_{drf0} implement M_{rc}, and hence are sequentially consistent for PL programs. Thus, particular implementations of these consistency conditions may be proven correct by mapping them directly to M_{rc}.

1.5 Outline of the paper

Section 2 begins with a description of the generic automaton M_{base}, and is followed by an informal description of the release consistency model. This model is made precise by restricting the actions of M_{base} to produce the generic release consistent memory M_{rc}. Section 3 presents a proof that M_{rc} is sequentially consistent for PL programs. Following [ABM89], it begins with a definition of a serial memory, M_s, that will serve as the programmer's view. Both sequential consistency and PL programs are defined in terms of this simple automaton. A series of lemmas lead to a useful alternative characterization of PL programs. Then an inductive argument establishes the main result. The proof is only sketched in this extended abstract. Section 4 states our second main result, that M_{dash}, a specification of the consistency algorithm used in the Stanford DASH Multiprocessor, implements M_{rc}. The complete M_{dash} specification and correctness proof, omitted in this extended abstract, appear in the full paper [GMG91]. Section 5 provides discussion and some concluding remarks.

2 Formal models of high-performance shared memories

2.1 Architectural assumptions implicit in previous work

Relaxed consistency models are described in the literature using phrases such as "no access to global data is issued before a previous access to a synchronizing variable has been globally performed" [DSB86], "at a point in time when an issued load to the same address returns the value defined by a store" [DSB86], "a write commits when its value could be dispatched for some read" [AH90b], "the value to be returned is bound" [GLL+90]. These phrases are difficult to interpret outside the context of a particular implementation.

Moreover, these models are expressed as conditions upon a memory system that preserves uniprocessor dependences and is kept *coherent*, defined in [GLL+90] as "all writes to the same location are serialized in some order and are performed in that order with respect to any processor". (A similar notion is used in [AH90b].)

A natural interpretation, drawing on more traditional work on cache consistency, is that these statements refer to a context in which each processor maintains a separate view, not necessarily in its cache, of the data stored in each address. Some centralized mechanism maintains a separate logical view, perhaps physically distributed, and is used to order the writes of that address. Other values may be held in a communication network. Then, for example, a write to an address might commit (or perform) when all views for that address are at least as

recent as the write. This interpretation is formalized in the automaton M_{base}, described in Section 2.3.

2.2 The I/O Automata model

We will model memory systems of multiprocessors using the I/O automata model developed by Lynch and Tuttle [LT87, Lyn88], defined as follows.

Definition 1 *A <u>system</u> is a set of states and a set of actions which are symbols labeling the arcs of a transition relation on the states. An <u>execution</u> is a finite or infinite sequence $s_0, \pi_1, s_1, \ldots$ of alternating states and actions in the system where s_0 is the initial state and $s_i \in \pi_i(s_{i-1})$. The <u>schedules</u> of a system are the sequences of actions described by its executions.*

An *event* is the occurrence of an action in a sequence. An action is denoted *internal* or *external*. The set of external events comprise the *signature* of a system: these are the only events visible to the external world (states are not visible). External events may be initiated by the external world (*requests*) or initiated by the system (*returns*).

Definition 2 *The <u>behaviors</u> of a system are the sequences of external actions described by its executions. If α is an execution or schedule, $beh(\alpha)$ denotes the sequence of external actions in α.*

In this paper, we consider memory systems with the following external actions, where $i \in ProcessorNum$, $a \in Address$, and $d \in Data$:

- **ReadRequest**$_i(t, a)$: A read request to address a by processor i.

- **ReadReturn**$_i(t, a, d)$: A corresponding read return to processor i, returning the value d for address a.

- **WriteRequest**$_i(t, a, d)$: A request by processor i to write the value d to address a.

- **WriteReturn**$_i(t, a, d)$: A corresponding write return to processor i.

The variable t indicates the "type" of the access, e.g. ordinary or synchronization, chosen from some set of types recognized by the particular memory system.

The external actions with subscript i comprise the interface between processor i and the memory system. Certain internal actions, done on behalf of processor i, will also have subscript i.

Definition 3 *If σ is a schedule with behavior β, then $\sigma|j$ is the subsequence of σ consisting of all actions with subscript j, and $\beta|j$ is the subsequence of β consisting of all (external) actions with subscript j.*

ReadRequest$_i(t,a)$ ::	$\text{Status}[i] := \textbf{ReadRequest}(t,a)$
	$rwc_i := rwc_i + 1$
	$\text{Reads}_i := \text{Reads}_i \cup \{(t,a,?,rwc_i,?)\}$
ServiceRead$_i(t,a,d)$ ::	
$\text{Status}[i] = \textbf{ReadRequest}(t,a)$ $\quad\rightarrow$	$\text{Status}[i] := \textbf{ReadReturn}(t,a,d)$
$\wedge\, (t,a,?,r_i,?) \in \text{Reads}_i$	$\text{Reads}_i := \text{replace}(\text{Reads}_i, (t,a,?,r_i,?),$
$\wedge\, \text{ProcView}_i[a] = (d,c_a)$	$\qquad\qquad\qquad\qquad (t,a,d,r_i,c_a))$
ReadReturn$_i(t,a,d)$ ::	
$\text{Status}[i] = \textbf{ReadReturn}(t,a,d) \quad\rightarrow$	$\text{Status}[i] := \text{null}$
WriteRequest$_i(t,a,d)$ ::	$\text{Status}[i] := \textbf{WriteRequest}(t,a,d)$
	$rwc_i := rwc_i + 1$
	$\text{Writes}_i := \text{Writes}_i \cup \{(t,a,d,rwc_i,\infty)\}$
	$\text{ProcView}_i[a] := (d,\infty)$
WriteReturn$_i(t,a,d)$ ::	
$\text{Status}[i] = \textbf{WriteRequest}(t,a,d) \quad\rightarrow$	$\text{Status}[i] := \text{null}$
ServiceWrite$_i(t,a,d)$ ::	
$(t,a,d,w_i,\infty) \in \text{Writes}_i \qquad\qquad\rightarrow$	$wc_a := wc_a + 1$
$\wedge\, (\forall(*,a,*,<w_i,c_a) \in \text{Writes}_i : c_a < \infty)$	$\text{Mem}[a] := (d, wc_a)$
	$\text{Writes}_i := \text{replace}(\text{Writes}_i, (t,a,d,w_i,\infty),$
/* An unserviced write can be serviced	$\qquad\qquad\qquad\qquad (t,a,d,w_i,wc_a))$
if all previous writes by i to the	**if** $\nexists(*,a,*,>w_i,*) \in \text{Writes}_i$ **then**
same address have been serviced. */	$\quad \text{ProcView}_i[a] := (d, wc_a)$
SendPerformWrite$_i(a,d)$ ::	
$\text{Mem}[a] = (d, c_a) \qquad\qquad\qquad\rightarrow$	$\text{ToPerform}_i[a] := \text{ToPerform}_i[a] \cup \{(d,c_a)\}$
PerformWrite$_i(a,d)$ ::	
$(d,c_a) \in \text{ToPerform}_i[a] \qquad\qquad\rightarrow$	$\text{ToPerform}_i[a] := \text{ToPerform}_i[a] - \{(d,c_a)\}$
	if $\text{ProcView}_i[a] = (*,<c_a)$ **then**
	$\quad \text{ProcView}_i[a] := (d,c_a)$

2.3 The base memory M_{base}

The generic base memory automaton, M_{base}, shown in Table 1, supports per-location consistency and the preservation of local dependences. The memory state, Mem, is used to serialize the order of writes to a specific location. Writes to that location are then "performed" independently at each processor in that order by updating the processor's current view of memory, ProcView. (It is important to understand that $\text{ProcView}_i[a]$ is the value processor i may return on a read of a; it should not be thought of as processor i's cache, since in a specific implementation, the data in ProcView may reside in memory or even another processor's cache.) Each processor i has an associated read history buffer, Reads_i, and a write history buffer, Writes_i. These contain records for every access (requested) by i, stored as five-tuple records $(type, address, data, counter_i, counter_a)$. The $counter_i$ and $counter_a$ entries record sequence numbers: this is the $counter_i$'th access requested by processor i, and when the access is a write, the $counter_a$'th write (by any processor) to address a. When the access is a read, $counter_a$ is initially "?", and is later updated with the sequence number in ProcView_i when the read is serviced. The variables rwc_i and wc_a maintain the latest value of the number of accesses by i and the number of writes to a, respectively. The $counter_a$ entry in a write record is ∞ until the address in Mem is updated during the corresponding **ServiceWrite** event; the order of these events determines the per-location serialization of the writes. A read access by i returns the value in ProcView_i when it is serviced. We assume here and throughout the paper that reads are blocking.[1]

No mechanism establishes global serialization (sequential consistency). A **WriteReturn** event indicates to the processor that the next write can be issued, not that the write has completed. (E.g. no corresponding **ServiceWrite** event may have occurred, or entries in other processors' ProcView's may not yet reflect the new value.) Depending on the order in which **SendPerformWrite** and **PerformWrite** events occur, writes to different addresses may appear and be read in

---

[1] A read is *blocking* in a memory system if the processor issuing a read request is stalled awaiting a read return until the value read is returned. We are currently working on extensions to handle non-blocking reads.

ReadView$_i$($\overline{\mathbf{O}}$, a, d) ::	
$\mathrm{Status}[i] = \mathbf{ReadRequest}(t, a) : t \in \{\mathbf{S}, \mathbf{N}\}$ $\to$	$\mathrm{Status}[i] := \mathbf{ReadReturn}(t, a, d)$
$\wedge\ (t, a, ?, r_i, ?) \in \mathrm{Reads}_i$	$\mathrm{Reads}_i := \mathrm{replace}(\mathrm{Reads}_i, (t, a, ?, r_i, ?),$
$\wedge\ \mathrm{ProcView}_i[a] = (d, c_a < \infty)$	$\qquad\qquad\qquad (t, a, d, r_i, c_a))$
$\wedge\ (\forall (\overline{\mathbf{O}}, a', *, < r_i, c_{a'}) \in \mathrm{Writes}_i : (c_{a'} < \infty$	/* Address order at i,
$\qquad \wedge\ \forall j\ \mathrm{ProcView}_j[a'] = (*, \geq c_{a'})))$	all non-ordinary writes by i are
$\wedge\ (\forall (\overline{\mathbf{O}}, a', *, < r_i, c_{a'} < \infty) \in \mathrm{Reads}_i :$	globally performed, and all previous
$\qquad ((\overline{\mathbf{O}}, a', *, *, c_{a'}) \in \mathrm{Writes}_{k \neq i}$	non-ordinary reads by i of non-ordinary
$\qquad\quad \Rightarrow \forall j\ \mathrm{ProcView}_j[a'] = (*, \geq c_{a'})))$	writes are globally performed. */
ReadBuffer$_i$($\overline{\mathbf{O}}$, a, d) ::	
$\mathrm{Status}[i] = \mathbf{ReadRequest}(t, a) : t \in \{\mathbf{S}, \mathbf{N}\}$ $\to$	$\mathrm{Status}[i] := \mathbf{ReadReturn}(t, a, d)$
$\wedge\ (t, a, ?, r_i, ?) \in \mathrm{Reads}_i$	$\mathrm{Reads}_i := \mathrm{replace}(\mathrm{Reads}_i, (t, a, ?, r_i, ?),$
$\wedge\ \mathrm{ProcView}_i[a] = (d, c_a)$	$\qquad\qquad\qquad (t, a, d, r_i, c_a))$
$\wedge\ (*, a, d, w_i, c_a) \in \mathrm{Writes}_i :$	/* Address order at i, reading own write,
$\qquad (|\{(\overline{\mathbf{O}}, *, *, \geq w_i, *) \in \mathrm{Writes}_i\}| \leq 1)$	looking past at most one non-ordinary
$\wedge\ (\forall (\overline{\mathbf{O}}, a', *, < r_i, c_{a'} < \infty) \in \mathrm{Reads}_i :$	write (inclusive), and all previous
$\qquad ((\overline{\mathbf{O}}, a', *, *, c_{a'}) \in \mathrm{Writes}_{k \neq i}$	non-ordinary reads by i of non-ordinary
$\qquad\quad \Rightarrow \forall j\ \mathrm{ProcView}_j[a'] = (*, \geq c_{a'})))$	writes are globally performed. */
ServiceWrite$_i$($\mathbf{S}$, a, d) ::	
$(\mathbf{S}, a, d, w_i, \infty) \in \mathrm{Writes}_i$ $\to$	$wc_a := wc_a + 1$
$\wedge\ (\forall (*, a', *, < w_i, c_{a'}) \in \mathrm{Writes}_i : (c_{a'} < \infty$	$\mathrm{Mem}[a] := (d, wc_a)$
$\qquad \wedge\ \forall j\ \mathrm{ProcView}_j[a'] = (*, \geq c_{a'})))$	$\mathrm{Writes}_i := \mathrm{replace}(\mathrm{Writes}_i, (\mathbf{S}, a, d, w_i, \infty),$
$\wedge\ (\forall (\overline{\mathbf{O}}, a', *, < w_i, c_{a'} < \infty) \in \mathrm{Reads}_i :$	$\qquad\qquad\qquad\qquad (\mathbf{S}, a, d, w_i, wc_a))$
$\qquad ((\overline{\mathbf{O}}, a', *, *, c_{a'}) \in \mathrm{Writes}_{k \neq i}$	**if** $\nexists (*, a, *, > w_i, *) \in \mathrm{Writes}_i$ **then**
$\qquad\quad \Rightarrow \forall j\ \mathrm{ProcView}_j[a'] = (*, \geq c_{a'})))$	$\qquad \mathrm{ProcView}_i[a] := (d, wc_a)$
/* Address order at i, all previous writes by i are globally performed, and all	
previous non-ordinary reads by i of non-ordinary writes are globally performed. */	
ServiceWrite$_i$($\mathbf{N}$, a, d) ::	
$(\mathbf{N}, a, d, w_i, \infty) \in \mathrm{Writes}_i$ $\to$	$wc_a := wc_a + 1$
$\wedge\ (\forall (*, a, *, < w_i, c_a) \in \mathrm{Writes}_i : c_a < \infty)$	$\mathrm{Mem}[a] := (d, wc_a)$
$\wedge\ (\forall (\overline{\mathbf{O}}, a', *, < w_i, c_{a'}) \in \mathrm{Writes}_i : (c_{a'} < \infty$	$\mathrm{Writes}_i := \mathrm{replace}(\mathrm{Writes}_i, (\mathbf{N}, a, d, w_i, \infty),$
$\qquad \wedge\ \forall j\ \mathrm{ProcView}_j[a'] = (*, \geq c_{a'})))$	$\qquad\qquad\qquad\qquad (\mathbf{N}, a, d, w_i, wc_a))$
$\wedge\ (\forall (\overline{\mathbf{O}}, a', *, < w_i, c_{a'} < \infty) \in \mathrm{Reads}_i :$	**if** $\nexists (*, a, *, > w_i, *) \in \mathrm{Writes}_i$ **then**
$\qquad ((\overline{\mathbf{O}}, a', *, *, c_{a'}) \in \mathrm{Writes}_{k \neq i}$	$\qquad \mathrm{ProcView}_i[a] := (d, wc_a)$
$\qquad\quad \Rightarrow \forall j\ \mathrm{ProcView}_j[a'] = (*, \geq c_{a'})))$	
/* Address order at i, all previous non-ordinary writes by i are globally performed, and	
all previous non-ordinary reads by i of non-ordinary writes are globally performed. */	

processors' ProcView's in different orders. However, M_{base} provides an architectural context in which sufficient conditions for sequential consistency can be stated. For example, such terms as "performed" and "committed," discussed in the beginning of this section, can now be given formal interpretations in the context of executions of M_{base}.

Definition 4 *Consider an execution of M_{base}.*

- *An* _operation_ *(read or write) of processor i is a successive pair of* **ReadRequest**$_i$ *and* **ReadReturn**$_i$ *or* **WriteRequest**$_i$ *and* **WriteReturn**$_i$ *events. An operation is* _issued_ *when the* **Request** *event occurs, and is* _pending_ *if there is a* **Request** *event and no corresponding* **Return**.

- *A write operation is* _serviced_ *(or* _committed_*) when the corresponding* **ServiceWrite** *event occurs. (This event assigns the operation the next sequence number for that address.)*

- *A write operation of processor i to address a is* _performed with respect to j_ *when* $ProcView_j[a]$ *contains a sequence number greater than or equal to that of the operation. The operation is* _globally performed (or performed)_ *when it is performed with respect to all processors.*

- *A read operation is* _bound_ *(or* _performed_*) when a corresponding* **ServiceRead** *event occurs.*

- *A read operation is* _globally performed_ *when the write it reads from is* _globally performed_.

2.4 The generic release consistent memory M_{rc}

We now show how a formal specification for a release consistent memory, M_{rc}, can be developed from M_{base}.

In [GLL$^+$90], the following conditions are given for release consistency (RCsc):[2]

1. Uniprocessor data dependences are respected.

2. All writes to the same location are serialized in some order and are performed in that order with respect to any processor.

3. Before a sync write access is allowed to perform with respect to any other processor, all previous ordinary write accesses by the same processor must be performed.

4. Sync and nsync accesses are kept sequentially consistent with respect to one another. A sufficient condition for sequential consistency is: Before a sync/nsync access is allowed to perform with respect to any other processor, all previous sync/nsync accesses by the same processor must be globally performed.

M_{base} is a concrete instantiation of the first two conditions above. The third and fourth conditions can be imposed as additional restrictions placed on sync and nsync accesses. Such restrictions are presented in Table 2. The resulting restricted version of M_{base} is called M_{rc}. As discussed below, restriction 4 above can be weakened slightly, while retaining sequential consistency for PL programs. The restrictions for M_{rc} reflect this weakening.

There are three types of accesses for M_{rc}: ordinary (O), sync (S), and nsync (N). The **Read-Request**, **ReadReturn**, **WriteRequest**, **WriteReturn**, **SendPerformWrite**, and **PerformWrite** actions are unchanged from M_{base}. There are no new constraints on ordinary accesses, so $\text{ServiceRead}_i(O, a, d)$ and $\text{Service-Write}_i(O, a, d)$ are unchanged as well. The new (restricted) actions are shown in Table 2. For ease of presentation, the $\text{ServiceRead}_i(\overline{O}, a, d)$ actions are replaced by $\text{ReadBuffer}_i(\overline{O}, a, d)$ and $\text{ReadView}_i(\overline{O}, a, d)$ actions, which distinguish between reading a local or remote write. $\text{ServiceWrite}_i(S, a, d)$ and $\text{Service-Write}_i(N, a, d)$ are new restricted actions for the servicing of non-ordinary writes.

The condition for $\text{ReadView}_i(\overline{O}, a, d)$ formalizes condition 4, by restricting the binding of non-ordinary reads. The condition for $\text{ReadBuffer}_i(\overline{O}, a, d)$ weakens condition 4 by allowing a processor to return certain unperformed write values, including that of the most recent unperformed sync or nsync write. The conditions for $\text{ServiceWrite}_i(S, a, d)$ and $\text{ServiceWrite}_i(N, a, d)$ are straightforward formalizations of conditions 3 and 4.

3 RC memories are sequentially consistent for PL programs

This section presents a proof that M_{rc} is sequentially consistent for PL programs. It begins with a definition of a serial memory, M_s; both sequential consistency and PL programs are defined in terms of this simple automaton. A series of lemmas lead to a useful alternative characterization of PL programs. Then an inductive argument establishes the main result.

3.1 The serial memory M_s

As in [ABM89], we define a particular memory system, the serial memory, M_s, that will serve as the programmer's view of the memory. For completeness, the definition is given in Table 3.

M_s contains a single memory state, Mem. Write accesses update Mem; read accesses return the value in Mem. We argue that M_s is a simple intuitive model for a memory system and a suitable abstraction for programmers of parallel processors. In environments which obey the handshake, i.e. await a **Return**$_i$ event before issuing a second **Request**$_i$, memory operations consist of sequences of three events: a **Request** from the environment, an internal (**MemoryWrite** or **MemoryRead**) event performing the operation as a single atomic act, and a **Return** signaling the completion of the operation and, for reads, returning the value. Thus, the environment knows that each operation is performed atomically at some time between the **Request** and **Return** events, and the sequence of internal **Memory** events is the serialization order of the operations.[3] Thus reads and writes can be viewed as accessing memory one at a time, just as in a uniprocessor, providing a familiar interface to the programmer.

The following definitions and lemmas concerning schedules of M_s will be useful in developing an alternative characterization of PL programs.

3.1.1 Causal order

Definition 5 *An execution of a memory system M is <u>driven</u> by a program P if (1) the processors communicate only using M, and (2) each processor obeys the handshake convention provided by M, i.e. a processor does not issue its next **Request** until after the **Return** event of its previous **Request**.*

---

[2]In this paper, we consider the RCsc variant of release consistency in which sync and nsync accesses are kept sequentially consistent. Also, our assumption that reads are blocking simplifies the conditions.

[3]This is called the linearization order in [HW87], and M_s is called a dynamic atomic memory in [HA90].

Table 3: M_s	
$\mathbf{ReadRequest}_i(t, a) ::$	$\mathrm{Status}[i] := \mathbf{ReadRequest}(t, a)$
$\mathbf{MemoryRead}_i(t, a, d) ::$ $\mathrm{Status}[i] = \mathbf{ReadRequest}(t, a)$ $\wedge \mathrm{Mem}[a] = d$ $\quad\longrightarrow\quad$	$\mathrm{Status}[i] := \mathbf{ReadReturn}(t, a, d)$
$\mathbf{ReadReturn}_i(t, a, d) ::$ $\mathrm{Status}[i] = \mathbf{ReadReturn}(t, a, d)$ $\quad\longrightarrow\quad$	$\mathrm{Status}[i] := \mathrm{null}$
$\mathbf{WriteRequest}_i(t, a, d) ::$	$\mathrm{Status}[i] := \mathbf{WriteRequest}(t, a, d)$
$\mathbf{MemoryWrite}_i(t, a, d) ::$ $\mathrm{Status}[i] = \mathbf{WriteRequest}(t, a, d)$ $\quad\longrightarrow\quad$	$\mathrm{Mem}[a] := d$ $\mathrm{Status}[i] := \mathbf{WriteReturn}(t, a, d)$
$\mathbf{WriteReturn}_i(t, a, d) ::$ $\mathrm{Status}[i] = \mathbf{WriteReturn}(t, a, d)$ $\quad\longrightarrow\quad$	$\mathrm{Status}[i] := \mathrm{null}$

Definition 6 *Consider a schedule, σ, of M_s driven by a program, and let $\beta = beh(\sigma)$.*

- *Let $<_\sigma^{DC}$, the <u>direct causal relation</u> for σ, be a relation on the events in σ, where $a <_\sigma^{DC} b$ for events a and b in σ provided either (1) a precedes b in $\sigma|i$ for some i, or (2) b is a $\mathbf{MemoryRead}$ and a is the $\mathbf{MemoryWrite}$ to the same address that immediately precedes b in σ.*

- *Let $\leq_\sigma^{DC}$ be the reflexive closure of $<_\sigma^{DC}$.*

- *Let $<_\sigma^C$, the <u>causal order</u> for σ, be the (irreflexive) transitive closure of $<_\sigma^{DC}$.*

Definition 7 *Let σ be a sequence of M_s actions, and σ' be a subsequence of σ. Then σ' is a <u>causally closed subsequence</u> of σ if for every event y in σ', if $x <_\sigma^C y$, then x is also in σ'.*

Lemma 1 *Let σ be a schedule of M_s driven by a program P, and let σ' be a causally closed subsequence of σ. Then σ' is a schedule of M_s driven by P.*

The proof appears in the full paper [GMG91].

3.1.2 Causal chains

Definition 8 *Let σ be a sequence of M_s actions, and let x_i and y_j be events in σ. A <u>causal chain</u> connecting x_i and y_j in σ is a subsequence of σ consisting of alternating $\mathbf{MemoryWrite}$ and $\mathbf{MemoryRead}$ events; $\mathbf{MemoryWrite}_{i_1}$, $\mathbf{MemoryRead}_{i_2}, \ldots,$ $\mathbf{Memory}$-$\mathbf{Write}_{i_{2k-1}}$, $\mathbf{MemoryRead}_{i_{2k}}$, $k \geq 1$, such that*

- $i = i_1$, *i.e. x_i and $\mathbf{MemoryWrite}_{i_1}$ occur at the same processor.*

- $j = i_{2k}$, *i.e. y_j and $\mathbf{MemoryRead}_{i_{2k}}$ occur at the same processor.*

- *For all t, $1 \leq t \leq k$, $i_{2t-1} \neq i_{2t}$ i.e. $\mathbf{MemoryWrite}_{i_{2t-1}}$ and $\mathbf{MemoryRead}_{i_{2t}}$ occur at different processors.*

- *For all t, $1 \leq t < k$, $i_{2t} = i_{2t+1}$ i.e. $\mathbf{MemoryRead}_{i_{2t}}$ and $\mathbf{MemoryWrite}_{i_{2t+1}}$ occur at the same processor.*

- $x_i \leq_\sigma^{DC} \mathbf{MemoryWrite}_{i_1} <_\sigma^{DC} \mathbf{MemoryRead}_{i_2} <_\sigma^{DC}$ $\cdots <_\sigma^{DC} \mathbf{MemoryRead}_{i_{2k}} \leq_\sigma^{DC} y_j.$

Lemma 2 *Let σ be a schedule of M_s driven by a program. If x_i and y_j are events in σ at different processors with x_i preceding y_j in σ, then $x_i <_\sigma^C y_j$ if and only if there is a causal chain in σ connecting x_i and y_j.*

3.2 PL programs

The PL programs [GLL$^+$90] are the class of programs supported by release consistent memories; their definition also depends upon the classification of memory operations into the three classes, ordinary, sync and nsync. The pattern of operations issued by the programs is required to satisfy a property defined below, which formalizes the intuition that ordinary accesses are data-race free. As we have seen, the memory system M_{rc} makes use of this constrained pattern of operations to more efficiently process ordinary accesses.

Two accesses <u>conflict</u> if they access the same location and at least one is a write. Two accesses <u>PL-conflict</u> if they conflict, take place at two different processors, and at least one is an ordinary access.

In [GLL$^+$90], the PL programs are defined for the general case, in which reads are non-blocking. Since we assume in this paper that reads are blocking, there is no need to distinguish between sync reads (acquires) and nsync reads as is done for the general case. Thus, the following simplified definition of PL, PL$_{br}$, suffices for the purposes of this paper.

Definition 9 *A PL_{br} program with respect to M_s is a program such that for any schedule, σ, on M_s driven by the program, the following property holds: for any two PL-conflicting accesses, x_i by processor i and z_j by processor j, if x_i precedes z_j in σ, then there is a release access, y_i, by i (an occurrence of a sync MemoryWrite$_i$ action) between x_i and z_j in σ. (The events x_i and y_i could be the same.)*

The following lemma states an important equivalent characterization of PL_{br} programs.

Lemma 3 *Let σ be a schedule of M_s driven by a PL_{br} program P, with x_i and z_j Request's for two PL-conflicting accesses such that x_i precedes z_j in σ. Then there is a causal chain connecting x_i and z_j in σ, consisting only of non-ordinary accesses and beginning with a sync MemoryWrite$_i$ event.*

The proof appears in the full paper [GMG91].

3.3 The correctness proof for M_{rc}

The proof is structured as an induction on executions of M_{rc}. The main theorem proves that there is actually a family of sequential schedules that are consistent with any particular execution of M_{rc}. Some of this nondeterminism is due to the fact that conflicting write operations may have returned to the calling processors, but have not yet been serviced—their serialization order is indeterminate as yet, and may be resolved in either order. An invariant argues that there are corresponding serial schedules with both serializations, so that when future steps require a particular choice (to *have been* made), the required serialization is known to exist.

The set of serializations corresponding to a given schedule of M_{rc} is constructed explicitly, and provides some insight into the workings of the automaton. Since the construction is the most interesting aspect of the proof, we describe it in detail in this extended abstract. This is followed by a brief sketch of the induction proof based on this construction.

3.3.1 The serializations construction

In a finite schedule α_{rc} of M_{rc} driven by a program, certain events can be naturally grouped as processing specific accesses. The read accesses, for example, are processed by each consecutive ReadRequest$_i$ReadView$_i$ReadReturn$_i$, ReadRequest$_i$ReadBuffer$_i$ReadReturn$_i$, or ReadRequest$_i$ServiceRead$_i$ReadReturn$_i$ subsequence of $\alpha_{rc}|i$.

Because of the buffering of writes, so that their processing continues after the associated WriteReturn event, the correspondence for write accesses is somewhat more complicated, but still natural. The ServiceWrite$_i$ events are associated with a specific prior WriteRequest$_i$ event, and, if it occurs in α_{rc}, a corresponding WriteReturn$_i$ event. They are also associated with

the specific value of wc_a just after the ServiceWrite$_i$ occurs. These values also serve to identify the SendPerformWrite and PerformWrite events, which together with the ServiceWrite$_i$ event, can naturally be said to be processing the associated write operation. Further, the ServiceWrite events at each address a are naturally ordered by the successive values of wc_a. Call this value of wc_a the <u>counter value</u> of the associated events in α_{rc}. Note that ReadRequest events, ReadReturn events, and any WriteRequest and WriteReturn events without associated ServiceWrite events do not have counter values.

Let α_{rc} be a finite schedule of M_{rc} driven by a PL_{br} program P. The development that follows defines $f(\alpha_{rc})$ to be a set of sequences of events of M_s, derived from α_{rc}, and shows that each is a schedule of M_s driven by P.

Simple properties of M_{rc}. Some simple monotonicity properties of M_{rc} (as well as M_{base}), established via an easy induction, will be useful:

Lemma 4 *In any execution of M_{rc} the following are true:*

- *The sequence of finite counter values stored at each address in ProcView$_i$ and Mem never decrease.*

- *The counter in Mem$[a]$ is never less than any finite value in ToPerform$_i[a]$ or ProcView$_i[a]$.*

- *The counter value in ProcView$_i[a]$ is infinite if and only if there is an unserviced write by i to address a. (E.g. $(*, a, *, *, \infty) \in$ Writes$_i$.)*

- *The property "performed at i" is stable.*

The events in $f(\alpha_{rc})$. Each sequence in $f(\alpha_{rc})$ contains the same set of events, $f_e(\alpha_{rc})$, consisting of:

- All external actions in α_{rc}, i.e. all ReadRequest, ReadReturn, WriteRequest, and WriteReturn events,

- MemoryWrite$_i(t, a, d)$ whenever a corresponding WriteReturn$_i(t, a, d)$ or ServiceWrite$_i(t, a, d)$ occurs in α_{rc}, and

- MemoryRead$_i(t, a, d)$ whenever a corresponding ServiceRead$_i(O, a, d)$, ReadView$_i(\overline{O}, a, d)$, or ReadBuffer$_i(\overline{O}, a, d)$ occurs in α_{rc}.

The events of $f_e(\alpha_{rc})$ with subscript i are naturally ordered according to their occurrence in α_{rc}, with MemoryWrite$_i$ and MemoryRead$_i$ events ordered after the corresponding Request$_i$ and before the corresponding Return$_i$ (if the latter exists). The result is n sequences of M_s events, $\sigma_1, \ldots, \sigma_n$.

We extend the definitions of servicing and performing reads and writes in α_{rc} to the corresponding **MemoryWrite** event in $f_e(\alpha_{rc})$. If $\pi \in f_e(\alpha_{rc})$ is a **MemoryRead** or **MemoryWrite** event and a corresponding **ServiceRead**, **ReadBuffer**, **ReadView**, or **ServiceWrite** occurs in α_{rc}, we say π is <u>serviced</u> in α_{rc}. If π is a **MemoryWrite** event, we assign the same counter value to π as is assigned to the **ServiceWrite** event. We say that π is <u>performed at j</u> in a state s of M_{rc}, and in an execution which ends in s or a schedule which can end in s, if π is serviced and if ProcView$_j[a]$ contains a counter value greater than or equal to π's. Finally, π is <u>globally performed</u> if the corresponding read or write operation is globally performed in α_{rc}.

Each **MemoryRead** event in $f_e(\alpha_{rc})$ is naturally said to <u>read from</u> a particular **MemoryWrite** event as follows. If the **MemoryRead** corresponds to a **ReadView**$_i(t, a, d)$ event in α_{rc}, the corresponding **MemoryWrite** has the (necessarily finite) counter value in ProcView$_i[a]$ when the **ReadView**$_i$ event occurs. If the **MemoryRead** corresponds to a **ReadBuffer**$_i(t, a, d)$ event in α_{rc}, the corresponding **MemoryWrite** is the preceding **MemoryWrite**$_i$ in σ_i. If the **MemoryRead** corresponds to a **ServiceRead**$_i(O, a, d)$ event in α_{rc}, then if the counter value in ProcView$_i[a]$ when the **ServiceRead**$_i$ event occurs is finite, the corresponding **MemoryWrite** has that value, and if the value is infinite, the corresponding **MemoryWrite** is the next previous **MemoryWrite** to a in σ_i.

Critical events. As we will see, the key actions of M_{rc} that determine the serialization order are the nonordinary **ServiceWrite** actions and those **ReadView** actions that read from non-ordinary writes by other processors. The "analogs" of these actions in the serialization are the non-ordinary **MemoryWrite**'s, and non-ordinary **MemoryRead**'s for which corresponding **ReadView** events occur in α_{rc}, and which read from non-ordinary writes by other processors. Call occurrences of these latter actions in $f_e(\alpha_{rc})$ <u>critical events</u>. The serializations of the events in $f_e(\alpha_{rc})$ are obtained by first serializing the critical events in $f_e(\alpha_{rc})$.

The performed before order. We can define a "performs before" relation on the critical **MemoryWrite** events, as follows: If π and ϕ are critical **MemoryWrite** events in $f_e(\alpha_{rc})$, we say that π is <u>performed before</u> ϕ if both are globally performed, in that order, or if π is globally performed and ϕ is not, in α_{rc}. Since being performed is stable, performed-before partially orders the globally performed, critical **MemoryWrite** events in $f_e(\alpha_{rc})$.

Note that several **MemoryWrite** events may be globally performed simultaneously: a **ServiceWrite**(t, a, d) event can overwrite an earlier value in Mem$[a]$ that has yet to be entered in some ToPerform$[a]$ set. In addi-

tion, the counter value it stores in ProcView$_i[a]$ will dominate any currently in ToPerform$_i[a]$. Hence, the sequence of finite counter values occurring at a ProcView$[a]$ entry may not be consecutive numbers. But since only one entry of any ProcView$_i$ array is changed in any single step of M_{rc}, two **MemoryWrite** events for *different* locations cannot globally perform simultaneously.

The serviced-by-address before order. However, the different critical **MemoryWrite** events to the same address can be ordered by their associated address counter values. If π and ϕ are critical events to the same address in $f_e(\alpha_{rc})$, we say that π is <u>serviced-by-address before</u> ϕ if both are serviced, in that order, or if π is serviced and ϕ is not, in α_{rc}. Note that this relation totally orders the critical, serviced accesses to each address.

The requested-by-processor before order. Next, the critical events by the same processor can be ordered according to the order of the associated requests in α_{rc}. That is, if π and ϕ are critical events in $f_e(\alpha_{rc})$ by the same processor, we say that π is <u>requested-by-processor before</u> ϕ if the **Request** for π occurs before the **Request** for ϕ in α_{rc}. This relation totally orders the critical events by each processor.

Ordering reads before writes. In the full paper, the transitive closure of the performed-before, serviced-by-address, requested-by-processor and reads-from partial orders on the critical events in $f_e(\alpha_{rc})$ is proven to be an acyclic relation on the critical events in $f_e(\alpha_{rc})$. Define $f_w(\alpha_{rc})$ to be the set of total orders on critical events in $f_e(\alpha_{rc})$ that extend this relation. Note that these sequences order each critical **MemoryRead** after the **MemoryWrite** from which it reads but do not ensure that the **MemoryRead** precedes other critical **MemoryWrite** events to the same address.

Accordingly, each total order $<^w_{\alpha_{rc}} \in f_w(\alpha_{rc})$ is used to assign sequence numbers to the critical events in $f_e(\alpha_{rc})$. First, assign to each critical **MemoryWrite** event in $f_e(\alpha_{rc})$ its index in the order $<^w_{\alpha_{rc}}$. For each processor i, sequence numbers are assigned to the critical **MemoryRead** events at i inductively on their order in σ_i. Let π be a critical **MemoryRead** event at i. Assign π the maximum of the set containing the sequence numbers of it's predecessor at i (if one exists) and of the critical **MemoryWrite** from which it reads.

These sequence numbers are used to define a relation $<^{rw}_{\alpha_{rc}}$ on the critical events in $f_e(\alpha_{rc})$, containing the pairs (π, ϕ) such that:

- π and ϕ are **MemoryWrite** events and $\pi <^w_{\alpha_{rc}} \phi$,

- π precedes ϕ at the same processor,

- π is assigned a lower sequence number than ϕ

- π and ϕ have the same sequence number, π is a **MemoryWrite** event and ϕ is a **MemoryRead** event.

The relation $<_{\alpha_{rc}}^{rw}$ serializes the **MemoryWrite** events in the same order as $<_{\alpha_{rc}}^{w}$, and orders the **MemoryRead** events "as soon as possible".

Lemma 5 *Let α_{rc} be an execution of M_{rc}, and let $<_{\alpha_{rc}}^{w} \in f_w(\alpha_{rc})$. Then $<_{\alpha_{rc}}^{rw}$ is acyclic.*

Blocks. The critical events in $f_e(\alpha_{rc})$ are now used to divide each σ_i into consecutive subsequences, called <u>blocks</u>, so that each critical event at i begins a new block, and blocks end just before the next critical event. (The first block does not contain a critical event.)

Each $<_{\alpha_{rc}}^{w} \in f_w(\alpha_{rc})$ is used to construct a relation $<_{\alpha_{rc}}^{bw}$ on blocks, using $<_{\alpha_{rc}}^{rw}$. That is, for two blocks B_1 and B_2, $B_1 <_{\alpha_{rc}}^{bw} B_2$ precisely if B_1 is the first block at some processor and B_2 is not the first block at any processor, or both have critical events, π_1 and π_2, respectively, and $\pi_1 <_{\alpha_{rc}}^{rw} \pi_2$.

The sequences in $f(\alpha_{rc})$. By Lemma 5, each relation $<_{\alpha_{rc}}^{bw}$ is acyclic, and the linear extensions of $<_{\alpha_{rc}}^{bw}$ are used to define the serializations of α_{rc}. That is, the sequences in $f(\alpha_{rc})$ are precisely those that can be obtained by concatenating the blocks in a linear order consistent with some $<_{\alpha_{rc}}^{bw}$.

In the full paper, an inductive argument demonstrates that each such element σ of $f(\alpha_{rc})$ is a serialization of α_{rc}; that is, σ is a schedule of M_s driven by P, and $\mathrm{beh}(\alpha_{rc})|i = \mathrm{beh}(\sigma)|i$, for all processors i.

3.3.2 The induction

Theorem 1 *Let α_{rc} be a finite schedule of M_{rc} driven by a PL_{br} program P.*

1. *Every $\sigma \in f(\alpha_{rc})$ is a schedule of M_s driven by P, and $\mathrm{beh}(\alpha_{rc})|i = \mathrm{beh}(\sigma)|i$, for all processors i.*

2. *If $\mathbf{MemoryWrite}_i <_{\sigma}^{DC} \mathbf{MemoryRead}_j$, for $\sigma \in f(\alpha_{rc})$, then $\mathbf{MemoryRead}_j$ reads from $\mathbf{MemoryWrite}_i$ in α_{rc}.*

Proof sketch. Note first that the condition $\mathrm{beh}(\alpha_{rc})|i = \mathrm{beh}(\sigma)|i$, for all processors i, is an easy consequence of the construction of f.

The proof of the theorem is an induction on the prefixes $\alpha\pi$ of α_{rc}, where π is a single event. The proof examines cases based on the different actions of M_{rc} of which π is an occurrence.

The argument shows that the counters and waiting conditions in M_{rc} allow the critical accesses to be serialized consistently with respect to each other.

Inductive appeal to invariant 1 allows us to apply the PL condition to argue that appropriate causal chains

connect other pairs of events in the serialization σ' of α'. Invariant 2 is used to argue that corresponding sequences of events exist in α_{rc}, which in turn imply appropriate orderings in σ. $\square$

4 The DASH implementation

The full paper [GMG91] gives a formal description of a memory system, M_{dash}, that appears to be M_s when driven by a PL_{br} program. The memory system is suitable for scalable shared-memory multiprocessors, and forms the basis of the Stanford DASH machine. The DASH protocol is an invalidation-based coherence protocol using a distributed "directory" data structure to hold information on the state of the caches [LLG$^+$90].

Theorem 2 *If σ_{dash} is a finite schedule of M_{dash} driven by an arbitrary program P, then there exists a schedule σ_{rc} of M_{rc} driven by P with an identical behavior.*

The proof appears in the full paper. Note that the behavior of the two schedules is identical. Thus the proof is simplified since we need not reason about reorderings of external events; the desired result (involving reorderings) can be obtained by applying Theorem 1:

Corollary 1 *M_{dash} provides a sequentially consistent memory when driven by a PL_{br} program.*

5 Discussion

5.1 Previous work

This paper presents a formal framework for relating restricted classes of programs and corresponding efficient memory implementations, focusing on the release consistency model of [GLL$^+$90]. In doing so, it generalizes the class of programs and implementations in [AH90b] and [DSB86], and makes explicit the architectural assumptions implicit in all of these papers.

The DRF0 consistency model defined by Adve and Hill [AH90b] differs from the release consistency model in the following two respects. First, DRF0 consistency does not distinguish between acquires, releases, and nsyncs: all non-ordinary accesses are considered syncs. Thus the performance gains obtained by the finer classification in release consistency are lost in DRF0 consistency [GGH91]. Second, PL_{br} programs are defined by the existence of a release separating any two PL-conflicting accesses in any execution on M_s. DRF0 programs are defined in terms of the existence of a synchronization chain ordering any two conflicting accesses in any execution on an "idealized" memory system. However, since this idealized memory system can be formalized as M_s, Lemma 3 shows that these two definitions are equivalent (ignoring nsyncs and non-blocking reads). This equivalence holds as well for the more general PL condition (i.e. when reads are non-blocking), which requires that any two PL-conflicting accesses be separated by both a release and an acquire. In other words, the existence of a release (and an acquire, in the general case) separating two PL-conflicting accesses in any execution implies the existence of a synchronization chain, which in turn must begin with a release (and end with an acquire).

A more minor point distinguishes this paper and [AH90b]—the definition of sequential consistency in [AH90b] places conditions on the final state of the memory. So stated, sequential consistency is not an interface property, as it assumes there is a component of the implementation that can be naturally referred to as the "memory". Following [ABM89], we consider that the memory can only be observed by reading it, and so this condition is unnecessary. Sequential consistency is stated as a pure interface property, with no assumptions about the implementation.

The model used here was introduced in [ABM89], where it was used to study memory systems in isolation, placing no restrictions on the programs.

Another approach based on compilers is taken in [SS88]. Parallel programs are subjected to off-line analysis, to determine the specific dependences between memory accesses. These are used to specify delays between specific pairs of events at the same processor, so that one must be globally performed before the other is requested. For general programs, determining exact dependences is undecidable, and these relations must be approximated. The distinction between sync, nsync and ordinary can be viewed as a programmer-specified approximation, supplementing or replacing the compiler's limited ability to compute delay relations.

5.2 Future work

There are many opportunities for interesting extensions of this work:

An obvious weakness of our proof framework is the assumption that reads are blocking. This restriction does not appear in existing consistency models such as release consistency, and limits the performance advantage of weakly consistent memories over sequentially consistent ones. We are exploring extensions which permit a read to return before it is performed, just as a write does. In this way, both reads and writes can be pipelined in an implementation.

The release consistency conditions imposed in M_{rc} are slightly weaker than those embodied in the DASH multiprocessor; for example, there is no precise analog to the non-ordinary **ReadBuffer** actions of M_{rc} in DASH. These distinctions represent possible extensions to the DASH algorithm which should be examined for potential performance gains.

A good test of the framework would be to carry out a

careful correctness proof of an implementation of different relaxed consistency conditions, such as the implementation of DRF0 consistency described in [AH90b].

Perhaps the most interesting opportunities are in exploring the interplay of the automaton M_{base} and classes of parallel programs. Are there alternative restrictions of M_{base} that support sequential consistency for other natural classes of parallel programs? In another direction, can M_{base} be used to explore potential shared memory semantics that are strictly weaker than sequential consistency, such as processor consistency [Goo89], slow memories [HA90], or Lipton and Sandberg's PRAM model [LS88]?

5.3 Implications for release consistent memories

Relaxed consistency models are designed to strike a balance between performance and programmer ease, admitting efficient implementations for a useful class of programs. This paper presents a framework for formal specification and proof of consistency algorithms, including what we believe are useful intermediate abstractions, M_{base} and M_{rc}. In the case of release consistency, this fills in the details missing from our initial paper [GLL$^+$90] by providing:

1. A formal specification of a release consistent memory.
2. A rigorous proof that RC + PL = SC, i.e. that a release consistent memory driven by a PL$_{br}$ program is sequentially consistent.
3. A proof that the memory system of a particular multiprocessor supports RC.

In [GG91], we fill in the last piece needed to make this a viable framework, that can be used in practice with confidence. Namely, we present a new implementation of release consistency such that, for each of its executions, it either signals that a PL violation has occurred or signals that the execution's behavior is sequentially consistent. Moreover, it does not make any errors. Thus a programmer gets exact information about whether or not the hardware has provided a sequentially consistent memory for each run of the program. This partly relieves the programmer of the burden of guaranteeing that a program is PL.

Acknowledgements

The authors thank Sarita Adve and Dan Lenoski for their helpful comments on this paper.

References

[ABM89] Y. Afek, G. M. Brown, and M. Merritt. A lazy cache algorithm. In *1989 ACM Sym-*

posium on Parallel Architectures and Algorithms, pages 209–222, June 1989.

[AH90a] S. V. Adve and M. D. Hill. Implementing sequential consistency in cache-based systems. In *1990 International Conference on Parallel Processing*, pages I47–I50, August 1990.

[AH90b] S. V. Adve and M. D. Hill. Weak ordering - a new definition. In *17th Annual International Symposium on Computer Architecture*, pages 2–14, May 1990.

[AL88] M. Abadi and L. Lamport. The existence of refinement mappings. In *Third Annual Symposium on Logic in Computer Science*, pages 165–175, July 1988. Also available as a Digital Systems Research Center technical report.

[DS90] M. Dubois and C. Scheurich. Memory access dependencies in shared-memory multiprocessors. *IEEE Transactions on Software Engineering*, 16(6):660–673, June 1990.

[DSB86] M. Dubois, C. Scheurich, and F. Briggs. Memory access buffering in multiprocessors. In *13th Annual International Symposium on Computer Architecture*, pages 434–442, June 1986.

[GG91] K. Gharachorloo and P. B. Gibbons. Detecting violations of sequential consistency. In *3rd Annual ACM Symposium on Parallel Algorithms and Architectures*, July 1991.

[GGH91] K. Gharachorloo, A. Gupta, and J. Hennessy. Performance evaluation of memory consistency models for shared-memory multiprocessors. In *Fourth International Conference on Architectural Support for Programming Languages and Operating Systems*, pages 245–257, April 1991.

[GLL$^+$90] K. Gharachorloo, D. Lenoski, J. Laudon, P. Gibbons, A. Gupta, and J. Hennessy. Memory consistency and event ordering in scalable shared-memory multiprocessors. In *17th Annual International Symposium on Computer Architecture*, pages 15–26, May 1990.

[GMG91] P. B. Gibbons, M. Merritt, and K. Gharachorloo. Proving sequential consistency of high-performance shared memories. Technical report, AT&T Bell Laboratories, May 1991. Full version.

[Goo89] J. R. Goodman. Cache consistency and sequential consistency. Technical report no. 61, SCI Committee, March 1989.

[HA90] P. Hutto and M. Ahamad. Slow memory: Weakening consistency to enhance concurrency in distributed memories. In *10th Annual International Conference on Distributed Computing Systems*, pages 302–309. IEEE Computer Society Press, 1990.

[HW87] M. P. Herlihy and J. M. Wing. Axioms for concurrent objects. In *14th Annual ACM Symposium on Principles of Programming Languages*, pages 13–25, January 1987.

[Lam79] Leslie Lamport. How to make a multiprocessor that correctly executes multiprocess programs. *IEEE Transactions on Computers*, C-28:690–691, 1979.

[LLG$^+$90] D. Lenoski, J. Laudon, K. Gharachorloo, A. Gupta, and J. Hennessy. The directory-based cache coherence protocol for the DASH multiprocessor. In *17th Annual International Symposium on Computer Architecture*, pages 148–159, May 1990.

[LS88] R. Lipton and J. Sandberg. Pram: A scalable shared memory. Technical Report CS-TR-180-88, Princeton University, September 1988.

[LT87] N. Lynch and M. Tuttle. Hierarchical correctness proofs for distributed algorithms. In *6th Annual ACM Symposium on Principles of Distributed Computation*, pages 137–151, August 1987. Expanded version available as MIT technical report number MIT/LCS/TM-387.

[Lyn88] N. Lynch. I/O automata: A model for discrete event systems. In *22nd Annual Conference on Information Science and Systems*. Princeton University, March 1988. Also MIT technical report number MIT/LCS/TM-351.

[Mer90] M. Merritt. Completeness theorems for automata. In J. W. de Bakker, W.-P. de Roever, and G. Rozenberg, editors, *Stepwise Refinement of Distributed Systems*. Springer-Verlag, 1990. Lecture Notes in Computer Science, Vol. 430, Proceedings of the REX Workshop, Mook, The Netherlands, May/June 1989.

[Mil80] R. Milner. *A Calculus of Communicating Systems*. Springer Verlag, 1980. Lecture Notes in Computer Science 92.

[SS88] D. Shasha and M. Snir. Efficient and correct execution of parallel programs that share memory. *Transaction on Programming Languages and Systems*, 10(2):282–312, 1988.

Sequential Consistency versus Linearizability

(EXTENDED ABSTRACT)

Hagit Attiya[*]
Department of Computer Science
The Technion
Haifa 32000, Israel

Jennifer L. Welch[†]
Department of Computer Science
University of North Carolina
Chapel Hill, NC 27599-3175

Abstract

The power of two well-known consistency conditions for shared memory multiprocessors, *sequential consistency* and *linearizability*, is compared. The cost measure studied is the worst-case response time in distributed implementations of virtual shared memory supporting one of the two conditions. The memory is assumed to consist of read/write objects. The worst-case response time is very sensitive to the assumptions that are made about the timing information available to the system. All the results in this paper assume that processes have clocks that run at the same rate as real time and that all message delays are in the range $[d - u, d]$ for some known constants u and d, $0 \leq u \leq d$. If processes have perfectly synchronized clocks or if every message has delay exactly d, then there are linearizable implementations in which one operation (either read or write) is performed instantaneously and the response time of the other operation is d. These upper bounds match exactly

*Email: hagit@cs.technion.ac.il. Part of this work was performed while the author was at the Laboratory for Computer Science, MIT, supported by ONR contract N00014-85-K-0168, by NSF grants CCR-8611442 and CCR-8915206, and by DARPA contracts N00014-89-J-1988 and N00014-87-K-0825.

†Email: welch@cs.unc.edu. The work of this author was supported in part by NSF grant CCR-9010730 and an IBM Faculty Development Award.

a lower bound for sequential consistency, proved by Lipton and Sandberg, on the sum of the response times of read and write operations. If clocks are not perfectly synchronized and if message delays are variable, i.e., $u > 0$, then such a tradeoff cannot be achieved by linearizable implementations: the response time for both read and write operations is at least $\Omega(u)$. In contrast, we present sequentially consistent implementations for this weaker timing model in which one operation (either read or write) is performed instantaneously, and the worst-case response time of the other operation is $O(d)$.

1 Introduction

A fundamental problem in concurrent computing is how to provide programmers with a useful model of logically shared data that can be accessed atomically, without sacrificing performance. The model must specify how the data can be accessed and what guarantees are provided about the results. Shared memory is an attractive paradigm for communication among computing entities because it is familiar from the uniprocessor case, it can be considered more high level than message passing, and many of the classical solutions for synchronization problems were developed for shared memory (e.g., mutual exclusion [13]).

This problem arises in many situations at different levels of abstraction. These situations include implementing a single shared variable out of weaker shared variables, cache coherence, building multiprocessors (with both physical and distributed shared memory), and high-level applications for loosely-coupled distributed systems such as distributed file systems and transaction systems.

To enhance performance (e.g., response time, availability, or fault-tolerance), many implementations employ multiple copies of the same logical piece of shared data (*caching*). Also, multiple user programs must be able to execute "concurrently," either with interleaved steps, or truly in parallel. More complications arise because at some level, each access to shared data has duration in time, from its start to its end; it is not instantaneous.

Thus, the illusion of atomic operations on single copies of objects must be supported by a *consistency mechanism*. The consistency mechanism guarantees that although operations may be executed concurrently on various copies and have some duration, they will *appear* to have executed atomically, in some sequential order that is consistent with the order seen at individual processes.[1] When this order must preserve the global (external) ordering of non-overlapping operations, this consistency guarantee is called *linearizability* ([18]);[2] otherwise, the guarantee is called *sequential consistency* ([20]). Obviously, linearizability implies sequential consistency.

Sequential consistency and linearizability are probably the two best-known consistency conditions. As the definitions of these two conditions are similar, it is important to study the relationships between them. In this paper we present a quantitative comparison of the cost to implement sequential consistency and linearizability in a non-bused distributed system. Distributed implementations are of great interest because of their ability to scale up in size. The comparison is based on time complexity — the inherent response time of the best possible distributed implementation supporting each consistency condition. That is, we present upper and lower bounds on the worst-case response time for performing an operation on an object. We concentrate on read/write objects.

We consider a collection of application programs running concurrently and communicating via virtual shared memory. The shared memory consists of a collection of *read/write objects*. The application programs are running in a distributed system consisting of a collection of nodes and a complete communication network.[3] The shared memory abstraction is implemented by a *memory consistency system* (mcs), which uses local memory at the various nodes and some protocol executed by the mcs processes (one at each node). (Nodes that are dedicated storage are modeled by nullifying the application process.) Fig. 1 illustrates a node, on which is running an application process and an mcs process. The application process sends calls to access shared data to the mcs process; the mcs process returns the responses to the application process, possibly based on messages exchanged with mcs processes on other nodes.

The correctness conditions are defined at the interface between the application processes (written by the user) and the mcs processes (supplied by the system). Thus, the mcs must provide the proper semantics when the values of the responses to calls are considered, throughout the network.

It turns out that timing information available in the model has a crucial impact on the time complexity of implementing sequential consistency and linearizability. We assume that on each node there is a real-time clock readable by the mcs process at that node, that runs at the same rate as real-time. We assume that every message incurs a delay in the interval $[d - u, d]$, for some known constants u and d, $0 \le u \le d$ (u stands for *uncertainty*). If $u = 0$, then the message delays are constant.

If processes have perfectly synchronized clocks and the message delays are constant, we show that the sum of the worst-case response times for a read operation and a write operation is at least d. The result is proved for sequential consistency, and thus, holds also for linearizability. (This formalizes and strengthens a result of Lipton and Sandberg [23].) We then show that this tradeoff is tight—it is possible to have the response time of *only one* of the operations depend on the network's latency. Specifically, we present an algorithm in which a read operation is performed instantaneously (locally), while a write operation returns within time d; we also present an algorithm in which the roles are reversed. These algorithms achieve linearizability, and hence, sequential consistency. (This upper bound indicates that separating sequential consistency from linearizability is not as obvious as it may seem.)

---

[1] This condition is similar in flavor to the notion of *serializability* from database theory ([7, 27]); however, serializability applies to *transactions* which aggregate many operations.

[2] Also called *atomicity* ([17, 21, 26]) in the case of read/write objects.

[3] The assumption of a complete communication network can be omitted and is made here only for clarity of presentation.

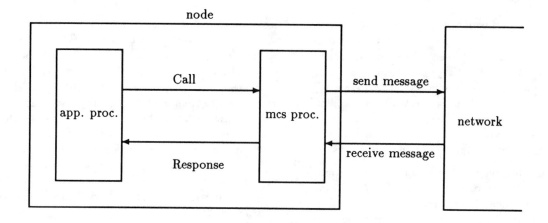

Figure 1: System Architecture

We then turn to the more realistic case of approximately synchronized clocks and uncertain message delays. We show that if linearizability is desired, neither operation can be performed instantaneously, regardless of the response time for the other operation. Specifically, we show that the worst-case response time of a read operation must be at least $u/4$ and the worst-case response time of a write operation must be at least $u/2$. (Note that u can be as big as d.) In contrast, we present sequentially consistent implementations of read/write objects in which one operation (either read or write) is performed instantaneously (locally), and the response time of the other operation is $O(d)$. Thus, sequential consistency admits significantly more efficient implementations than linearizability, when there are significantly more operations of one type and under certain timing assumptions.

Our proofs make use of techniques from the theory of distributed systems: The lower bounds for implementations of linearizable objects are proved using *shifting* arguments, originally used in [24] for clock synchronization problems. Our efficient implementations of sequential consistency use *timestamps* in a way that was inspired by the *atomic broadcast* algorithm of [9].

Several papers have proposed sequentially consistent implementations of read/write objects, which were claimed to achieve a higher degree of concurrency (e.g., [2, 3, 6, 10, 14, 25, 29]). In particular, Afek, Brown, and Merritt ([3]) present a sequentially consistent implementation of read/write objects, for systems where processes communicate via a bus. A bus enforces global ordering on all messages delivered to the processes; such a prop-

erty is not provided in a communication network. None of these papers provides an analysis of the response time of the implementations suggested (or any other complexity measure). Furthermore, none of these papers proves that similar improvements cannot be achieved for linearizability. To the best of our knowledge, this is the first time such a result is shown.

This paper addresses a simplification of the problem of memory coherence in loosely-coupled multiprocessors ([6, 10, 8, 14, 22, 25, 28, 29]). Our formal model ignores several important practical issues, e.g., limitations on the size of local memory storage, network topology, clock drift and "hot-spots". Since our lower bounds are proved in a very strong model, they clearly hold for more practical systems. We believe our algorithms can be adapted to work in more realistic systems.

2 Correctness Conditions

We begin with an informal description of the system model. A memory consistency system (mcs) consists of a collection of processes, one on each node of a distributed system.

Process p interacts with the application program using *call* events $\text{Read}_p(X)$ and $\text{Write}_p(X, v)$ for all objects X and value v, and *response* events $\text{Return}_p(X, v)$ (for Read) and $\text{Ack}_p(X)$ (for Write). It communicates with other processes using *message-send* and *message-receive* events. It sets timers for itself (to go off at some future clock time) and responds to them using *timer-set* and *timer* events. The process is modeled as an automaton with states and a transition function that takes as input the current state, clock time, and a call or message-receive or timer event, and produces a new state, a set of response events, a set of message-send events, and a set of timer-set events. A *history* of a process describes what steps (i.e., applications of the transition function) the process takes at what real times; it must satisfy certain natural "consistency" conditions.

An *execution* of a set of processes is a set of histories, one for each process, satisfying the following two conditions: (1) A timer is received by p at clock time T if and only if p has previously set a timer for T. (2) There is a one-to-one correspondence between the messages sent by p to q and the messages received by q from p, for any processes p and q. We use the message correspondence to define the *delay* of any message in an execution to be the real time of receipt minus the real time of sending. (The network is not explicitly modeled, although the constraints on executions imply that the network reliably delivers all messages sent.) An execution is *admissible* if the delay of every message is in the range $[d - u, d]$, for fixed nonnegative integers d and u, $u \leq d$, and for every p, at any time at most one call at p is *pending* (i.e., lacking a matching subsequent response).

Every object is assumed to have a *serial specification* (cf. [18]) defining a set of *operations*, which are ordered pairs of call and response events, and a set of operation sequences, which are the allowable sequences of operations on that object. In the case of a read/write object, the ordered pair of events $[\text{Read}_p(X), \text{Return}_p(X, v)]$ forms an *operation* for any p, X, and v, as does $[\text{Write}_p(X, v), \text{Ack}_p(X)]$. The set of operation sequences consists of all sequences in which every read operation returns the value of the latest preceding write operation (the usual read/write semantics). A sequence τ of operations for a collection of processes and objects is *legal* if, for each object X, the restriction of τ to operations of X is in the serial specification of X. Given an execution σ, let $ops(\sigma)$ be the sequence of call and response events appearing in σ in real-time order, breaking ties by ordering all response events before any call event and then using process ids.

Our formal definitions of sequential consistency and linearizability follow. These definitions imply that every call gets an eventual response and that calls and responses alternate at each process.

Definition 2.1 (Sequential consistency) *An execution σ is sequentially consistent if there exists a legal sequence τ of operations such that, for each process p, the restriction of $ops(\sigma)$ to operations of p is equal to the restriction of τ to operations of p.*

Definition 2.2 (Linearizability) *An execution σ is linearizable if there exists a legal sequence τ of operations such that, for each process p, the restriction of $ops(\sigma)$ to operations of p is equal to the restriction of τ to operations of p, and furthermore, whenever the response for operation op_1 precedes the call for operation op_2 in $ops(\sigma)$, then op_1 precedes op_2 in τ.*

An mcs is a *sequentially consistent* implementation of a set of objects if any admissible execution of the mcs is sequentially consistent; similarly, an mcs is a *linearizable* implementation of a set of objects if any admissible execution of the mcs is sequentially consistent.

We measure the efficiency of an implementation by the worst-case response time for any operation on the object. Given a particular mcs and a read/write object X implemented by it, we denote by $|W(X)|$ the maximum time taken by a write operation on X and by $|R(X)|$ the maximum time taken by a read operation on X, in any admissible execution. Denote by $|W|$ the maximum of $|W(X)|$, and by $|R|$ the maximum of $|R(X)|$, over all objects X implemented by the mcs.

3 Perfect Clocks

We start by considering the case in which processes have perfectly synchronized (*perfect*) clocks and message delay is constant and known.[4] We first show that the sum of the worst-case response times of read and write operations is at least d, even in this strong model, and even under sequential consistency. This is a formalization of a result of Lipton and Sandberg ([23]) making precise the timing assumptions made on the system. We then show that the lower bound is tight for this model by describing two algorithms that match the lower bound exactly: In the first algorithm, reads are performed instantaneously, while the worst-case response time

---

[4] We remark that the assumptions that processes have perfect clocks and that message delays are constant (and known) are equivalent.

for a write is d. In the second algorithm, writes are performed instantaneously, while the worst-case response time for a read is d. The algorithms actually implement linearizability, which is a stronger condition than sequential consistency.

3.1 Lower Bound for Sequential Consistency

We start with a formal proof of a theorem presented in [23, Theorem 1]. We show that the result holds even in highly synchronous systems, in which processes have perfect clocks and message delays are constant and known. Perfect clocks are modeled by letting $C_p(t) = t$ for all p. The constant message delay is modeled by letting $u = 0$; d is known (and can be used by the mcs).

Theorem 3.1 (Lipton and Sandberg) *For any memory-consistency system that is a sequentially consistent implementation of two read/write objects X and Y, $|W| + |R| \geq d$.*

Proof: Let p and q be two processes that access X and Y. We prove that either $|W(X)| + |R(Y)| \geq d$ or $|W(Y)| + |R(X)| \geq d$. Assume by way of contradiction that there exists a sequentially consistent implementation of X and Y for which both $|W(X)| + |R(Y)| < d$ and $|W(Y)| + |R(X)| < d$. Without loss of generality, assume that 0 is the initial value of both X and Y.

By the specification of Y, there is some admissible execution α_1 such that $ops(\alpha_1)$ is

$$\text{Write}_p(X, 1)\ \text{Ack}_p(X)\ \text{Read}_p(Y)\ \text{Return}_p(Y, 0)$$

and $\text{Write}_p(X, 1)$ occurs at real time 0 and $\text{Read}_p(Y)$ occurs immediately after $\text{Ack}_p(X)$. By assumption, the real time at the end of α_1 is less than d. Thus no message is received at any node during α_1.

By the specification of X, there is some admissible execution α_2 such that $ops(\alpha_2)$ is

$$\text{Write}_q(Y, 1)\ \text{Ack}_q(Y)\ \text{Read}_q(X)\ \text{Return}_q(X, 0)$$

and $\text{Write}_q(Y, 1)$ occurs at real time 0 and $\text{Read}_q(X)$ occurs immediately after $\text{Ack}_q(Y)$. By assumption, the real time at the end of α_2 is less

than d. Thus no message is received at any node during α_2.

Since no message is ever received in α_1 and α_2, the execution α obtained from α_1 by replacing q's history with q's history in α_2 is admissible. Then $ops(\alpha)$ consists of the operations $[\text{Write}_p(X, 1), \text{Ack}_p(X)]$ followed by $[\text{Read}_p(Y), \text{Return}_p(Y, 0)]$, and $[\text{Write}_q(Y, 1), \text{Ack}_q(Y)]$ followed by $[\text{Read}_q(X), \text{Return}_q(X, 0)]$.

By assumption, α is sequentially consistent. Thus there is a legal operation sequence τ consisting of the operations $[\text{Write}_p(X, 1), \text{Ack}_p(X)]$ followed by $[\text{Read}_p(Y), \text{Return}_p(Y, 0)]$, and $[\text{Write}_q(Y, 1), \text{Ack}_q(Y)]$ followed by $[\text{Read}_q(X), \text{Return}_q(X, 0)]$. Since τ is a sequence of operations, either the read of X follows the write of X, or the read of Y follows the write of Y. But each possibility violates the serial specification of either X or Y, contradicting τ being legal. ∎

3.2 Upper Bounds for Linearizability

In this section we show that the tradeoff indicated by Theorem 3.1 is inherent, and that a sequentially consistent implementation may choose which operation to slow down. More precisely, we present an algorithm in which a read operation is instantaneous (local) while a write operation returns within time d; we also present an algorithm in which the roles are reversed. These algorithms actually ensure the stronger condition of linearizability. They assume that clocks are perfect and message delays are constant.

Informally, the algorithm for fast reads and slow writes works as follows. Each process keeps a copy of all objects in its local memory. When a $\text{Read}_p(X)$ occurs, p reads the value v of X in its local memory and immediately does a $\text{Return}_p(X, v)$. When a $\text{Write}_p(X, v)$ occurs, p sends "write(X, v)" messages to all other processes. Then p waits d time units, after which it changes the value of X to v in its local memory and does an $\text{Ack}_p(X)$. Whenever a process receives a "write(X, v)" message, it changes the value of X to v in its local memory. (If it receives several at the same time, it "breaks ties" using sender ids, that is, it writes the value in the message from the process with the largest id and ignores the rest of the messages.) Clearly the time for every read is 0 and the time for every write is d, and $|W| + |R| = d$.

308

Theorem 3.2 *The algorithm just described implements linearizability.*

The proof, which is omitted from this extended abstract, proceeds by explicitly constructing, for every admissible execution, a legal operation sequence satisfying the necessary conditions. In creating the operation sequence, each operation in the execution is serialized to occur at the time of its response.

The algorithm for slow reads and fast writes is similar to the previous one. Each process keeps a copy of all objects in its local memory. When a $\text{Read}_p(X)$ occurs, p waits d time units, after which it reads the value v of X in its local memory and immediately does a $\text{Return}_p(X, v)$. When a $\text{Write}_p(X, v)$ occurs, p sends "write(X, v)" messages to all other processes (including a dummy message to itself which is delayed d time units) and does an Ack immediately. Whenever a process receives a "write(X, v)" message, it changes the value of X to v in its local memory. Ties are resolved as in the previous algorithm. Clearly the time for every read is d and the time for every write is 0, and $|W| + |R| = d$.

Theorem 3.3 *The algorithm just described implements linearizability.*

The proof is the same as the proof of Theorem 3.2 except that each operation is serialized to occur at the time it is called.

4 Imperfect Clocks

Obviously, the assumptions of the previous section are unrealistically strong. In this section we relax them, and assume a system in which clocks run at the same rate as real time but are not initially synchronized, and in which message delays are in the range $[d - u, d]$ for some $u > 0$.

Under these assumptions, the lower bound of Theorem 3.1 still holds, but the algorithms of Theorems 3.2 and 3.3 do not work. We start by showing that for linearizability this is not a coincidence—in any linearizable implementation of a read/write object the worst-case response time of *both* read and write operations must depend on u, the message delay uncertainty. We then show that this is not

the case for sequential consistency by presenting two algorithms, one in which reads are performed instantaneously while the worst-case response time for a write is $O(d)$, and another in which the roles are reversed. These algorithms match (within constant factors) the lower bound of Theorem 3.1.

4.1 Lower Bounds for Linearizability

We now show that, under reasonable assumptions about the pattern of sharing, in any linearizable implementation of an object, the worst-case time for a read is $u/4$ and the worst-case time for a write is $u/2$. The proofs of these lower bounds use the technique of *shifting*. Shifting is used to change the timing and the ordering of events in the system while preserving the local views of the processes. It was originally introduced in [24] to prove lower bounds on the precision achieved by clock synchronization algorithms. Here we describe the technique and its properties informally.

Given an execution with a certain set of clocks, if process p's history is changed so that the real times at which the events occur are shifted by some amount s and if p's clock is shifted by the same amount, then the result is another execution in which every process still "sees" the same events happening at the same real time. The intuition is that the changes in the real times at which events happen at p cannot be detected by p because its clock has changed by a corresponding amount. It is possible to quantify the resulting changes to message delays in the new execution: the delay of any message to p is s less, the delay of any message from p is s more, and the delay of any message not involving p has the same delay as in the original execution.

Theorem 4.1 *Assume X is a read/write object with at least two readers. Then any linearizable implementation of X must have $|R(X)| \geq \frac{u}{4}$.*

Proof: Let p and q be two processes that read X and r be a process that writes X. Assume in contradiction that there is an implementation with $|R(X)| < \frac{u}{4}$. Without loss of generality, assume that the initial value of X is 0. The idea of the proof is to consider an execution in which p reads 0 from X, then q and p alternate reading X while r writes 1 to X, and then q reads 1 from X. Thus there exists a read R_1, say by p, that returns 0

and is immediately followed by a read R_2 by q that returns 1. If q is shifted earlier by $u/2$, then in the resulting execution R_2 precedes R_1. Since R_2 returns the new value 1 and R_1 returns the old value 0, this contradicts linearizability.

Let $k = \lceil \frac{|W(X)|}{u} \rceil$. By the specification of X, there is an admissible execution α, in which all message delays are $d - \frac{u}{2}$, consisting of the following operations (see Fig. 2(a)):

- At time $\frac{u}{4}$, r does a $\text{Write}_r(X, 1)$.

- Between times $\frac{u}{4}$ and $(4k+1) \cdot \frac{u}{4}$, r does an $\text{Ack}_r(X)$. (By definition of k, $(4k+1) \cdot \frac{u}{4} \geq \frac{u}{4} + |W(X)|$, and thus r's write operation is guaranteed to finish in this interval.)

- At time $2i \cdot \frac{u}{4}$, p does a $\text{Read}_p(X)$, $0 \leq i \leq 2k$.

- Between times $2i \cdot \frac{u}{4}$ and $(2i+1) \cdot \frac{u}{4}$, p does a $\text{Return}_p(X, v_{2i})$, $0 \leq i \leq 2k$.

- At time $(2i+1) \cdot \frac{u}{4}$, q does a $\text{Read}_q(X)$, $0 \leq i \leq 2k$.

- Between times $(2i+1) \cdot \frac{u}{4}$ and $(2i+2) \cdot \frac{u}{4}$, q does a $\text{Return}_q(X, v_{2i+1})$, $0 \leq i \leq 2k$.

Thus in $ops(\alpha)$, p's read of v_0 precedes r's write, q's read of v_{4k+1} follows r's write, no two read operations overlap, and the order of the values read from X is $v_0, v_1, v_2, \ldots, v_{4k+1}$. By linearizability, $v_0 = 0$ and $v_{4k+1} = 1$. Thus there exists j, $0 \leq j \leq 4k$, such that $v_j = 0$ and $v_{j+1} = 1$. Without loss of generality, assume that j is even, so that v_j is the result of a read by p.

Define $\beta = \text{shift}(\alpha, q, \frac{u}{2})$. I.e., we shift q earlier by $\frac{u}{2}$. (See Fig. 2(b).) The result is admissible since the message delays to q become $d - u$, the message delays from q become d, and the remaining message delays are unchanged.

As a result of the shifting, we have reordered read operations with respect to each other at p and q. Specifically, in $ops(\beta)$, the order of the values read from X is $v_1, v_0, v_3, v_2, \ldots, v_{j+1}, v_j, \ldots$. Thus in β we now have $v_{j+1} = 1$ being read before $v_j = 0$, which violates linearizability. ∎

Theorem 4.2 *If X is a read/write object with at least two writers, then any linearizable implementation of X must have $|W(X)| \geq \frac{u}{2}$.*

The proof uses techniques similar to the proof of Theorem 4.1. It constructs an execution in which, if write operations are too short, linearizability can be violated by appropriately shifting histories.

The assumptions about the number of readers and writers made in Theorems 4.1 and 4.2 are crucial to the results, since it can be shown that the algorithms from Theorems 3.2 and 3.3 are correct if there is only one reader and one writer.

4.2 Upper Bounds for Sequential Consistency

Inspecting the algorithm for fast reads (Theorem 3.2) reveals that the key point of its correctness is the fact that write updates are handled by all processes in the same order and at the same time. In order to guarantee sequential consistency, it suffices for processes to update their local copies in the same order (not necessarily at the same time). A simple way to achieve this property is for a centralized controller to collect update messages and broadcast them. This idea can be developed into two algorithms, one in which each read operation is performed instantaneously and the response time for write is $O(d)$, and another where the roles are reversed. We now present algorithms that are fully distributed and do not rely on a centralized controller. These algorithms use atomic broadcast to guarantee that all messages are delivered at the same order at all processes. Our algorithms are inspired by the atomic broadcast algorithm of Birman and Joseph [9].[5]

We start with an informal description of the algorithm for fast reads (time 0) and slow writes (times at most $6d$). Each process keeps a local copy of every object, a counter, and a set of updates that it is waiting to make to its local copies. A read returns the value of the local copy immediately. When a write comes in to p, p requests "candidate" timestamps from all processes for this write. When a process q receives a request for a candidate timestamp, it increments its counter and sets the timestamp to be the pair (counter, id). q sends this timestamp to p and also keeps a copy of the update marked as unready. Once p receives candidate timestamps from everyone, it chooses the maximum as the final timestamp for that write and sends it to everyone.

---

[5] Birman and Joseph credit Skeen for the original idea, which is based on *two-phase commit*.

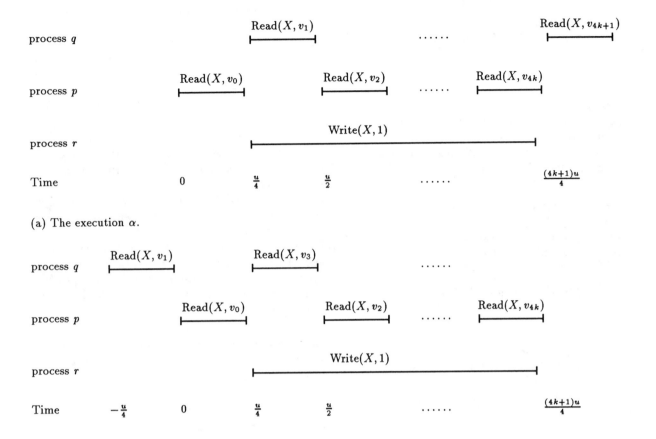

(a) The execution α.

(b) The execution β.

Figure 2: Executions used in the proof of Theorem 4.1.

p also sets a timer to go off $4d$ time later,[6] when it can be sure that every process has received the final timestamp and updated its local copy. When the timer goes off, p Acks the write. When q receives a final timestamp, it updates the timestamp for that write, marks it as ready, and sorts all the pending updates by timestamp. Then it does the updates in order of increasing timestamps until hitting an unready update. q also updates its counter to be at least as large as the counter in the final timestamp just received.

The algorithm uses the following data types:

timestamp — (integer, id) (break ties with processor ids);

write — record with fields:

---

[6]The algorithm can be made completely asynchronous by replacing the timer with explicit acknowledgements; this will increase the time complexity of a write to $7d$.

obj : name of an object (object to be written),
val : value of obj (value to be written),
uid : timestamp (unique id of this write request, assigned by initiator),
ts : timestamp (candidate or final),
ready : boolean (have final timestamp?),
cands : set of timestamp (candidate timestamps, only used by initiator).

The state of each process consists of the following variables:

count : integer, initially 0 (generates successive integers for creating timestamps);

updates : set of write, initially empty (set of updates waiting to be made to local copies);

pending-write : name of an object (write is pending on this object);

Read$_p(X)$:
  generate Return$_p(X, v)$,
    where v is the value of p's copy of X

Write$_p(X, v)$:
  count := count + 1
  pending-write := X
  add $(X, v, (\text{count}, p), (\text{count}, p), \text{false}, \{(\text{count}, p)\})$
    to updates
  send REQ-TS$(X, v, (\text{count}, p))$ to all processes
    (except self)

receive REQ-TS(X, v, u) from q:
  count := count + 1
  add $(X, v, u, (\text{count}, p), \text{false}, \emptyset)$ to updates
  send CAND-TS$(X, v, u, (\text{count}, p))$ to q

receive CAND-TS(X, v, u, T) from q:
  let E be the entry in updates with
    $E.\text{obj} = X$, $E.\text{val} = v$, and $E.\text{uid} = u$
  add T to $E.\text{cands}$
  if $|E.\text{cands}| = n$ then
    send MAX-TS$(X, v, u, \max(E.\text{cands}))$
      to all processes (including self)
    set timer for current time $+4d$
  endif

receive MAX-TS$(X, v, u, (i, r))$ from q:
  let E be the entry in updates with
    $E.\text{obj} = X$, $E.\text{val} = v$, and $E.\text{uid} = u$
  count := max(count,i)
  $E.\text{ts} := (i, r)$
  $E.\text{ready} := \text{true}$
  while E', element in updates with smallest ts,
    is ready do
      write $E'.\text{val}$ to local copy of $E'.\text{obj}$
      remove E' from updates
  endwhile

Timer$_p$:
  generate Ack$_p$(pending-write)

Figure 3: The transition function.

copy of every object X, initially equal to its initial
  value.

Each process also knows n, the total number of processes, and d, the maximum message delay. The
transition function of process p appears in Fig. 3.

We first sketch the proof. To show sequential
consistency, we must demonstrate, for any admissible execution σ, a sequential order for all operations
in σ such that the order at each process is preserved and each read returns the value of the latest
write. The operations are ordered by first ordering
all writes in final timestamp order, and then placing each read, say on object X at process p, after
the latest of (1) the previous operation for p, and
(2) the write that generated the latest update to p's
copy of X preceding the read's return. The resulting sequence respects the order at each process by
construction and because of the way timestamps
are assigned. Showing that the sequence satisfies
the specification of read-write objects depends on
two facts: (1) that updates are done at each process in final timestamp order, and (2) that if a read
operation follows a write operation at any process
p, then p reads its local copy for the read after it
updates its local copy for the write.

Lemma 4.3 *Let σ be any admissible execution of
the algorithm. Then every write operation in σ is
given a unique final timestamp.*

Lemma 4.4 *Let σ be any admissible execution of
the algorithm. Then the final timestamps assigned
to write operations in σ form a total order.*

Lemma 4.5 *Let σ be any admissible execution of
the algorithm. Then for any process p, p's local
copies of the objects take on all the values contained
in writes and the updates are done in timestamp
order.*

Proof: The final timestamp order of the writes
in σ is uniquely defined, by Lemmas 4.3 and 4.4.
Clearly every write is eventually assigned a final
timestamp, which is at least as large as all its candidate timestamps.

First we show that the update associated with
every write is made at every process. Consider
the set of writes whose updates are not made at
all processes; let W be the write in this set with
the smallest final timestamp and let p be a process where W's update is not made. Let t be the
time when p receives W's final timestamp. Since
p increments count to be at least as large as the
count in W's final timestamp, every write that is
added to p's updates set subsequently has a timestamp larger than W's. Let W' be any write in p's

updates set at time t whose timestamp is less than W's. If W' is not ready, then eventually it will be. If W'''s final timestamp is greater than W's, then it cannot block W's update at p. If W'''s final timestamp is less than W's, then by the choice of W, its update is eventually done at p, after which it does not block W's update at p. Thus eventually nothing prevents W's update from being made at p.

Now we show that at each process p, updates are made in final timestamp order. Suppose in contradiction that the final timestamp of write W_1 is less than the final timestamp of write W_2, but p performs W_2's update before W_1's. When p performs W_2's update, it cannot yet have an entry for W_1, because otherwise it would either block (if W_1 was not ready) or perform W_1's update before W_2's. But then p's candidate timestamp for W_1 would be greater than W_2's final timestamp, since p's count is increased when MAX-TS is received, implying that W_1's final timestamp is greater than W_2's. ■

Lemma 4.6 *Let σ be any admissible execution of the algorithm and p be any process. If W_1 precedes W_2 in $ops(\sigma)|p$[7], then the final timestamp of W_1 is less than the final timestamp of W_2.*

Lemma 4.7 *Let σ be any admissible execution of the algorithm and p be any process. If read R of object Y follows write W to object X in $ops(\sigma)|p$, then R's read of p's local copy of Y follows W's write of p's local copy of X.*

Theorem 4.8 *This algorithm ensures sequential consistency with $|R| = 0$ and $|W| = 6d$.*

Proof: (Sketch) Clearly the time for any read is 0. The time for any write is the time for the REQ-TS messages to be received, the subsequent CAND-TS messages to be received, and the $4d$ timeout to expire, which is at most $6d$.

We now show sequential consistency. Fix some admissible execution σ. We define a legal sequence of operations τ, such that for every process p, $ops(\sigma)|p = \tau|p$. In τ, we order the writes in σ by final timestamps. To insert the reads, we proceed in order from the beginning of σ. $[\text{Read}_p(X), \text{Return}_p(X, v)]$ goes immediately after the latest

of (1) the previous operation for p (either read or write, on any object), and (2) the write that spawned the latest update to p's local copy of X preceding the generation of the $\text{Return}_p(X, v)$. (Break ties using process ids.)

We must show $ops(\sigma)|p = \tau|p$ for all processes p. Two reads are ordered correctly by definition of τ. Two writes are ordered correctly by Lemma 4.6. The interesting case is when a read R precedes write W, in $ops(\sigma)|p$. Suppose in contradiction that R comes after W in τ. Then in σ there is some read $R' = [\text{Read}_p(X), \text{Return}_p(X, v)]$ and some write $W' = [\text{Write}_q(X, v), \text{Ack}_q(X)]$ such that (1) R' occurs before R in σ, (2) the final timestamp of W' is greater than the final timestamp of W, and (3) W' spawns the latest update to p's copy of X that precedes R''s read. But W' must have already received its final timestamp before R''s read occurs, which means before W starts. But then the timestamp of W would be greater than the timestamp of W', which is a contradiction.

To show τ is legal, first note that for every read R of X by p, the write W, whose update to p's local copy of X provides the value returned, follows R. Lemmas 4.5 and 4.7 and the definition of τ can be used to prove that no other write falls between W and R in τ. ■

Theorem 4.1 implies that this algorithm does not guarantee linearizability. We can also explicitly construct an admissible execution that violates linearizability as follows. The initial value of X is 0. Process p writes 1 to X. The final timestamp for the write is sent at time t. It arrives at process r at time t and at process q at time $t + d$. Meanwhile, r performs a read at time t and gets the new value 1, while q performs a read at time $t + d/2$ and gets the old value 0. No permutation of these operations can both conform to the read/write specification and preserve the relative real-time orderings of all non-overlapping operations.

We now discuss the algorithm that ensures sequential consistency with fast writes (time 0) and slow reads (time at most $3d$). (Its detailed code and proof of correctness are omitted from this abstract.) This algorithm is similar to the previous algorithm. When a Read(X) comes in to p, if p has no updates (to any object, not just X) that it initiated waiting to be made, then it Returns the current value of its copy of X. Otherwise, it marks the waiting update (that it initiated) with the largest timestamp

---

[7] $ops(\sigma)|p$ is the restriction of $ops(\sigma)$ to the operations of p.

313

and Returns once this update is made. When a Write(X) comes in to p, it is handled very similarly to the other algorithm; however, it is Acked immediately. Since a process p may be handling several writes at a time, it is important that q respond to timestamp requests from p in the correct order.[8] Effectively, the algorithm pipelines write updates generated at the same process. We have:

Theorem 4.9 *The algorithm just described implements sequential consistency with* $|R| = 3d$ *and* $|W| = 0$.

The structure of the proof is the same as for the previous algorithm, while making concession to the fact that the writes are acknowledged immediately and that reads are sometimes delayed.

Theorem 4.2 implies that this algorithm does not guarantee linearizability. It is also not difficult to construct an explicit scenario.

5   Conclusions and Further Research

The impact of the correctness guarantee on the efficiency of supporting it was studied under various timing assumptions. Although we still do not have a complete picture of this problem, our results indicate that supporting sequential consistency can be more cost-effective than supporting linearizability, for read/write objects and under certain timing assumptions. Two other conclusions can be drawn from our results: First, perfect clocks admit more efficient implementations, and thus it may be worthwhile to provide such clocks. Second, knowing in advance the sharing patterns of the object (i.e., how many processes read it and how many processes write it) results in faster implementations. Thus, the mcs can benefit from having the application program (the user) supply "hints" about the sharing patterns of the object.

Our work leaves open many interesting questions. Obviously, it is desirable to narrow the gaps between our upper and lower bounds. It will be interesting to understand how practical issues such as local memory size and clock drift influence the bounds. We have studied only read/write objects, although our definitions can be extended in a straightforward way to apply to other data objects. It will be very interesting to obtain bounds on the response time of implementing other objects, e.g., FIFO Queues and Test-and-Set registers, under sequential consistency and linearizability. Preliminary results in this direction appear in [5]. The cost measure we have chosen to analyze is response time, but there are other interesting measures, including throughput and network congestion.

The problem that we have studied is closely related to the problem of designing cache consistency schemes in which some sort of global ordering must be imposed on the operations ([10, 11, 12, 16, 20]). Our results show that making the definitions of these orderings more precise is important since seemingly minor differences in the definitions result in significant differences in the inherent efficiency of implementing them. Recently, several non-global conditions that are weaker than sequential consistency have been suggested, e.g., weak ordering ([15, 8, 1]), pipelined memory ([23]), slow memory ([19]), causal memory ([4]), loosely coherent memory ([6]), and the definitions in [12] and [28]. It would be interesting to investigate the inherent efficiency of supporting these consistency guarantees. In order to do so, crisp and precise definitions of these conditions are needed.

It is clear that efficiency, in general, and response time, in particular, are not the only criteria for evaluating consistency guarantees. In particular, the ease of designing, verifying, programming, and debugging algorithms using such shared memories is very important.

As multiprocessor systems become larger, distributed implementations of shared virtual memory are becoming more common. (Truly shared memories, or even buses, cannot be used in systems with a large number of processors.) Such implementations and their evaluation relate issues concerning multiprocessor architecture, programming language design, software engineering, and the theory of concurrent systems. We hope our work contributes toward a more solid ground for this interaction.

Acknowledgements: The authors thank Sarita Adve, Roy Friedman, Mark Hill, and Rick Zucker for helpful comments on an earlier version of this paper.

---

[8]For simplicity, we assume FIFO channels, but this assumption can be removed if sequence numbers are employed.

References

[1] S. Adve and M. Hill, "Weak Ordering—A New Definition," *Proc. 17th ISCA*, 1990, pp. 2–14.

[2] S. Adve and M. Hill, "Implementing Sequential Consistency in Cache-Based Systems," *Proc. ICPP*, 1990.

[3] Y. Afek, G. Brown, and M. Merritt. "A Lazy Cache Algorithm," *Proc. 1st SPAA*, 1989, pp. 209–222.

[4] M. Ahamad, P. Hutto, and R. John, *Implementing and Programming Causal Distributed Shared Memory*, TR GIT-CC-90-49, Georgia Inst. of Tech., December 1990.

[5] H. Attiya, "Implementing FIFO Queues and Stacks," in preparation.

[6] J. Bennett, J. Carter, and W. Zwaenepoel, "Munin: Distributed Shared Memory Based on Type-Specific Memory Coherence," *Proc. 2nd PPoPP*, 1990, pp. 168–176.

[7] P. Bernstein, V. Hadzilacos, and H. Goodman, *Concurrency Control and Recovery in Database Systems*, Addison-Wesley, Reading, MA, 1987.

[8] R. Bisiani, A. Nowatzyk, and M. Ravishankar, "Coherent Shared Memory on a Distributed Memory Machine," *Proc. ICPP*, 1989, pp. I-133–141.

[9] K. Birman and T. Joseph, "Reliable Communication in the Presence of Failures," *TOCS*, vol. 5, no. 1, pp. 47–76.

[10] W. Brantley, K. McAuliffe, and J. Weiss, "RP3 Processor-Memory Element," *Proc. ICPP*, 1985, pp. 782–789.

[11] L. M. Censier and P. Feautrier, "A New Solution to Coherence Problems in Multicache Systems," *IEEE Trans. on Computers*, vol. C-27, no. 12, pp. 1112–1118.

[12] W. W. Collier, "Architectures for Systems of Parallel Processes," IBM TR 00.3253, Poughkeepsie, NY, January 1984.

[13] E. W. Dijkstra, "Hierarchical Ordering Of Sequential Processes," *Acta Informatica*, 1971, pp. 115–138.

[14] M. Dubois and C. Scheurich, "Memory Access Dependencies in Shared-Memory Multiprocessors", *IEEE Trans. on Software Engineering*, vol. 16, no. 6 (June 1990), pp. 660–673.

[15] M. Dubois, C. Scheurich, and F. A. Briggs, "Memory Access Buffering in Multiprocessors," *Proc. 13th ISCA*, June 1986, pp. 434–442.

[16] M. Dubois, C. Scheurich, and F. A. Briggs, "Synchronization, Coherence and Event Ordering in Multiprocessors," *IEEE Computer*, vol. 21, no. 2, pp. 9–21.

[17] M. Herlihy, "Wait-Free Implementations of Concurrent Objects," *Proc. 7th PODC*, 1988, pp. 276–290.

[18] M. Herlihy and J. Wing, "Linearizability: A Correctness Condition for Concurrent Objects," *TOPLAS*, vol. 12, no. 3, pp. 463–492.

[19] P. Hutto and M. Ahamad, *Slow Memory: Weakening Consistency to Enhance Concurrency in Distributed Shared Memories*, TR GIT-ICS-89/39, Georgia Inst. of Tech., October 1989.

[20] L. Lamport, "How to Make a Multiprocessor Computer that Correctly Executes Multiprocess Programs," *IEEE Trans. on Computers*, vol. C-28, no. 9, pp. 690–691.

[21] L. Lamport, "On Interprocess Communication. Parts I and II," *Distributed Computing*, vol. 1, no. 2 (1986), pp. 77–101.

[22] K. Li and P. Hudak, "Memory Coherence in Shared Virtual Memory Systems," *TOCS*, vol. 7, no. 4, pp. 321–359.

[23] R. Lipton and J. Sandberg, *PRAM: A Scalable Shared Memory*, TR CS-TR-180-88, Princeton University, September 1988.

[24] J. Lundelius and N. Lynch, "An Upper and Lower Bound for Clock Synchronization," *Information and Control*, vol. 62, Nos. 2/3, pp. 190–204.

[25] S. Min and J. Baer, "A Timestamp-Based Cache Coherence Scheme," *Proc. ICPP*, 1989, pp. I-23–32.

[26] J. Misra, "Axioms for Memory Access in Asynchronous Hardware Systems," *TOPLAS*, vol. 8, no. 1, pp. 142–153.

[27] C. Papadimitriou, *The Theory of Concurrency Control*, Computer Science Press, Rockville, MD, 1986.

[28] U. Ramachandran, M. Ahamad, and M. Y. Khalidi, "Coherence of Distributed Shared Memory: Unifying Synchronization and Data Transfer," *Proc. ICPP*, 1989, pp. II-160–169.

[29] C. Scheurich and M. Dubois, "Correct Memory Operation of Cache-Based Multiprocessors," *Proc. 14th ISCA*, 1987, pp. 234–243.

Detecting Violations of Sequential Consistency

Kourosh Gharachorloo

Center for Integrated Systems
Stanford University
Stanford, CA 94305

Phillip B. Gibbons

600 Mountain Avenue
AT&T Bell Laboratories
Murray Hill, NJ 07974

Abstract

The performance of a multiprocessor is directly affected by the choice of the memory consistency model supported. Several different consistency models have been proposed in the literature. These range from *sequential consistency* on one end, allowing limited buffering of memory accesses, to *release consistency* on the other end, allowing extensive buffering and pipelining. While the relaxed models such as release consistency provide potential for higher performance, they present a more complex programming model than sequential consistency. Previous research has addressed this tradeoff by showing that a release consistent architecture provides sequentially consistent executions for programs that are free of data races. However, the burden of guaranteeing that the program is free of data races remains with the programmer or compiler.

This paper presents a new implementation of release consistency. For every execution, the implementation conclusively determines *either* that the execution is sequentially consistent *or* that the program has data races. This is achieved with minor additional hardware while maintaining the higher performance associated with release consistency.

1   Introduction

Techniques that cope with the large latency of memory accesses are essential for achieving high processor utilization in large scale shared-memory multiprocessors. Buffering and pipelining of accesses are two such techniques that can be used to hide memory latency. Unfortunately, unconstrained buffering and pipelining can result in an intractable programming model for the machine. The role of the con-

sistency model is to provide a more reasonable programming model by placing certain restrictions on the ordering of accesses.

Several memory consistency models have been proposed in the literature. The strictest model is *sequential consistency* (SC) [16], which requires the execution of a parallel program to appear as some interleaving of the execution of the parallel processes on a sequential machine. Sequential consistency imposes severe restrictions on buffering and pipelining of memory accesses. One of the least strict models is *release consistency* (RC) [12], which allows significant overlap of memory accesses given synchronization accesses are identified and classified into acquires and releases. Other relaxed models that have been discussed in the literature are *processor consistency* [12, 14], *weak consistency* [8, 9], and *data-race-free-0* (DRF0) [2]. These models fall between the sequential and release consistency models in terms of strictness.

While the relaxed models provide a higher potential for performance [10], the programmer is burdened with a more complex programming model. To partially remedy this problem, it has been shown that programs that are free of data races provide sequentially consistent executions on weak or release consistent architectures [12]. A similar equivalence is proven for DRF0 [2]. Thus, programmers can use the well-defined semantics of sequential consistency to reason about their programs, and as long as the programs are free of data races, the programs can be safely executed on hardware with a relaxed model.

Much research has been done on detecting data races in parallel programs. However, exactly determining whether a program is free of data races is known to be undecidable [6]. Dynamic techniques have been proposed to detect whether a particular execution exhibits data races [3, 4, 7, 15, 19, 21]. These techniques involve analyzing access traces on-the-fly or in a post-mortem fashion. Tracing the accesses and analyzing the trace can adversely affect the execution time [7], making such techniques useful for debugging purposes only. In addition, the absence of data races in several executions of the program during debugging is insufficient proof that the program is data-race-free. Thus, the programmer is still responsible for guaranteeing that the program is free of data races if sequentially consistent executions are desired on architectures with relaxed models.

Given the difficulty in determining whether a program is data-race-free, an alternative approach is to directly detect whether sequential consistency is violated in executions on architectures supporting a relaxed model. Unfortunately, exactly determining whether or not an execution is sequentially consistent is NP-complete. However, a conservative detection for violations of sequential consistency can still be useful.

This paper presents a new implementation for relaxed consistency models that dynamically detects possible violations of sequential consistency. For every execution, the implementation exactly determines *either* that the execution is sequentially consistent *or* that the program has data races. If the execution is sequentially consistent, the programmer is assured that the relaxed consistency model did not affect the correctness of that execution. And if it is determined that the program has data races, then the programmer knows that it is possible to get sequentially inconsistent results if that program is executed on architectures supporting relaxed models.

The proposed detection technique has several advantages. First, the programmer is guaranteed exact information either about the execution or about the program. Second, the detection mechanism does not adversely affect the performance of the architecture and maintains the high performance associated with relaxed consistency models. Thus, the mechanism can be used for all executions of the program. Third, the implementation involves minor hardware complexity, making the scheme practical.

The next section provides background information on consistency models and their implementation. Section 3 describes the general approach for detecting violations of sequential consistency. Section 4 outlines the basic detection mechanism. Implementation constraints required to make the detection more accurate and extensible are presented in Sections 5 and 6. Related work is discussed in Section 7. Finally, we conclude in Section 8.

2 Background on Consistency Models

The ordering restrictions imposed by a consistency model can be presented in terms of when an access is allowed to perform. A read is considered *performed* when the return value is bound and can not be modified by other write operations. Similarly, a write is considered *performed* when the value written by the write operation is visible to all processors. For simplicity, we assume a write is made visible to all other processors at the same time. Our detection scheme can be trivially extended for the case when a write is made

visible to different processors at different times. The notion of being performed and having completed will be used interchangeably in the rest of the paper. We assume uniprocessor (data and control) dependences and general cache coherence are also satisfied. In [13], a formal automaton is given as an instantiation of the above architectural assumptions. Condition 2.1 presents sufficient conditions for providing sequential consistency [12]. Each process has to satisfy this condition among its memory accesses.

> **Condition 2.1: Sufficient Conditions for Sequential Consistency**
> (A) before a LOAD or STORE is allowed to perform, all previous LOAD and STORE accesses must be performed.

A more relaxed consistency model can be derived by relating memory request ordering to synchronization points in the program. The weak consistency model (WC) proposed by Dubois et al. [8, 9] is based on the above idea and guarantees a consistent view of memory only at synchronization points. As an example, consider a process updating a data structure within a critical section. Under SC, every access within the critical section is delayed until the previous access completes. But such delays are unnecessary if the programmer has already made sure that no other process can rely on the data structure to be consistent until the critical section is exited. Weak consistency exploits this by allowing accesses within the critical section to be pipelined. Correctness is achieved by guaranteeing that all previous accesses are performed before entering or exiting each critical section.

Release consistency (RC) [12] is an extension of weak consistency that exploits further information about synchronization by classifying them into acquire and release accesses. An *acquire* synchronization access (e.g., a lock operation or a process spinning for a flag to be set) is performed to gain access to a set of shared locations. A *release* synchronization access (e.g., an unlock operation or a process setting a flag) grants this permission. An acquire is accomplished by reading a shared location until an appropriate value is read. Thus, an acquire is always associated with a read synchronization access (see [12] for discussion of read-modify-write accesses). Similarly, a release is always associated with a write synchronization access. In contrast to WC, RC does not require accesses following a release to be delayed for the release to complete; the purpose of the release is to signal that previous accesses are complete, and it does not have anything to say about the ordering of the accesses following it. Similarly, RC does not require an acquire to be delayed for its previous accesses. The conditions to satisfy the DRF0 model [2] are similar to release consistency, although DRF0 does not distinguish between acquire and release accesses. Condition 2.2 presents sufficient conditions for ensuring release consistency. These conditions are for RCsc, as described in [12].

317

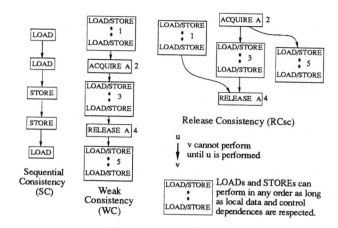

Figure 1: Ordering restrictions on memory accesses.

Condition 2.2: Sufficient Conditions for Release Consistency

(A) before an ordinary LOAD or STORE access is allowed to perform, all previous *acquire* accesses must be performed, and

(B) before a *release* access is allowed to perform, all previous ordinary LOAD and STORE accesses must be performed, and

(C) *synchronization* accesses are sequentially consistent with respect to one another.

Figure 1 graphically shows the restrictions imposed by each of the consistency models on memory accesses from the same process. As shown, sequential consistency can be guaranteed by requiring shared accesses to perform in program order. Weak consistency and release consistency differ from SC in that they exploit information about synchronization accesses. Both WC and RC allow accesses between two synchronization operations to be pipelined, as shown in Figure 1. The numbers on the blocks denote the order in which the accesses occur in program order. The figure shows that RC provides further flexibility by exploiting information about the type of synchronization.

We now discuss the class of programs that provide sequentially consistent executions under WC and RC architectures. First we introduce some terminology. Two accesses *conflict* if they are to the same memory location and at least one of the accesses is a store. Consider a pair of conflicting accesses a_1 and a_2 on different processors. If the two accesses are not ordered, they may execute simultaneously thus causing a race condition. Such accesses a_1 and a_2 form a *competing pair*. If an access is involved in a competing pair under any execution, then the access is considered a *competing access*.

The notion of *properly-labeled* (PL) programs was originally defined in [12]. A program is considered PL if all competing accesses are identified appropriately as either acquire or release synchronization accesses.[1] Thus, in a PL

program, any access that may be involved in a race condition is identified as synchronization and other ordinary accesses are guaranteed to be race-free.

A PL program is known to provide sequentially consistent results when executed on WC or RC architectures [12]. A similar equivalence is shown for the DRF0 model [2]. A more formal framework for proving such equivalences is presented in [13]. Thus, if the programmer or compiler properly identifies the competing accesses as synchronization, the program can be safely executed on architectures supporting these relaxed consistency models and the executions are guaranteed to be sequentially consistent.

3 General Approach

Our goal is to present a technique to detect possible violations of sequential consistency on an architecture supporting a relaxed model such as release consistency. Exactly determining whether or not an execution is sequentially consistent is NP-complete.[2] Therefore, we settle for a conservative detection for violations of sequential consistency. This section describes the constraints we impose on the accuracy of the detection.

For the detection to be conservative, we have to guarantee that a violation is detected if the execution is not sequentially consistent. Condition 3.1 summarizes this.

Condition 3.1: Conservative Detection
If execution E is not sequentially consistent, the detection mechanism will detect a violation in E.

Condition 3.1 can be trivially satisfied by *always* detecting a violation for every execution. However, such a detection scheme is clearly not useful. Therefore, it is important to make the detection more accurate for it to be useful. We know that programs with no data races (i.e. PL programs) are guaranteed to produce sequentially consistent executions on release consistent architectures. A useful detection scheme is one that obeys Condition 3.1, but does not detect a violation if the program is free of data races. The latter requirement is stated in Condition 3.2.

Condition 3.2: Bound on Conservative Detection
If program P is a PL program, then the detection mechanism is guaranteed not to detect a violation in *any* execution of P.

Therefore, if no violation is detected for an execution, then the execution is sequentially consistent (by Condition 3.1). And if a violation is detected, then the program is known to have a data race (by Condition 3.2). In the first case, the programmer is assured that the correctness of the

---

[1]This is a simplified definition for PL programs since we are ignoring the distinction between synchronization and non-synchronization

competing accesses. See [12] for the more general definition.

[2]The proof, omitted here, is similar in structure to the NP-completeness proof in [22].

execution was not affected by the fact that the architecture supports a relaxed model. In the second case, the programmer knows that the program has a data race and can result in sequentially inconsistent results on architectures supporting the relaxed models.

The next section describes a basic detection mechanism that satisfies Condition 3.1. Section 5 shows how this detection scheme can be modified to satisfy Condition 3.2. The detection mechanism is initially described in the context of an invalidation-based cache coherent architecture with a one word cache line size. Section 6 provides extensions of the scheme for larger cache line sizes and Appendix A considers update-based coherence schemes.

4   Basic Detection Mechanism

This section describes the basic mechanism for conservatively detecting violations of sequential consistency. The first subsection describes the intuition behind the technique. The second subsection presents an example implementation.

4.1   Description

The idea behind the detection mechanism is simple. Assume u and v are two accesses in program order. Sequential consistency is guaranteed if the completion of v is delayed until u completes (Condition 2.1). However, if the multiprocessor supports a relaxed consistency model, it is possible that the model does not enforce such a completion order on the two accesses. Thus, sequential consistency may be violated. The purpose of the detection mechanism is to determine whether the violation of the completion order in the relaxed architecture may result in a sequentially inconsistent execution.

We now describe how the detection mechanism works. A violation may arise if v completes before u. First consider the case where v is a read access. Assume the read completes before u completes. Thus, the return value for v is bound before u completes. This does not necessarily lead to a violation of sequential consistency, however. At the time u completes, if the return value for v is the same as the current value of the location accessed by v, then sequential consistency is not violated. Clearly, any computation based on the access is correct since even if v was delayed until u completed, the value the access would return would be the same. However, if the current value is different from the value returned by access v, then sequential consistency may have been violated and the detection scheme conservatively detects a violation.

Now consider the case where v is a write access. Assume the write completes before u completes. Even so, sequential consistency is guaranteed if no other processor attempts to access the location touched by v until u completes. Again,

if the location is accessed only after u completes, then it is *as if* v was delayed until u completes. However, in case of an attempt to access the location touched by v while u is pending, the detection scheme conservatively detects a violation.

Architectures with invalidation-based cache coherence provide an efficient base for the detection mechanism. (Update-based schemes are discussed in Appendix A.) The detection mechanism monitors the coherence transactions to determine whether a violation of SC is likely. Let us refer back to accesses u and v. If v is a read access, an invalidation for the location accessed by v before u has completed indicates that the value bound by access v is old and may result in a violation of SC. In addition, the lack of invalidation messages indicates that the value bound by v is current. Similarly, if v is a write access, a read or invalidation (ownership) message to the location accessed by v before u has completed indicates a possible violation of SC. Cache line replacements need to be handled properly.[3] If the location accessed by v is replaced from the cache before u completes, then coherence messages for v may no longer reach the cache and we need to conservatively assume a violation. However, to make the detection less conservative, it is possible to delay the replacement of v until u completes. A detection mechanism that obeys the above constraints satisfies Condition 3.1. The next subsection provides further implementation details for this mechanism.

4.2   Example Implementation

We assume an architecture with invalidation-based cache coherence such as the DASH multiprocessor [17]. To implement the detection mechanism, only the load/store (memory) unit of the base processor needs to be modified and the rest of the architecture remains unchanged. Figure 2 shows the components of a typical memory unit. We first describe the components shown on the left side of the figure. These components are present regardless of whether the detection mechanism is supported. The only new component that is required for supporting the detection mechanism is the *detection buffer* (right side of the figure) that will be described later.

As shown in Figure 2, the processor generates the address and data for load and store accesses. We assume that the accesses are presented to the memory unit in program order. The *address unit* is responsible for doing the virtual to physical translation. Once the physical address is obtained, the address and data for a store operation are placed into the *store buffer*. The retiring of stores from the store buffer is done in a FIFO manner. However, stores are allowed to be pipelined (i.e. may complete out of order). Load operations are allowed to bypass the store buffer and

---

[3]A replacement is required if the processor accesses an address that maps onto a cache line with valid data for a different address.

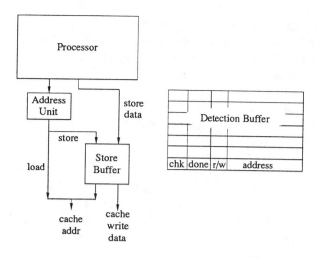

Figure 2: Organization of a typical load/store unit.

dependence checking is done on the store buffer to ensure the correct return value for the load (i.e. the latest value for that address if it exists in the store buffer). Although the above implementation is sufficient for a uniprocessor, we need to add mechanisms to enforce consistency constraints for a multiprocessor.

We now consider how access order can be guaranteed for release consistency. The conventional way to provide RC is to delay accesses following an acquire until the acquire completes and to delay a release access until its previous accesses complete. To satisfy the requirement for acquires, further generation of memory accesses by the processor can be stalled until an issued acquire access completes. The release requirement can be effectively satisfied by allowing the release to be buffered in the store buffer and by stalling the issue of the release from the buffer until all previously issued loads and stores complete. To provide sequential consistency among acquires and releases, we also require the processor to delay the generation of an acquire until its previous release has completed. The above constraints satisfy Condition 2.2 for RC. For more details on implementation issues for consistency models, see [10, 12].

The detection buffer provides the capability to detect violations of sequential consistency. The buffer works as follows. Loads and stores that are generated by the processor are immediately placed into the buffer in addition to being issued to the memory system. There are four fields per entry (as shown in Figure 2): chk, done, r/w, and address. The r/w field indicates whether the operation is a read or a write and the address field contains the corresponding address for the operation. The done field is set when the operation is completed. The chk field indicates whether the entry's address should be checked during the monitoring of coherence transactions. For a read operation, the chk field is set as soon as the entry is put in the detection buffer. For write operations, the chk field is originally clear and is set when the store buffer issues the write access to the memory.

This is because the completion of writes is delayed until the store buffer issues them and there is no need to check for a violation until that time. Entries are retired in a FIFO manner. The entry at the head of the buffer is retired only if its done field is set. Therefore, an entry remains in the buffer until all previous load and store accesses complete and the access it refers to completes. The generation of accesses by the processor is stalled if the buffer is full. A reasonable size for the buffer is the maximum number of outstanding accesses per processor that is desired for the architecture.

We now describe the detection mechanism. The following coherence transactions are monitored by the detection buffer: read request, invalidation (or ownership) request, and replacement request. The addresses in the buffer are associatively checked for a match with such transactions. Only entries with the chk field set are involved in the check. The entry at the head of the buffer is not checked since all accesses previous to it are completed, thus eliminating the possibility that this access can cause a violation of SC due to early issue. Multiple matches are possible. Only one match needs to be reported and an entry corresponding to a write operation has priority over an entry for a read operation. An invalidation for a matching read entry results in the conservative detection of a violation. A read or invalidation for a matching write entry also triggers the detection mechanism to report a violation. A violation of SC is reported if any processor's detection buffer detects a violation.

A cache replacement request for a line that has a matching entry in the detection buffer is treated differently. The replacement is delayed until there are no more matching entries in the buffer corresponding to the line that is to be replaced. In addition, matching involves all entries, including entries with the chk field clear. Therefore, a future access is not allowed to delay the completion of an access that occurs before it in program order. This ensures that delaying the replacement does not result in deadlock.

Although the above implementation satisfies Condition 3.1, the detection mechanism is too conservative to satisfy Condition 3.2. That is, there will be cases where a violation of SC is detected for PL (data-race-free) programs. The next section provides possible solutions to this given there is no false sharing (i.e. the cache line size is one word). Section 6 extends the solution for larger line sizes.

5 More Accurate Detection

This section describes why the detection mechanism proposed in the previous section is too conservative to satisfy Condition 3.2. In addition, we propose two solutions to remedy this problem. Condition 3.2 is a bound on how conservative the detection can be and demands that if the program is PL, no violation should be detected. If the program is PL, we are guaranteed that the ordinary accesses are not involved in any data races. This is precisely why relaxed

P1	P2	P1	P2
rel A (1)	write B (4)	rel A (2)	read B (4)
rel A (3)	acq A (2)	write B (3)	acq A (1)
PL Program		**non−PL Program**	

Figure 3: Example PL and non-PL programs.

models such as release consistency can provide sequentially consistent executions for such programs. There are two difficulties with PL programs, however. First, synchronization accesses are allowed to be involved in races. Second, false sharing (arising from locations being mapped to different words within the same cache line) does not constitute a data race and is allowed in PL programs. However, the presence of coherence messages caused by accesses to other words in the same line complicates the detection mechanism.

In this section, we assume away the problem of false sharing by only considering a cache line size of one word. The next section will relax this assumption. With this assumption, let us consider why Condition 3.2 is not satisfied by the implementation proposed in the previous section. A violation is reported if a race is detected on a matching entry in the detection buffer. The matching entry corresponds either to an ordinary access or to a synchronization access. If the matching entry corresponds to an ordinary access, then the presence of a race signifies that the program is not PL. Therefore, reporting a violation of SC, even if it is conservative, still satisfies Condition 3.2. However, for a matching entry corresponding to a synchronization access, the presence of a race involving another synchronization access is inconclusive in determining whether the program is PL or not. After all, PL programs allow races among synchronization accesses. Moreover, a race that is detected among synchronization accesses in a non-PL program may indicate a true violation of SC. Figure 3 shows an example of each case. We describe the code segments below.

Figure 3 depicts code segments from two programs, one PL and one not. Each segment involves two processors. The numbers in parentheses represent the order in which the accesses complete in some execution on an RC implementation.

The code segment on the left side of Figure 3 is an example PL program. The write access to B is the only ordinary access and is free of data races. The execution as ordered is sequentially consistent (i.e. the return values correspond to a total order of accesses that is consistent with program order). However, it will result in a conservative detection of a violation arising from the invalidation caused by the second release to location A while the acquire access is in the detection buffer of P2 (the acquire is in the detection buffer since the write has not completed). Therefore, a violation is reported even though the program is PL, thus violating Condition 3.2. One possible solution is to ignore violations

that arise from synchronization accesses. However, this will violate Condition 3.1 if the program is non-PL. The code segment on the right side of Figure 3 illustrates this. There is a race possible on the ordinary accesses to location B. The execution order, as specified, is in violation of sequential consistency. Indeed, a violation will be detected by our mechanism due to the release access invalidating location A while the acquire access is in the detection buffer of P2. However, ignoring the violation arising from the synchronization accesses would cause this true violation of SC to remain undetected. Thus, while a race on synchronization accesses can be safely ignored in PL programs, such races can cause violations of SC in non-PL programs. Since we do not know *a priori* whether the program is PL or not, we cannot safely ignore violations that are detected due to synchronization accesses. Below, we provide two possible solutions to this problem.

5.1   Simple Solution

One way to remedy the above problem is to ensure that races on synchronization accesses do not result in violations of SC, whether the program is PL or not. This can be achieved by constraining synchronization accesses such that their completion is delayed until all previous accesses have completed. In this way, the synchronization access completes when it would have been allowed under an SC implementation (Condition 2.1). The above requirement is automatically guaranteed for release accesses under RC. However, we need to constrain acquire accesses under RC as specified by Condition 5.1.[4]

> **Condition 5.1: Extra Constraint for Acquires under RC**
> (A) before an *acquire* access is allowed to perform, all previous accesses must be performed.

Given the above restriction, we are guaranteed that (i) races on synchronization accesses can not lead to violations of SC and (ii) our detection mechanism will never notice a race arising from synchronization accesses. This allows us to satisfy Condition 3.2 in bounding the conservative nature of the detection.

Condition 5.1 in conjunction with Condition 2.2 of RC make the release consistent system less different from a weakly consistent (WC) system. An aggressive RC system is less strict than WC because (i) an acquire is not delayed by its previous ordinary accesses and (ii) a release doesn't delay future ordinary accesses. However, with Condition 5.1 added to an RC implementation, only the second difference remains.

---

[4]For the general definition of RC, as specified in [12], all special accesses (i.e. nsync read, nsync write, and acquire) need to satisfy a similar condition.

Our previous studies have shown that the different constraints for WC and RC sometimes lead to a noticeable performance difference [10]. However, this performance difference arises mainly from the fact that RC allows accesses following a release to proceed (case (ii) above). Detailed simulation results for the program that exhibited a difference between WC and RC show that virtually all release accesses are followed by a read access within a few cycles. However, only 30% of the acquires are delayed under WC due to previous write misses and the miss occur on average 20 cycles before the acquire. In addition, with new techniques such as hardware-controlled non-binding prefetch [11], the latency of the acquire access can be hidden through prefetching while the access is being delayed for previous accesses to complete. Therefore, even when Condition 5.1 is satisfied, we expect the performance of the system to be close to that of an unconstrained RC system.

5.2 Alternative Solution

There is an alternative way to remedy the problem of invalidations for matching entries corresponding to synchronization accesses that does not require delaying the issue of the synchronization access as prescribed in the previous section. The solution is as follows. We now require an incoming invalidation request to specify whether it arises from an ordinary write or a synchronization write. In case the invalidation arises from an ordinary write, a matching entry corresponding to an acquire access results in a violation to be detected. However, an invalidation arising from a synchronization write that matches an entry corresponding to an acquire is simply delayed and a retry message is sent to the originating processor.[5] The processor that receives the retry message can retry the request and the resulting invalidation action will take place if there is no longer a matching entry corresponding to an acquire in the target processor's buffer. Although the above scheme delays the completion of synchronization writes by other processors, there is no deadlock problem since synchronization accesses are sequentially consistent (as specified by Condition 2.1) under RCsc and hence a cycle consisting only of synchronization accesses is not possible.

---

[5]The above scheme can be easily extended for the general definition of RC (see [12]). The nsync read accesses can be handled in the same way as acquires and invalidations arising from release or nsync write accesses are delayed until the nsync read is retired from the detection buffer. For nsync writes, both read requests and invalidation requests are monitored. Requests arising from ordinary accesses that match an entry corresponding to an nsync write result in a violation to be detected. However, requests arising from special (nsync read, nsync write, acquire, or release) accesses are delayed and a retry signal is sent to the originator.

P1	P2
write A (3)	write C (4)
read D (1)	read B (2)

Figure 4: Example PL program with false sharing.

6 Extension for Larger Line Sizes

The implementation described so far assumes an invalidation-based coherence scheme with a cache line size of one word. This section presents an extension of the implementation to allow for more than one word per cache line.

The major difficulty with line sizes of greater that one word is that a coherence message for a cache line may be caused by an access to a different word than the word that is present in the detection buffer of the target processor. This is usually referred to as false sharing. One choice is to allow the coherence action to take place. However, since no more coherence messages may be received for the entry in the detection buffer, we need to conservatively report a violation of SC. This approach satisfies Condition 3.1, but not Condition 3.2. Another choice is to disallow the coherence action to take place. In other words, the completion of another processor's access is delayed until the appropriate entry is retired from the target processor's detection buffer. However, as will be shown, this technique can lead to deadlock. Therefore, we need to find a hybrid solution that satisfies Condition 3.2 and does not result in deadlock.

Figure 4 shows an example PL program with false sharing. Assume A and B map to different words on the same cache line. Assume the same for C and D. The numbers represent the order in which the accesses complete in some execution on an RC architecture. Therefore, in both processors, the reads complete before the writes. Both writes result in invalidation messages to be generated for the other processor and at least one of the processors receives an invalidation while the read entry is in the detection buffer. Since there are no data races in the program, the program results in sequentially consistent executions. Therefore, Condition 3.2 prohibits us from conservatively detecting a violation of SC. However, the implementation of the detection mechanism as presented in Sections 4 and 5 will result in a violation to be detected. The problem can not be solved by simply delaying the invalidations while there is a matching entry in the detection buffer since deadlock will result. For example, in the execution shown in Figure 4, deadlock will arise if both reads delay invalidations from the two writes.

We now describe the changes to the basic detection mechanism to properly handle false sharing. First, we require coherence messages to specify the word address instead of the line address so that the specific word in the line can be identified. In the following, we will refer to a match as a *true match* if the coherence message specifies a word address that matches an entry corresponding to that word. If the word address corresponds to another word in the same cache line, we refer to the match as a *false match*. In case of a true match, the detection mechanism remains unchanged. For example, an invalidation for a word that has a corresponding entry in the detection buffer would result in a violation to be detected. The detection mechanism is different for a false match. An invalidation that results in a false match for a read entry is not serviced and a retry message is sent to the originating processor. A read or invalidation request that results in a false match for a write entry is treated in the same way. The processor that receives the retry message can retry the access again and the resulting coherence action will take place if there is no longer a matching entry in the target processor's detection buffer. Unfortunately, this is not a complete solution since deadlock can arise (as in the example in Figure 4).

To remedy the deadlock problem, we need a new category of read and write accesses that we will label *remote-service* accesses. Adve and Hill have proposed such accesses to remedy deadlocks in their implementation of DRF0 [1]. Remote-service accesses get performed at the target processor without changing the ownership of the cache line. A remote-service read access returns the full line in shared mode if the target processor does not have ownership of the line. However, if the processor does have ownership, the read access returns an uncachable value for the word. A remote-service write access simply performs a write to the specific word at the target processor's cache copy. This is similar to an updating write. Clearly, a remote-service write access has to specify the value to be written. An acknowledgement is sent to the originating processor when the update takes place.[6]

We now explain how deadlock is avoided through selective use of remote-service accesses. When an access that needs to be retried reaches the head of the detection buffer, the access is issued as a remote-service access. Thus, the access gets performed as a remote-service access at the target processor instead of possibly resulting in another retry. This permits each of the two writes in Figure 4 to complete while the reads are still in the detection buffer. The target processor can treat a remote-service access as a normal access if there is no longer a match in its detection buffer.

---

[6]A remote-service write can make the new value visible to different processors at different times. This arises when the remote-service write is to a line that is in shared mode (i.e. not owned by the target cache). To make it appear as if the value is made visible to all other processors at the same time, the word needs to be especially marked in the target cache. A future read by the target processor to that word needs to be delayed until the originating processor sends another message to signify that the remote-service write has updated all other shared copies.

7 Related Work and Discussion

This section briefly describes previous research in detecting data races and compares them with our proposed detection mechanism. Previous research has been mainly concerned with detecting data races in programs written for sequentially consistent systems. The proposed techniques can be classified as static or dynamic. Static techniques use compile-time information and analysis to detect all possible data races that could potentially occur in any possible execution of a program [5, 23]. Dynamic techniques analyze a dynamically generated trace of the program and determine whether that particular execution exhibited a data race [3, 4, 7, 15, 19, 21]. The following discusses these techniques in more detail.

The advantage of static techniques is that any data race that may potentially occur in any possible execution of a program is detected. Therefore, the programmer is assured that the program is data-race-free if no data races are reported. However, the problem of exactly determining whether a program is free of data races or not is known to be undecidable [6]. Exact analysis has been shown to be NP-complete even for restricted classes of programs and synchronization primitives [20, 22]. Therefore, practical algorithms for static detection are extremely conservative. Thus, many programs that are actually data-race-free may be reported as having data races.

Dynamic techniques have the advantage of determining exactly whether a specific execution of the program has data races. These techniques use a trace gathering mechanism to monitor the order among memory accesses in an execution and analyze this information to determine whether the execution exhibits any data races. The tracing and analysis can be either done on-the-fly (e.g., [7]) or in a post-mortem fashion (e.g., [19]). The on-the-fly techniques buffer trace information in memory and detect data races as they occur. In contrast, post-mortem techniques generate trace files containing information on the order of accesses and the files are analyzed after the execution completes. Most dynamic techniques are designed for use in architectures that are sequentially consistent. More recently, dynamic techniques have been proposed for use in architectures that support a relaxed consistency model [3].

The dynamic techniques have several disadvantages. First, the gathering and analysis of memory traces can adversely affect the execution time for the program. A two to five times increase in execution time has been reported for on-the-fly techniques [7]. Recently, a more efficient on-the-fly technique has been proposed that uses information from the underlying cache coherence protocol to detect anomalies in a limited class of programs [18]. In this scheme, the parallel program being monitored is interrupted only on cache misses instead of on every access. However, the overhead is still expected to be unacceptable for normal executions of the program. Thus, dynamic techniques are limited to use during debugging only. The second problem with the dynamic techniques arises from the fact that exact information is provided for only a single execution of the program. No information is given about other possible executions. This is further complicated by the fact that the extra overhead of tracing can affect the critical timing in the program, resulting in possibly different executions than would have normally occurred. Therefore, a program may not be data-race-free even if all executions during debugging are determined to be free of data races.

The detection technique proposed in this paper provides useful feedback to programmers of architectures with relaxed consistency models. In contrast to the work on data-race detection, our technique does not exactly determine whether or not the program or execution is data-race-free. Instead, the technique detects whether sequential consistency may be violated in an execution of the program. In addition, the technique is efficient enough to be used for all executions of the program. An exact property is asserted either for the execution or for the program. If no violation is detected for an execution, then the programmer knows that the execution is sequentially consistent. If a violation is detected, then the programmer knows that the program has data races and may lead to sequentially inconsistent executions on architectures with relaxed consistency. Although the above technique is presented for an RC architecture, simple changes will allow the mechanism to be used for architectures that support the WC or DRF0 models.

An interesting addition to the detection mechanism is to point the programmer to the data races when a violation of SC is detected. We believe that this information can be recovered by analyzing the contents of the detection buffers once a violation is detected and are currently working on this extension. However, with our detection scheme, it is inherently impossible to guarantee that the data race reported is the first data race or a data race that could occur on an SC machine (see [3]). This is because the first data races may go undetected if they do not result in a violation of SC and can in turn affect the presence of future data races.

The detection mechanism described can be used when the consistency model is relaxed at the hardware level. Relaxing the model can also affect performance at the software level, mainly through enabling compiler optimizations (e.g., register allocation) for shared variables. However, our detection mechanism inherently depends on the original program order among memory references and can not be used if the compiler reorders or eliminates (through register allocation) shared accesses unless the compiler guarantees that the transformed program is equivalent (under the SC model) to the original program.

The detection buffer implementation described in this paper is similar to an implementation we proposed in [11] for a slightly different purpose. There, we present a technique for speculatively performing read accesses and detecting whether the speculation may lead to a violation of sequential consistency. If it is determined that a violation may result, the read access and the computation depending on it are repeated to provide a sequentially consistent result. Since there is a correction mechanism, the detection mechanism can afford to be conservative. In addition, since we guarantee sequential consistency at all times, writes are not allowed to occur speculatively, thus requiring no detection. The detection mechanism proposed in this paper is different in that we need to bound its conservatism due to the absence of a correction mechanism. In addition, the detection needs to check for violations of SC due to either reads or writes since both read and write accesses are allowed to perform out of order.

8 Concluding Remarks

To achieve higher performance, relaxed consistency models have been proposed for shared-memory multiprocessors as an alternative to sequential consistency. Unfortunately, relaxed models present a more complex programming model to the user. Relaxed consistency models such as weak consistency, data-race-free-0, and release consistency are known to provide sequentially consistent executions for programs with no data races. In spite of the research on data-race detection, current techniques for automatic detection are quite limited. Hence, the programmer is still responsible for guaranteeing that the program is data-race-free if sequentially consistent results are desired on architectures with relaxed models.

This paper presented a unique architectural feature to help programmers determine whether sequential consistency is violated in an architecture supporting a relaxed consistency model. For every execution of the program, the technique determines *either* that the execution is sequentially consistent *or* that the program has data races and may result in sequentially inconsistent executions. Practical and efficient implementations of the technique were described.

9 Acknowledgments

We thank Anoop Gupta and John Hennessy for their comments. Sarita Adve provided comments on an earlier version of the paper. We also thank Rohit Chandra, Dan Lenoski, and Jaswinder Pal Singh for useful discussions. Kourosh Gharachorloo is supported by DARPA contract N00014-87-K-0828 and by Texas Instruments.

References

[1] Sarita Adve. Personal communication. February 1991.

[2] Sarita Adve and Mark Hill. Weak ordering - A new definition. In *Proceedings of the 17th Annual International Symposium on Computer Architecture*, pages 2–14, May 1990.

[3] Sarita Adve, Mark Hill, Barton Miller, and Robert Netzer. Detecting data races on weak memory systems. In *Proceedings of the 18th Annual International Symposium on Computer Architecture*, May 1991.

[4] Todd R. Allen and David A. Padua. Debugging Fortran on a shared memory machine. In *Proceedings of the 1987 International Conference on Parallel Processing*, pages 721–727, August 1987.

[5] Vasanth Balasundaram and Ken Kennedy. Compile-time detection of race conditions in a parallel program. In *Proceedings of the 3rd International Conference on Supercomputing*, pages 175–185, June 1989.

[6] A. J. Bernstein. Analysis of programs for parallel processing. *IEEE Transactions on Electronic Computers*, EC-15(5):757–763, October 1966.

[7] Anne Dinning and Edith Schonberg. An empirical comparison of monitoring algorithms for access anomaly detection. In *Proceedings of ACM Symposium on Principles and Practice of Parallel Programming*, pages 1–10, March 1990.

[8] Michel Dubois and Christoph Scheurich. Memory access dependencies in shared-memory multiprocessors. *IEEE Transactions on Software Engineering*, 16(6):660–673, June 1990.

[9] Michel Dubois, Christoph Scheurich, and Fayé Briggs. Memory access buffering in multiprocessors. In *Proceedings of the 13th Annual International Symposium on Computer Architecture*, pages 434–442, June 1986.

[10] Kourosh Gharachorloo, Anoop Gupta, and John Hennessy. Performance evaluation of memory consistency models for shared-memory multiprocessors. In *Fourth International Conference on Architectural Support for Programming Languages and Operating Systems*, pages 245–257, April 1991.

[11] Kourosh Gharachorloo, Anoop Gupta, and John Hennessy. Two techniques to enhance the performance of memory consistency models. In *Proceedings of the 1991 International Conference on Parallel Processing*, August 1991.

[12] Kourosh Gharachorloo, Dan Lenoski, James Laudon, Phillip Gibbons, Anoop Gupta, and John Hennessy. Memory consistency and event ordering in scalable shared-memory multiprocessors. In *Proceedings of the 17th Annual International Symposium on Computer Architecture*, pages 15–26, May 1990.

[13] Phillip B. Gibbons, Michael Merritt, and Kourosh Gharachorloo. Proving sequential consistency of high-performance shared memories. In *Symposium on Parallel Algorithms and Architectures*, July 1991.

[14] James R. Goodman. Cache consistency and sequential consistency. Technical Report no. 61, SCI Committee, March 1989.

[15] Robert Hood, Ken Kennedy, and John M. Mellor-Crummey. Parallel program debugging with on-the-fly anomaly detection. In *Supercomputing '90*, pages 74–81, November 1990.

[16] Leslie Lamport. How to make a multiprocessor computer that correctly executes multiprocess programs. *IEEE Transactions on Computers*, C-28(9):241–248, September 1979.

[17] Dan Lenoski, James Laudon, Kourosh Gharachorloo, Anoop Gupta, and John Hennessy. The directory-based cache coherence protocol for the DASH multiprocessor. In *Proceedings of the 17th Annual International Symposium on Computer Architecture*, pages 148–159, May 1990.

[18] Sang Lyul Min and Jong-Deok Choi. An efficient cache-based access anomaly detection scheme. In *Fourth International Conference on Architectural Support for Programming Languages and Operating Systems*, pages 235–244, April 1991.

[19] Robert Netzer and Barton Miller. Detecting data races in parallel program executions. Technical Report CS-894, University of Wisconsin - Madison, November 1989.

[20] Robert Netzer and Barton Miller. On the complexity of event ordering for shared-memory parallel program executions. In *Proceedings of the 1990 International Conference on Parallel Processing*, pages II: 93–97, August 1990.

[21] Robert Netzer and Barton Miller. Improving the accuracy of data race detection. In *Proceedings of ACM Symposium on Principles and Practice of Parallel Programming*, pages 133–144, April 1991.

[22] Richard N. Taylor. Complexity of analyzing the synchronization structure of concurrent programs. *Acta Informatica*, 19:57–84, 1983.

[23] Richard N. Taylor. A general-purpose algorithm for analyzing concurrent programs. *Communications of the ACM*, 26(5):362–376, May 1983.

Appendix A: Update-Based Coherence Schemes

This appendix presents extensions to the implementation to accommodate update-based coherence schemes. An update-based coherence scheme is inherently different from an invalidation-based scheme in the way writes are handled. An invalidation scheme acquires an exclusively owned copy of the cache line for the writing processor. This allows us to monitor whether another processor tries to access the new value while the write access remains in the detection buffer. In contrast, an update scheme simply sends the new value to other cache copies. Thus, the writing processor is not notified when another processor tries to read the new value. As a result, we can no longer detect if a violation of sequential consistency arises due to a write that completes out of order.

Since violations of SC arising from out-of-order writes are no longer detected, we need to make sure that writes do not result in violations. This can be achieved by delaying the completion of writes until all previous accesses have completed. This is similar to the condition imposed on acquires in Section 5.1. As a result of this constraint on writes, the detection mechanism for update-based schemes is less efficient than for invalidation-based schemes.[7] Disallowing pipelined writes can degrade performance in two ways. First, the store buffer can fill up more often if writes are not pipelined, although a reasonably large store buffer may alleviate the problem somewhat. The second performance difference arises from the fact that, in an unconstrained RC architecture, releases may complete earlier due to the pipelining of writes that occur before them. Forcing writes to complete in order may hurt performance when such releases occur in the critical path of the computation. We refer the reader to [10] for an in-depth discussion of the effects of pipelining writes on performance.

Since writes complete in order, the detection mechanism needs to only monitor out-of-order read accesses for possible violation of SC. Thus, the operation of the detection buffer is slightly different. First of all, only read accesses are placed in the detection buffer. The detection buffer requires only the following three fields per entry: done, store tag, and address. The done and address fields are the same as before. The store tag uniquely identifies the previous store access for the load that is placed in the buffer. A null store tag specifies that the load depends on no previous stores. When a load is placed into the detection buffer, the store tag is set to point to the store immediately preceding the load in program order (the most recent store in the store buffer). If the immediate access preceding the load

is another load, the store tag is set to null. When a store completes, its corresponding tag in the detection buffer is nullified if present. Entries are still retired in a FIFO manner. The entry at the head of the buffer is retired when the done field is set and the store tag is equal to null. Therefore, a load entry remains in the buffer until all its previous accesses complete and the load itself completes.

The detection mechanism is similar to before. We explain the differences below. Update and replacement messages are monitored by the detection buffer. The addresses in the buffer are associatively checked for a match as before. The entry at the head of the buffer is included in the check if the store tag is not null. A matching entry for an update to the same word results in a violation to be detected. Updates to other words in the line can be ignored as far as detection is concerned. Replacement requests are handled as before except that addresses in the store buffer are also checked. This is because stores are no longer kept in the detection buffer.

---

[7]In addition, supporting sequential consistency either requires atomic writes or requires a globally performed signal for writes (see [12]). In large scale multiprocessors, either requirement results in an inefficient implementation of update writes.

326

Impossibility Results for Asynchronous PRAM
(extended abstract)

Maurice Herlihy

Digital Equipment Corporation

Cambridge Research Laboratory

One Kendall Square

Cambridge MA, 02139

herlihy@crl.dec.com

Abstract

In the asynchronous PRAM model, processes communicate by atomically reading and writing shared memory locations. This paper investigates the extent to which asynchronous PRAM permits long-lived, highly concurrent data structures. An implementation of a concurrent object is *non-blocking* if some operation will always complete in a finite number of steps, it is *wait-free* if every operation will complete in a finite number of steps, and it is *k-bounded wait-free*, for some $k > 0$, if every operation will complete within k steps. It is known that asynchronous PRAM cannot be used to construct a non-blocking implementation of any object that solves two-process consensus, a class of objects that includes many common data types. It is natural to ask whether the converse holds: does asynchronous PRAM permit non-blocking implementations of any object that does not solve consensus? This papers shows that the answer is *no*. There is a strict infinite hierarchy among objects that do not solve consensus: there exist objects (1) without non-blocking implementations, (2) with implementations that are non-blocking but not wait-free, (3) with implementations that are wait-free but not bounded wait-free, and (4) with implementations that are K-bounded wait-free but not k-bounded wait-free for all $k > 0$ and some $K > k$.

1 Introduction

In the "classical" parallel random access machine (PRAM) model, a set of processes executing in lock-step communicate by applying read and write operations to a shared memory. Existing shared memory architectures,
however, are inherently *asynchronous:* processors' relative speeds are unpredictable, at least in the short term, because of timing uncertainties introduced by variations in instruction complexity, page faults, cache misses, and operating system activities such as preemption or swapping. A number of researchers have noted this mismatch, and have proposed the *asynchronous PRAM* model as an alternative [8, 9, 14, 25]. In this model, asynchronous processes communicate by applying atomic read and write operations to the shared memory [1]. Techniques for implementing these memory locations, often called *atomic registers*, have also received considerable attention [4, 5, 20, 21, 24, 26, 27].

Much of the work on asynchronous PRAM models addresses the problem of computing functions, such as parallel summation, whose inputs reside in the shared memory. Many practical applications, however, such as operating systems and data bases, are not organized around functional computation. Instead, they are organized around long-lived *data objects* such as sets, queues, directories, and so on. In this paper, we investigate the extent to which the asynchronous PRAM model supports long-lived, highly-concurrent data objects. There are several reasons why long-lived objects are inherently more difficult than functional computation. A data object has an unbounded lifetime during which each process can execute an arbitrary sequence of operations, requiring that data structures be reused. It must retain enough information to ensure that "sleepy" processes that arbitrarily suspend and resume execution can continue to progress, while discarding enough information to keep the object size bounded. Care must be taken to guard against starvation, since one operation can be "overtaken" by an arbitrary sequence of other operations.

An implementation of a concurrent object is *non-blocking* if some non-faulty process always completes an operation in a finite number of steps, despite failures

---

[1]Some of these models also include primitives for barrier synchronization.

of other processes. It is *wait-free* if every non-faulty process has this property, and it is *k-bounded wait-free*, for some fixed $k > 0$, if every non-faulty process always completes an operation within k steps. These properties form a hierarchy: bounded wait-free implies wait-free, and wait-free implies non-blocking. The non-blocking property permits individual processes to starve, but it guarantees that the system as a whole will make progress. The wait-free property excludes starvation; any process that continues to take steps will finish its operation, and the bounded wait-free property bounds how long it will take. Each of these properties rules out conventional synchronization techniques such as barrier synchronization, busy-waiting, conditional waiting, or critical sections, since the failure or delay of a single process within a critical section or before a barrier will prevent the non-faulty processes from making progress.

Which objects have non-blocking implementations in asynchronous PRAM? Elsewhere [17, 15], we have shown that any object X can be assigned a *consensus number*, which is the largest number of processes (possibly infinite) that can achieve consensus asynchronously [13] by applying operations to a shared X. It is impossible to construct a non-blocking implementation of any object with consensus number n from objects with lower consensus numbers in a system of n or more processes, although any object with consensus number n is universal (it supports a wait-free implementation of any other object) in a system of n or fewer processes. A memory with atomic read and write operations has consensus number 1 (it cannot solve consensus between two processes), and therefore the asynchronous PRAM model is too weak to support non-blocking implementations of any object with a higher consensus number, including common data types such as sets, queues, stacks, priority queues, or lists, most if not all the classical synchronization primitives, such as *test&set*, *compare&swap*, and *fetch&add*, and simple memory-to-memory operations such as *move* or *swap*.

It is natural to ask whether the converse holds: does asynchronous PRAM permit non-blocking implementations of the remaining objects, objects that do *not* solve two-process consensus? In this paper, we show that the answer is *no*. In a system of two processes, we demonstrate the existence of the following strict infinite hierarchy among objects with consensus number 1.

- Objects without non-blocking implementations. These objects are too weak to solve two-process consensus, yet they cannot be implemented (in asynchronous PRAM) without critical sections.

- Objects with implementations that are non-blocking, but not wait-free. These objects can be

implemented without critical sections, but it is impossible to guarantee fairness.

- Objects with implementations that are wait-free, but not bounded wait-free. Each operation requires a finite number of steps, but there is no bound common to all operations.

- For all $k > 0$, objects with implementations that are K-bounded wait-free for some $K > k$, but not k-bounded wait-free.

This hierarchy is shown schematically in Figure 1. Our impossibility results (e.g., this object has no wait-free implementation) apply to systems with arbitrary numbers of processes, but some of our constructions (e.g., this object does have a non-blocking implementation) apply only to systems of two processes.

A specific contribution of this paper is the hierarchy itself, which shows that even relatively "weak" concurrent objects have a rich mathematical structure. Moreover, each level of the hierarchy requires a different kind of proof technique. Another, more general, contribution is to raise basic questions about the value of the asynchronous PRAM model. Although some synchronous PRAM algorithms can be adapted to asynchronous PRAM [8, 9, 14, 25], our results show that there is little hope of constructing useful highly-concurrent long-lived data structures in this model. Fortunately, however, one can argue that asynchronous PRAM is an incomplete reflection of current practice. Starting with the IBM System/370 architecture [19] in the early 1970's, nearly every major architecture has provided some kind of atomic read-modify-write primitive. We have shown elsewhere that one can construct a bounded wait-free implementation of any object by augmenting the read and write operations with sufficiently powerful read-modify-write primitives, such as *compare&swap* [16]. It is not our intent here to suggest a specific alternative model, but we do believe that the research community would benefit from a more realistic and powerful model of concurrent shared-memory computation.

2   The Model

A *concurrent system* consists of a collection of n *processes* that communicate through shared typed *objects*. Processes are *sequential* — each process applies a sequence of operations to objects, alternately issuing an invocation and then receiving the associated response. We make no fairness assumptions about processes. A process can halt, or display arbitrary variations in speed. In particular, one process cannot tell whether another has halted or is just running very slowly.

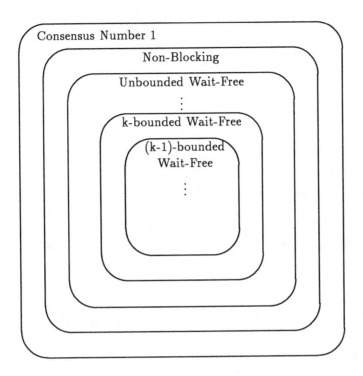

Figure 1: Hierarchy of Objects with Consensus Number 1

Objects are data structures in memory. Each object has a *type*, which defines a set of possible *values* and a set of primitive *operations* that provide the only means to manipulate that object. Each object has a *sequential specification* that defines how the object behaves when its operations are invoked one at a time by a single process. For example, the behavior of a queue object can be specified by requiring that *enq* insert an item in the queue, and that *deq* remove the oldest item in the queue. In a concurrent system, however, an object's operations can be invoked by concurrent processes, and it is necessary to give a meaning to interleaved operation executions. An object is *linearizable* [18] if each operation appears to take effect instantaneously at some point between the operation's invocation and response. Linearizability implies that processes appear to be interleaved at the granularity of complete operations, and that the order of non-overlapping operations is preserved.

A *consensus protocol* is a system of n processes that communicate through a set of shared objects. The processes each start with an input value, either 0 or 1. Each process communicates with the others by applying operations to shared objects, and each process eventually chooses an output value and halts. A consensus protocol is required to be:

- *Consistent*: distinct processes never decide on distinct values.

- *Wait-free*: each process decides after a finite number of steps.

- *Valid*: the common decision value is the input to some process.

It is impossible to solve consensus for two or more processes in the asynchronous PRAM model [1, 6, 7, 10, 17, 22].

3 The Wait-Free Hierarchy

In this section, we construct a family of objects with the property that, for all k, there exists an object whose implementations are K-bounded wait-free but not k-bounded wait-free, for some $K > k$. There also exists an object whose implementations are wait-free but not k-bounded wait-free for any k. We prove the lower bounds by reducing the (difficult) problem of analyzing all possible implementations of a particular object to the (more tractable) problem of analyzing solutions to a related decision problem.

If S is a set of real numbers, let $range(S) = [\min(S), \max(S)]$, $midpoint(S) = (\min(S)+\max(S))/2$, and $|S| = \max(S) - \min(S)$. An *approximate agreement object* provides two operations:

```
Object State:
    X is a set of reals, initially ∅.
    Y is a set of reals, initally ∅.

input(P, x)
    pre: true
    post: X' = X ∪ {x}

y := output(P)
    pre: X ≠ ∅
    post: Y' = Y ∪ {y} ∧
          range(Y) ⊂ range(X) ∧
          |Y| < ε.
```

Figure 2: Sequential Specification for Approximate Agreement

```
input(P: process, x: real)
output(P: process) returns (real)
```

A sequential specification for these operations, expressed in terms of pre- and post-conditions, appears in Figure 2. The object's abstract state has two components: a set of real *input values* X and a set of real *output values* Y, initially both empty. In postconditions, X' and Y' denote the components' new states. The *input* operation inserts its argument value in X. The *output* operation is defined only when X is non-empty. It inserts its result in Y, ensuring that $range(Y) \subset range(X)$ and $|Y| < \epsilon$ for some fixed $\epsilon > 0$. For brevity, we leave unspecified how *output* behaves when X is empty. As a decision problem, approximate agreement has been studied in a variety of message-passing models [3, 11, 12, 23], and Attiya, Lynch, and Shavit [2] independently derive upper and lower bounds for approximate agreement in shared memory that imply those given here.

A wait-free implementation of an approximate agreement object appears in Figure 3. The object is represented by an n-element array r of *entries*, where each entry has two fields: an integer round initially zero, and a real prefer, initially ⊥. A process is a *leader* if its round field is greater than or equal to any other process's round field. P *advances* its entry by setting its preference to the midpoint of the leaders' preferences and by incrementing its round field by one. P *scans* the entries by reading them in an arbitrary order.

The first time P calls *input*, it sets prefer to its input value. Subsequent calls have no effect. When P calls *output*, it returns the results of executing a wait-free approximate agreement protocol. This protocol consists of a loop in which P scans the entries, and discards those whose round fields trail its own by two or more. If the diameter of the remaining preferences is less than $\epsilon/2$,

```
input(P: process, x: real)
    if r[P].prefer = ⊥
        then r[P] := [prefer: x, round: 1]
    end if
end input

output(P: process)
    advance := false
    loop
        E := entries that trail mine by 1 or less
        L := leading entries
        if |E| < ε/2
            then return r[P].prefer
            elseif |L| < ε/2 or advance
                then r := [prefer: midpoint(L),
                           round: r.round + 1]
                     advance := false
            else  advance := ¬ advance
        end if
    end loop
end output
```

Figure 3: Wait-Free Implementation of Approximate Agreement Object

P returns its own preference. If the diameter of the leaders' preferences is less than $\epsilon/2$, then P advances its entry and resumes the loop. If the diameter of the leaders' preferences exceeds $\epsilon/2$, then P rescans the entries once more before advancing its entry. For brevity, "P's r-entry" (or r-preference) refers to P's entry (or preference) with round number r.

First, we show that this implementation is correct. Let X_r denote the set of entries having round number r. (We sometimes abuse notation and use X_r to stand for the set of r-preferences; the exact meaning should be clear from context.)

Lemma 1 $X_r \subset X_{r-1}$.

Proof: By induction on round numbers. P's initial preference is trivially in $range(X_1)$. Assume the result for rounds less than r, and suppose P creates an r-preference x_p. If $\mathcal{L}_P$ is the set of leaders P observes, then $\mathcal{L}_P \subset range(X_{r-1})$ by the induction hypothesis, hence $x_p = midpoint(\mathcal{L}_P) \in range(X_{r-1})$. ∎

P *expands* X_r if it writes a preference that increases $|X_r|$.

Lemma 2 *If P expands X_r after observing the set of leaders $\mathcal{L}_P$, then the entries in $\mathcal{L}_P$ have round number $r-1$.*

Proof: They cannot have a lower round number, since P observes its own entry, and they cannot have a higher round number, since then $midpoint(\mathcal{L}_P) \in range(X_r)$.
∎

Lemma 3 $|X_r| \leq |X_{r-1}|/2$.

Proof: Let P be the first process to write $x_p = \min(X_r)$, Q be the first process to write $x_q = \max(X_r)$, and let $\mathcal{L}_P$ and $\mathcal{L}_Q$ their respective sets of leaders. Since both writes expand X_r, Lemma 2 implies that all entries in $\mathcal{L}_P$ and $\mathcal{L}_Q$ have round number $r-1$. One of P or Q must have observed the other's $(r-1)$-preference, so $\mathcal{L}_P \cap \mathcal{L}_Q \neq \emptyset$. Therefore, $|x_p - x_q| \leq |\mathcal{L}_P|/2 + |\mathcal{L}_Q|/2 \leq |X_{r-1}|/2$.
∎

Lemma 4 *If P returns x_p at round r, and Q writes x_q at round r, then $|x_p - x_q| < \epsilon$.*

Proof: By contradiction. Let Q be the first process to write x_q such that $|x_p - x_q| \geq \epsilon$, let $\mathcal{L}_P$ be the set of leaders observed by P *after* writing x_p, and let $\mathcal{L}_Q$ be the set of leaders observed by Q *before* writing x_q. Note that $x_p \in range(\mathcal{L}_P)$ and $x_q \in range(\mathcal{L}_Q)$. Moreover, $x_q \notin \mathcal{L}_P$ because $|\mathcal{L}_P| < \epsilon/2$, and $x_p \notin \mathcal{L}_Q$, by Lemma 2.

Suppose $|\mathcal{L}_Q| < \epsilon/2$. Because each process wrote its $(r-1)$-entry before reading the other's entry, and because neither process read the other's r-entry, one of the two processes must have read the other's $(r-1)$-entry, and therefore $\mathcal{L}_P \cap \mathcal{L}_Q \neq \emptyset$. It follows that $|\mathcal{L}_P \cap \mathcal{L}_Q| \leq |\mathcal{L}_P| + |\mathcal{L}_Q| < \epsilon$. Because x_p and x_q lie within $range(\mathcal{L}_P \cup \mathcal{L}_Q)$, $|x_p - x_q| < \epsilon$.

Otherwise, if $|\mathcal{L}_Q| \geq \epsilon/2$, then Q reads twice before writing x_q. Let $\mathcal{L}'_Q$ be the set of leaders it saw during the first read. Since Q reads twice, $|\mathcal{L}'_Q| \geq \epsilon/2$. If Q finished reading $\mathcal{L}'_Q$ before Q wrote x_p, then $\mathcal{L}'_Q \subset \mathcal{L}_P$, and $|\mathcal{L}'_Q| \leq |\mathcal{L}_P| < \epsilon/2$, a contradiction. If Q finished reading $\mathcal{L}'_Q$ after Q wrote x_p, then it started reading $\mathcal{L}_Q$ afterwards, and $x_p \in \mathcal{L}_Q$, a contradiction.
∎

Theorem 5 *There exists a wait-free implementation of the approximate agreement object in asynchronous PRAM.*

Proof: We show that the protocol in Figure 3 is correct. There are three points to check: (1) that every output value lies within the original input range, (2) that the diameter of the output set is less than ϵ, and (3) that the algorithm is wait-free.

The first point is an immediate consequence of Lemma 1. For the second point, suppose P returns x_p after round r and Q returns x_q after round s, where $r \leq s$. Lemma 4 states that every element of X_r lies within ϵ of x_p, and Lemma 1 that $X_s \subset X_r$, hence $|x_p - x_q| < \epsilon$. Finally, Lemma 3 states that $|X_r| < \epsilon/2$ for some r, implying that every process will return on or before round $r+1$.
∎

Lemma 6 *An adversary scheduler can force some process executing an output to execute $\lfloor \log_3(\Delta/\epsilon) \rfloor$ steps before finishing.*

Proof: It is enough to prove the result for two processes. Consider an execution in which P and Q have distinct input values, and each executes an *output*. Define a process's *preference* at any point to be the value it returns if it runs uninterruptedly to conclusion. The *output* operations cannot both terminate while their preferences differ by more than ϵ. Initially, each process's preference is its input.

Consider the following scenario. Run P until it is about to change Q's preference, then do the same for Q. Alternate P and Q in this way as long as neither process changes preference. Eventually, since the operations cannot run forever, the object reaches a state where each process is about to change the other's preference. The adversary now has a choice of running P, Q, or both. Let p_0 be P's current preference, p_1 its preference if Q takes the next step, and let q_0 and q_1 be defined similarly. Depending on whom the adversary schedules next, the new preferences will differ by either $|p_0 - q_1|$, $|p_1 - q_0|$, or $|p_1 - q_1|$. The sum of these quantities is at least $|p_0 - q_0|$, thus the adversary can always choose one that is greater than or equal to $|p_0 - q_0|/3$, preventing the gap between the preferences from shrinking by more than one third. Repeating this strategy for k rounds, an adversary scheduler can ensure that the range of the preferences is at least $\Delta/(3^k)$, yielding the desired lower bound.
∎

Theorem 7 *For all $k > 0$, there exists an object with a K-bounded wait-free implementation, for $K > k$, that is not k-bounded wait-free.*

Proof: Consider an approximate agreement object with the unit interval as potential input range, and $\epsilon = 1/3^k$.
∎

Theorem 8 *There exists an object with a wait-free implementation but no bounded wait-free implementation.*

Proof: Consider an approximate agreement object with the rational numbers as potential input range.
∎

```
Object State:
    x_p and x_q are reals, initially ⊥.
    y_p and y_q are reals, initially ⊥.
    r_p and r_q are integers, initially 0.

    input(P, x)
        pre:  x_p = ⊥
        post: x'_p = x

    y := output(P)
        pre:  x_p ≠ ⊥ ∧ x_q = ⊥
        post: y'_p = x ∧ r'_p = r_p + 1

    y := output(P)
        pre:  x_p ≠ ⊥ ∧ x_q ≠ ⊥
        post: y'_p = y ∧
              |y'_p - y_q| < ε/2^{r_p} ∧
              y'_p ∈ range(x_p, x_q) ∧
              r'_p = r_p + 1
```

Figure 4: Sequential Specification for Iterated Approximate Agreement

4 Non-Blocking

In this section, we construct an object having consensus number 1, a non-blocking implementation, but no wait-free implementation. This section illustrates an important difference between long-lived objects and short-lived decision problems: a decision problem, but definition, is executed once, and hence cannot distinguish between the non-blocking and wait-free properties.

We consider a system of two processes, P and Q. An *iterated approximate agreement* object has two operations:

```
input(P: process, x: real)
output(P: process) returns (real).
```

Each process P has a *starting estimate* x_p, and a *current estimate* y_p. As shown in Figure 4, P's starting estimate is initialized by *input*. Its current estimate is updated by *output* so that following P's i^{th} output, the range of the two processes' current estimates is less than $\epsilon/2^i$ for some fixed $\epsilon > 0$, and lies within the range of their original estimates. (The sequence of current estimates forms a Cauchy sequence that converges on a point in the range of the original estimates.) For simplicity, our specifications focus on executions in which any process that executes any operations executes an *input* followed by a sequence of *outputs*.

A non-blocking implementation of the iterated approximate agreement object is shown in Figure 5. The

```
input(P: process, x: real)
    r[P] := [prefer: x, round: 0]
    previous := [-∞, +∞]
end input

output(P: process) returns(real)
    p := r[P]
    p.round := p.round + 1
    loop
        r[P] := p
        q := r[Q]
        i := p.round + q.round
        range := [p.prefer ± ε/(2^i)]
        if q.prefer ∈ range or q.prefer ∉ previous
            then previous := range
                    return p.prefer
            elseif p.prefer < q.prefer
                then p.prefer := p.prefer + ε/(2^i)
                else  p.prefer := p.prefer - ε/(2^i)
            end if
        end loop
    end output
```

Figure 5: Non-Blocking Iterated Approximate Agreement Implementation

object is represented by a two-element array r of *entries*, where each entry has two fields: an integer round, initially 0, and a real prefer, initally ⊥. Each process also has a persistent local variable previous, which holds a real interval, and survives from one invocation to the next. When P calls *input*, it initializes round to zero, prefer to the input value, and previous to the real line. When P calls *output*, it reads its entry, increments round, and enters the loop. Each time through the loop, it updates its own entry and reads Q's. It sums the two entries' round fields in variable i, and constructs a *desired* interval of radius $\epsilon/(2^i)$. If Q's preference lies outside P's previous interval, then it returns immediately. If Q's preference lies within the desired interval, then it returns, otherwise it chooses a new preference closer to the other's.

Lemma 9 *Every current estimate lies within the range of the original estimates.*

Proof: Initially, every preference lies within the original range, and each new preference lies between two earlier preferences.   ∎

Lemma 10 *The operations in Figure 5 are non-blocking.*

Proof: It suffices to check that two concurrent *output* operations cannot both take an infinite number of steps without returning. If P takes only a finite number of steps, then Q's preference will converge to P's, and Q will return. If P and Q both take an infinite number of steps, then once P and Q have each written a preference and read the other's, then each time through the loop reduces the distance between their preferences by a fixed amount, and eventually one will return. ∎

We use the following notation: p and q are output operations of P and Q, $\pi(p)$ is p's current preference (if active) or final return value (if completed), $\alpha(p)$ is the first value p assigns to variable i, and $\omega(p)$ is the current value of i (if active) or last value (if completed).

We construct an explicit linearization order as follows: if $\alpha(p) < \alpha(q)$ then p is ordered before q, and if $\alpha(p) = \alpha(q)$ then p and q are ordered arbitrarily.

Lemma 11 *The α function defines a valid linearization order.*

Proof: If p finishes before q begins, then $\alpha(p) < \alpha(q)$. ∎

Define $B(p)$ to be the open ball of radius $\epsilon/(2^{\omega(p)})$ around $\pi(p)$. If p_i is P's i^{th} output, then $i \leq \alpha(p_i) \leq \omega(p_i)$. In particular, if $y \in B(p_i)$, then $|y - \pi(p_i)| < \epsilon/(2^i)$.

Lemma 12 *If p is a completed output of P, and p' a later output, either completed or active, then $B(p') \subset B(p)$.*

Proof: The distances from $\pi(p')$ to the endpoints of $B(p)$ are always integral multiples of $\omega(p')$. ∎

Theorem 13 *The algorithm in Figure 5 is a non-blocking implementation of an iterated approxmiate agreement object.*

Proof: Lemma 9 states that all estimates lie within the range of the current estimates, and Lemma 10 states that one operation will always complete in a finite number of steps. It remains to check that each process's i^{th} estimate lies within $\epsilon/(2^i)$ of the other's current estimate. Suppose p_i is linearized between q_j and q_{j+1}, and that p_i is the first to violate correctness.

Suppose p_i returns after observing that Q's preference lies outside P's prevously committed range. That preference must have been written by q_j, and q_j must still be active, thus p_i cannot be the first to violate correctness.

Suppose p_i returns after observing that $\pi(p_i)$ lies within $\epsilon/(2^{\omega(p)})$ of $\pi(q_k)$. Since $\omega(q_k) \leq \omega(p_i)$, $\pi(p_i) \in B(q_k)$. If $k = j$, then we are done, since q_{j+1} has no

return value yet. If $k \geq j$, Lemma 12 implies that $B(q_j) \subset B(q_{j+1}) \subseteq B(q_k)$, hence correctness is not violated. ∎

Although the algorithm in Figure 5 is non-blocking, one can easily check that it is not wait-free: an *output* operation can be forced to run forever if it is overtaken sufficiently often by other *outputs*. We now show that this property is inherent in any solution of iterated approximate agreement.

Consider an execution in which P and Q each performs an *input* followed by an *output*. Following the terminology of Fisher, Lynch, and Paterson [13], P is *bivalent* in any state where its output value is not yet determined, otherwise it is *univalent*. P's state is *x-valent* if it is univalent with eventual output value x. A *decision step* for P is an operation that carries P from a bivalent to a univalent state. P is *ambivalent* in a state s if there exists a state s' such that P is x-valent in s, y-valent in s', but s and s' are indistinguishable to Q.

Lemma 14 *From an initial state in which P and Q have different input values, it is possible to reach a state in which P is ambivalent.*

Proof: Assume without loss of generality that P has input 0, Q input 1, and $\epsilon < 1$. P is bivalent in this initial state: if P is run to completion before Q starts, its *output* returns 0, and if Q is run to completion before P starts, then P returns a value in $(1 - \epsilon, 1]$.

Consider the following execution, which leaves P bivalent. In the first stage, run P until it reaches a state where it cannot continue without becoming univalent. P must eventually reach such a state, since it cannot run forever. In the second stage, run Q until it cannot continue without making P univalent, and in successive stages, alternate running P and Q until each is about to make P univalent. Because the processes cannot run forever leaving P bivalent, it must eventually reach a state s in which any subsequent step of either process forces P to be univalent. Since P is still bivalent, however, some enabled step of P carries P to an x-valent state, and some enabled step of Q carries P to a y-valent state, where x and y are distinct.

We now do a case analysis of the operations executed by P and Q. In each case, we show that certain combinations are impossible by constructing two executions starting in s, one in which P returns x, and one in which P returns y, but where the protocol states appear identical to P.

- Suppose Q is about to read a shared register. (1) P runs to completion, returning x, and (2) Q reads, and P executes to completion, returning y.

- Suppose the processes are about to write to different registers. (1) P writes, Q writes, and P executes to completion, returning x, and (2) Q writes, P writes, and P executes to completion, returning y.

- Suppose the processes are about to write to the same register. (1) P writes and P executes to completion, returning x, and (2) Q writes, P writes, and P executes to completion, returning y.

The only remaining combination is that P is about to read a register which Q is about to write. As soon as Q writes, P's state becomes ambivalent, since P must be univalent, but Q has no way to predict P's output. ∎

Bivalence arguments have been used to show the impossibility of shared-memory consensus [1, 7, 10, 17, 22], and the *ambiguous choice lemma* of Burns and Peterson [6].

Theorem 15 *The iterated approximate agreement object has no wait-free implementation.*

Proof: Consider an execution in which P and Q respectively input 0 and 1 and execute a single *output*. By Lemma 14, it is possible to reach a state where P's *output* has returned, Q's has not, and Q is ambivalent. Let y and z be two possible values Q could return in this state. Pick a k such that $\epsilon/(2^k) < |y - z|$. If P executes k more *outputs* in isolation, then it will be unable to return a value consistent with both y and z. ∎

5 Final Impossibility Results

In this section, we construct an object having consensus number 1 but no non-blocking implementation. To prove this result, we exhibit an object with the curious property that although it itself is too weak to solve two-process consensus, it can only be implemented by "stronger" objects that do solve consensus.

A *blind consensus* object's state consists of two boolean variables, called *red* and *blue*, initially both *false*. It provides two operations:

fix(c: color) returns (boolean)
blind() returns (color,boolean)

The first time *fix* is called, it sets the argument variable to *true* and returns its previous value. Subsequent calls with the same argument leave the variables unaffected, and non-deterministically return either *true* or *false*. The *blind* operation non-deterministically chooses a variable, sets it to *true*, and returns the chosen variable's name and previous value.

Lemma 16 *The blind consensus object cannot solve two-process consensus.*

Proof: Suppose otherwise. By an argument similar to the one given above in the proof of Theorem 15, any two-process consensus protocol can be maneuvered into a state where the decision value is 0 if P takes the next step, and 1 if Q takes the next step. The rest is a case analysis.

Suppose P and Q both call *fix*. If the invocations have distinct arguments, then they commute, so assume the invocations both apply to *red*. One possible execution is: P's call to *fix* returns some value v, any subsequent calls to *fix* also return v, any subsequent calls to *blind* apply to *blue*, and P eventually decides 0. Another possible execution is: Q's call to *fix* returns v, P's subsequent calls to *fix* also return v, its subsequent calls to *blind* apply to *blue*, and P eventually decides 1. Since the two executions appear equivalent to P, we have a contradiction.

If P applies *fix* to *red* and Q calls blind, then *blind* can always choose *blue*, forcing the operations to commute. Similarly, if both processes call *blind*, the operations can always choose distinct variables. ∎

Theorem 17 *It is impossible to construct a non-blocking implementation of a blind consensus object in asynchronous PRAM.*

Proof: We show that any *implementation* of a blind consensus object can be transformed into a two-process consensus protocol.

An operation implementation is *deterministic* if it always returns the same response when run in the absence of concurrency. We may restrict our attention to deterministic implementations, since any non-deterministic implementation can always be rendered deterministic by fixing the outcome of any non-deterministic choices. Suppose the *blind* operation returns *red* when executed in isolation by P starting in the initial state (the case where it returns *blue* is symmetric). Now, we construct a consensus protocol as follows. P executes the implementation of *blind*, and Q executes the implementation of *red*. They decide 0 if P's result is (*red, false*) and Q's is *true*, and otherwise they decide 1. It is easily checked that this protocol is consistent, wait-free, and valid. ∎

We leave as an interesting open question whether every object whose sequential specification is *deterministic* has a non-blocking implementation in asynchronous PRAM.

Acknowledgments

Hagit Attiya's remarks helped improve this paper.

References

[1] J.H. Anderson and M.G. Gouda. The virtue of patience: Concurrent programming with and without waiting. University of Texas at Austin Technical Report.

[2] H. Attiya, N. Lynch, and N. Shavit. Are wait-free algorithms fast? In *31st Annual Symposium on the Foundations of Computer Science*, October 1990.

[3] O. Biran, S. Moran, and S. Zaks. A combinatorial characterization of the distributed tasks which are solvable in the presence of one faulty processor. In *Seventh ACM SIGACT-SIGOPS Symposium on Principles of Distributed Computing*, pages 263–273, August 1988.

[4] B. Bloom. Constructing two-writer atomic registers. In *Proceedings of the Sixth ACM Symposium on Principles of Distributed Computing*, pages 249–259, 1987.

[5] J.E. Burns and G.L. Peterson. Constructing multireader atomic values from non-atomic values. In *Proceedings of the Sixth ACM Symposium on Principles of Distributed Computing*, pages 222–231, 1987.

[6] J.E. Burns and G.L. Peterson. The ambiguity of choosing. In *Eighth ACM SIGACT-SIGOPS Symposium on Principles of Distributed Computing*, pages 145–157, August 1989.

[7] B. Chor, A. Israeli, and M. Li. On processor coordination using asynchronous hardware. In *Proceedings of the Sixth ACM Symposium on Principles of Distributed Computing*, pages 86–97, 1987.

[8] R. Cole and O. Zajicek. The apram: incorporating asynchrony into the pram model. In *Proceedings of the 1989 Symposium on Parallel Algorithms and Architectures*, pages 169–178, Santa Fe, NM, June 1989.

[9] R. Cole and O. Zajicek. The expected advantage of asynchrony. In *2nd ACM Symposium on Parallel Algorithms and Architectures*, pages 85–94, July 1990.

[10] D. Dolev, C. Dwork, and L Stockmeyer. On the minimal synchronism needed for distributed consensus. *Journal of the ACM*, 34(1):77–97, January 1987.

[11] D. Dolev, N.A. Lynch, S.S. Pinter, E.W. Stark, and William E. Weihl. Reaching approximate agreement in the presence of faults. *Journal of the ACM*, 33(3):499–516, July 1986.

[12] A. Fekete. Asymptotically optimal algorithms for approximate agreement. In *Fifth ACM SIGACT-SIGOPS Symposium on Principles of Distributed Computing*, pages 73–87, August 1986.

[13] M. Fischer, N.A. Lynch, and M.S. Paterson. Impossibility of distributed commit with one faulty process. *Journal of the ACM*, 32(2), April 1985.

[14] P.B. Gibbons. A more practical pram model. In *ACM Symposium on Parallel Algorithms and Architectures*, pages 158–168. ACM, July 1989.

[15] M.P. Herlihy. Impossibility and universality results for wait-free synchronization. In *Seventh ACM SIGACT-SIGOPS Symposium on Principles of Distributed Computing*, pages 276–290, August 1988.

[16] M.P. Herlihy. A methodology for implementing highly concurrent data structures. In *Proceedings of the Second ACM SIGPLAN Symposium on Principles and Practice of Parallel Programming*, pages 197–206, March 1990.

[17] M.P. Herlihy. Wait-free synchronization. *ACM Transactions on Programming Languages and Systems*, 13(1):124–149, January 1991.

[18] M.P. Herlihy and J.M. Wing. Linearizability: A correctness condition for concurrent objects. *ACM Transactions on Programming Languages and Systems*, 12(3):463–492, July 1990.

[19] IBM. System/370 principles of operation. Order Number GA22-7000.

[20] L. Lamport. Concurrent reading and writing. *Communications of the ACM*, 20(11):806–811, November 1977.

[21] L. Lamport. On interprocess communication, parts i and ii. *Distributed Computing*, 1:77–101, 1986.

[22] M.C. Loui and H.H. Abu-Amara. *Memory Requirements for Agreement Among Unreliable Asynchronous Processes*, volume 4, pages 163–183. JAI Press, 1987.

[23] S. Mahaney and F.B. Schneider. Inexact agreement: Accuracy, precision, and graceful degradation. In *Fourth ACM SIGACT-SIGOPS Symposium on Principles of Distributed Computing*, pages 237–249, August 1985.

[24] R. Newman-Wolfe. A protocol for wait-free, atomic, multi-reader shared variables. In *Proceedings of the Sixth ACM Symposium on Principles of Distributed Computing*, pages 232–249, 1987.

[25] N. Nishimura. Asynchronous shared memory parallel computation. In *2nd ACM Symposium on Parallel Algorithms and Architectures*, pages 76–84, July 1990.

[26] G.L. Peterson. Concurrent reading while writing. *ACM Transactions on Programming Languages and Systems*, 5(1):46–55, January 1983.

[27] G.L. Peterson and J.E. Burns. Concurrent reading while writing ii: the multi-writer case. Technical Report GIT-ICS-86/26, Georgia Institute of Technology, December 1986.

SESSION 9

Understanding Retiming
through
Maximum Average-Weight Cycles

Marios C. Papaefthymiou*

Laboratory for Computer Science
Massachusetts Institute of Technology
Cambridge, MA 02139

Abstract

A synchronous circuit built of functional elements
and registers is a simple implementation of the
semisystolic model of computation that can be used
to design parallel algorithms. Retiming is a well-
known technique that can transform a given circuit into a faster circuit by relocating its registers.
We give novel and tight bounds on the minimum
clock period that can be achieved by retiming a
synchronous circuit. These bounds are expressed
in terms of the maximum delay-to-register ratio of
the cycles in the circuit graph, and the maximum
propagation delay D of the circuit components.
Our bounds are of theoretical as well as practical interest. They are the first bounds presented
that do not depend on the size of the circuit, and
they characterize exactly the minimum clock period that can be achieved by retiming a unit-delay
circuit. They also lead to more efficient algorithms
for several important problems related to retiming.
In particular, we give an $O(V^{1/2}E\lg(VW))$ algorithm for minimum clock period retiming of unit-
delay circuitry, where W is the maximum number
of registers on any wire in the circuit. We also give

an $O(VE\lg D)$ algorithm for minimum clock period retiming of circuitry with arbitrary delays, and
an $O(E\lg D)$ algorithm for minimum clock period
pipelining of combinational circuitry. These running times are an improvement over the previous
best bounds for the same problems.

1 Introduction

The semisystolic model of computation affords
great flexibility and ease in designing parallel algorithms, and can be implemented by synchronous
circuits built of *functional elements* and globally
clocked *registers* [6]. Retiming, which was introduced in [7, 8, 9] and treated in [10], is a well-known
design automation technique which can be used to
transform a given synchronous circuit into a faster
circuit, that is, a circuit with shorter clock period,
by relocating the registers of the given circuit while
preserving its functionality. In this paper we further investigate retiming and provide results of theoretical as well as practical interest. Specifically, we
give novel and tight bounds on the minimum clock
period that can be achieved by retiming a circuit
in terms of the maximum delay-to-register ratio of
the cycles in the circuit graph and the maximum
propagation delay of the components in the circuit. These bounds characterize exactly the minimum clock period that can be achieved by retiming
a unit-delay circuit, and they are the first bounds
presented that do not depend on the size of the
circuit. We use these bounds to obtain improved
algorithms for several important problems related

*Supported in part by the Defense Advanced Research
Projects Agency under contract N00014-87-K-0825. Author's e-mail address marios@theory.lcs.mit.edu.

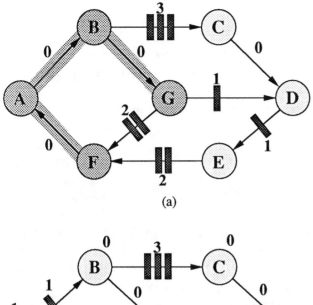

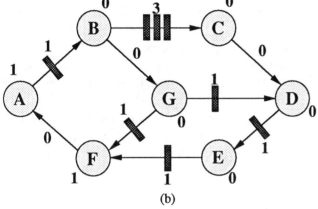

Figure 1: (a) A synchronous circuit G with unit-delay functional elements. The vertices represent functional elements, the edges represent wires, and the rectangles represent registers. The integers next to the edges indicate number of registers. The clock period of the circuit is 4 units of time (path FABG). (b) A retiming of G. The integer assignment is indicated next to the vertices. The clock period of this circuit is 2 units of time.

to retiming.

We model a synchronous circuit according to [7, 8, 9] by a *circuit graph* $G = (V, E, d, w)$. A vertex $v \in V$ corresponds to a functional element of the circuit, and an edge $u \xrightarrow{e} v \in E$ corresponds to a wire between the functional elements u and v. The integer edge-weight $w(e)$ is the number of registers on the directed edge e. The vertex-weight $d(v)$ is the propagation delay of the signals through the functional element v. For simplicity we assume that vertex-weights are integers. Figure 1(a) illustrates a synchronous circuit with unit-delay functional elements.

Intuitively, the circuit operates as follows. Between any two consecutive clock ticks, signals propagate along wires and ripple concurrently through the functional elements. By the end of a clock period all signals must have settled in the registers of the circuit. Although the functional elements of the circuit operate in parallel, some signals may require more time to settle than others, because they experience longer propagation delays along their paths. The *clock period* $\Phi(G)$ of the system is defined naturally as the propagation delay of the longest register-free path in the circuit, which is well defined for *synchronous circuits* in which every directed cycle contains at least one register. For example, the clock period of the unit-delay circuit in Figure 1(a) is 4 units of time (path FABG).

A *retiming* r of G is an assignment $r : V \to \mathbf{Z}$, such that $w(e) + r(u) - r(v) \geq 0$. Given r, we transform the circuit by removing $r(v)$ registers from every edge coming into v, and adding $r(v)$ registers to every edge going out of v. This results to a retimed circuit $G_r = (V, E, d, w_r)$, with $w_r(e) = w(e) + r(u) - r(v) \geq 0$ for every edge $u \xrightarrow{e} v \in E$. In Figure 1(b) we have retimed the circuit of Figure 1(a) so that the resulting circuit has a clock period of 2 units of time. Note that the total number of registers around any cycle in the circuit remains invariant after retiming.

The *delay-to-register* ratio of a directed cycle in a circuit is defined as the ratio of the total propagation delay around the cycle over the total number of registers in the cycle. For example, the delay-to-register ratio of the directed cycle ABCDEF in Figure 1 is $6/6 = 1$. Observe that the delay-to-register ratio of any cycle is the same in the original circuit G and in the retimed circuit G_r, since both the total delay and the number of registers around any cycle remain invariant after retiming. This observation suggests a relation between the minimum clock period that we can achieve by retiming G and the maximum delay-to-register ratio in G. Let us illustrate this relation by means of our example circuit in Figure 1. Consider the cycle ABGF with delay-to-register ratio $4/2 = 2$, which is the *maximum* among the three directed cycles in G. It is not possible to distribute the registers around ABGF in a way that achieves a clock period smaller than the average delay per register in

ABGF, since the delay-to-register ratio around any cycle in G_r remains invariant. Therefore, G cannot be retimed to achieve a clock period smaller than 2, the delay-to-register ratio of ABGF, and the circuit in Figure 1(b) has achieved its minimum possible clock period.

In this paper we prove that rounding up the maximum delay-to-register ratio in any unit-delay circuit yields a lower bound on the minimum clock period achievable by retiming. Moreover, we show that there always exists a retiming which achieves this lower bound. Therefore, the maximum delay-to-register ratio in any *unit-delay* circuit characterizes exactly the minimum clock period achievable by retiming. For circuits with arbitrary delays, we use the maximum delay-to-register ratio to obtain strong bounds on the minimum clock period achievable by retiming. These bounds yield better algorithms for several important problems related to retiming, such as minimum clock period retiming, retiming for approximately minimum clock period and minimum clock period pipelining.

The rest of the paper has eight sections. In Section 2 we introduce some notation and we state the tight bounds on the minimum clock period $\Phi_{min}(G)$ that can be achieved by retiming a circuit G. Specifically, we claim that $\Phi_{min}(G)$ is bounded from below by the ceiling of the maximum delay-to-register ratio, and that $\Phi_{min}(G)$ does not exceed this lower bound by more than an additive factor of $D - 1$, where D is the maximum propagation delay of the elements in the circuit. These are the first bounds presented that do not depend on the size of the circuit. For the special case of circuits with unit-delay functional elements, it follows directly from the given bounds that we can obtain the minimum clock period $\Phi_{min}(G)$ simply by rounding up the maximum delay-to-register ratio of these circuits. (This result for unit-delay has been claimed independently in [2].) In Section 3 we prove the lower bound, and in Section 4 we prove the upper bound for $\Phi_{min}(G)$.

In Sections 5 through 8, we focus on the algorithmic implications of the minimum clock period characterization for several specific problems related to retiming. Section 5 gives an $O(V^{1/2}E \lg(VW))$ procedure for retiming unit-delay circuits with the minimum possible clock period $\Phi_{min}(G)$, where W

is the maximum number of registers on any wire in the circuit. Our procedure utilizes known scaling algorithms for finding maximum average-weight cycles and single-source shortest-paths in a graph [11, 3]. Its running time improves the running time obtained using the techniques in [10] by a multiplicative factor of $O(\lg V)$.

In Section 6 we show how arbitrary delay circuits can be retimed to achieve their minimum clock period in $O(VE \lg D)$ steps. Our algorithm performs a preprocessing step for computing the maximum delay-to-register ratio in the circuit, followed by a binary search of an interval of D possible clock periods. Assuming that the maximum propagation delay D of the circuit components and the maximum number W of registers on any wire in the circuit grow subpolynomially with the size of the circuit (actually, it is realistic to assume that D and W do not depend at all on the size of the circuit), our algorithm is asymptotically more efficient than the previously known schemes [10], because our preprocessing step guarantees that the range of the binary search is small.

An $O(V^{1/2}E \lg(VWD) \lg(VD))$ procedure for retiming a circuit with arbitrary delays is described in Section 7. The retimed circuit achieves a clock period that does not exceed the minimum by more than an additive factor of $D - 1$. This algorithm is asymptotically more efficient than the algorithm for minimum clock period retiming in Section 6 by an $O(V^{1/2} \lg D/(\lg(VWD) \lg(VD)))$ multiplicative factor. Its running time is close to that of the algorithm in Section 5 for minimum clock period retiming of unit-delay circuitry.

In Section 8 we extend our minimum clock period characterization to cover the case of combinational circuits, that is, circuits with no directed cycles in their graphs. We show how to pipeline combinational circuits in $O(E \lg D)$ steps in order to achieve minimum clock period for a given number of stages in the pipeline. For circuits with unit-delay elements, the running time is optimal within a constant multiplicative factor. The previous general techniques required $O(VE \lg V)$ steps [10]. Finally, Section 9 concludes the paper and proposes an interesting open problem.

2 Minimum Clock Period Characterization

In this section we relate the minimum clock period $\Phi_{min}(G)$ that we can obtain by retiming a given general circuit $G = (V, E, d, w)$ to the maximum delay-to-register ratio of the cycles in the circuit graph G and the maximum propagation delay of the circuit components.

First, we give some definitions that will allow us to state and prove our results formally. Let $G = (V, E, d, w)$ be a circuit graph. We define the *delay-to-register* ratio $R(C)$ of a cycle $C = v_0 \overset{e_0}{\to} v_1 \overset{e_1}{\to} \ldots \overset{e_{k-2}}{\to} v_{k-1} \overset{e_{k-1}}{\to} v_0$ in the circuit G as follows:

$$R(C) = \frac{\sum\limits_{v \in C} d(v)}{\sum\limits_{e \in C} w(e)}.$$

We denote by $C^*(G)$ the directed cycle in G with maximum delay-to-register ratio. By definition, $R(C^*(G)) \geq R(C)$ for every cycle $C \in G$. Finally, we denote by $\Phi_{min}(G)$ the smallest possible clock period that we can achieve by retiming G:

$$\Phi_{min}(G) = \min\{\Phi(G_r) : r \text{ is a retiming of } G\}.$$

Our first theorem bounds the range of the minimum clock period of a circuit.

Theorem 1 *Let $G = (V, E, d, w)$ be a synchronous circuit with maximum delay-to-register ratio $R(C^*(G))$, and let $\Phi_{min}(G)$ be the minimum clock period we can obtain by retiming G. Then*

$$\lceil R(C^*(G)) \rceil \leq \Phi_{min}(G) \leq \lceil R(C^*(G)) \rceil + D - 1,$$

where $D = \max\{d(v) : v \in V\}$. □

The proofs of the lower and the upper bound are given in Sections 3 and 4 respectively. Observe that both the upper and the lower bound are independent of the size of the circuit.

For unit-delay circuits, the bounds in Theorem 1 yield an exact characterization of the minimum clock period.

Corollary 1 *Let $G = (V, E, 1, w)$ be a unit-delay synchronous circuit with maximum delay-to-register ratio $R(C^*(G))$, and let $\Phi_{min}(G)$ be the minimum clock period we can obtain by retiming G. Then*

$$\lceil R(C^*(G)) \rceil = \Phi_{min}(G).$$

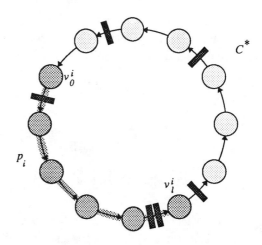

Figure 2: Path p_i used in the proof of the lower bound. Note that only the first and the last edge in the path have non-zero register count.

Proof: $D = 1$. □

As we shall see in Section 5, this property of the unit-delay circuits allows us to derive asymptotically more efficient schemes for their optimization.

3 Lower Bound

In this section we prove the lower bound of Theorem 1. Specifically, we prove the following lemma.

Lemma 1 *Let $G = (V, E, d, w)$ be a synchronous circuit with maximum delay-to-register ratio $R(C^*(G))$, and let $\Phi_{min}(G)$ be the minimum clock period we can obtain by retiming G. Then*

$$\lceil R(C^*(G)) \rceil \leq \Phi_{min}(G).$$

Proof: Assume that we have retimed G in such a way that it achieves the minimum possible clock period $\Phi_{min}(G)$. Let C^* be the cycle with maximum delay-to-register ratio in G (see Figure 2), and let $N = \{e \in C^* : w_r(e) > 0\}$. Now, consider a path $p_i = v_0^i \overset{e_0^i}{\to} v_1^i \overset{e_1^i}{\to} \ldots \overset{e_{l-2}^i}{\to} v_{l-1}^i \overset{e_{l-1}^i}{\to} v_l^i$ in C^*, such that $e_0^i, e_{l-1}^i \in N$ and $e_j^i \notin N$, for $j = 1, 2, \ldots, l-2$. Observe that only the first and the last edge in the path p_i have registers on them. Now, by definition of the clock period, the register-free part of p_i satisfies

$$\sum_{j=1}^{l-1} d(v_j^i) \leq \Phi_{min}(G).$$

There are $|N|$ paths around C^* that have the form of p_i. By summing up the $|N|$ corresponding inequalities for $\Phi_{min}(G)$, we obtain

$$\sum_{v \in C^*} d(v) \leq \Phi_{min}(G) \cdot |N|$$

$$\leq \Phi_{min}(G) \cdot \left(\sum_{e \in C^*} w_r(e) \right)$$

$$\leq \Phi_{min}(G) \cdot \left(\sum_{e \in C^*} w(e) \right),$$

since $w_r(e) = w(e) + r(u) - r(v)$ for every edge $u \xrightarrow{e} v$ and the sum $\sum_{e \in C^*} w_r(e)$ telescopes. Since the propagation delays are integers, $\Phi_{min}(G)$ must be an integer and therefore

$$\left\lceil \frac{\sum_{v \in C^*} d(v)}{\sum_{e \in C^*} w(e)} \right\rceil \leq \Phi_{min}(G).$$

The lemma follows directly from the definition of $R(C^*(G))$. □

4   Upper Bound

In this section we prove the upper bound of Theorem 1. Our proof uses a graph construction from [10], which we call *constraint graph*, and Lemma 2, whose correctness follows directly from the properties of the constraint graph [10] and basic properties of the shortest-paths [5].

Definition 1 *The* constraint graph *of a given circuit graph* $G = (V, E, d, w)$, *with respect to a given clock period* c, *is an edge-weighted graph* $G_c = (V, E_c, w_c)$ *with* $E_c = E \cup E'$, *where* $u_0 \xrightarrow{e} u_k \in E'$ *if and only if there exists a path* $p = u_0 \xrightarrow{e_0} u_1 \xrightarrow{e_1} \dots \xrightarrow{e_{k-2}} u_{k-1} \xrightarrow{e_{k-1}} u_k \in G$ *with* $\sum_{u_i \in p} d(u_i) > c$. *For every* $e \in E$ *we have* $w_c(e) = w(e)$ *and for every* $e \in E'$ *corresponding to a path* $p \in G$ *we have* $w_c(e) = \left(\sum_{e_i \in p} w(e_i) \right) - 1$.

Lemma 2 ([10]) *Given a circuit* $G = (V, E, d, w)$ *and a constant* c, *there exists a retiming* r *of* G *such that* $\Phi(G_r) \leq c$ *if and only if the constraint graph* G_c *has no negative edge-weight cycles.* □

Now, we can proceed with the proof of the upper bound.

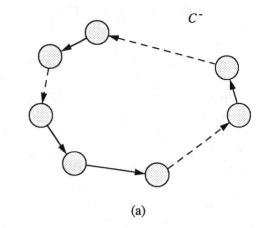

(a)

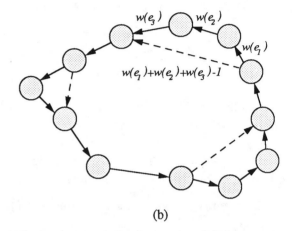

(b)

Figure 3: (a) The cycle C^- in G_c. The solid lines indicate edges in S. For simplicity, we have not indicated the registers on these edges. The broken lines indicate edges in S'. (b) After the introduction of the edges in S'' that correspond to the edges in S', the solid cycle has edges exclusively in G and its delay-to-register ratio is greater than $R(C^*(G))$.

Lemma 3 *Let* $G = (V, E, d, w)$ *be a synchronous circuit with maximum delay-to-register ratio* $R(C^*(G))$, *and let* $\Phi_{min}(G)$ *be the minimum clock period we can obtain by retiming* G. *Then*

$$\Phi_{min}(G) \leq \lceil R(C^*(G)) \rceil + D - 1.$$

Proof: The proof is by contradiction of the fact that $R(C^*(G))$ is the maximum delay-to-register ratio in G. Let us assume that there does not exist a retiming r, such that $\Phi(G_r) \leq \lceil R(C^*(G)) \rceil + D - 1$. Equivalently, according to Lemma 2, we assume that for $c = \lceil R(C^*(G)) \rceil + D - 1$ there exists a negative edge-weight cycle C^- in the constraint graph G_c (see Figure 3(a)). We can partition the edges of C^- into $C^- = S \cup S'$, where $S \subseteq E$ and $S' \subseteq E'$. Since the edge-weights are integral we have

$$\sum_{e \in S} w_c(e) + \sum_{e \in S'} w_c(e) \le -1. \tag{1}$$

Let $S'' = \{v_1 \to v_2 : u \to v \in S'$ corresponds to path $p \in G$, $v_1 \to v_2 \in p\}$ (see Figure 3(b)). Then, according to inequality (1), we have:

$$\sum_{e \in S} w(e) + \sum_{e \in S''} w(e)$$
$$= \sum_{e \in S} w(e) + \sum_{e \in S''} w(e) - |S'| + |S'|$$
$$= \sum_{e \in S} w(e) + \sum_{e \in S'} w_c(e) + |S'|$$
$$= \sum_{e \in S} w_c(e) + \sum_{e \in S'} w_c(e) + |S'|$$
$$\le |S'| - 1.$$

Note that $|S'| \ge 2$, because otherwise the cycle $S \cup S''$ would have no registers, which contradicts the fact that G is synchronous. Now, for the delay-to-register ratio of the cycle $S \cup S''$ in G we have:

$$\frac{\sum_{u \xrightarrow{e} v \in S} d(u) + \sum_{u \xrightarrow{e} v \in S''} d(u)}{\sum_{u \xrightarrow{e} v \in S} w(e) + \sum_{u \xrightarrow{e} v \in S''} w(e)}$$
$$\ge \frac{\sum_{u \xrightarrow{e} v \in S} d(u) + \sum_{u \xrightarrow{e} v \in S''} d(u)}{|S'| - 1}$$
$$\ge \frac{\sum_{u \xrightarrow{e} v \in S''} d(u)}{|S'| - 1}$$
$$> \frac{|S'|(c + 1 - D)}{|S'| - 1}$$
$$\ge \frac{|S'|}{|S'| - 1} R(C^*(G)).$$

Since $|S'|/(|S'| - 1) > 1$, we conclude that there exists a cycle in G with delay-to-register ratio greater than the maximum delay-to-register ratio $R(C^*(G))$, which is a contradiction. Therefore, G_c has no negative weight cycles and, according to Lemma 2, there exists a retiming r of G such that $\Phi(G_r) \le \lceil R(C^*(G)) \rceil + D - 1$. Consequently $\Phi_{min}(G) \le \lceil R(C^*(G)) \rceil + D - 1$. $\qquad\square$

5 Minimum Clock Period Retiming with Unit Delays

In this section we present the algorithmic implications of the minimum period characterization

for the retiming of unit-delay sequential circuitry. Specifically, we consider the problem: Given a unit-delay sequential circuit $G = (V, E, 1, w)$, determine a retiming r such that $\Phi(G_r)$ is minimum. Leiserson and Saxe [10] solve this problem by performing a binary search over the $|V|$ possible clock periods. Each iteration in the binary search requires the solution of a shortest-paths problem. The total running time is $O(V^{1/2} E \lg V \lg(VW))$, where W is the maximum number of registers on any wire in the circuit, using the Gabow-Tarjan algorithm for shortest-paths [3]. We present a procedure that solves this problem more efficiently by an $O(\lg V)$ multiplicative factor.

Our algorithm operates as follows. First, it identifies the minimum clock period $\Phi_{min}(G)$ directly, by computing the maximum delay-to-register ratio of the cycles in the circuit graph. Then, it solves a *single* shortest-paths problem on the graph $G' = (V, E, w')$, where $w'(e) = w(e) - 1/\Phi_{min}(G)$ for every edge $u \xrightarrow{e} v \in E$. According to the Retiming Theorem in [10], the rounded up lengths of these shortest-paths yield a retiming with clock period $\Phi_{min}(G)$.

In order to compute the minimum feasible period of the circuit, we can use Karp's $O(VE)$ strongly polynomial algorithm for finding maximum average-weight cycles in a graph [4]. For the shortest-paths problem we can use the Bellman-Ford $O(VE)$ algorithm [1]. For these choices the total running time is $O(VE)$. However, under the reasonable assumption that W is independent of the size of the circuit, we can use scaling algorithms to obtain improved running times. The minimum clock period can be found in $O(V^{1/2} E \lg(VW))$ steps, using the Ahuja-Orlin scaling algorithm [11] for maximum average-weight cycles in a graph, and the shortest-paths lengths can be found in $O(V^{1/2} E \lg(VW))$ steps, using the Gabow-Tarjan algorithm for shortest-paths [3]. The overall running time is $O(V^{1/2} E \lg(VW))$.

6 Minimum Clock Period Retiming with Arbitrary Delays

This section describes an $O(VE \lg D)$ procedure for the following problem: Given a sequential circuit $G = (V, E, d, w)$, determine a retiming r such that

343

$\Phi(G_r)$ is minimum. Leiserson and Saxe [10] give an $O(VE \lg V)$ algorithm for this problem. Their algorithm performs an $O(VE + V^2 \lg V)$ preprocessing step that computes all $O(V^2)$ possible clock periods. Subsequently, it binary searches this set of possible clock periods in order to find the minimum feasible one. We present a more efficient procedure with a different preprocessing phase that leads to the binary search of an interval with only D possible clock periods.

Our algorithm operates as follows. First, it finds $\lceil R(C^*(G)) \rceil$ by binary searching the interval $[1, \ldots, VD]$ of possible periods for the smallest integer n that does not induce negative-weight cycles in $G' = (V, E, w')$, where $w'(e) = w(e) - d(v)/n$ for every edge $u \xrightarrow{e} v \in E$. Each iteration in the binary search requires the solution of a shortest-paths problem on G' [5]. Subsequently, the algorithm binary searches the interval $[\lceil R(C^*(G)) \rceil, \ldots, \lceil R(C^*(G)) \rceil + D - 1]$ of possible values of $\Phi_{min}(G)$, for the minimum integer that yields a legal retiming of the circuit.

The computation of $\lceil R(C^*(G)) \rceil$ can be performed in $O(V^{1/2} E \lg(VWD) \lg(VD))$ steps, using the Gabow-Tarjan algorithm for shortest-paths [3]. Each iteration in the binary search for $\Phi_{min}(G)$ uses the $O(VE)$ retiming algorithm of Leiserson-Saxe [10]. Under the assumption that W and D grow subpolynomially with respect to the size of the circuit, we obtain an overall running time of $O(VE \lg D)$. In practice, we expect D and W to be independent of the size of the circuit.

7 Retiming for Approximately Minimum Clock Period

In this section we give an algorithm for determining a retiming of a circuit with arbitrary delays, such that its clock period is approximately minimized. Specifically, we consider the following problem: Given a sequential circuit $G = (V, E, d, w)$ determine a retiming r such that $\Phi(G_r) \leq \Phi_{min}(G) + D - 1$, where D is the maximum propagation delay of the circuit components. We show how to use scaling algorithms in order to solve this problem by an $O(V^{1/2} \lg D / (\lg(VWD) \lg(VD)))$ multiplicative factor faster than minimum clock period retiming.

Our algorithm for retiming with approximately

minimum clock period is based on Lemma 4 which follows below. Its proof relies on the definition of retiming and properties of the constraint graph, and can be found in Appendix A.

Lemma 4 *Let $G = (V, E, d, w)$ be a circuit graph with maximum delay-to-register ratio $R(C^*(G))$ and let $\Phi_{min}(G)$ be the minimum clock period we can obtain by retiming G. Moreover, let $n = \lceil R(C^*(G)) \rceil$, and let $l(v)$ be the solutions of a single-source shortest-paths problem on $G' = (V, E, w')$, where $w'(e) = w(e) - d(v)/n$ for every edge $u \xrightarrow{e} v \in E$. Then, the assignment $r(v) = \lceil l(v) \rceil$ for each vertex $v \in V$ is a retiming of G such that*

$$\Phi(G_r) \leq \Phi_{min}(G) + D - 1. \qquad \square$$

The algorithm for retiming with approximately minimum clock period proceeds as follows. Initially, it identifies $\lceil R(C^*(G)) \rceil$ by binary searching the interval $[1, \ldots, VD]$ for the smallest integer n that does not induce negative-weight cycles in G'. Each iteration requires the solution of one shortest-paths problem on G' [5]. Rounding up the lengths of the shortest-paths from the last of these iterations yields, according to Lemma 4, a retiming of the circuit with period that does not exceed $\Phi_{min}(G)$ by more than $D - 1$. The overall running time of this algorithm is $O(V^{1/2} E \lg(VWD) \lg(VD))$, using the Gabow-Tarjan scaling algorithm for shortest-paths [3].

8 Minimum Clock Period Pipelining

In this section we use ideas drawn from the characterization of the minimum clock period to develop an $O(E \lg D)$ algorithm for the problem of minimum clock period pipelining of combinational circuitry. For unit-delay circuitry, the running time of the algorithm is optimal within a constant multiplicative factor. The best known bound so far was $O(VE \lg V)$ and required the precomputation of all possible clock periods. Our algorithm avoids computing all possible clock periods, and exploits the special structure of the graph of a combinational circuit.

In a combinational circuit the graph is acyclic and has an input interface v_{in} and an output interface v_{out}. Initially, the circuit is assumed to have no registers. By retiming a combinational circuit G we add registers to the circuit in such a way that the retimed circuit G_r achieves a shorter clock period at the cost of introducing a *latency* of $r(v_{in}) - r(v_{out})$ clock ticks for the signals to propagate from the input interface v_{in} to the output interface v_{out}. The problem of minimum clock period pipelining is defined as follows: Given a combinational circuit $G = (V, E, d, 0)$ and a positive integer l, determine a retiming r such that G_r is a pipelined combinational circuit with latency no greater than l and with minimum clock period.

The algorithm for minimum clock period pipelining of combinational circuitry is based on Lemma 5 that bounds the minimum achievable clock period, and an $O(E)$ procedure for minimum latency pipelining of combinational circuitry with clock period no greater than a given upper bound. Lemma 5 bounds $\Phi_{min}(G)$ in terms of the delay Δ of the longest path in the circuit, the latency l, and the longest component delay D. Its proof, which can be found in Appendix B, relies on the constraint graph G_c of the circuit. In this case, G_c has been augmented by an edge $v_{out} \to v_{in}$ of weight l in order to account for the desired latency of the circuit.

Lemma 5 *Let $G = (V, E, d, 0)$ be a combinational circuit with input interface v_{in} and output interface v_{out}. Let Δ be the delay of the path $p_\Delta = v_{in} \rightsquigarrow v_{out}$ in G with the longest propagation delay, and let l be a positive integer. Then the minimum clock period $\Phi_{min}(G)$ for any pipelined version of G with latency l satisfies:*

$$\left\lceil \frac{\Delta}{l+1} \right\rceil \le \Phi_{min}(G) \le \left\lceil \frac{\Delta}{l+1} \right\rceil + D,$$

where D is the longest component delay in the circuit. □

Algorithm MLP *(Minimum Latency Pipelining)* Given a combinational circuit G and a desired clock period c, this algorithm determines a pipelined combinational circuit G_r with clock period $\Phi(G_r) \le c$ and minimum latency.

1. For each vertex $v \in V$, set $r(v) \leftarrow 0$ and $\delta(v) \leftarrow d(v)$.

2. Visit the edges $u \to v$ in topological sort order. For each edge $u \to v$ do:

   2.1. If $r(v) > r(u)$, then $r(v) \leftarrow r(u)$.

   2.2. If $\delta(u) + d(v) > c$ and $r(v) \ge r(u)$, then $r(v) \leftarrow r(u) - 1$.

   2.3. If $\delta(u) + d(v) > \delta(v)$ and $r(u) = r(v)$, then $\delta(v) \leftarrow \delta(u) + d(v)$.

3. For each edge $u \xrightarrow{e} v \in E$, set $w_r(e) = w(e) + r(u) - r(v)$. □

The correctness proof and the running time argument for Algorithm MLP can be found in [12]. Intuitively, the idea behind the algorithm is to visit the vertices of the graph keeping track of the longest propagation delay up to the vertex currently visited. New registers are introduced greedily: whenever the longest propagation delay exceeds the desired clock period c, a pipeline stage is introduced.

The $O(E \lg D)$ algorithm for minimum period pipelining of combinational circuitry is described below. Its correctness follows directly from Lemma 5 and the correctness of Algorithm MLP.

Algorithm MPP *(Minimum Period Pipelining)* Given a combinational circuit $G = (V, E, d, 0)$ with input interface v_{in} and output interface v_{out}, and a positive integer l, determine a retiming r such that G_r is a pipelined combinational circuit with latency l and minimum clock period.

1. Determine the delay Δ of the longest path p_Δ in G from v_{in} to v_{out}.

2. Binary search among the $D + 1$ possible values of $\Phi_{min}(G)$ applying Algorithm MLP on G. □

Step 1 is a depth-first search in G and requires $O(E)$ steps [1]. Step 2 performs $O(\lg D)$ applications of Algorithm MLP. Therefore, Algorithm MPP terminates in $O(E \lg D)$ steps. Observe that for unit-delay circuits the running time is optimal within a constant multiplicative factor.

9 Conclusion

In this paper we presented the first tight bounds on the minimum clock period that can be achieved by retiming a circuit. The bounds were given in terms of the maximum delay-to-register ratio in the circuit and the maximum propagation delay D of the circuit components. Using these bounds we gave an exact characterization of the minimum clock period that we can achieve by retiming unit-delay circuits, and we presented improved algorithms for several problems related to retiming. In particular, we gave an $O(V^{1/2}E \lg(VW))$ algorithm for minimum clock period retiming of unit-delay circuitry, where W is the maximum number of registers on any wire in the circuit, and an $O(VE \lg D)$ algorithm for minimum clock period retiming of circuitry with arbitrary delays. We also gave an $O(E \lg D)$ algorithm for minimum clock period pipelining of combinational circuitry. These running times improve the previous best bounds for the same problems, under the reasonable assumption that W and D grow subpolynomially with the size of the circuit. Finally, we described an $O(V^{1/2}E \lg(VWD) \lg(VD))$ algorithm for retiming circuits with arbitrary delays, in order to achieve a clock period that does not exceed the minimum by more than $D - 1$.

An interesting open problem is finding an algorithm for minimum clock period pipelining of circuits with arbitrary delays, whose running time is comparable to that for minimum period retiming of unit-delay circuits.

Acknowledgements

I would like to thank my advisor Charles Leiserson for his research directions and for suggestions that significantly improved the presentation of this work. Thanks to Michel Goemans, Cliff Stein and Joel Wein for helpful discussions. Also, thanks to Lenore Cowen, Tom Leighton and Eric Schwabe for helpful comments.

References

[1] T. H. Cormen, C. E. Leiserson, and R. L. Rivest. *Introduction to Algorithms.* McGraw-Hill, MIT Press, 1990.

[2] S. Even and A. Litman. On the capabilities of systolic systems. *3rd ACM Symposium on Parallel Algorithms and Architectures*, 1991.

[3] H. Gabow and R. Tarjan. Faster scaling algorithms for network problems. *SIAM J. Computing*, October 1989.

[4] R. Karp. A characterization of the minimum cycle mean in a digraph. *Discrete Mathematics*, 23:309–311, 1978.

[5] E. L. Lawler. *Combinatorial Optimization, Networks and Matroids.* Holt, Rinehart and Winston, New York, 1976.

[6] F. T. Leighton. *Introduction to Parallel Algorithms and Architectures: Arrays, Trees and Hypercubes.* Morgan Kaufman, to appear this year.

[7] C. E. Leiserson. *Area-efficient VLSI Computation.* PhD thesis, Carnegie-Mellon University, 1981. Published in book form by the MIT Press, Cambridge, Massachusetts, 1983.

[8] C. E. Leiserson, F. M. Rose, and J. B. Saxe. Optimizing synchronous circuitry by retiming. *3rd Caltech Conference on VLSI*, 1983. R. Bryant, ed., pp. 87-116.

[9] C. E. Leiserson and J. B. Saxe. Optimizing synchronous systems. *Journal of VLSI and Computer Systems*, 1(1):41–67, 1983.

[10] C. E. Leiserson and J. B. Saxe. Retiming synchronous circuitry. *Algorithmica*, 6(1), 1991. Also available as MIT/LCS/TM-372.

[11] J. B. Orlin and R. K. Ahuja. New scaling algorithms for the assignment and minimum cycle mean problem. Technical Report 2019-88, MIT Sloan School of Management, 1988.

[12] M. C. Papaefthymiou. On retiming synchronous circuitry and mixed-integer optimization. Master's thesis, Massachusetts Institute of Technology, September 1990. Available as MIT/LCS/TR-486.

Appendix A: Proof of Lemma 4

Before we proceed with the proof, we note that since $n = \lceil R(C^*(G)) \rceil$, the graph G' has no negative edge-weight cycles and therefore the shortest-paths lengths $l(v)$ are well-defined. Now, in order to prove that $r(v) = \lceil l(v) \rceil$ is a legal retiming with clock period $\Phi(G_r) \leq \Phi_{min}(G) + D - 1$, we must show that every edge $e \in G_r$ has $w_r(e) = w(e) + r(u) - r(v) \geq 0$, and that every path $p \in G_r$ with delay $\sum_{v \in p} d(v) > \Phi_{min}(G) + D - 1$ has at least one register.

First, we prove that $r(v) = \lceil l(v) \rceil$ for each $v \in V$ satisfies $w_r(e) \geq 0$ for every edge e in the retimed circuit G_r. Since l is a single-source shortest-paths solution on G', we have $l(v) - l(u) \leq w(e) - d(v)/n$ for every edge $u \xrightarrow{e} v$ in G'. Therefore

$$
\begin{aligned}
\lceil l(v) \rceil - \lceil l(u) \rceil &\leq \lceil l(v) - l(u) \rceil \\
&\leq \lceil w(e) - d(v)/n \rceil \\
&\leq \lceil w(e) \rceil \\
&= w(e),
\end{aligned}
$$

since $\lceil x \rceil - \lceil y \rceil \leq \lceil x - y \rceil$ for every real x, y, and since $w(e)$ is an integer. Therefore, $w_r(e) \geq 0$.

Now, we show that the assignment $r(v) = \lceil l(v) \rceil$ for each $v \in V$ satisfies the clock period constraint. Consider any path $p = u_0 \xrightarrow{e_0} u_1 \xrightarrow{e_1} \ldots \xrightarrow{e_{k-2}} u_{k-1} \xrightarrow{e_{k-1}} u_k$ in the retimed circuit G_r with delay $\sum_{i=0}^{k} d(u_i) > \Phi_{min}(G) + D - 1$. For this path we have:

$$
\begin{aligned}
l(u_k) &- l(u_0) \\
&\leq \left(\sum_{i=0}^{k-1} w(e_i) \right) - \left(\sum_{i=1}^{k} \frac{d(u_i)}{n} \right) \\
&= \left(\sum_{i=0}^{k-1} w(e_i) \right) - \left(\sum_{i=0}^{k} \frac{d(u_i)}{n} \right) + \frac{d(u_0)}{n} \\
&\leq \left(\sum_{i=0}^{k-1} w(e_i) \right) - \frac{\Phi_{min}(G) + D}{n} + \frac{d(u_0)}{n} \\
&\leq \left(\sum_{i=0}^{k-1} w(e_i) \right) - \frac{\Phi_{min}(G)}{\lceil R(C^*(G)) \rceil} - \frac{D - d(u_0)}{\lceil R(C^*(G)) \rceil} \\
&\leq \left(\sum_{i=0}^{k-1} w(e_i) \right) - 1,
\end{aligned}
$$

since $D \geq d(u_0)$ by definition, and $\Phi_{min}(G) \geq \lceil R(C^*(G)) \rceil$ from Theorem 1. Therefore,

$$
\begin{aligned}
\lceil l(u_k) \rceil - \lceil l(u_0) \rceil &\leq \lceil l(u_k) - l(u_0) \rceil \\
&\leq \left\lceil \left(\sum_{i=0}^{k-1} w(e_i) \right) - 1 \right\rceil \\
&= \left(\sum_{i=0}^{k-1} w(e_i) \right) - 1.
\end{aligned}
$$

Since the number of registers along the path p is $\sum_{i=0}^{k-1} w_r(e_i) = r(u_0) - r(u_k) + \sum_{i=0}^{k-1} w(e_i)$, we conclude that there exists at least one register along p and therefore the clock period constraint is met. $\qquad \square$

Appendix B: Proof of Lemma 5

Any retiming r of the circuit that gives a pipelined version of the circuit with latency l and clock-period no greater than c, satisfies

$$
r(u) - r(v) \geq 0
$$

for every edge $u \xrightarrow{e} v$ in E, and

$$
r(u) - r(v) \geq 1
$$

for all vertices $u, v \in V$ connected by a path p of delay $d(p) > c$. It also satisfies a latency constraint

$$
r(v_{in}) - r(v_{out}) \leq l.
$$

This constraint introduces an edge $v_{out} \xrightarrow{e_l} v_{in}$ in the constraint graph G_c with weight $w(e_l) = l$. Note that every cycle in G_c must use this edge.

First, we derive the lower bound of the inequality. Let r be a retiming of the circuit with latency l and clock period $\Phi_{min}(G)$. Every path in G_r from v_{in} to v_{out} has $l + 1$ register-free parts. Adding up all the delays of the register-free parts along the longest such path p_Δ, yields $\Delta \leq \Phi_{min}(G)(l + 1)$, which implies $\Phi_{min}(G) \geq \Delta/(l + 1)$. Therefore, $\Phi_{min}(G) \geq \lceil \Delta/(l + 1) \rceil$, since $\Phi_{min}(G)$ must be an integer as a consequence of the fact that $d(v) \in \mathbf{Z}$ for every vertex $v \in V$.

Now, we establish the upper bound of the inequality by proving that $\lceil \Delta/(l + 1) \rceil + D$ is a feasible clock period. According to Lemma 2, it suffices to show that G_c has no negative-weight cycles for $c = \lceil \Delta/(l + 1) \rceil + D$. The only negative weight edges of G_c are the ones in S' with weight -1. The maximum number of such edges in any path from v_{in} to v_{out} is

$$\left\lfloor \frac{\Delta - 1}{(\lceil \Delta/(l+1) \rceil + D) - D} \right\rfloor = \left\lfloor \frac{\Delta - 1}{\lceil \Delta/(l+1) \rceil} \right\rfloor .$$

We can easily show that this number is bounded from above by l.

$$\left\lfloor \frac{\Delta - 1}{\lceil \Delta/(l+1) \rceil} \right\rfloor \leq \left\lfloor \frac{\Delta - 1}{\Delta/(l+1)} \right\rfloor$$

$$= \left\lfloor l + 1 - \frac{l+1}{\Delta} \right\rfloor$$

$$\leq l,$$

since $l + 1 > 0$. Since every cycle in G_c must use e_l, we conclude that G_c has no negative-weight cycles, and therefore the clock period $c = \lceil \Delta/(l+1) \rceil + D$ can be achieved by retiming G. $\quad \square$

A One-Way Array Algorithm for Matroid Scheduling

Matthias F.M. Stallmann
Department of Computer Science
North Carolina State University
Raleigh, NC 27695-8206
e-mail: matt@euler.csc.ncsu.edu

Abstract

The greedy algorithm is a standard paradigm for solving matroid optimization problems on sequential computers. This paper presents a greedy algorithm suitable for a fully-pipelined linear array of processors, a generalization of Huang's algorithm [8] for minimum spanning trees. Application of the algorithm to uniprocessor scheduling with release times and deadlines is discussed in detail. A key feature of the algorithm is its use of matroid contraction.

1 Introduction

Algorithms on one-dimensional arrays of processors with one-way data flow (*one-way arrays*) have several practical advantages. They are simple, fault-tolerant (can work correctly when faulty processors are bypassed), and allow for pipelining of successive problem instances. They are also intriguing from a theoretical point of view. Several combinatorial problems that have efficient sequential algorithms also have one-way array algorithms. These include connected components [2, 14], biconnected components [11], and minimum spanning trees [8]. These algorithms are typically more elegant than their sequential counterparts, and require nontrivial insights. The purpose of this work is to propose a paradigm for solving matroid problems on one-way arrays, generalizing the algorithm of Huang [8]. The paradigm yields an efficient one-way array algorithm for the scheduling problem described in the following paragraph, and suggests future work on one-way array algorithms for matroid problems.

The *deadline scheduling problem* is defined as follows. Given a collection of m tasks, where each task i has an integer deadline d_i and a profit w_i, find a one-processor schedule, i.e. assign each task i an integer *time slot* t_i, corresponding to the interval $(t_i - 1, t_i]$, so that the total profit of tasks assigned before their deadline, $\sum_{\{i | t_i \le d_i\}} w_i$, is maximized. Note that it suffices to schedule the (max profit) set of tasks that can all be scheduled before their deadlines. The remaining tasks can be scheduled arbitrarily late (or not at all). The best sequential time bound for deadline scheduling, $O(m + n \log n)$, is due to Gabow and Tarjan [5].

The one-way array algorithm also extends to the scheduling problem if release times as well as deadlines are considered, as long as the release times and deadlines obey a monotonicity restriction. Each task has a release time r_i in addition to its deadline and profit, and task i must be assigned to time slot t_i with $r_i < t_i \le d_i$ to earn profit. The *monotone scheduling problem* requires that any two tasks i and j having $r_i < r_j$ also have $d_i \le d_j$ Monotone scheduling is a generalization of deadline scheduling. Gabow and Tarjan [5] give a sequential time bound of $O(m \log m + n^2)$ for scheduling with release times and deadlines (without the monotonicity restriction).

The tasks in a one-processor scheduling problem with release times and deadlines define a matroid in which a set of tasks is independent if all may be scheduled after their release times and before their deadlines. A *matroid* $\mathcal{M} = (E, \mathcal{I})$ is defined on a set of elements E, where $\mathcal{I} \subseteq 2^E$ denotes the class of *independent* subsets of E. This class obeys two axioms: (1) $A \in \mathcal{I}$ and $B \subseteq A$ implies $B \in \mathcal{I}$ (a subset of an independent set is independent), and (2) $A \in \mathcal{I}$ and $B \in \mathcal{I}$ with $|B| > |A|$ implies $\exists e \in B - A$ such that $A \cup \{e\} \in \mathcal{I}$ (an independent set can always be increased in size as long as a larger independent set exists). Classic examples of matroids include the set of columns of a matrix, where a subset is independent if the columns are linearly independent, and the set of edges in a graph, where a

© 1991 ACM 089791-438-4/91/0007/0349 $1.50

subset is independent if it induces no cycles.

Matroids are useful in the study of algorithmic paradigms. Suppose that each element of a matroid is assigned a weight and the objective is to find the *base* (maximum cardinality independent set), having maximum weight. Call this a *matroid optimization problem*. Specific instances of matroid optimization include finding a maximum (or minimum) weight spanning tree and finding a maximum profit schedule in any of the scheduling problems discussed previously. It is not hard to show that any problem of this general form can be solved by the *greedy algorithm*, which repeatedly adds the largest weight element that can be added without violating independence (see, e.g. [9]).

This paper discusses a variant of the greedy algorithm for a linear array of processors with one-way data flow. A generic linear-array algorithm for matroid optimization is presented, along with an efficient implementations for the deadline and monotone scheduling. The generic algorithm simplifies and generalizes an algorithm for the minimum spanning tree problem due to Huang [8].

The one-way array algorithm has several advantages over the sequential greedy algorithm. First, it is an on-line algorithm, able to deal with matroid elements presented to it one at a time, in random order. The standard greedy algorithm either requires the matroid elements to be stored internally or to be sorted by decreasing weight prior to execution. If m denote $|E|$ and $n = r(E)$ denote the *rank* of E, the maximum cardinality of an independent subset of E. The sequential greedy algorithm requires $\Theta(m)$ storage locations capable of holding a matroid element, while an on-line algorithm only requires $\Theta(n)$ locations of random-access memory. Note that $n \leq m$ and m can be $\Omega(n^2)$ for spanning tree or monotone scheduling matroids (m can be arbitrarily large in relation to n if redundant elements are allowed; for general matroids m can be exponential in n or worse even without redundant elements).

On-line algorithms on the RAM model exist for both the minimum spanning tree problem (using dynamic trees [13]), and the deadline scheduling problem (using a data structure described in [5]). In each case, the *period* (time between processing successive inputs) is $\Theta(\log n)$. The one-way array algorithm requires the same area (in this case n processors, each capable of storing a constant number of matroid elements) and has a constant period for both problems.

Another advantage of a one-way array algorithm is that it is pipelineable, namely that successive instances of the same problem can be pushed through the array without an initialization delay between instances. Finally, a one-way array algorithm is fault-tolerant in the sense that, if faulty processors can be bypassed, the algorithm will work without modification as long as there are sufficient non-faulty processors. Both these advantages hinge upon the unidirectional dataflow of the one-way array model.

The model of computation is a one-way linear array consisting of n processors (*cells*), numbered from 1 to n (recall that n is the rank of the matroid). During a single *time unit* cell i (for $i = 2, \ldots, n-1$) reads input from its left neighbor (cell $i-1$), performs a fixed number of arithmetic operations, and generates output for its right neighbor (cell $i+1$) to be read during the next time unit. Cells 1 and n are special cases in that cell 1 reads input from an external host instead of its left neighbor and cell n produces output for the external host instead of its right neighbor. It is assumed that each cell has a fixed number of registers, with each register capable of storing a matroid element. We also assume that data in each cell is initialized to some dummy value. A cell does not have to know its position in the array.

Input to the array consists of a stream of matroid optimization instances, consecutive instances separated by a marker, say $\$$. Each instance consists of a list of matroid elements in random order. Output is a stream of optimum (maximum weight) bases for the instances. Since n_j, the rank of the jth instance, is, in general, less than or equal to m_j, the number of elements in the jth instance, there are gaps long enough to compensate for this difference between output instances.

We conclude this section with some additional matroid terminology. Section 2 then describes the generic one-way array algorithm. Section 3 gives details and correctness arguments for deadline and monotone scheduling. Section 4 describes further details of the array implementation, such as the output of the optimum base. Section 5 presents some conclusions and open problems.

A *circuit* is a minimal set that is not independent. In the spanning-tree matroid a circuit corresponds to the edges of a cycle. In scheduling, a circuit is a minimal set of $d - r + 1$ tasks all having deadlines $\leq d$ and release times $\geq r$. A matroid element e is called a *loop* if $\{e\}$ is a circuit. If $\mathcal{M} = (E, \mathcal{I})$ is a matroid, then $\mathcal{M}/A$, $\mathcal{M}$ *contracted* wrt A, is the matroid $\mathcal{M}' = (E - A, \mathcal{I}')$, where $B \in \mathcal{I}'$ iff $B \cup A \in \mathcal{I}$. In the spanning tree matroid, the contracted matroid wrt a set of edges A is obtained by identifying the endpoints of all edges in A. Contraction in the scheduling matroid has a more complicated description, which is the key to understanding the array algorithm for this special case. If A is an independent set and $A \cup \{f\}$ contains a circuit C, while $A \cup \{f\} - \{g\}$ is independent ($g \in C$), then f, g is called a *swap* wrt A.

2 The Generic Algorithm

Some simplifications are used to describe the array algorithm. First note, as was observed by Savage et al. [11], that the actions of a one-way array can be described by tracing the actions of each individual input record as it propagates through the array. That is, a generic algorithm for a one-way array can be described as

$$\textbf{for } i := 1 \textbf{ to } n \textbf{ do}$$
$$(r, c_i) := F(r, c_i)$$

where r is the new input record, c_i denotes the contents of cell i, and F is any function that can be computed during a time unit, namely by a constant number of arithmetic operations or comparisons. This is true because the current contents of c_i only depend on the initial state and previous input records. Second, assume that each cell has the same initial value (a dummy record) before computation begins. This could be arranged by having a start marker propagate through the array before the first input record (see [12]).

Subsequent description of the algorithm ignores any complications having to do with output. The generic algorithm only ensures that after all elements of the jth instance have been processed, the elements of the jth optimum base are stored in cells $1, \ldots, n_j$ (the remaining $n - n_j$ cells, if any, will contain dummy records). The solution (optimum base) can then be "pushed" out using techniques described in [11, 12]. A more detailed description of how this is accomplished, and how the tasks of the optimum schedule in the scheduling problem can be tagged with their time slot assignments, is given in Section 4.

The generic one-way-array algorithm for matroid optimization problems maintains the following invariant: If $\hat{E}$ is the set of elements that have entered the array so far, the first $r(\hat{E})$ cells contain a maximum-weight independent subset B of $\hat{E}$, and cell i holds the element of B with ith largest weight. Initially all cells contain dummy elements with weight $-\infty$, and, if $r(\hat{E}) < n$, dummy elements occupy the last $n - r$ cells. Suppose $e_1, e_2, \ldots, e_n$ are the elements currently stored in the array (with $w(e_1) \geq w(e_2) \geq \ldots \geq w(e_n)$) and let f be the new element to enter the array. The goal is to compute B', the largest weight independent subset of $\hat{E} \cup \{f\}$. Let index p be such that $w(f) \leq w(e_p)$ and $w(f) > w(e_{p+1})$, i.e. f's rightful position in the sorted order of the elements is between e_p and e_{p+1}.

If $\{e_1, \ldots, e_p, f\}$ is not independent (f is in some circuit of $\{e_1, \ldots, e_p, f\}$), then B' does not include f. On the other hand if $\{e_1, \ldots, e_p, f\}$ is independent, f is added to B' and e_q is deleted (f, e_q is a swap wrt B'), where $q = \min\{i \mid \{e_1, \ldots, e_i, f\} \notin \mathcal{I}\}$. If $B \cup f$ is independent then e_q is the first dummy element — here and in what follows, we pretend that dummy elements extend an independent set so that it becomes a base. The contents of the array then become $e_1, \ldots, e_p, f, e_{p+1}, \ldots, e_{q-1}, e_{q+1}, \ldots, e_n$. Note that, due to sorting by weight, e_q is the least-weight element in the circuit containing f. Thus the swap f, e_q yields the best possible improvement when f is added. The following lemma ensures that the deleted element (either f or e_q) need never be considered for inclusion in any future base.

Lemma 1 If f_2, g_2 is a swap wrt $B \cup \{f_1\} - \{g_1\}$ (where f_1, g_1 is a swap wrt B) but not wrt B, then both f_1, g_2 and f_2, g_1 are swaps wrt B.

Proof. See [4]. $\square$

Suppose f (or e_q) is deleted and let B' be the earliest base (after the deletion) for which f, e is a swap wrt B' having $w(f) > w(e)$. Let $B' = B \cup \{g\} - \{h\}$, where B is the base preceding B'. Thus $w(g) > w(h)$. From Lemma 1 we know that g, e and f, h are also swaps wrt B. We also know $w(e) \geq w(h)$, otherwise e would have been deleted in place of h. But then f, h is a swap wrt B having $w(f) > w(e) \geq w(h)$, contradicting the choice of B'.

The index p can be easily computed as f traverses the array. To determine whether or not f is to be inserted, and the identity of e_q, the algorithm requires an efficient independence oracle, one for which independence can be detected on the fly, by inspecting one element at a time. The key to the scheduling algorithm (and Huang's spanning tree algorithm) is the maintenance of an efficient representation of f', the element f in the matroid $\mathcal{M}/\{e_1, \ldots, e_i\}$. Note that f' is a loop iff f is contained in a circuit of $\{e_1, \ldots, e_i\}$ in $\mathcal{M}$.

The representation of f' is computed by the non-commutative binary operation $/$, applied to (representations of) individual matroid elements (e/f is referred to as e contracted wrt f). The ith cell in the array stores e'_i, where $e'_1 = e_1$ and $e'_i = (\ldots((e_i/e'_1)/e'_2)/ \ldots e'_{i-1})$. In the spanning tree case, an element (edge) e is initially represented by its two endpoints, lower-numbered vertex first (vertices are assumed to be integers in the range $1, \ldots, 2n$ — there are at most $2n$ vertices in a spanning forest having n edges). The operation $(i', j') = (i, j)/(k, l)$ is defined by $i' = k$ if $i = l$, and $i' = i$ otherwise, and similarly for j'. In other words, the effect is as if k and l are contracted to a single vertex whose label is k.

The algorithm relies on three properties of $/$, as follows.

1. *Order invariance*: $(e/a)/(b/a) = (e/b)/(a/b)$. This is used to argue (by a straightforward induction) that the representation e'_i depends only on the set of elements $\{e_1, \ldots, e_{i-1}\}$, not the order

in which they appear. If f is inserted into the array, representations $e'_{p+1}, \ldots, e'_{q-1}$ can be updated by contracting them wrt f'. Henceforth, we may use f/A to denote $(\ldots((f/e'_1)/e'_2)/\ldots e'_k)$, where $A = \{e_1, \ldots, e_k\}$ and e'_i is defined as above.

2. *Faithfulness*: f is in a circuit of $A \cup f$ iff f/A represents a loop. This property ensures that the decision whether not to insert f can be made correctly and that e_q can be correctly identified.

3. *Swap invariance*: if f, g is a swap wrt A then $e/(A \cup \{f\} - \{g\}) = e/A$. This ensures that $e'_{q+1}, \ldots, e'_n$ do not need to be updated when f replaces e_q.

The array algorithm can now be described as follows (i is used to indicate the current cell as the new record containing f propagates through the array):

Algorithm Array-Greedy

$i := 1;\ f' := f$
while $w(f) \leq w(e_i)$ **do**
    $f' := f'/e'_i;\ i := i + 1$ **end do**

/* $i = p + 1$ at this point */
if f' is a loop **then** exit
    (a dummy record traverses the remaining cells)

/* f' is inserted and $e'_{p+1}, \ldots, e'_{q-1}$ are pushed one
    cell to the right (note: this requires two records,
    f' and *previous*, to be propagated to the next
    cell each time unit) */

previous := f'
repeat
    /* update representations of both e'_i and f' */
    $newf := f'/e'_i;\quad e'_i := e'_i/f';\quad f' := newf$

    /* store e'_{i-1} (or f') here; send e'_i to next cell */
    swap e'_i and *previous*
until *previous* is a loop

/* here $i = q + 1$ and subsequent cells of the array
    remain unaltered */

In case of the spanning tree algorithm, it is straightforward to show that the contraction operation is order invariant, and that $(i, j)/A$, where A is a set of edges, is just $(s_A(i), s_A(j))$, where $s_A(x)$ is the lowest numbered vertex of x's connected component in the subgraph defined by A. Faithfulness and swap invariance follow immediately. These observations give a simplified proof of correctness for Huang's algorithm.

3 The Scheduling Algorithm

The same generic algorithm can be used for the monotone scheduling problem (with deadline scheduling being a special case). Note that a task i is characterized by the pair (r_i, d_i) (weights can be ignored in defining contraction). The contraction $(r', d') = (r, d)/(r_0, d_0)$ is defined as follows.

$$(r', d') = \begin{cases} (r-1, d-1) & \text{if } r_0 < r,\ d_0 \leq d \\ (r, d-1) & \text{if } r_0 \geq r,\ d_0 \leq d \\ (r, d) & \text{if } d_0 > d \end{cases} \quad (1)$$

A loop in this context is a task (r, d) with $d - r = 0$.

Lemma 2 *The contraction operation defined in (1) is order invariant.*

Proof. Let (r', d') denote the result of two contractions $((r, d)/(r_1, d_1))/((r_2, d_2)/(r_1, d_1))$. By case analysis, we show that r' and d' depend only on the set $\{(r_1, d_1), (r_2, d_2)\}$ and not on the order. First observe that $d' = d - 2$ iff $d_1, d_2 \leq d$; also, $d' = d$ iff $d_1, d_2 \geq d + 1$ and $d_1 \neq d_2$. This takes care of showing order invariance for d'. Similarly, when $d' = d - 2$, it follows that $r' = r$ iff $r_1, r_2 \geq r$, and that $r' = r - 2$ iff $r_1, r_2 \leq r - 1$ and $r_1 \neq r_2$. When $d' = d$ it must be the case that $r' = r$. That leaves us with $d' = d - 1$. Here r' is either r or $r - 1$. In order for r' to be $r - 1$, at least one of the r_i, say r_1, must be strictly less than r. Because of monotonicity, $d_1 \leq d$, so from earlier arguments d_2 must be strictly greater than d. Thus when $d' = d - 1$, the new release time r' will be $r - 1$ iff exactly one of $i = 1, 2$ has $r_i < r$ and $d_i \leq d$. $\square$

In order to establish faithfulness and swap invariance, we first define the notion of *slack*: Let $\delta(A, s, t) = t - s - |\{(r, d) \in A \mid r \geq s, d \leq t\}|$, so $\delta(A, s, t)$, the slack between s and t wrt A, is the amount of empty space between time slots s and t in the schedule for A. It is easy to see that $f = (r, d)$ is in a circuit of $A \cup \{f\}$ iff there exist $s \leq r$ and $t \geq d$ such that $\delta(A, s, t) = 0$. We now show that if $(r', d') = (r, d)/A$ then $d' - r' = \min\{\delta(A, s, t) \mid s \leq r, t \geq d\}$. First we prove two lemmas that are sufficient to establish faithfulness and swap invariance for deadline scheduling, where a loop corresponds to a deadline of 0. These lemmas are also used in the proofs for the more general monotone case.

Lemma 3 *If $(r', d') = (r, d)/A$, then for any $t \geq d$, $d' \leq \delta(A, 0, t)$.*

Proof. Proof is by induction on $|A|$. If $A = \emptyset$ then $d' = d$ and the lemma is trivially true. Otherwise let $\hat{A} = A - \{(r_0, d_0)\}$, where (r_0, d_0) is any task in A. Let $(\hat{r}, \hat{d}) = (r, d)/\hat{A}$ and $(\hat{r_0}, \hat{d_0}) = (r_0, d_0)/\hat{A}$. By induction hypothesis, $\hat{d} \leq \delta(\hat{A}, 0, t)$. If $d_0 > t$, then $d' \leq \hat{d} \leq \delta(\hat{A}, 0, t) = \delta(A, 0, t)$. If $d_0 \leq t$ and $\hat{d} \leq \delta(\hat{A}, 0, t) - 1 = \delta(A, 0, t)$, then $d' \leq \delta(A, 0, t)$.

Finally, if $d_0 \leq t$ and $\hat{d} = \delta(A, 0, t)$, we apply the induction hypothesis to $\hat{d}_0$, to get $\hat{d}_0 \leq \delta(\hat{A}, 0, t)$. This means $\hat{d}_0 \leq \hat{d}$ and, by (1), $d' = \hat{d} - 1 \leq \delta(A, 0, t)$. $\square$

Lemma 4 *If $(r', d') = (r, d)/A$, then there exists $t \geq d$ such that $d' \geq \delta(A, 0, t)$.*

Proof. Again, proof is by induction on $|A|$ with a trivial basis. Define $\hat{A}$, (r_0, d_0), $(\hat{r}, \hat{d})$, and $(\hat{r}_0, \hat{d}_0)$ as in the previous proof. Using the induction hypothesis, let $\hat{t} \geq d$ be such that $\hat{d} \geq \delta(\hat{A}, 0, \hat{t})$; similarly choose $t_0 \geq d_0$ so that $\hat{d}_0 \geq \delta(\hat{A}, 0, t_0)$. If $d_0 \leq \hat{t}$, then $d' \geq \hat{d} - 1 \geq \delta(\hat{A}, 0, \hat{t}) - 1 = \delta(A, 0, \hat{t})$, and we choose $t = \hat{t}$. If $d_0 > \hat{t}$ and $d' = \hat{d} \geq \delta(\hat{A}, 0, \hat{t}) = \delta(A, 0, \hat{t})$, we choose $t = t$. Finally, if $d_0 > \hat{t}$ and $d' = \hat{d} - 1$ then $\hat{d}_0 \leq \hat{d}$, and we are done by choosing $t = t_0$, since $d' = \hat{d} - 1 \geq \hat{d}_0 - 1 \geq \delta(\hat{A}, 0, t_0) - 1 = \delta(A, 0, t_0)$. $\square$

We have shown that $d' = \min\{\delta(A, 0, t) \mid t \geq d\}$, where $(r', d') = (r, d)/A$. So in deadline scheduling $d' = 0$ iff the task $(0, d)$ forms a circuit with the tasks of A. The following lemma, which is straightforward to prove by induction, is used throughout the remaining arguments. It shows, among other things, that monotonicity is preserved by the contraction operation.

Lemma 5 *Let $(r_i', d_i') = (r_i, d_i)/A$ for $i = 1, 2$. Then $r_1 \geq r_2$ implies $r_1' \geq r_2'$, and $d_1 \geq d_2$ implies $d_1' \geq d_2'$.* $\square$

We now introduce constraints involving the release times after contraction, which, together with Lemmas 3 and 4 give us what we need for faithfulness, namely that $d' - r' = \min\{\delta(A, s, t) \mid s \leq r, d \leq t\}$.

Lemma 6 *If $(r', d') = (r, d)/A$, then for any s, t with $s \leq r, d \leq t$ we have $r' \geq \delta(A, 0, t) - \delta(A, s, t)$.*

Proof. Again we use induction on $|A|$ with a trivial basis. Here we carefully define $A = A - \{(r_0, d_0)\}$ so that r_0 is as small as possible. The pairs $(\hat{r}, \hat{d})$ and $(\hat{r}_0, \hat{d}_0)$ are as in earlier proofs. If $r' = \hat{r}$ then the lemma follows easily by induction. Suppose $r' = \hat{r} - 1$. This means $\hat{r}_0 < \hat{r}$ so, by Lemma 5, $r_0 < n$, which means $d_0 \leq d$. If $r_0 < s$ then $r' = \hat{r} - 1 \geq \delta(\hat{A}, 0, t) - \delta(\hat{A}, s, t) - 1 = \delta(A, 0, t) - \delta(A, s, t)$. Otherwise note that the choice of r_0 implies $\hat{r}_0 = r_0$. Since the induction hypothesis applies to $\hat{r}_0$, we have $r' = \hat{r} - 1 \geq \hat{r}_0 \geq \delta(\hat{A}, 0, t) - \delta(\hat{A}, r_0, t) = \delta(A, 0, t) - \delta(A, r_0, t)$. We also know from the choice of r_0 that $\delta(A, r_0, t) \leq \delta(A, s, t)$ when $r_0 \geq s$, so the final expression is $\geq \delta(A, 0, t) - \delta(A, s, t)$ as desired. $\square$

Note that Lemma 6, together with Lemma 3, ensures that $d' - r' \leq \delta(A, s, t)$ for all relevant s, t. This means that when (r, d) is in a circuit of $A \cup \{(r, d)\}$ the algorithm will detect the circuit because $d' - r'$ will be

0. We complete the faithfulness argument by showing, via a more general argument, that when $d' - r'$ is 0, a circuit really does exist.

Lemma 7 *If $(r', d') = (r, d)/A$, then there exist s, t with $s \leq r, d \leq t$ such that $\delta(A, s, t) \leq d' - r'$.*

Proof. Proof is by induction on $|A|$. In the basis, choose $s = r$ and $t = d$. In the induction step choose a task $(r_0, d_0) \in A$ with r_0 as small as possible. The definitions of $\hat{A}$ $(\hat{r}, \hat{d})$, and $(\hat{r}_0, \hat{d}_0)$ are as in earlier proofs. We also use the induction hypothesis to define $\hat{s}, \hat{t}$ with $\hat{s} \leq r, d \leq \hat{t}$ and $\delta(\hat{A}, \hat{s}, \hat{t}) \leq \hat{d} - \hat{r}$.

If $r' = \hat{r}, d' = \hat{d}$ or $r' = \hat{r} - 1, d' = \hat{d} - 1$ we can choose $s = \hat{s}$ and $t = \hat{t}$ and the lemma follows easily by induction. We are left only with the situation where $r' = \hat{r}$ and $d' = \hat{d} - 1$. Three separate cases need to be considered. In the first two cases we choose s, t so that $\delta(A, s, t) \leq \delta(\hat{A}, \hat{s}, \hat{t}) - 1$ and the lemma follows by induction. In the third case the lemma follows directly using earlier lemmas.

Case 1. $r_0 \geq \hat{s}, d_0 \leq \hat{t}$. Here choose $s = \hat{s}, t = \hat{t}$ and note that $\delta(A, s, t) = \delta(\hat{A}, \hat{s}, \hat{t}) - 1$.

Case 2. $r_0 < \hat{s}, d_0 \leq \hat{t}$. In this case choose $s = r_0$ and $t = \hat{t}$. Because r_0 was chosen to be as small as possible, we have $r_0 = \hat{r}_0 \geq \hat{r}$ and $\delta(A, s, t) = \delta(\hat{A}, 0, \hat{t}) - r_0 = \delta(\hat{A}, 0, \hat{t}) - 1 - r_0 \leq \delta(\hat{A}, 0, \hat{t}) - 1 - \hat{r}$. Lemma 6 says that $\hat{r} \geq \delta(\hat{A}, 0, \hat{t}) - \delta(\hat{A}, \hat{s}, \hat{t})$, so the final expression is $\leq \delta(\hat{A}, \hat{s}, \hat{t}) - 1$ as desired. This case arises, for example, when $(r, d) = (1, 3)$, $(r_0, d_0) = (0, 1)$, and $\hat{A} = \{(0, 2)\}$.

Case 3. $d_0 > \hat{t}$. Here choose $s = r$ and $t = t_0$, where $t_0 \geq d_0$ and $\hat{d}_0 \geq \delta(\hat{A}, 0, t_0)$; such a t_0 exists by Lemma 4. We have $\delta(A, s, t) = \delta(\hat{A}, r, t_0) - 1$. Because of monotonicity we know that $r_0 \geq r$. So by the choice of r_0 there are no tasks in $\hat{A}$ with deadlines less than r, implying that $\delta(A, s, t) = \delta(\hat{A}, 0, t_0) - r - 1$. By the choice of t_0 this is $\leq \hat{d}_0 - r - 1 \leq d' - r'$, as desired. An example of this case is when $(r, d) = (0, 2)$, $(r_0, d_0) = (1, 3)$, and $\hat{A} = \{(1, 3)\}$. $\square$

Lemmas 3, 6, and 7 together imply faithfulness of (1): we have established that (r, d) is in a circuit of $A \cup \{(r, d)\}$ iff there exist s, t with $s \leq r, d \leq t$ and $\delta(A, s, t) = 0$, which is true iff $d' - r' = 0$. To establish swap invariance we prove that the *minimum surrounding slack* for arbitrary $a \leq b$, defined to be $\min\{\delta(A, s, t) \mid s \leq a, b \leq t\}$, does not change in value as the result of a swap. This suffices because $d' - r'$ is determined by the minimum surrounding slack for r, d and d' is determined by the minimum surrounding slack for $0, d$ (by Lemmas 3 and 4). The following lemma gives us what we need to complete the proof of swap invariance for (1).

Lemma 8 *Let $(r_0, d_0), (r_1, d_1)$ be a swap wrt A and let $A' = A \cup \{(r_0, d_0)\} - \{(r_1, d_1)\}$. Then for any*

$a \leq b$, (i) there exist a', b' satisfying $a' \leq a, b \leq b'$ and $\delta(A', a', b') \leq \delta(A, a, b)$, and (ii) if $\delta(A', a, b) < \delta(A, a, b)$ then there exist $\hat{a}, \hat{b}$ with $\hat{a} \leq a, b \leq \hat{b}$ and $\delta(A, \hat{a}, \hat{b}) < \delta(A, a, b)$.

Proof. It is known (see, e.g. [5]) that $s \leq r_1, d_1 \leq t$, where s and t are chosen so that $s \leq r_0, d_0 \leq t$ and $\delta(A, s, t) = 0$. If $s \leq a, b \leq t$, the lemma follows immediately. If $a \leq s, t \leq b$ then $\delta(A', a, b) = \delta(A, a, b)$ follows by the choice of s, t and again the lemma is established. The remaining case is when $a < s < b < t$ (or, symmetrically, $s < a < t < b$). Here, note that the definition of slack implies $\delta(A', a, t) = \delta(A, a, t) \leq \delta(A, a, b) + \delta(A, s, t) - \delta(A, s, b) \leq \delta(A, a, b)$. So part (i) has been shown with $a' = a, b' = t$. For part (ii) observe that $\delta(A', a, b) < \delta(A, a, b)$ only if $d_0 \leq b$. Thus $\delta(A, a, t) = \delta(A', a, t) \leq \delta(A', a, b) < \delta(A, a, b)$ and we are done by choosing $\hat{a} = a, \hat{b} = t$. □

Monotonicity appears to be essential in this particular approach to scheduling. Order invariance is violated, for example, if $a = (0, 3)$, $b = (1, 2)$, and $c = (0, 3)$. Then $(a/b)/(c/b) = (0, 2)$ but $(a/c)/(b/c) = (0, 1)$. This example could leave open the possibility of a more clever contraction operation for non-monotone scheduling. We dispel this notion by observing that matroids based on scheduling with release times and deadlines are not closed under contraction (unless they are monotone). Consider a scheduling matroid $\mathcal{M}$ in which $a_i = b_i = (i - 1, i)$ for $i = 1, 2, 3$ and let $c = (0, 3)$. Then $\mathcal{M}/\{c\}$ has circuits $\{a_i, b_i\}$ for $i = 1, 2, 3$ and all 8 sets of the form $\{x_1, x_2, x_3\}$, where each x_i is either a_i or b_i. It can be shown, using for example the characterization of Bondy and Welsh (see [1], page 378), that $\mathcal{M}/\{c\}$ is not even a transversal matroid, much less a monotone scheduling matroid. Intuitively, at least 3 time slots are needed to represent the fact that $\{a_i, b_i\}$ is a circuit for each i, but the rank of $\mathcal{M}/\{c\}$ is 2. The smallest contraction-closed class of matroids known to contain monotone scheduling is the class of *gammoids* (see [1]). Elements of a gammoid cannot be represented as succinctly as those of a scheduling matroid.

4 Implementation Details

We now describe how the optimum base is produced as output and illustrate, with an example, how the array algorithm works. When the separator $ is received by a cell, the cell enters "push mode". A cell receiving $ at time t sends its matroid element, marked for output, to the next cell at time $t + 1$ and sends $ at time $t + 2$. A cell receiving an element marked for output at time t may send either its own matroid element or the one it has just received to the next cell at time $t + 1$, and the remaining element at time $t + 2$. The

ability to choose which element to send first allows the array to sort its output by any desired key. A sort by increasing release time (and increasing deadline as a secondary key) would allow the last cell to assign time slots to the elements it outputs using the algorithm of Glover [7] (the next feasible slot is assigned to a task with earliest release time — earliest deadline is used to break ties). Note that the last cell does not need to know it is last — all other cells can assign time slots using the same algorithm, but these assignments are superceded by the assignment of the last cell, which reaches the host.

Figure 1 shows an example of monotone scheduling with 4 tasks having rank 3. The top half of each cell i shows the current representation of e'_i as the pair r'_i, d'_i. The bottom half shows the original element e_i as r_i, d_i, w_i. Arrows indicate the input/output values at the start of the current time unit. When both f' and *previous* are sent to the next cell (see Algorithm Array-Greedy on page 4), f' is shown above the arrow and *previous* is shown below. The output phase is initiated at time unit 4. During time unit 5, cell 1 reinitializes itself to a dummy value and is ready to process the next problem instance. The output is sorted by release time and then deadline in cell 2 during time unit 6 and cell 3 during time units 7 and 8.

The actions of the generic algorithm (page 4) may be traced for an input record f appearing at time j by looking at cell i, time $j + i$, for $i = 1$ to n. Task $a = 0, 2, 5$ (which appears at time 0) is inserted in cell 1 at time 1. Task $b = 0, 1, 6$ is inserted in cell 1 at time 2, causing $a' = a/b$ to replace the dummy record in cell 2 at time 3. Task $c = 2, 3, 4$ moves past b (cell 1, time 3) and a' (cell 2, time 4) to find its proper position in cell 3 at time 5. Task $d = 1, 3, 7$ inserts itself in front of b (cell 1, time 4), which in turn pushes forward b' (from cell 1 to cell 2, time 4) and a' (from cell 2 to cell 3, time 5). Finally, d' and c' discover a circuit (d'/c' is a loop) in cell 3 at time 6, causing c' to be deleted (a' is inserted in its place). The optimal schedule includes tasks a, b, and d with b assigned to slot 1, a to slot 2, and d to slot 3.

5 Conclusions

What has been described is a generic one-way array algorithm for matroid problems that is analogous to the greedy algorithm in the sequential model. Like the greedy algorithm, the one-way array algorithm can, theoretically, be adapted to solve any matroid optimization problem. The primary issue, however, is the efficiency of testing for a circuit. For example, were we to store all of A in our representation of f/A, and allow sufficient computational power per time unit to solve a linear system of equations, the generic one-way algorithm could be used to solve optimization problems on arbitrary *linear* matroids (see [1] for a definition). Linear matroids include most problems that are of practical interest. A straightforward implementation of this idea would require $\Theta(n^3)$ total area and a period in $\Theta(M(n))$, where $M(n)$ is the time for $n \times n$ matrix multiplication (the period can be reduced if each cell is allowed to be a parallel machine, or is custom designed in VLSI). It is likely that efficient implementations of the one-way algorithm (constant period and roughly linear area) exist for matroids which have efficient (subquadratic) greedy algorithms, as has already been demonstrated for minimum spanning trees and monotone scheduling (the author is not aware of sequential algorithms specifically for monotone scheduling, but it is possible that techniques for deadline scheduling described by Gabow and Tarjan [5] can be generalized).

One interesting open question related to one-way array algorithms for matroid problems is whether there exists an efficient one-way array algorithm for the non-monotone scheduling problem. The fact that non-monotone scheduling is not closed under contraction rules out an approach based on the generic greedy algorithm given here — the most efficient result would have to be based on linear matroids (gammoids are linear matroids). It may, however, be possible to obtain an efficient algorithm if tasks are sorted in the array by some other criterion than weight, or auxiliary information is cleverly encoded throughout the array. Lack of closure under contraction may also explain why the best time bound known for non-monotone scheduling is $O(m \log n + n^2)$ [5] and the known efficient algorithms for independence testing appear to require non-trivial data structures and use of random access memory [3, 6, 10].

References

[1] M. AIGNER, *Combinatorial Theory*, Springer Verlag, 1979.

[2] S. ASHTAPUTRE AND C. SAVAGE, *Systolic arrays with embedded tree structures for connectivity problems*, IEEE Transactions on Computers, C-34 (1985), pp. 483 – 484.

[3] G. N. FREDERICKSON, *Scheduling unit-time tasks with integer release times and deadlines*, Inf. Process. Lett., 16 (1983), pp. 171 – 173.

[4] G. N. FREDERICKSON AND M. A. SRINIVAS, *Online updating of solutions to a class of matroid intersection problems*, Information and Computation, 74 (1987), pp. 113 – 139.

[5] H. N. GABOW AND R. E. TARJAN, *Efficient algorithms for a family of matroid intersection problems*, Journal of Algorithms, 5 (1984), pp. 80 – 131.

[6] ——, *A linear-time algorithm for a special case of disjoint set union*, J. Comput. System Sci., 30 (1985), pp. 209 – 221.

[7] F. GLOVER, *Maximum matching in a convex bipartite graph*, Naval Research Logistics Quarterly, 14 (1967), pp. 313 – 316.

[8] S.-T. HUANG, *A fully pipelined minimum-cost-spanning tree constructor*, Journal on Parallel and Distributed Computing, 9 (1990), pp. 55 – 62.

[9] E. L. LAWLER, *Combinatorial Optimization: Networks and Matroids*, Holt, Rinehart and Winston, 1976.

[10] W. LIPSKI, JR. AND F. P. PREPARATA, *Efficient algorithms for finding maximum matchings in convex bipartite graphs and related problems*, Acta Inf., 15 (1981), pp. 329 – 346.

[11] C. SAVAGE, M. STALLMANN, AND J. PERRY, *Solving some combinatorial problems on arrays with one-way dataflow*, Algorithmica, 5 (1990), pp. 179 – 199.

[12] C. D. SAVAGE, M. F. STALLMANN, AND A. Z. KOTOB, *Simulation of two-way computations on arrays with one-way data flow*, Tech. Rep. CCSP-TR-87/6, North Carolina State University Center for Communications and Signal Processing, 1987.

[13] D. D. SLEATOR AND R. E. TARJAN, *A data structure for dynamic trees*, J. Comput. System Sci., 26 (1983), pp. 362 – 391.

[14] M. TCHUENTE AND L. MELKEMY, *Reseaux systoliques pour le calcul des composantes connexes et le triangularisation des matrices bandes*, Tech. Rep. 366, Laboratoire d'Informatique et de Mathematiques Appliquees de Grenoble, 1983.

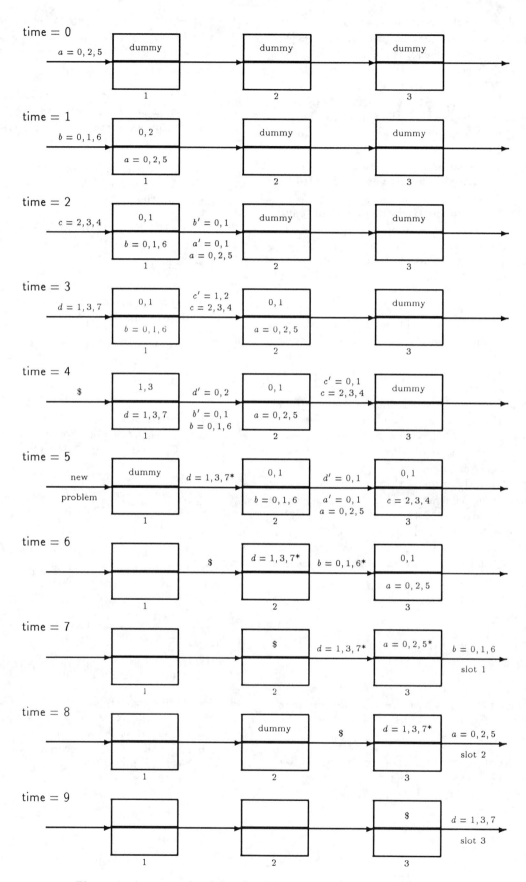

Figure 1: An example of the algorithm for monotone scheduling

356

On the Capabilities of Systolic Systems

(extended abstract)

Shimon Even* and Ami Litman

Bellcore
445 South St.
Morristown, NJ 07960-1910

Abstract

This paper investigates the capabilities of systolic systems. We show that any synchronous system can be transformed into an equivalent systolic system via two opposite techniques, one syntactic and the other semantic.

The syntactic technique considers the topology of the system, but ignores its behavior and the behavior of its functional elements. Leiserson and Saxe [LS] have developed such a technique, which does not preserve the behavior of the system. Our technique leaves the behavior of the system intact.

The semantic technique considers the functionality of the system as a whole, but ignores its internal structure. For each alphabet, used by a system to communicate with the external world, there is a single functional element, called the *universal* functional element for this alphabet. Systems which are built from copies of the universal functional element are called *restricted*. We show that every synchronous system can be transformed into a restricted systolic one. For binary systems, our technique produces a systolic system with a feasible clock period of $O(i + \log(o))$, where i and o are the numbers of input and output ports of the system. This clock period is independent of the size and complexity of the given system.

In the context of language recognizers, we show that any language, even nonrecursive, can be defined by an infinite restricted systolic system, while every regular language can be defined by a finite restricted system.

---

* On leave from the Computer Science Dept., Technion, Haifa, Israel.

© 1991 ACM 089791-438-4/91/0007/0357 $1.50

1. Introduction

Consider a large digital system built of *functional elements* and *registers*. All the registers are triggered by the same central clock and all the connections between components are point-to-point (no buses). The functional elements have the property that their outputs, at a given time, are determined by their inputs at that time; that is, they have no memory. Although we usually ignore the propagation delays of the functional elements, these delays determine the feasible period of the central clock. The registers are clocked memory elements. Assume the clock period is one, then for an integer τ the output of a register during the time interval $(\tau, \tau+1]$ is equal to its input at time τ.

Following Leiserson et al. [LS, LRS] the structure of the system is modeled by a directed weighted multigraph $G = (V, E, H, w)$ called the *communication graph* (in short, *c-graph*), which is defined as follows:

(1) V is a set of *vertices*. A vertex represents a functional element.

(2) E is a set of directed *edges*. An edge $u \xrightarrow{e} v$ represents a connection from an out-port of the functional element represented by u to an in-port of the functional element represented by v.

(3) $H \in V$ is the *host*. It represents the user of the system, and the edges to and from H are the only connections of the system to the outside world.

(4) w is a function from E to the nonnegative integers. $w(e)$ represents the number of registers on the edge e.

Following [LS], a system is called *synchronous* if in every cycle (directed circuit) of G there is at least one edge e such that $w(e) > 0$. This condition is essential for a proper operation of the system; it prevents possible instability as well as inconsistency. However, a synchronous system may have long directed paths, in which all edges have no registers. In such a case, signals may ripple through long paths before they stabilize. This forces the slowing of the central clock to allow for such transitory effects to die down, rendering the system inefficient.

A synchronous system is called *systolic* if every edge e, except those emanating from the host, satisfies $w(e) > 0$. Systolic systems are attractive for several reasons. If we consider the registers to be an integral part of the vertex preceding them, then each vertex becomes a finite automaton (Moore's finite state machine). Networks of finite automata are conceptually simpler than synchronous systems, and have been popular models of parallel computation since the 'fifties [SM]. A practical advantage of a systolic system is that if each functional element can operate at a certain rate of the central clock, then the system as a whole can operate at this rate, whatever its structure or size.

We will investigate the computational capability of systolic systems. While our main interest is finite systems, we will also consider infinite ones; that is, systems having infinitely many vertices and edges while any of their components is finite.

This paper presents transformations of systems (synchronous, systolic and others) into systolic systems with related functionality. We will describe two opposite transformation techniques, one syntactic and the other semantic.

1.1. Syntactic technique

The syntactic technique considers the topology of the system, but ignores its behavior and the behavior of its functional elements. The topology of the resulting system is strongly related to the original topology, and the new functional elements are built of copies of the old ones. Clearly, we are not interested in transformations that glue the whole system into a single finite state machine, and prefer those that keep the functional elements small.

Our technique extends the work of Leiserson et al. [LS, LRS]. However, they have not considered any modification of the topology of the system or its functional elements; the only modification they have investigated was the addition and deletion of registers over the edges of the system.

We will show that any synchronous system can be syntactically transformed into an equivalent† systolic system. This is an extension of a result of [LS]. They have built a systolic system which is similar to the original system, but is k times slower for some integer k. This requires a modification of the host. While the original host produced input and received output each clock tick, their modified host must recognize the one tick, out of every k consecutive ticks, to produce input and the one

tick out of every k ticks to read the output. Our transformation leaves the behavior of the system intact, therefore, there is no need to modify the host. However, the system we produce does not work k times faster (in real time) than that of [LS]; in practice our functional elements will have longer propagation delay, thus a slower clock rate will be required.

There are two powerful computational mechanisms, *broadcast* and *instant-accumulation,* which seem at odds with the framework of systolic systems. Broadcast is a mechanism that makes signals, sent by the host over a single edge, immediately available to all other vertices. Instant-accumulation is a mechanism that instantaneously presents to the host, via a single edge, a value which depends on values produced, for this purpose, by all functional elements. For example, an AND function of binary values produced by all functional elements.

Consider a systolic system augmented by an auxiliary mechanism of either broadcast or instant-accumulation. We will show that this auxiliary mechanism may be eliminated via a syntactic transformation. Sieferas [S] has proved that broadcast can be eliminated in the framework of iterative arrays, a special case of infinite systolic systems, and Leiserson and Saxe [LS] have shown that any one of these two mechanisms can be eliminated in the framework of systolic systems with a 2-slowdown penalty, hence requiring modification of the host.

A k-speedup of a given system is another system that computes in a single tick what the original system computes in k clock ticks. Cole [C] has shown how to speed up an iterative array. We will present a syntactic speedup transformation for systolic systems in general.

1.2. Semantic technique

The semantic technique considers the functionality of the system as a whole, but ignores its internal structure. For each alphabet, used by a system to communicate with the external world, one can define a single functional element called the *universal* functional element for this alphabet. Systems that are built from copies of the universal functional element are called *restricted*. We show that every synchronous system can be transformed into a restricted systolic one. If the alphabet over all the edges of the system is binary, our technique produces a systolic system with a feasible clock period of $O(i+\log(o))$, where i and o are the numbers of input and output ports of the system. This clock period is independent of the size and the complexity of the given system.

In the context of language recognizers, we prove the following results.

(1)   Any language, even nonrecursive, can be defined by an infinite restricted systolic system.

---

† The meaning of this ''equivalent'' will be described later.

(2) Any regular language can be defined by a finite restricted systolic system.

Foster and Kung [FK] have described a transformation from a regular expression into a synchronous system that defines the same regular language. Their system is built from copies of three functional elements, and the size of the system is linear in the length of the given expression, while the size of our system is superexponential. However, their system is not systolic and may have arbitrarily long paths with no registers.

2. Syntax of Retiming

In this work we will extensively apply the concept of retiming introduced by Leiserson and Saxe [LS]. To keep the paper self-contained, we will repeat some of their work.

The concept of retiming in its basic form is as follows. Let v be a vertex of a synchronous system Y such that each edge emanating from v has at least one register. Assume that we remove one register from each edge emanating from v, add one register to each edge entering v, and call the resulting system Y'. In Y', v will receive the same sequence of inputs as in Y, but one tick later. We say that v has been *retimed* to *lag* its original image by one tick. Since outputs produced by v in Y' will take one tick less to reach the neighbors of v, the rest of the system will not notice any change. Similarly, we may remove one register from any entering edge, and add one to any emanating edge, retiming v to *lead* by one tick.

It seems that, as far as the host is concerned, the systems Y and Y' are identical, but it is not necessarily so. There is a difficulty with the mapping of initial states from one system to the other. For simplicity, let us assume that the edges incident to v have no other registers except those manipulated by the retiming transformation. Given values of the old registers (on the emanating edges), we should assign values to the new registers (on the entering edges) in an appropriate manner. However, this may be impossible; for example, two old registers may have different values, while the functional element of v always sends an identical value over all its emanating edges. We will deal with this semantic difficulty in the next section.

Let $G = (V, E, H, w)$ and $G' = (V, E, H, w')$ be two c-graphs sharing the same V, E and H. Following [LS], we say that G' *is a retiming of G by r* iff $r : V \to \mathbf{Z}$ (the integers) and $w'(e) = w(e) + r(v) - r(u)$ for all $u \xrightarrow{e} v$. Notice that if G' is a retiming of G by r then G' is a retiming of G by $r+k$ for any constant k. Hence, without loss of generality, we may assume that $r(H) = 0$.

We say that G' *is a retiming of G* ($G' \cong G$) if there is an r such that G' is a retiming of G by r. Note that the relation $\cong$ is reflexive, symmetric, and transitive; i.e., it is an equivalence relation.

It is convenient to consider general edge-weighted directed graphs in which the weights are real numbers, rather than non-negative integers, and the sum of weights over a cycle is not necessarily positive. We will refer to such graphs as *g-graphs*. For any g-graph G, we extend its weight-function w to be defined on every directed path in G as follows. For a path $p = v_0 \xrightarrow{e_1} v_1 \cdots \xrightarrow{e_l} v_l$, set

$$w(p) \triangleq \sum_{i=1}^{i=l} w(e_i).$$

If G' is a retiming of G by r, then

$$\begin{aligned} w'(p) &= \sum_{i=1}^{i=l} [w(e_i) + r(v_i) - r(v_{i-1})] \qquad (2.1) \\ &= w(p) + r(v_l) - r(v_0) \end{aligned}$$

Hence, $w(c) = w'(c)$ for every cycle c.

For g-graphs $G = (V, E, H, w)$ and $\bar{G} = (V, E, H, \bar{w})$, we denote $G \geq \bar{G}$ iff $w(p) \geq \lfloor \bar{w}(p) \rfloor$ for every path p. Note that in the special case where G and $\bar{G}$ are c-graphs, $G \geq \bar{G}$ means that $w(e) \geq \bar{w}(e)$ for every e.

Assume we are given a c-graph G and a partition of its vertices into disjoint sets, and we wish to retime G such that any inter-partition edge will have at least one register. If we can do so, we can make the system systolic by merging each partition into a single functional element. This raises the following question: Given a c-graph G and a g-graph $\bar{G}$, the weights of $\bar{G}$ being either zero or one, is there a $G' \cong G$ such that $G' \geq \bar{G}$? This question and similar ones are resolved by the following lemma.

Lemma (2.1) (The retiming lemma)

Let $G = (V, E, H, w)$ be a finite c-graph and $\bar{G} = (V, E, H, \bar{w})$ be a g-graph, sharing the same V, E and H. Then there is a $G' \cong G$ such that $G' \geq \bar{G}$ iff $w(c) \geq \bar{w}(c)$ for every cycle c.

A special case of this lemma, where both graphs are c-graphs, has been proved by Commoner et al. [CHEP] in the context of marked graphs. Several consequences of this lemma appear in Leiserson et al. [LS, LRS].

Proof:

Assume there is a G' such that $G' \cong G$, $G' \geq \bar{G}$ and yet there is a cycle c such that $w(c) < \bar{w}(c)$. Let nc be an n-repetition of c. For n large enough, $n \cdot w(c) < \lfloor n \cdot \bar{w}(c) \rfloor$, hence $w(nc) < \lfloor \bar{w}(nc) \rfloor$. Since $G' \cong G$, $w'(nc) = w(nc) < \lfloor \bar{w}(nc) \rfloor$, but this contradicts $G' \geq \bar{G}$.

Assume that $w(c) \geq \bar{w}(c)$ for every cycle c. Define $\hat{w}(e) \triangleq w(e) - \bar{w}(e)$ for all $e \in E$. For every cycle c, $\hat{w}(c) = w(c) - \bar{w}(c) \geq 0$. Choose any $t \in V$. We will construct a retiming G' by solving the *single-destination-shortest-paths* problem to the target t with the $\hat{w}$ weights.

Without loss of generality, we assume that there is a path from any $v \in V$ to t. (Otherwise, we may add edges $v \xrightarrow{e} t$, and assign them large w weights and small $\overline{w}$ weights to maintain $w(c) \geq \overline{w}(c)$. Once we have G', we will discard the additional edges.)

For every $v \in V$ set $\lambda(v) \triangleq \min\{\hat{w}(p) | p$ a path from v to $t\}$. λ is well defined since we assume that there is a path from every v to t and since $\hat{w}(c) \geq 0$ for every cycle c. For every path p going from u to v, $\lambda(v) + \hat{w}(p) \geq \lambda(u)$, and by definition of $\hat{w}$:

$$\lambda(v) + w(p) - \overline{w}(p) \geq \lambda(u)$$

Hence,
$\lambda(v) + w(p) \geq \lambda(u) + \overline{w}(p) \geq \lfloor \lambda(u) \rfloor + \lfloor \overline{w}(p) \rfloor$. Since the w weights are integers, $\lfloor \lambda(v) \rfloor + w(p) \geq \lfloor \lambda(u) \rfloor + \lfloor \overline{w}(p) \rfloor$. Rewriting the last inequality, we get:

$$w(p) + \lfloor \lambda(v) \rfloor - \lfloor \lambda(u) \rfloor \geq \lfloor \overline{w}(p) \rfloor$$

Let G' be the retiming of G by $r(v) \triangleq \lfloor \lambda(v) \rfloor$. By (2.1), for any path p from u to v, $w'(p) = w(p) + \lfloor \lambda(v) \rfloor - \lfloor \lambda(u) \rfloor$. It follows that $w'(p) \geq \lfloor \overline{w}(p) \rfloor$. ∎

Lemma (2.2)

Let $G = (V, E, H, w)$ be a finite c-graph and $\overline{G} = (V, E, H, \overline{w})$ be a g-graph such that for every cycle c, $w(c) \geq \overline{w}(c)$. Then for any given $z \in V$:
(1) There is $G' \cong G$ such that $G' \geq \overline{G}$, and $w'(e) \geq \overline{w}(e)$ for every edge $v \xrightarrow{e} z$.
and
(2) There is $G'' \cong G$ such that $G'' \geq \overline{G}$ and $w''(e) \geq \overline{w}(e)$ for every edge $z \xrightarrow{e} v$.
Proof omitted.

The graphs G' and G'', which exist by lemmas (2.1) and (2.2), may be computed in time $O(|V| \cdot |E|)$. The only non-trivial computation there is the *single-destination-shortest-paths* problem, which can be solved in time $O(|V| \cdot |E|)$ by Ford's algorithm ([F], [FF]; also described in [E]).

The following theorem of Commoner et al. [CHEP] explains why cycles are significant for retiming.

Theorem (2.1)

For strongly connected c-graphs $G = (V, E, H, w)$ and $\overline{G} = (V, E, H, \overline{w})$: $G \cong \overline{G}$ iff $w(c) = \overline{w}(c)$ for every cycle c.
Proof omitted.

2.1. Infinite graphs

Up to here we assumed that the graphs in question are finite. In fact, lemmas (2.1) and (2.2) do not hold for infinite graphs. A counter-example is an acyclic graph having a source s and a sink t with infinitely many paths $\{p_i | i \in \mathbf{N}\}$ from s to t, such that $\lim_{i \to \infty}[\overline{w}(p_i) - w(p_i)] = \infty$. (There exists such a graph with bounded degrees.) If G' is a retiming of G by r and $G' \geq \overline{G}$ then by (2.1), $r(t) - r(s) = \infty$.

Let us show that lemmas (2.1) and (2.2) hold for infinite graphs, if the graphs are restricted to be strongly connected. Theorem (2.1) is already restricted and therefore holds for infinite graphs. To accommodate the infinite case in the proof of lemma (2.1), redefine λ to be $\lambda(v) \triangleq \mathrm{glb}^\dagger\{\hat{w}(p) | p$ a path from v to $t\}$. It is easy to verify that this set is bounded from below and not empty. Except for the redefinition of λ, the arguments in this section are valid for the infinite case as well. Let us restate lemma (2.2) for the sake of reference.

Lemma (2.3)

Let $G = (V, E, H, w)$ be an infinite, strongly connected c-graph and $\overline{G} = (V, E, H, \overline{w})$ be a g-graph such that for every cycle c, $w(c) \geq \overline{w}(c)$. Then for any given $z \in V$:
(1) There is $G' \cong G$ such that $G' \geq \overline{G}$, and $w'(e) \geq \overline{w}(e)$ for every edge $v \xrightarrow{e} z$.
and
(2) There is $G'' \cong G$ such that $G'' \geq \overline{G}$ and $w''(e) \geq \overline{w}(e)$ for every edge $z \xrightarrow{e} v$.

3. Semantics of Retiming

Let Y be a synchronous system with a c-graph G. A state of Y is an aggregate state of all the registers of Y. Let S denote the set of all states of Y. Since G has no register-less cycle, the output of Y (to the host) is independent of the current input. Let $O(s)$ be the output produced by the system when in state s. Let Θ be the set of all potential inputs. Every $\theta \in \Theta$ is a vector of letters, one for each edge emanating from the host. Since G has no register-less cycle, the next state of Y is determined by the current state s and the current input θ. Let $f(s, \theta)$ denote the next state of Y. As usual, we extend f to be defined over Θ^* by $f(s, \phi) = s$ and $f(s, U\theta) = f(f(s, U), \theta)$.

Let Y and Y' be two synchronous systems having the same input alphabet Θ and the same output alphabet, as is the case when Y' is a retiming of Y. Let S', f', etc., denote the corresponding entities for Y'. For $s \in S$ and $s' \in S'$, we say that $\langle Y, s \rangle$ is *equivalent* to $\langle Y', s' \rangle$

---
† Greatest Lower Bound

$(\langle Y, s \rangle \equiv \langle Y', s' \rangle)$ if $O(f(s, U)) = O'(f'(s', U))$ for any $U \in \Theta^*$. (In other words, the host cannot distinguish between $\langle Y, s \rangle$ and $\langle Y', s' \rangle$.) In the special case where $Y = Y'$, we will shorten $\langle Y, s \rangle \equiv \langle Y, s' \rangle$ to $s \equiv s'$.

We say that a state $s \in S$ is m-old if there is a state $q \in S$ and a word $U \in \Theta^*$ such that $|U| = m$ and $f(q, U)$ is equivalent to s. We say that a state $s \in S$ is ∞-old if it is m-old for every integer m.

We say that Y' *strongly-simulates* Y if for every $s \in S$ there is an $s' \in Y$ such that $\langle Y, s \rangle \equiv \langle Y', s' \rangle$. We say that Y' *weakly-simulates* Y if there is an integer m such that for every m-old $s \in S$ there is an $s' \in Y'$ satisfying $\langle Y, s \rangle \equiv \langle Y', s' \rangle$. We say that Y' *poorly-simulates* Y if for every ∞-old $s \in S$ there is an $s' \in Y'$ satisfying $\langle Y, s \rangle \equiv \langle Y', s' \rangle$.

If Y is finite, then for $m = |S|$ and every $s \in S$: s is m-old iff s is ∞-old. Hence, the relations "weakly-simulate" and "poorly-simulate" are identical in the context of finite systems. These two relations are distinct in the context of infinite systems.

We say that Y' is *strongly-equivalent* to Y if Y and Y' strongly-simulate each other. We say that Y' is *weakly-equivalent* to Y if Y and Y' weakly-simulate each other. We say that Y' is *poorly-equivalent* to Y if Y and Y' poorly-simulate each other.

The following theorem has been proved by Leiserson and Saxe [LS].

Theorem (3.1)

Let Y be a finite synchronous system, and let Y' be a retiming of Y, then Y' is weakly-equivalent to Y. Moreover, let Y' be a retiming of Y by r, where $r(H) = 0$ and $m = \max\{r(v) | v \in V\}$. Then for every m-old $s \in S$ there is an $s' \in S'$ such that $\langle Y, s \rangle \equiv \langle Y', s' \rangle$.

3.1. Infinite Systems

The infinite systems we consider have infinitely many vertices and edges, but each of their components is finite. Any edge may pass letters out of a finite alphabet, and the degree of each vertex (except the host) is finite. The size of the alphabets or the degrees may be unbounded. In this section we will extend theorem (3.1) for infinite systems. Toward this end, we will apply the compactness theorem of propositional calculus.

Infinite systems may have a pathological structure that do not occur in finite systems. They may have a simple, infinite, register-less, incoming path. That is, an infinite sequence of edges ($\cdots v_2 \overset{e_1}{\to} v_1 \overset{e_0}{\to} v_0$), such that all the v_i are distinct, and the edges have no registers. We refer to such a path as *i-path*.

It is interesting to compare the effects of i-paths and register-less cycles. In both cases, there may be more than one assignment of values to the register-less edges that is consistent with the behavior of the functional elements. For example, this is the case with a register-less cycle of an even number of inverters.

The effects of i-paths and register-less cycles differ in two ways. First, register-less cycles are invariant under retiming, while i-paths may be created and eliminated by retiming. Second, a (non-synchronous) system with a register-less cycle may lack any consistent assignment of values to the register-less edges; e.g., a system with a register-less cycle of an odd number of inverters. This is never the case with i-paths. Any infinite synchronous system has at least one consistent assignment of values to the edges, for any given state and host input. This last fact can be proved by techniques similar to those below. However, we will not study systems having i-paths in this paper; hence, we will neither prove, nor use this fact.

Theorem (3.2)

Let Y be a (finite or infinite) synchronous system, and let Y' be a retiming of Y, such that Y and Y' have no i-paths. Then Y' is poorly-equivalent to Y. Moreover, let Y' be a retiming of Y by r, where $r(H) = 0$, and $m \triangleq \text{lub}^{\dagger}\{r(v) | v \in V\}$ (m is either an integer or ∞). Then for every m-old $s \in S$ there is an $s' \in S'$ such that $\langle Y, s \rangle \equiv \langle Y', s' \rangle$.
Proof omitted.

4. System Initialization

In most practical applications of digital systems, there must be a mechanism that forces the system into a predefined state. Such a mechanism is usually applied to initialize the system upon power-up, and may be used for error recovery as well. This mechanism could be outside the scope of our model. For example, the system may have a single wire called *master-clear* which is connected to all the registers. A single pulse on this wire resets all the registers to a predefined state before the clock starts ticking.

Initialization could also be done within the scope of our model. There may be a word $W \in \Theta^*$ which resets the system whenever provided by the host. Some systems need to be specially designed to be reset in this way, while others have it naturally. For example, a k-stage pipeline is reset by any word of size k.

There are two types of resets, a *hard-reset* and a *soft-reset*. A hard-reset forces the system into a predefined state s, while a soft-reset guarantees only that the new state y is equivalent to a predefined state s. (It brings the system into the equivalence class $s/\equiv$.) We will

---
† Least Upper Bound

361

consider soft-resets only, since – as discussed below – they behave nicely under retiming.

Given a (finite or infinite) synchronous system Y, we say that a word $W \in \Theta^*$ is *decisive* if there is an $s \in S$ such that $f(q, W) \equiv s$ for all $q \in S$. In this case we say that s is *reproducible,* and that W *reproduces s.* Note that if W is decisive, so is $U'WU''$ for any $U', U'' \in \Theta^*$. Hence, every reproducible state is ∞-old. If s is reproducible and there is a run which starts in state s and ends in state y, then y is reproducible as well. Therefore, after the host initializes the system with any decisive word, the system will visit reproducible states only. The definitions above and the following two lemmas hold for both finite and infinite systems.

Lemma (4.1)

Let Y' poorly-simulate Y. Then for every reproducible $s \in S$ there is an $s' \in S'$ such that $\langle Y, s \rangle \equiv \langle Y', s' \rangle$.

Lemma (4.2)

Let Y' be weakly-equivalent to Y. Then for every reproducible $s \in S$ there is a reproducible $s' \in S'$ such that $\langle Y, s \rangle \equiv \langle Y', s' \rangle$.

Proofs omitted.

5. From Synchronous to Systolic

Let G be a (finite or infinite) c-graph. Define the *minimum-cycle-mean* of G by:

$$\mathrm{mcm}(G) \triangleq \mathrm{lub}^{\dagger}\{(w(c)/|c|)\,|\,c \text{ is a cycle in } G\}$$

where $|c|$ is the number of edges in c. If G is acyclic, we arbitrarily define $\mathrm{mcm}(G) = 1$. Since G is a c-graph, it has no cycles without registers. Hence, if G is finite, $\mathrm{mcm}(G) > 0$. Karp [K] has described an algorithm that computes $\mathrm{mcm}(G)$ in time $O(|V| \cdot |E|)$. Leiserson et al. [LRS] have proved a lemma similar to the following one.

Lemma (5.1)

Let G be a finite c-graph, then there is G', a retiming of G, such that in G' every path of length $\lceil 1/\mathrm{mcm}(G) \rceil$ has at least one register, and every edge entering H has at least one register.

Proof:

Apply lemma (2.2) for $\overline{w}(e) \triangleq \mathrm{mcm}(G)$. ■

Given G, the total time complexity of constructing G' is $O(|V| \cdot |E|)$, a slight improvement over [LRS].

---

† Least Upper Bound

Lemma (5.2)

Let G be an infinite, strongly connected c-graph with $\mathrm{mcm}(G) > 0$, then there is G', a retiming of G, such that in G' every path of length $\lceil 1/\mathrm{mcm}(G) \rceil$ has at least one register, and every edge entering H has at least one register.

Proof:

Apply lemma (2.3) for $\overline{w}(e) \triangleq \mathrm{mcm}(G)$. ■

Lemma (5.3)

Let Y' be a (finite or infinite) synchronous system and k an integer such that every path of length k has at least one register, and every edge entering H has at least one register. Then there is a systolic system Y^* that strongly-simulates Y.

Although k does not appear in the consequence of the lemma, it plays a role in bounding the complexity of the functional elements of Y^*. These elements will be built out of (copies of) functional elements of Y, and the "depth" of these elements will be at most k. More about this later.

Outline of proof:

Let G' be the c-graph of Y'. The system Y^* will have the same set of vertices, V, as Y', but these vertices will contain new functional elements, and the interconnection of these vertices in G^* will be "close", but not identical, to G'. Let $F(v)$ denote the functional element of the vertex v in Y^*. Instead of defining $F(v)$ by a table which maps input values to output values, we will describe $F(v)$ as a synchronous system which has no registers. Altogether, we will have two types of graphs: the (global) graph G^*, and a graph $F(v)$ for each v.

$F(v)$ is composed of vertices of G', but the host, which have a register-less path leading to v, as well as the register-less edges between them. $F(v)$ is a directed acyclic graph whose depth is, at most, k. v is the only vertex of $F(v)$ that produces inputs for other functional elements of G^*. These inputs correspond to edges out of v, in G', which have positive weights. The sequence of signals transmitted over these edges will be the same, both in G' and G^*.

To insure the proper operation of the subsystem $F(v)$, its components should get the right signals at the right places. Consider an edge $a \xrightarrow{e} b$ of G' where $b \in F(v)$. If $w'(e) = 0$ and $a \neq H$, then this input is provided internally by $F(v)$. Otherwise, we may define G^* in such a way that this input will be provided via an edge of G^*. ■

Y^* is not strongly-equivalent to Y' due to a minor point; Y^* contains several copies of each register of Y', hence, Y' may not simulate the initial states of Y^* in which the values of corresponding registers do not match.

There is another technical difficulty with Y^*; it has several copies of original edges emanating from H. Strictly speaking, the interface of Y' to the external world has been changed. To overcome this problem, for each edge that emanates from the host in G', we should merge all the heads of its copies in G^* into one vertex.

Theorem (5.1)

For every finite synchronous system Y there is a systolic system Y^* that weakly-simulates Y.

Proof:

Retime Y into the synchronous system Y' via lemma (5.1). By theorem (3.1) Y' is weakly-equivalent to Y. Transform Y' into the systolic system Y^* via lemma (5.3). ∎

This last theorem by itself is trivial. One may glue all the functional elements into a single functional element and come with a systolic system strongly-equivalent to the original. The key issue here are the size and depth of the resulting functional elements. Let Δ_{in} be an upper bound on the in-degree of vertices of G other than H, let $k \triangleq \lceil 1/\text{mcm}(G) \rceil$ and consider the original functional elements to be of size one and depth one. The depth of the resulting functional elements is bounded by k, and — ignoring the merge of the host neighbors — their size is bounded by either $(\Delta_{in}^k - 1)/(\Delta_{in} - 1)$ or k (the former in the case that $\Delta_{in} > 1$, the latter otherwise).

Leiserson and Saxe [LS] have introduced a technique to convert a synchronous system into a systolic one. However, their systolic system is not equivalent to the original one — it works k times slower for some integer k — and hence the host must be modified.

Theorem (5.2)

Let Y be an infinite synchronous system with c-graph G, such that G is strongly connected, $\text{mcm}(G) > 0$, and G has no infinite register-less incoming path (i-path). Then there is a systolic system Y^* that poorly-simulates Y.

Proof:

Retime Y into the synchronous system Y' via lemma (5.2). By theorem (3.2) Y' is poorly-equivalent to Y. Transform Y' into the systolic system Y^* via lemma (5.3). ∎

6. Broadcast and Instant-accumulation

We consider here two powerful computational mechanisms which seem at odds with the framework of systolic systems, but are easily done in synchronous systems. We will show that each of these mechanisms can be effectively done in the framework of systolic systems.

Broadcast is a mechanism that makes signals, sent by the host over a single edge, immediately available to all other vertices. Consider a systolic system augmented by an auxiliary broadcast mechanism. We will show that this mechanism can be eliminated via a syntactic transformation.

Theorem (6.1)

Let Y be a finite (infinite) systolic system augmented by an auxiliary broadcast mechanism. (In the infinite case, let the in-degree of the host be finite.) Then there is a systolic system Y^* that weakly-simulates (poorly-simulates) Y.

Proof:

Let such a Y be given, and let G be its c-graph (which does not include the broadcast mechanism). Without loss of generality, we may assume that any $v \in V$ has a directed path from v to H (otherwise, remove the superfluous vertices).

Let (V, A) be a directed breadth-first spanning tree of G, where the edges lead to the root H. Let (V, A^r) be the graph generated by reversing all the edges of (V, A). Define $G' = (V, E', H, w')$ as follows:

(1) $E' \triangleq E \cup A^r$

(2) $w'(e) \triangleq \begin{cases} w(e) & \text{if } e \in E \\ 0 & \text{if } e \in A^r \end{cases}$

With additional simple logic in each vertex, we may use the register-less edges of A^r to disseminate the broadcast signal instantaneously. Let us call the resulting synchronous system Y'. Clearly, Y' is strongly-equivalent to Y. There is one difficulty, however. A^r may have several edges emanating from the host. We will correct this later.

In every cycle of G', the number of edges with registers is greater than or equal to the number of register-less edges. Thus, $\text{mcm}(G') \geq 1/2$. If Y is finite, then by theorem (5.1) there is a systolic system Y^* that weakly-simulates Y'. If Y is infinite, then Y' satisfies the conditions of theorem (5.2); that is, G' is strongly connected, $\text{mcm}(G') \geq 1/2$, and G' has no infinite register-less incoming path. By theorem (5.2) there is a systolic system Y^* that poorly-simulates Y'.

Y^* may have several edges emanating from the host, which are copies of edges of A^r, while the host should send the broadcast signals via a single edge. To overcome that, merge the heads of all these edges into a single vertex. ∎

Let Δ be an upper bound on the degree of vertices in G (including the host). If we ignore the simple logic for broadcasting and consider the original functional elements to be of depth one and size one, then the depth of a functional element of Y^* is at most two, and its size is bounded by a function of Δ. This function is independent of the size and topology of Y.

Let us turn our attention to instant-accumulation. Instant-accumulation is a mechanism that instantaneously presents to the host, via a single edge, a value which depends on values produced, for this purpose, by all functional elements. A common example is an AND function of binary values produced by all functional elements. The exact computation performed by the instant-accumulation mechanism is immaterial, but we assume that it combines its inputs by a binary operator which is commutative and associative, like $+$.

We assume that all the inputs to the instant-accumulation mechanism pass through registers, as they come out of the functional elements. This is in concert with the assumption that every edge has at least one register, except those emanating from the host.

Theorem (6.2)

Let Y be a finite systolic system augmented by an auxiliary instant-accumulation mechanism, then there is a systolic system Y^* that weakly-simulates Y.

The elimination of instant-accumulation in finite systems is similar to the elimination of broadcast, with the direction of all edges reversed. Hence, we will not describe it.

We cannot use the same technique to eliminate instant-accumulation in an infinite system, since this will create a synchronous system having i-paths. We do not study such systems in this paper.

7. Speedup

Let k be a positive integer. Informally, a system Y' is a *k-speedup* of a system Y if the computation performed by Y, in n clock ticks, is performed by Y' in n/k ticks. Formally, let Y be a system with input alphabet Σ and output alphabet Θ, and let Y' be a system with input alphabet Σ^k and output alphabet Θ^k. For $w \in (\Sigma^k)^*$, let $\overline{w}$ denote the word of Σ^* generated from w by considering each letter of w to be a word (of length k) of Σ^* and catenating all these words. Let s be a state of Y, and $u \in \Sigma^*$. Define $Y_s(u) \in \Theta^*$ to be the word produced by the system Y at ticks $1, 2, \cdots, |u|$ when Y starts in state s and receives the word u at ticks $0, 1, \cdots, |u|-1$. We say that Y' is a *k-speedup* of Y if for every state s of Y there is a state s' of Y' such that $Y'_{s'}(w) = Y_s(\overline{w})$ for all $w \in (\Sigma^k)^*$.

Theorem (7.1)

Let Y be a systolic system and k a positive integer, then there is a systolic system Y' such that Y' is a k-

speedup of Y.

Outline of proof:

Let $G = (V, E, H, w)$ be the c-graph of Y. Without loss of generality, $w(e) = 0$ if e emanates from the host and $w(e) = 1$ otherwise. Let the graph K be the cycle of k vertices, $K = (0 \rightarrow 1 \rightarrow 2 \cdots \rightarrow k-1 \rightarrow 0)$. Let G' be the product of G and K. Let e be an edge of G' entering the vertex $\langle v, j \rangle$. Define $w'(e) = 1$ if $v = H$ or $j = 0$, and $w'(e) = 0$ otherwise. Assign to each vertex of G' the functional element of the corresponding vertex of G, merge all the "hosts" into one and call the resulting system Y'.

The system Y' is synchronous and a k-speedup of Y, but it is not systolic. In Y', every directed path of length k has at least one register, and every edge entering the host has a register. By lemma (5.3) there is a systolic system that strongly-simulates Y'. ∎

8. A Theorem About Finite Automata

The transformations we described so far were syntactic. They consider the topology of the system, but ignore its behavior and the behavior of its functional elements. From here on we will discuss semantic transformations. These transformations consider the functionality of the system as a whole, but ignore its internal structure. Since the behavior of a synchronous system is equivalent to that of a (deterministic) finite automaton, we will consider transformations of a finite automaton into a systolic system.

One may view a finite automaton $A = (S, \Sigma, q_0, f, F)$ as a directed labeled graph, called the *state diagram* of A. The set of vertices is S, and there is an edge labeled a going from s to t ($s \xrightarrow{a} t$) iff $f(s, a) = t$. In this context we are interested in a bound on the in-degree of the states. (The out-degree of every state is clearly $|\Sigma|$.)

Theorem (8.1)

For every regular language $L \subset \Sigma^*$, there is a deterministic finite automaton A which defines L, such that the in-degree of every state of A is at most $|\Sigma| + 1$.
Proof omitted.

9. Restricted Systolic Systems – The Finite Case

A synchronous system Y whose output alphabet is binary may be considered as a language recognizer. That is, Y *accepts* the word W if Y outputs a 1 at the next tick after receiving W. If Σ is the input alphabet, then Y *defines* the language $L \subset \Sigma^*$ of all words accepted by Y.

Clearly, if the system is finite then L is regular. However, the system may not be systolic, and it may have arbitrarily large functional elements. We will show that every regular L is defined by a systolic system whose functional elements are all identical, and equal a predefined functional element.

Let Ψ be a (type of) functional element, and let Y be a synchronous system. We say that Y is *restricted* to Ψ if all the functional elements of Y are copies of Ψ. A copy of Ψ may have some unconnected out-ports, but all its in-ports are, of course, connected.

Theorem (9.1)

Let Σ be a finite alphabet. Then there is a functional element Ψ (called a *universal* functional element) such that for any regular language $L \subset \Sigma^*$ there is a systolic system restricted to Ψ which defines L.

Proof:

Let $L \subset \Sigma^*$ be a regular language, and let $\sigma = |\Sigma|$. Consider the language L^r, which consists of all the words of L written in the reverse order. It is well known that L^r is regular [RS]. Thus, by theorem (8.1) there is a deterministic finite automaton A^r that defines L^r, and in which the in-degrees are bounded by $\sigma+1$. Being deterministic, A^r has a single initial state, but may have several accepting states.

Transform A^r to a nondeterministic automaton A which defines L as follows. Reverse all the transitions; make all accepting states of A^r initial states in A; make the initial state of A^r the (unique) accepting state of A. In A, the in-degree of each state is (exactly) σ, and the out-degree is bounded by $\sigma+1$. Let $A = (S, \Sigma, S_0, f, F)$, where S is the finite set of states; Σ is the input alphabet of σ letters; S_0 is the set of initial states; f is the next-state function, $S \times \Sigma \rightarrow 2^S$; F is the set which contains the single accepting state g.

Construct a systolic system with broadcast, Y, whose c-graph, $G = (V, E, H, w)$, is as follows.

(1) $V \triangleq S$.

(2) $E \triangleq \{u \xrightarrow{e} v \mid u, v \in V, \exists a \in \Sigma$ such that $v \in f(u, a)\}$
$\cup \ \{g \xrightarrow{\rho} H\}$.

Note that g, which is the accepting state of A, is the only vertex of G that "reports" to the host.

(3) $\forall e \in E \ w(e) \triangleq 1$.

Each register of Y may contain either a token or a blank. The initial state q is defined as follows: a register has a token iff it follows a vertex that corresponds to an initial state of A.

Each functional element has exactly σ in-ports, labeled by distinct letters of Σ. The edge $u \xrightarrow{e} v$ enters the in-port labeled a if $v \in f(u, a)$. In every tick, the host broadcasts a letter of Σ. Let the current letter be a; each functional element takes the input of the in-port labeled a,

and passes it to all its out-ports.

It is easy to see that H gets a token at time t iff the word, broadcast up to time t (exclusive of the letter broadcast at t), belongs to L; that is, the system defines L. All the functional elements are essentially identical, differing only by the number of out-ports. Moreover, the functional element depends on the alphabet Σ, but not on the language L.

Except for the broadcast mechanism, the system Y is systolic. By theorem (6.1) we can eliminate the broadcast and come with a systolic system that weakly-simulates Y. Unfortunately, this is not good enough. The system Y has a specific initial state q defined above, and we need to simulate this initial state and no other.

To overcome this difficulty we slightly modify Y to make the state q reproducible (see section 4). We add to Σ a new letter R (meaning reset). This addition is temporary; the eventual systolic system will never receive R from its host. We use two types of functional elements. These functional elements differ from each other and from the original one only when the host broadcasts an R. In this case, one of them sends a token over all its out-ports, while the other sends a blank. We assign these functional elements to the vertices of Y in such a way that q will be reproducible by R. That is, whenever the host sends the letter R, the system will enter state q.

Let Y^* be a systolic system that weakly-simulates the modified Y. Since q is reproducible, by lemma (4.1) there is a state q^* of Y^* such that $\langle Y, q \rangle$ is equivalent to $\langle Y^*, q^* \rangle$.

The system Y has only two types of functional elements and these types do not depend on L. A functional element of Y^* is composed of a finite number of elements of Y, and this number depends only on σ. Hence, there is a finite set Γ, which does not depend on L, such that all the functional elements of Y^* are copies of members of Γ.

We now construct a systolic system $Y^\#$ that strongly-simulates Y^*, and is restricted to a functional element Ψ, which does not depend on L. The c-graph of $Y^\#$ is that of Y^* augmented by self-loops having one register. We artificially modify the functional elements of Γ, so that all of them will have the same number of in-ports and the same number of out-ports. This is done by adding dummy ports, and using self-loops to keep all the in-ports connected.

One can build a functional element Ψ capable of simulating all the members of Γ, if Ψ somehow knows which member to simulate. Toward this end, Ψ has a designated self-loop called the *configuration* loop. Each tick Ψ reads a letter from the configuration loop and writes it back into the loop. Using $|\Gamma|$ distinct letters on the configuration loop, the initial value of the register on

365

this loop can be used to configure Ψ to simulate any member of Γ. ∎

10. Restricted Systolic Systems – The Infinite Case

Theorem (10.1)

Let Σ be a finite alphabet. Then there is a functional element Ψ and an infinite systolic system Y restricted to Ψ, such that for any language $L \subset \Sigma^*$, even nonrecursive, there is an s, a state of Y, such that $\langle Y, s \rangle$ defines L.

Proof:

Construct an infinite systolic system with broadcast. Each of its functional elements has one out-port and σ in-ports, labeled by distinct letters of Σ. Its c-graph $G = (V, E, H, w)$ is an infinite directed in-tree. Every vertex $v \neq H$ has exactly σ incoming edges. The root, g, has an edge $g \xrightarrow{\rho} H$. For every $e \in E$, $w(e) = 1$. In addition, the system has an auxiliary broadcast mechanism. The description, so far, is independent of L, but of course, depends on σ.

Each register may contain either a token or a blank. The initial state q is defined as follows: the register on the edge emanating from v contains a token iff the sequence of labels (of in-ports) on the directed path from v to g belongs to L.

From this point on, all the constructions, difficulties and remedy of the finite case apply here. Using the same technique, we can construct an infinite systolic system that simulates our system starting in state q. Moreover, since the c-graph of the resulting system is independent of L, we have a universal systolic system that can define every $L \subset \Sigma^*$. ∎

A theorem similar to (10.1) is not true for finite systems and regular languages. A finite system has a finite number of states and, therefore, can define only a finite number of languages.

11. Feasible Clock period

We say that a synchronous system is *binary* if the alphabet of every edge of the system is binary. In this case the functional elements can be built out of gates. Assume a finite and complete set of (types of) gates is given, where each gate has a specified propagation delay, and assume that the functional elements should be implemented by these gates, and the fan out of the gates should be bounded by a constant. In this context, it is of interest to estimate the minimum feasible clock period of all the binary systolic systems that are "equivalent" to a given system Y.

We will be satisfied by an estimate up to a constant factor. Hence, the given set of gates is immaterial. Without loss of generality, we may assume that all gates

of one and two inputs are available, and the delay of every gate is one.

The construction of section (9) provides an upper bound on the minimum clock period. This bound does not depend on the size, complexity, or functionality of the system, but only on the number of edges incident to the host.

Theorem (11.1)

Let Y be a finite binary synchronous system, and let s be a state of Y. Let i and o be the numbers of edges emanating from and entering the host. Then there is a binary systolic system Y^* with a state s^* such that $\langle Y^*, s^* \rangle$ is equivalent to $\langle Y, s \rangle$, and Y^* has a feasible clock period of $O(i + \log(o))$.

Proof:

Let a binary synchronous system be given, and let i and o be the numbers of edges emanating from and entering the host. Assume, for the time being, that $o = 1$. In this case we can apply theorem (9.1) with $\Sigma = \{0,1\}^i$ and $\sigma = |\Sigma| = 2^i$.

Let Y be the (unmodified) system Y constructed in the proof of theorem (9.1). All the functional elements of Y are identical. The functional element has i binary inputs that encode the broadcast letter, and 2^i inputs which are labeled by distinct letters of Σ. We will refer to the latter as *local* inputs. We claim that the functional element can be implemented by a network of one and two input gates such that the fan out of each gate is, at most, two and the depth of the network is $O(i)$.

The network can be composed of four subnetworks connected in series as follows. The first subnetwork, of depth i, decodes the i broadcast inputs into 2^i terms, one term for each letter of Σ. The second subnetwork, of depth one, ANDs each term with the local input labeled by the corresponding letter of Σ. The third subnetwork, of depth i, ORs together all the 2^i outputs of the previous subnetwork. The fourth subnetwork, of depth $i+1$, fans out the single output of the previous subnetwork into $2^i + 2$ outputs.

As part of the broadcast elimination transformation, we add to each functional element a logic for distributing the broadcast signals to its neighboring vertices in a breadth-first spanning tree of Y. Since each vertex has 2^i neighbors, this logic can be implemented by a network of depth i. We then transform the system into a systolic one. This increases the depths of the functional elements by a factor of, at most, two. Altogether, the depths of the resulting functional elements are $O(i)$. This proves the theorem in the case of $o = 1$.

In the general case, we can build a system Y^* composed of disjoint systolic systems, $Y_1^*, Y_2^*, \cdots Y_o^*$, where

366

each system provides one binary output, and the depth of each functional element is $O(i)$. However, the signals produced by the host need to be distributed to all these subsystems. This can be done with a network of depth $O(\log(o))$. To keep the system systolic, we merge all the neighbors of the host into a single functional element that contains the distribution network as well. ■

12. Acknowledgements

We wish to thank Bill Aiello, Tom Leighton, Peter Winkler, and Michael Yoeli for helpful discussions.

13. References

[C]   Cole, S. N., "Real-Time Computation by n-Dimensional Iterative Arrays of Finite-State Machines", *IEEE Trans. on Computers*, Vol. C-18(4), 1969, pp. 349-365.

[CHEP] Commoner, F., Holt A. W., Even S., and Pnueli A., "Marked Directed Graphs", *Journal of Computer and System Sciences*, Vol. 5, 1971, pp. 511-523.

[E]   Even, S., *Graph Algorithms*, Computer Sci. Press, 1979, page 15.

[F]   Ford, L. R., Jr., "Network Flow Theory", The Rand Corp., P-923, August 1956.

[FF]   Ford, L. R., Jr., and D. R. Fulkerson, *Flows in Networks*, Princeton Univ. Press, 1962, Chap. III, Sec. 5.

[FK]   Foster, M. J., and H. T. Kung, "Recognize Regular Languages With Programmable Building Blocks", *Journal of Digital Systems,* Vol. 6, 1982, pp. 323-332.

[K]   Karp, R. M., "A Characterization of the Minimum Cycle Mean in a Digraph", *Discrete Mathematics*, Vol. 23, 1978, pp. 309-311.

[LS]   Leiserson, C. E., and J. B. Saxe, "Optimizing Synchronous Systems", *Twenty-Second Annual Symposium on Foundations of Computer Science*, IEEE, 1981, pp. 23-36. Also, *Journal of VLSI and Computer Systems*, Vol. 1, 1983, pp. 41-67.

[LRS]   Leiserson, C. E., F. M. Rose and J. B. Saxe, "Optimizing Synchronous Circuitry by Retiming", *Third Caltech Conference on Very Large Scale Integration*, ed. R. Bryant, Computer Science Press, 1983, pp. 87-116.

[RS]   Rabin, M. O., and D. Scott, "Finite Automata and their Decision Problems", *IBM J. Res.*, Vol. 3, No. 2, 1959, pp. 115-125.

[S]   Sieferas, J. I., "Iterative Arrays with Direct Central Control", *Acta Informatica*, Vol. 8, 1977, pp. 177-192.

[SM]   Shannon, C. E., and McCarthy, J. (eds.), "Automata Studies", *Princeton University Press,* 1956.

367

AUTHOR INDEX

NOTES

NOTES

NOTES

NOTES

NOTES

NOTES